Robert Keating O'Neill is Director of the Jo[...] D1583854
Faculty, Political Science, at Boston College, [...] .... He
has been Burns Librarian since 1987. He holds both the PhD in History and the
MA in Library Science from the University of Chicago. Previously he was
Director of the Indiana Historical Society Library in Indianapolis and Head of
Special Collections at Indiana State University, where he was also Associate
Professor of Library Science in the College of Arts and Sciences.

His many publications include *Irish Libraries, Archives, Museums and
Genealogical Centres: A Visitors' Guide* (1st ed., 2002; 2nd ed., 2007), *Management
of Library and Archival Security: From the Outside Looking In* (1998), co-published
simultaneously as *Journal of Library Administration*, Volume 25, Number 1, 1998;
Ulster Libraries, Archives, Museums & Ancestral Heritage Centres (1997); and
*English Language Dictionaries, 1604–1900: The Catalogue of the Warren N. and
Suzanne B. Cordell Collection* (1988). He co-edited *The Art of the Book from the
Early Middle Ages to the Renaissance: A Journey through a Thousand Years* (2000).
He has written numerous articles and reviews, most recently 'The History of the
Irish Book in the U.S, 1890–2000: An Overview', Chapter 17 in *The Oxford
History of the Irish Book*, Volume V: *The Irish Book in English, 1891–2000*; edited
by Clare Hutton, co-edited by Patrick Walsh (2011).

O'Neill is a past president of the Manuscript Society, 1992–4, and the Eire
Society of Boston, 1995–7. He continues to serve as a member of the boards of
both these organisations, and currently serves as Vice-President of the Charitable
Irish Society of Boston, founded in 1737. He serves as the Clerk of the Linen Hall
Library Foundation. He is a member of the Royal Dublin Society, Dublin, the
Grolier Club in New York, and the Union Club in Boston, and is a Fellow of the
Massachusetts Historical Society. He is also a Fellow of the Manuscript Society,
and received the Society's award of distinction. He serves on the Library Board of
Directors of the McClelland Irish Library, Phoenix, Arizona.

O'Neill was honoured by the Irish and American governments for his role in
the recovery of stolen Irish artefacts in 1991. In 2003 he was named to *Irish
America* magazine's list of Top 100 Irish Americans, and that same year received
the Eire Society of Boston's Gold Medal. In 2004 he was honoured by the
Holyoke, MA St. Patrick's Day Parade Committee with its Ambassador's Award.
In each year from 2009 to 2011, he was named to *Irish Echo's* list of Top 100 Irish
in Education. In 2010 he was invested with the Government of Chile's Order of
Bernardo O'Higgins. In 2012 he received the Anam Cara award from the Phoenix
Irish Cultural Center, Phoenix, Arizona.

O'Neill is married to the former Helen Ann Parke. The couple have six grown
children and five grandchildren.

To my grandchildren,
Sebastian John Southworth, Charles Dylan O'Neill,
Delcan Hernandez-O'Neill, Kennedy Alexandra O'Neill
and Evelyn Mei O'Neill.

A VISITORS' GUIDE

IRISH
LIBRARIES

ARCHIVES, MUSEUMS &
GENEALOGICAL CENTRES

Robert K. O'Neill

ULSTER HISTORICAL
FOUNDATION
2013

Third edition published 2013

First edition 2002, second edition 2007
by Ulster Historical Foundation
49 Malone Road,
Belfast BT9 6RY
www.ancestryireland.com
www.booksireland.org.uk

© R.K. O'Neill
ISBN: 978-1-909556-05-8

Printed by Sprint-PRINT Ltd.
Typeset by Ulster Historical Foundation
Cover Design by Dunbar Design

CONTENTS

ACKNOWLEDGEMENTS

As with the compilation of the previous two editions of this guide in 2002 and 2007, I have had the indispensable help of numerous librarians, archivists and genealogical centre managers, co-ordinators and researchers throughout the island of Ireland. Their names can usually be found as the contact persons in the entry for their respective institutions, but this is not always the case, as a number of people who were very helpful preferred not to have a specific contact person listed or recommended another name. E-mails, letters, visits, and telephone enquiries were no doubt unwelcome intrusions into the already overcrowded schedules of these professionals, yet their generous and gracious gifts of knowledge and time give proof to the adage that if you want a job done well, give it to a busy person.

Many individuals in Ireland provided helpful advice and assistance in the compilation of this work. At the great risk of overlooking some, I wish to express my special gratitude to the following, in alphabetical order: Jonathan Armstrong, Janet Atherton, Sean Aylward, Hugh Beckett, Darragh Begley, Peter Beirne, Leah Benson, Ken Bergin, Elizabethanne Boran, Marie Boran, Liam Bradley, Mary Bradley, Damien Brady, Ellen Breen, Pauline Brennan, Eddie Byrne, Ursula Byrne, Jane Cantwell, Bernie Casey, Mary Clark, Bernadette Cogan, Katherine Collins, Ciaran Cregan, Bernadette Cunningham, Damien Burke, Carol Conlin, Imelda Conlon, Elizabeth Consiglia, Mario Corrigan, Charlotte Crowe, John F. Deane, Maura Deering, Gerard M. Delaney, Anne-Marie Diffley, Roger Dixon, Gráinne Doran, Mark Dorman, Noelle Dowling, Anne Durkin, Stephen Edgar, Robena Elliott, Helen Fallon, Richard Farrell, Donal Fenlon, Rev Ignatius Fennessy, OFM, Lydia Ferguson, John FitzGerald, Siobhán Fitzpatrick, Evelyn Flanagan, Mary Flood, Pauline Flood, Bernie Foran, Rene Franklin, Noel E. French, Tom French, Jude Flynn, Cailin Gallagher, Sheena Gamble, Caroline Ganley, Mary Glennon, Bridie Greavy, Helen Grimes, Daire Guidera, Mary Guinan-Darmody, Ivor Hamrock, Alan Hand, Fionnuala Hanrahan, Bobbie Hanvey,

Jacqui Hayes, Margaret Hayes, Rebecca Hayes, Roddy Hegarty, Seamus
Helferty, Rev Mark Patrick Hederman, OSB, Kieran Hoare, Anne Hodge,
Monica Hynes, Christine Johnston, Jacinta Judge, Miriam Kaempf, John
Kearney, Bernie Kelly, Diarmuid Kennedy, Maíre Kennedy, Maureen Kerr,
Karel Kiely, John Killen, Bishop John Kirby, Elizabeth Kirwan, The Very Rev
Dr Philip Knowles, Edward Law, Catriona Lennon, Andrea Lydon, Michael
Lynch, Most Rev John McAreavey, Declan Macauley, Lorraine (née
Buchanan) McCann, Sinéad McCoole, Catherine McCullough, Jason
McElligott, John McFarland, Brian McGee, Frances McGee, Siobhan Mc
Guinness, Stephanie Mclaughlin, Theo McMahon, Helen McNutt, Róisín
McQuillan, Colm McQuinn, Katherine McSharry, Patria Mc Walter, Gerard
Madden, Joan Magee, Donal Maguire, Michael Maguire, Paul E. Maher,
Catherine Malone, Nora Maloney, Bernadette Marks, Brendan Martin,
Bernard Meehan, Carmel Meehan, Brian Mitchell, Gerardine Moloney,
Grace Moloney, Donal Moore, Maureen Moran, Christopher Moriarty,
Martin Morris, Nicola Morris, Phil Mowat, Thirza Mulder, Fintan Mullan,
Orla Nic Aodha, Deirdre Nugent, Ciara O'Brien, Eileen O'Brien, Gearoid
O'Brien, Rev Colmán Ó Clabaigh, OSB, Kasandra O'Connell, Yvonne
Altman O'Connor, Paula O'Dornan, Mgr. Christy O'Dwyer, Rev Fergus
O'Donoghue, SJ, Colette O'Flaherty, Willie O'Kane, Nora O'Meara,
Siobhan O'Rafferty, Colum O'Riordan, Trevor Peare, Carol Quinn, Joanna
Quinn, Raymond Rafaussé, Greer Ramsey, Adrian Regan, Mark Reynolds,
Declan Roche, Eibhlin Roche, Liam Ronayne, Fiona Ross, Joanne Rothwell,
Stephen Scarth, Paul Sheehan, Mary Skelly, Tony Storan, Tom Sullivan,
Pauline Swords, Frances Tallon, Grace Toland, Brian Trainor, Austin
Vaughan, Bernadette Walsh, Deirdre Walsh, Celine Ward, Harriet Wheelock,
Gerard Whelan, Teresa Whitington, Joseph Woods, Penny Woods, and
Catherine Wright.

   Professor Kevin Whelan, former Burns Library Visiting Scholar in Irish
Studies at Boston College and current Director of the University of Notre
Dame's Keough-Naughton Institute in Dublin, graciously read over the
glossary and contributed a number of helpful improvements and
clarifications. Ulster Historical Foundation Executive Director Fintan Mullan
and *emeritus* Research Director Dr Brian Trainor encouraged me to undertake
this work, and provided support throughout this project. I wish to
acknowledge in particular the assistance of Dr Trainor, whose enthusiasm,
energy and help have been a constant source of inspiration from the start of
this guide process in 1991. He also prepared the valuable appendix, 'Tithe
and Valuation Records for Ireland, *c.* 1823–*c.* 1930,' an expanded version of
the appendix he originally prepared for my Ulster Guide (1997), and which
subsequently appeared in the previous two editions of this current work. I am

grateful to the Public Record Office of Northern Ireland, Belfast, and to the National Archives, Dublin, for their permission to list, as an appendix to this book, the references to their tithe and valuation holdings for the parishes of Ireland. I wish also to thank Karel Kiely, Secretary, Irish Family History Foundation, for preparing the valuable appendix piece on the Irish Family History Foundation, the website www.rootsireland.ie and a short guide to the main sources for tracing Irish ancestry. Wendy Dunbar lent her award-winning design talent and expertise to this work, as she has done with its three predecessors. Her contributions made this book a more aesthetically pleasing as well as user-friendly one.

That I was able to bring this work to a timely conclusion is due in no small measure to the support of my employer, Boston College. In addition to providing me with leave time to undertake this third edition, Boston College also provided substantial technical and support services. I wish to express my appreciation to two Boston College administrators in particular for their support and encouragement: Thomas Hachey, University Professor and Executive Director, Center for Irish Programs; and Leo Sullivan, Vice President for Human Resources. No acknowledgement would be complete, however, without recognizing the deep debt I owe to my wife, Helen, and to our children – Kathleen, Kevin, Kerry, Daniel, MaryAnn and Timothy – for their support and love. I dedicated the 2007 edition to my first and then only grandchild, Sebastian John Southworth. It is with great pride and joy that I, 'Papa', now dedicate this edition to Sebastian and his four cousins, Charles Dylan O'Neill, Declan Javier Hernandez-O'Neill, Kennedy Alexandra O'Neill, and Evelyn Mei O'Neill.

INTRODUCTION

In 1997 the Ulster Historical Foundation published a book I compiled entitled *Ulster Libraries, Archives, Museums & Ancestral Heritage Centres: A Visitors' Guide*. When time came to update this guide, UHF Executive Director Fintan Mullan asked if I would expand coverage to include the entire island of Ireland. I agreed. The first edition appeared in 2002, followed by the second edition in 2007.

The need for a new edition has never been greater. The rapid growth of new and improved services, particularly electronic services, and the expansion of resources and delivery capabilities offered by Irish libraries, archives, museums and genealogical centres since the publication of the second edition of *Irish Libraries* in 2007 has been breathtaking. Many institutions now offer remote access not only to their catalogues, but also to their information databases and to their digitised holdings. Indeed, many institutions have devoted substantial resources to the digitisation of their holdings and have made these resources readily accessible online.

The primary target of this guide is the visitor, chiefly the North American visitor, who may be taking or contemplating a trip to Ireland for the first time. In most instances this visitor will primarily be interested in family history, and this guide is consciously oriented towards the needs of the genealogist. Nevertheless, it is hoped that all researchers, including serious academic researchers, will find it useful. That they do so will be due in no small measure to the incredible support I have received from colleagues in libraries, archives and genealogical centres throughout Ireland and Northern Ireland. These good people have been very generous with their time, content contributions and advice, and the extensive information that they have unselfishly made available has made this guide possible. Users of this Guide can be assured that the level of professionalism, courtesy and assistance that they will find in Ireland will be second to none.

When I first started compiling entries for the earlier editions of this work,

I relied heavily on printed surveys and personal visits. In preparing this revised edition, I depended mostly on e-mails, copying and pasting entries from the 2007 edition and asking contacts in Ireland to review and amend these entries as needed. The response was truly gratifying. Every institution represented in the 2007 edition, which is still active, responded positively. Several institutions not included in the 2007 edition have been added as well. Once I revised the entries with the information provided, I sent the copy to my contacts for final approval. The final product represents a sincere effort to reflect the information provided to me as accurately and as fully as possible. If I have failed to do so, I apologise and accept full responsibility for any errors or misunderstandings that may appear in this guide.

This is not intended to be a comprehensive guide to libraries, archives and genealogical centres in Ireland. Rather, it is an effort to include those institutions that are likely to be most attractive to and welcoming of visitors, with a focus on local and family history. No doubt some will find institutions that they believe should have been listed here but that are not. To be sure some institutions specifically asked not to be included, but I may have simply overlooked others, and I welcome readers' suggestions. In the 2001 and 2007 editions of this guide, for example, I did not include The Edward Worth Library (1733) in Dublin, an oversight that was brought to my attention by my friend Sean Aylward. Because this guide is not intended to be comprehensive, I refer the reader to several other very helpful and valuable reference sources. I recommend in particular the *Directory of Irish Archives*, 5th edn, edited by Seamus Helferty and Raymond Refaussé (Dublin: Four Courts Press, 2011). This work includes many of the religious and specialised archives that are not included in this guide, primarily because access for visitors is limited or because holdings fall outside the scope of this guide. The Library Association of Ireland published five editions of its *Directory of Libraries and Information Services in Ireland*, but discontinued the printed version after 1996 in favour of an online version that is not currently available to the public. Copies of the published guides were distributed primarily to libraries and librarians, and were not made widely available to the general public. Another valuable source is RASCAL. The RASCAL (Research and Special Collections Available Locally) project was originally founded to provide online access to information resources held in local libraries and archives in Northern Ireland. RASCAL represented a collaborative initiative undertaken by Queen's University Belfast, The University of Ulster, Library & Information Services (Northern Ireland), the Public Record Office of Northern Ireland, Linen Hall Library and Belfast Public Libraries, not only to make local resources better known, but also to encourage more effective use of these resources. In 2008 RASCAL was expanded to include collections throughout Ireland in association with the Committee on Library Co-operation in Ireland. It is administered and managed by Information Services at Queen's University Belfast. The RASCAL Directory is accessible at www.rascal.ac.uk.

In compiling this guide I was struck both by the wealth of resources available in Ireland and by the warm welcome extended to me and to all visitors. Naturally, in doing research, especially family history research, the reader will be drawn in particular to the large repositories in Dublin, such as the National Archives, the National Library of Ireland, the General Register Office and the Valuation Office, or the Public Record Office and the General Register Office in Belfast. But one should not overlook the bounty to be found in the local history collections of city, county and even some branch libraries, which often contain important local resources, including databases for church and civil records, copies of Griffith's Valuation, Ordnance Survey maps, and local newspapers. The entries for the Centre for Dublin and Irish Studies and the Belfast Central Library, for example, reveal an exceptional wealth of materials that visitors too often overlook. Many of the county libraries, such as those of Westmeath and Kildare, also offer rich and varied resources, and competition for computers and microform readers may be less intense. Staff are very knowledgeable and helpful.

Though this publication is aimed primarily at a North American audience, it is published in Belfast; hence, orthography practice follows the UK-English rather than US-English model. Examples include: acknowledgement (acknowledgment), artefact (artifact), catalogue (catalog), centre (center), colour (color), defence (defense), favour (favor), gaol (jail), judgement (judgment), kilometre (kilometer), and labour (labor).

ENTRY FORMAT

ARRANGEMENT

Entries are arranged alphabetically by city or town within county. This arrangement, in addition to providing a 32-county organisational structure with which most visitors are familiar, also offers visitors a convenient and easy way to get around to institutions that are grouped together within a relatively small geographical area, especially in the cities of Dublin, Belfast and Cork. To assist visitors who might be uncertain or even confused about geographical location, I have made generous use of 'See' references. County Dublin, in particular, offers some interesting challenges to those unfamiliar with its administrative divisions. In 1994, County Dublin was divided into three separate administrative units, called South Dublin, Dún Laoghaire-Rathdown, and Fingal. Nevertheless, all listings here are under the single county of Dublin, subdivided alphabetically by city or town in the following order: Dublin City, Dún Laoghaire, Killiney and Swords, with See references under Dublin City to avoid possible misunderstanding. The entries for Fingal Local Studies and Archives, previously found among the listings for the City of Dublin within the County of Dublin, as they were both located at the end of O'Connell Street on the near north side of Dublin City, are now to be found under Swords, County Dublin. They join the headquarters for this library system in the town of Swords, the administrative seat of County Fingal, which embraces the area of County Dublin north of the River Liffey. Fingal Genealogy is also located in Swords.

The city of Belfast presents yet another interesting problem, as it is actually located within two counties, Down and Antrim. But since all but two entries in this guide for Belfast City – PRONI and the Police Museum – are geographically located within the borders of County Antrim, Belfast is listed under County Antrim, with a note to this effect in the heading. While this arrangement may cause some confusion, especially to those accustomed to thinking of County Dublin and Dublin City as one, the alternative of listing institutions alphabetically by county, without regard to city or town, would present, I believe, even more confusion in certain counties, especially Antrim and Londonderry (Derry).

Elsewhere, the geographical listings are fairly uncomplicated, but it might be helpful to note that Galway Family History Society West precedes East Galway Family History Society because the former is located in Galway City while the latter is located in the town of Woodford. To make finding institutions even easier, an alphabetically arranged listing by type of institution is provided in the preliminaries under the following categories:

Academic Libraries and Archives
Archives
Genealogical and Heritage Centres and Services
Government Organizations and Offices
Public Libraries
Private and Special Libraries

While visitors may be familiar and comfortable with the county system, it should be noted that the this system was gradually introduced into Ireland by the Anglo-Normans beginning at the end of the twelfth century, but completed in the north only in the seventeenth century with the Flight of the Earls (1607) and the establishment of the Ulster Plantation. Hence, there never was officially a County Derry. It was named Londonderry in 1613, and County Londonderry is therefore used as the geographical designation. But within County Londonderry, entries are arranged under the city of Derry, as this is both the historic name of the city founded as a monastic site in the sixth century by St Columcille (St Columba) and the name officially adopted by the Derry City Council, though the British Government has not officially recognised this name change.

County Laois was initially called Queen's County, and County Offaly was King's County. 'See' references are provided for each of these former names, which were changed to their present names following Ireland's independence. Visitors should also be aware that two of the important ports from which many Irish emigrated also underwent name changes with Ireland's independence: Kingstown became Dún Laoghaire and Queenstown became Cobh.

'See' references are also used wherever there might be confusion about the official name of an institution. Trinity College Dublin (TCD) is also the University of Dublin, and University College Dublin (UCD) is also the National University of Ireland, Dublin. The Historical Library, Religious Society of Friends, in Dublin, is more popularly known as either The Friends' Historical Library or the Quaker Library. Some headings have changed. For example, the Royal College of Physicians of Ireland, Dublin, is now listed under Heritage Centre, the Royal College of Physicians of Ireland. Similarly, The Military Archives, Dublin, is now listed under An Chartlann Mhíleata/The Military Archives. As a rule, the official name of the institution, as preferred by the institution itself, is the name used as the heading in this guide, with 'See' references to other names by which the institution might be known.

TELEPHONE AND FAX NUMBERS

Telephone and fax numbers are given as if you were calling from within Ireland or from within Northern Ireland. The international code is 353 for Ireland and 44 for Northern Ireland. For direct-dialed calls from Canada and the United States, first dial 011, then the country code, the area code (dropping the 0) and the telephone number. Thus, if you were calling the National Archives of Ireland in Dublin from the United States, you would dial 011 353 1 407 2300. If you were calling the Public Record Office of Northern Ireland (PRONI) in Belfast, you would dial 011 44 28 9053 4800, again dropping the 0 before the Belfast city code of 028. To call Northern Ireland from within Ireland, dial 048 before the area code; hence, PRONI would be: 048 9025 2000. The international code for the UK (44) is not needed. To call Ireland from Northern Ireland, however, the international code for Ireland is needed, preceded by 00; hence, to call the National Archives in Dublin from Belfast, you would dial 00 353 1 407 2300, again dropping the 0 from the Dublin city code (01). Remember, there is a five- to eight-hour time difference between the United States and Ireland. When it is noon in Boston, it is 17:00 in Ireland, except for a short period in the spring and fall when the U.S. and Europe start and end Daylight Savings Time differently.

E-MAIL ADDRESSES AND WEBSITES

These are perhaps the two areas most subject to change. The information given is as current as the printed format will allow. Indeed, in more than a few cases, changes occurred between the time the information was originally collected and the time the final copy was sent to the institution for editing. Some website addresses were given even though they are currently not accessible. In these cases, it was believed that the sites would be operational by the time this publication appears in print, but there are no guarantees.

HOURS

Opening hours are also subject to change, and it is wise to contact institutions in advance to be sure that the hours are as indicated. All libraries and archives are closed on Sundays unless otherwise noted. In particular, please note that many of the smaller institutions have limited staffing, and vacations and illness may affect announced operating hours. **Please note** that hours in this edition, unlike previous editions, are given according to the EU or military standard, i.e. a 24-hour format. Even though the old AM-PM standard is still in use in much of Ireland, the adoption of the 24-hour format is becoming more widespread, especially among institutions.

ACCESS AND SERVICES

Information here is provided with the visitor chiefly in mind. Access is treated broadly, encompassing not only physical access, i.e. wheelchair-accessible, reader's card required, advance notice, letter of recommendation, etc., but also fax or e-mail services and online access to the institution's OPAC (Online Public Access Catalogue) and databases. Services include reference, photocopying, microfilm reader/printer access, Internet access, exhibits, and publications. Fees, if applicable, are provided, but only as a guideline, as they are subject to change. **Note:** Ireland adopted the euro in January 2002, but Northern Ireland, as part of the United Kingdom, continues to use the pound sterling, and there are no immediate plans to convert to the euro.

CONTACT

In most instances, the name of the person most likely to be able to help the visitor with his or her question is given. But please keep in mind that because of personnel changes, holidays or leaves, the contact(s) listed in this guide may not be available. In certain cases, institutions have asked that an individual not be listed as the contact; rather, that a title only be listed, e.g. Archivist. Academic titles, such as Dr, and degrees, such as PhD, for contact persons are not given, as most did not supply them, and I wanted to be consistent. It can be assumed, however, that most of the contact persons, especially in academic settings, have advanced degrees, many of them holding the doctorate. Titles are provided in the case of clerical, military, or police personnel.

DESCRIPTION

This area is used to provide the visitor with some understanding of the history and place of the institution within a broader context. It is helpful to know, for example, the origin of the name 'Linen Hall Library' or the source of financial support for institutions so that visitors may have a better appreciation of the demands that they may be making on that institution. Many institutions in Ireland, even government-supported ones, are hard pressed to serve their principal clientele due to staff shortages and limited resources. It is important for visitors to understand this and to be patient, polite, courteous and considerate. I am always surprised as the Librarian of a private, American, academic, research library how demanding some enquirers can be, sometimes receiving requests from people with absolutely no ties to the institution demanding prompt answers to a long list of research questions. Such impolite demands invariably are filed away in the wastebasket, without the courtesy of a reply. Visitors take heed! If you find institutions especially helpful, a note of appreciation is always welcome. For those wishing to express their appreciation to a library or archive in more tangible ways, financial contributions may be sent directly to the institution or channelled through several not-for-profit organisations based in America, such as the Irish-American Partnership, which has made the funding of libraries in Ireland a priority.

HOLDINGS

This is the most important element of this guide. Despite the devastation wrought by the destruction of the Public Record Office in 1922 during the Civil War, Ireland is still rich in resources. Many of these repositories are well-kept secrets, even among the Irish. A quick perusal of the breadth and depth of holdings to be found in Irish libraries and archives should impress even the most seasoned researcher. The holdings statement, however, is not intended to be comprehensive. Rather, it is meant to highlight the strengths of the institution's collection, with a particular focus on local studies and genealogy. Even in the areas of local history and genealogy, there is a good deal more depth and breadth to the collections than may be indicated by the information provided. I was heavily dependent on the information that institutions made available to me, and, frankly, some were rather modest in describing their holdings. I was often able to collect additional material through personal contacts or from institutional publications and websites, but this could not be done in every case.

LOCATION

Brief directions are given to each entry's location, often with information on parking or access by public transportation. Public transportation in Ireland is very good. Virtually every entry in this guide can be reached by rail or bus, with perhaps no more than a ten to fifteen-minute walk from the station or depot. Rail service between Dublin and Belfast is especially good, taking only two hours along a scenic route, and upgrades of other rail services are planned. Taxi fares in Ireland and Northern Ireland are quite reasonable, and often the conversation alone is worth the fare. As a concession to this guide's primary audience, distance is given in miles, not kilometres, even though Ireland has officially adopted the metric system. A kilometre is roughly equal to 0.6 mile. Thus, 100 kilometres is equal to 60 miles.

CLASSIFIED LIST OF INSTITUTIONS

1
ACADEMIC LIBRARIES AND ARCHIVES

DUBLIN CITY UNIVERSITY LIBRARY, Dublin City, County Dublin

EDGEHILL THEOLOGICAL COLLEGE, Belfast, County Antrim

MARY IMMACULATE COLLEGE LIBRARY, Limerick City, County Limerick

NATIONAL UNIVERSITY OF IRELAND, CORK (UCC) – BOOLE LIBRARY, Cork City, County Cork

NATIONAL UNIVERSITY OF IRELAND, GALWAY – JAMES HARDIMAN LIBRARY, Galway City, County Galway

NATIONAL UNIVERSITY OF IRELAND, MAYNOOTH – JOHN PAUL II LIBRARY, Maynooth, County Kildare

NATIONAL UNIVERSITY OF IRELAND, MAYNOOTH – RUSSELL LIBRARY, Maynooth, County Kildare

QUEEN'S UNIVERSITY BELFAST LIBRARY, Belfast, County Antrim

RUSSELL LIBRARY. See NATIONAL UNIVERSITY OF IRELAND, MAYNOOTH – RUSSELL LIBRARY, Maynooth, County Kildare

ST MARY'S UNIVERSITY COLLEGE LIBRARY, Belfast, County Antrim

ST PATRICK'S COLLEGE – CREGAN LIBRARY, Dublin City, County Dublin

ST PATRICK'S COLLEGE – RUSSELL LIBRARY. See NATIONAL UNIVERSITY OF IRELAND, MAYNOOTH – RUSSELL LIBRARY, Maynooth, County Kildare

STRANMILLIS UNIVERSITY COLLEGE LIBRARY, Belfast, County Antrim

TRINITY COLLEGE DUBLIN LIBRARY, Dublin City, County Dublin

UCD ARCHIVES, Dublin City, County Dublin

UNION THEOLOGICAL COLLEGE – GAMBLE LIBRARY, Belfast, County Antrim

UNIVERSITY COLLEGE DUBLIN LIBRARY (UCD), Dublin City, County Dublin

UNIVERSITY OF LIMERICK LIBRARY AND INFORMATION SERVICES, Limerick City, County Limerick

UNIVERSITY OF ULSTER LIBRARY, BELFAST CAMPUS, Belfast, County Antrim

UNIVERSITY OF ULSTER LIBRARY, COLERAINE CAMPUS, Coleraine, County Londonderry

UNIVERSITY OF ULSTER LIBRARY, JORDANSTOWN CAMPUS, Newtownabbey, County Antrim

UNIVERSITY OF ULSTER LIBRARY, MAGEE CAMPUS, Derry City, County Londonderry

2
ARCHIVES

AN CHARTLANN MHÍLEATA/THE MILITARY ARCHIVES, Dublin City, County Dublin

THE ARCHIVES OF THE RELIGIOUS SOCIETY OF FRIENDS IN ULSTER, Lisburn, County Antrim

BANTRY HOUSE, Bantry, County Cork. See NATIONAL UNIVERSITY OF IRELAND, CORK (UCC) – BOOLE LIBRARY– SPECIAL COLLECTIONS AND ARCHIVES, Cork City, County Cork

CARDINAL TOMÁS Ó FIAICH MEMORIAL LIBRARY AND ARCHIVE, Armagh, County Armagh

CASHEL AND EMLY ARCHDIOCESAN ARCHIVES, (ROMAN CATHOLIC), Thurles, County Tipperary

CLARE COUNTY ARCHIVES SERVICE, Ennis, County Clare

CORK ARCHIVES INSTITUTE, Cork City, County Cork

CORK PUBLIC MUSEUM (MÚSAEM POIBLÍ CHORCAÍ), Cork City, County Cork

DIOCESAN ARCHIVE, DROMORE (ROMAN CATHOLIC), Newry, County Down

DIOCESE OF CLONFERT ARCHIVE, Loughrea, County Galway

DONEGAL COUNTY ARCHIVES SERVICE, Lifford, County Donegal

DOWN & CONNOR DIOCESAN ARCHIVES (ROMAN CATHOLIC), Belfast, County Antrim

DUBLIN CITY PUBLIC LIBRARY AND ARCHIVES, Dublin City, County Dublin

DUBLIN DIOCESAN ARCHIVES, Dublin City, County Dublin

FINGAL LOCAL STUDIES AND ARCHIVES, Swords, County Dublin

THE GAA MUSEUM, Dublin City, County Dublin

GALWAY CITY LIBRARY – LOCAL HISTORY DEPARTMENT AND ARCHIVES, Galway, County Galway

GARDA MUSEUM/ARCHIVES, Dublin City, County Dublin

GENERAL REGISTER OFFICE (Reading Room), Dublin City, County Dublin

GENERAL REGISTER OFFICE, Roscommon Town, County Roscommon

GRAND LODGE OF FREEMASONS OF IRELAND: LIBRARY, ARCHIVES AND MUSEUM, Dublin City, County Dublin

GUINNESS ARCHIVE, Dublin City, County Dublin

HERITAGE CENTRE, ROYAL COLLEGE OF PHYSICIANS OF IRELAND, Dublin City, County Dublin

HISTORICAL LIBRARY, RELIGIOUS SOCIETY OF FRIENDS IN IRELAND, Dublin City, County Dublin

IRISH ARCHITECTURAL ARCHIVE, Dublin City, County Dublin

IRISH FILM INSTITUTE, Dublin City, County Dublin

IRISH JESUIT ARCHIVES, Dublin City, County Dublin

IRISH JEWISH MUSEUM, Dublin City, County Dublin

IRISH THEATRE ARCHIVE, Dublin City, County Dublin

IRISH TRADITIONAL MUSIC ARCHIVE, Dublin City, County Dublin

JAMES HARDIMAN LIBRARY. See NATIONAL UNIVERSITY OF IRELAND, GALWAY – JAMES HARDIMAN LIBRARY – DEPARTMENT OF SPECIAL COLLECTIONS AND ARCHIVES, Galway City, County Galway

KERRY LOCAL HISTORY AND ARCHIVES COLLECTION, Kerry County Library, Tralee, County Kerry

KILDARE COLLECTIONS AND RESEARCH SERVICES – ARCHIVES, Newbridge, County Kildare

LIMERICK ARCHIVES, Limerick City, County Limerick

LOUTH LOCAL AUTHORITIES ARCHIVES SERVICE, Dundalk, County Louth

MICHAEL DAVITT MUSEUM, Foxford, County Mayo

THE MILITARY ARCHIVES, Dublin, County Dublin. See AN CHARTLANN MHÍLEATA/THE MILITARY ARCHIVES, Dublin City, County Dublin

NATIONAL ARCHIVES OF IRELAND, Dublin City, County Dublin

NATIONAL GALLERY OF IRELAND RESEARCH SERVICES, Dublin City, County Dublin

NATIONAL PHOTOGRAPHIC ARCHIVE, Dublin City, County Dublin. See NATIONAL LIBRARY OF IRELAND — NATIONAL PHOTOGRAPHIC ARCHIVE, Dublin City, County Dublin

NATIONAL UNIVERSITY OF IRELAND, GALWAY – JAMES HARDIMAN LIBRARY – DEPARTMENT OF SPECIAL COLLECTIONS AND ARCHIVES, Galway City, County Galway

NATIONAL UNIVERSITY OF IRELAND, MAYNOOTH – RUSSELL LIBRARY, Maynooth, County Kildare

PUBLIC RECORD OFFICE OF NORTHERN IRELAND, Belfast, County Antrim

REGISTRY OF DEEDS, Dublin City, County Dublin

REPRESENTATIVE CHURCH BODY LIBRARY, Dublin City, County Dublin

ST PATRICK'S COLLEGE, MAYNOOTH ARCHIVES, RUSSELL LIBRARY, Maynooth, County Kildare. See NATIONAL UNIVERSITY OF IRELAND, MAYNOOTH – RUSSELL LIBRARY, Maynooth, County Kildare

TRINITY COLLEGE LIBRARY – MANUSCRIPTS & ARCHIVES RESEARCH LIBRARY (M&ARL), Dublin City, County Dublin

UCD ARCHIVES, Dublin City, County Dublin

ULSTER FOLK AND TRANSPORT MUSEUM, Holywood, County Down

UNIVERSITY COLLEGE DUBLIN – ARCHIVES DEPARTMENT. *See* UCD ARCHIVES, Dublin City, County Dublin

WATERFORD CITY ARCHIVES, Waterford City, County Waterford

WATERFORD COUNTY ARCHIVES SERVICE, Dungarvan, County Waterford

WESTMEATH COUNTY LIBRARY AND ARCHIVES SERVICE – LOCAL STUDIES AND ARCHIVES COLLECTION, Mullingar, County Westmeath

WEXFORD COUNTY ARCHIVE & RECORDS CENTRE, Ardcavan, County Wexford

WICKLOW COUNTY ARCHIVES, Wicklow Town, County Wicklow

3
GENEALOGICAL AND HERITAGE CENTRES AND SERVICES

ARMAGH ANCESTRY, Armagh City, County Armagh

ASSOCIATION OF PROFESSIONAL GENEALOGISTS IN IRELAND, Dublin City, County Dublin

BRIAN MITCHELL GENEALOGY SERVICE, *See* HERITAGE AND MUSEUM SERVICE DERRY CITY COUNCIL, Derry City, County Londonderry

BRÚ BORÚ CULTURAL CENTRE, Cashel, County Tipperary

CARLOW GENEALOGY PROJECT, Carlow Town, County Carlow [closed]

CAVAN GENEALOGY, Cavan, County Cavan

CLARE HERITAGE AND GENEALOGICAL CENTRE, Corofin, County Clare

CORK CITY ANCESTRAL PROJECT, Cork City, County Cork

COUNTY DERRY OR LONDONDERRY GENEALOGY CENTRE, Derry, County Londonderry *See* HERITAGE AND MUSEUM SERVICE DERRY CITY COUNCIL – Brian Mitchell Genealogy Service, Derry City, County Londonderry

COUNTY ROSCOMMON HERITAGE AND GENEALOGY COMPANY, Strokestown, County Roscommon

COUNTY SLIGO HERITAGE AND GENEALOGY SOCIETY, Sligo Town, County Sligo

COUNTY WEXFORD HERITAGE AND GENEALOGY SOCIETY, Tagoat, County Wexford [closed]

DONEGAL ANCESTRY, Ramelton, County Donegal

DÚN LAOGHAIRE-RATHDOWN HERITAGE CENTRE, Dún Laoghaire, County Dublin

DÚN NA SÍ HERITAGE CENTRE, Moate, County Westmeath

EAST CLARE HERITAGE COMPANY, Tuamgraney, County Clare

EAST GALWAY FAMILY HISTORY SOCIETY, Woodford, Loughrea, County Galway

FINGAL GENEALOGY, Swords Historical Society Co. LTD, Swords, County Dublin

GALWAY FAMILY HISTORY SOCIETY WEST, Galway City, County Galway

IRISH MIDLANDS ANCESTRY (LAOIS AND OFFALY FAMILY HISTORY RESEARCH CENTRE), Tullamore, County Offaly

IRISH WORLD FAMILY HISTORY CENTRE, Coalisland, County Tyrone

KILDARE COLLECTIONS AND RESEARCH SERVICES – KILDARE GENEALOGY, Newbridge, County Kildare

KILKENNY FAMILY HISTORY, Rothe House & Garden, Kilkenny Town, County Kilkenny

KILLARNEY GENEALOGICAL CENTRE, Killarney, County Kerry [closed]. *See* KERRY LOCAL HISTORY AND ARCHIVES COLLECTION, Tralee

KERRY ARCHAEOLOGICAL AND HISTORICAL SOCIETY. *See* KERRY LOCAL HISTORY AND ARCHIVES COLLECTION, Kerry County Library, Tralee, County Kerry

LAOIS AND OFFALY FAMILY HISTORY RESEARCH CENTRE. *See* IRISH MIDLANDS ANCESTRY (LAOIS AND OFFALY FAMILY HISTORY RESEARCH CENTRE), Tullamore, County Offaly

THE LIBRARY, KILKENNY ARCHAEOLOGICAL SOCIETY, Kilkenny Town, County Kilkenny

LEITRIM GENEALOGY CENTRE (SINSEARLANN LIATROMA), Ballinamore, County Leitrim

LIMERICK ANCESTRY, Limerick, County Limerick [closed]

LONGFORD RESEARCH CENTRE, Longford Town, County Longford

MALLOW HERITAGE CENTRE, Mallow, County Cork

MAYO NORTH FAMILY HERITAGE CENTRE, Ballina, County Mayo

MEATH HERITAGE AND GENEALOGY CENTRE, Trim, County Meath

MEATH–LOUTH FAMILY RESEARCH CENTRE. *See* MEATH HERITAGE AND GENEALOGY CENTRE, Trim, County Meath

MONAGHAN ANCESTRY, Monaghan Town, County Monaghan

OFFALY HISTORICAL & ARCHAEOLOGICAL SOCIETY. *See* IRISH MIDLANDS ANCESTRY, Tullamore, County Offaly

OFFICE OF THE CHIEF HERALD/GENEALOGICAL OFFICE, Dublin, County Dublin. *See* NATIONAL LIBRARY OF IRELAND – OFFICE OF THE CHIEF HERALD, Dublin City, County Dublin

ORDNANCE SURVEY OF NORTHERN IRELAND. *See* LAND & PROPERTY SERVICES, ARCHIVE OF ORDNANCE SURVEY OF NORTHERN IRELAND® MAPPING & PHOTOGRAPHY, Belfast, County Antrim

SOUTH MAYO FAMILY RESEARCH CENTRE, Ballinrobe, County Mayo

TIPPERARY FAMILY HISTORY RESEARCH, Tipperary Town, County Tipperary

TIPPERARY NORTH GENEALOGY CENTRE, Nenagh, County Tipperary

ULSTER HISTORICAL FOUNDATION, Belfast, County Antrim

WATERFORD HERITAGE SERVICES, Waterford Town, County Waterford

THE WICKLOW FAMILY HISTORY CENTRE, Wicklow Town, County Wicklow

4
GOVERNMENT ORGANISATIONS AND OFFICES

GENERAL REGISTER OFFICE, Belfast, County Antrim

GENERAL REGISTER OFFICE (READING ROOM), Dublin City, County Dublin

GENERAL REGISTER OFFICE, Roscommon Town, County Roscommon

LAND & PROPERTY SERVICES, ARCHIVE OF ORDNANCE SURVEY OF NORTHERN IRELAND® MAPPING & PHOTOGRAPHY, Belfast, County Antrim

LIBRARIES NI HERITAGE COLLECTION, THE MELLON CENTRE FOR MIGRATION STUDIES, Ulster American Folk Park, Castletown, Omagh, County Tyrone

NATIONAL ARCHIVES OF IRELAND, Dublin City, County Dublin

NATIONAL GALLERY OF IRELAND RESEARCH SERVICES, Dublin City, County Dublin

NATIONAL LIBRARY OF IRELAND, Dublin City, County Dublin

NATIONAL PHOTOGRAPHIC ARCHIVE, Dublin City, County Dublin

OFFICE OF THE CHIEF HERALD/GENEALOGICAL OFFICE, Dublin City, County Dublin

NATIONAL MUSEUM OF IRELAND
Museum of Country Life, Turlough Park, Castlebar, County Mayo
Museum of Decorative Arts and History, Collins Barracks, Dublin City, County Dublin
Museum of Archaeology, Dublin City, County Dublin
Museum of Natural History, Dublin City, County Dublin

NORTHERN IRELAND ASSEMBLY LIBRARY, Belfast, County Antrim

NORTHERN IRELAND HOUSING EXECUTIVE – LIBRARY INFORMATION SERVICES, Belfast, County Antrim

ORDNANCE SURVEY OF NORTHERN IRELAND. See LAND & PROPERTY SERVICES, ARCHIVE OF ORDNANCE SURVEY OF NORTHERN IRELAND® MAPPING & PHOTOGRAPHY, Belfast, County Antrim

PUBLIC RECORD OFFICE OF NORTHERN IRELAND, Belfast, County Antrim

REGISTRY OF DEEDS, Dublin City, County Dublin

ULSTER AMERICAN FOLK PARK. See LIBRARIES NI HERITAGE COLLECTION, THE MELLON CENTRE FOR MIGRATION STUDIES, Ulster American Folk Park, Castletown, Omagh, County Tyrone

ULSTER FOLK AND TRANSPORT MUSEUM, Cultra, Holywood, County Down

VALUATION OFFICE, Dublin City, County Dublin

5

PUBLIC LIBRARIES

ATHLONE PUBLIC LIBRARY, Athlone, County Westmeath

BAILIEBORO LIBRARY, Bailieboro, County Cavan

BALLYMENA CENTRAL LIBRARY. *See* LIBRARIES NI HERITAGE COLLECTION, BALLYMENA, Ballymena, County Antrim

BALLYMONEY LIBRARY, Ballymoney, County Antrim

BANGOR LIBRARY, Bangor, County Down

BELFAST CENTRAL LIBRARY, Belfast, County Antrim

CARLOW CENTRAL LIBRARY, Carlow Town, County Carlow

CARRICKFERGUS LIBRARY, Carrickfergus, County Antrim

CASTLEBAR CENTRAL LIBRARY – LOCAL STUDIES DEPARTMENT, Castlebar, County Mayo

CAVAN COUNTY LIBRARY, Cavan Town, County Cavan

CENTRAL LIBRARY, Derry City, County Londonderry. *See* LIBRARIES NI HERITAGE COLLECTION, DERRY CENTRAL LIBRARY, Derry City, County Londonderry

CENTRE FOR DUBLIN AND IRISH STUDIES, Dublin City, County Dublin

CLARE COUNTY LIBRARY – LOCAL STUDIES CENTRE, Ennis, County Clare

CORK CITY LIBRARY, Cork City, County Cork

CORK COUNTY LIBRARY, Cork City, County Cork

DONEGAL COUNTY LIBRARY, Letterkenny, County Donegal

DUBLIN AND IRISH COLLECTIONS — Dublin City Library and Archive, Dublin City, County Dublin

DUBLIN CITY PUBLIC LIBRARIES AND ARCHIVE, Dublin City, County Dublin

DUBLIN CITY PUBLIC LIBRARIES – CENTRAL LIBRARY, Dublin City, County Dublin

DÚN LAOGHAIRE LIBRARY – LOCAL HISTORY DEPARTMENT, Dún Laoghaire, County Dublin

ENNISKILLEN LIBRARY, Enniskillen, County Fermanagh. *See* LIBRARIES NI HERTITAGE COLLECTION, ENNISKILLEN, Enniskillen, County Fermanagh

FINGAL COUNTY LIBRARIES, Dublin, County Dublin

GALWAY CITY LIBRARY, Galway, County Galway

GALWAY CITY LIBRARY – LOCAL HISTORY DEPARTMENT AND ARCHIVES HOLYWOOD BRANCH LIBRARY, Holywood, County Down

KERRY LOCAL HISTORY AND ARCHIVES COLLECTION, Tralee, County Kerry

KILKENNY COUNTY LIBRARY, Kilkenny Town, County Kilkenny

LAOIS COUNTY LIBRARY – LOCAL STUDIES COLLECTION, Portlaoise, County Laois

LIBRARIES NI IRISH & LOCAL STUDIES LIBRARY, ARMAGH, Armagh City, County Armagh

LIBRARIES NI HERITAGE COLLECTION, BALLYMENA, Ballymena, County Antrim

LIBRARIES NI HERITAGE COLLECTION, BALLYMONEY LIBRARY, Ballymoney, County Antrim

LIBRARIES NI HERITAGE COLLECTION, DERRY CENTRAL LIBRARY, Derry City, County Londonderry

LIBRARIES NI HERITAGE COLLECTION, DOWNPATRICK, Downpatrick, County Down

LIBRARIES NI HERTITAGE COLLECTION, ENNISKILLEN, Enniskillen, County Fermanagh

LIBRARIES NI HERITAGE COLLECTION, THE MELLON CENTRE FOR MIGRATION STUDIES, Ulster American Folk Park, Castletown, Omagh, County Tyrone

LIBRARIES NI HERITAGE COLLECTION, Newry City Library, Newry, County Down

LIBRARIES NI HERITAGE COLLECTION, OMAGH, Omagh, County Tyrone

LEITRIM COUNTY LIBRARY, Ballinamore, County Leitrim

LIMERICK CITY PUBLIC LIBRARY, Limerick City, County Limerick

LIMERICK COUNTY LIBRARY – LOCAL STUDIES COLLECTION, Limerick City, County Limerick

LONGFORD BRANCH LIBRARY – LOCAL STUDIES, Longford Town, County Longford

LOUTH COUNTY LIBRARY, Dundalk, County Louth

MEATH COUNTY LIBRARY HEADQUARTERS, Navan, County Meath

MONAGHAN COUNTY LIBRARY, Clones, County Monaghan

M'SKIMIN ROOM, Carrickfergus Library, Carrickfergus, County Antrim. *See* CARRICKFERGUS LIBRARY, Carrickfergus, County Antrim

NEWRY BRANCH LIBRARY, Newry, County Down. *See* LIBRARIES NI HERITAGE COLLECTION, Newry City Library, Newry, County Down

NEWTOWNARDS BRANCH LIBRARY, Newtownards, County Down

OFFALY COUNTY LIBRARY – LOCAL STUDIES SECTION, Tullamore, County Offaly

OMAGH LIBRARY, Omagh, County Tyrone. *See* LIBRARIES NI HERITAGE COLLECTION, OMAGH, Omagh, County Tyrone

ROSCOMMON COUNTY LIBRARY, Roscommon Town, County Roscommon

SLIGO COUNTY LIBRARY, Sligo Town, County Sligo

TIPPERARY LIBRARIES, Thurles, County Tipperary

WATERFORD COUNTY LIBRARY HEADQUARTERS, Lismore, County Waterford

WATERFORD MUNICIPAL LIBRARY, Waterford City, County Waterford

WESTMEATH COUNTY LIBRARY HEADQUARTERS – LOCAL STUDIES COLLECTION, Mullingar, County Westmeath

WEXFORD COUNTY LIBRARY, Ardcavan, County Wexford

WICKLOW COUNTY LIBRARY – LOCAL HISTORY COLLECTION AND RCHIVES, Bray, County Wicklow

6
SPECIAL LIBRARIES

ARMAGH COUNTY MUSEUM, Armagh City, County Armagh

ARMAGH OBSERVATORY, Armagh City, County Armagh

ARMAGH PUBLIC LIBRARY, Armagh City, County Armagh

AUSTIN CLARKE LIBRARY – POETRY IRELAND/EIGSE EIREANN, Dublin City, County Dublin. *See* POETRY IRELAND/ÉIGSE ÉIREANN, Dublin City, County Dublin

CARDINAL TOMÁS Ó FIAICH LIBRARY AND ARCHIVE, Armagh City, County Armagh

CENTRAL CATHOLIC LIBRARY, Dublin City, County Dublin

CENTRE FOR MIGRATION STUDIES, Omagh, County Tyrone. *See* LIBRARIES NI HERITAGE COLLECTION, THE MELLON CENTRE FOR MIGRATION STUDIES, Ulster American Folk Park, Castletown, Omagh, County Tyrone

CHESTER BEATTY LIBRARY, Dublin City, County Dublin

CORK PUBLIC MUSEUM (Músaem Poiblí Chorcaí), Cork City, County Cork

DONEGAL COUNTY MUSEUM, Letterkenny, County Donegal

THE EDWARD WORTH LIBRARY (1733), Dublin City, County Dublin

FRANCISCAN LIBRARY, Killiney, County Dublin

GPA BOLTON LIBRARY, Cashel, County Tipperary

HERITAGE CENTRE, ROYAL COLLEGE OF PHYSICIANS OF IRELAND, Dublin City, County Dublin

HISTORICAL LIBRARY, RELIGIOUS SOCIETY OF FRIENDS, Dublin City, County Dublin

HISTORY AND FAMILY RESEARCH CENTRE – LOCAL STUDIES DEPARTMENT, Newbridge, County Kildare

HERITAGE CENTRE, ROYAL COLLEGE OF PHYSICIANS OF IRELAND, Dublin City, County Dublin

THE HONORABLE SOCIETY OF KING'S INNS, Dublin City, County Dublin

INVEST NORTHERN IRELAND – BUSINESS INFORMATION CENTRE & ENTERPRISE EUROPE NETWORK, Belfast, County Antrim

IRISH JEWISH MUSEUM, Dublin City, County Dublin

THE JESUIT LIBRARY, Dublin City, County Dublin

LIFFORD OLD COURTHOUSE, Lifford, County Donegal

LINEN HALL LIBRARY, Belfast, County Antrim

MARSH'S LIBRARY, Dublin City, County Dublin

MICHAEL DAVITT MUSEUM, Foxford, County Mayo

MONAGHAN COUNTY MUSEUM, Monaghan Town, County Monaghan

MUSEUM OF COUNTRY LIFE, Castlebar, County Mayo. See NATIONAL MUSEUM OF IRELAND, Dublin City, County Dublin

NATIONAL GALLERY OF IRELAND RESEARCH SERVICES, Dublin City, County Dublin

NATIONAL LIBRARY OF IRELAND, Dublin City, County Dublin

NATIONAL MUSEUM OF ARCHAEOLOGY & HISTORY. See NATIONAL MUSEUM OF IRELAND, Dublin City, County Dublin

NATIONAL MUSEUM OF COUNTRY LIFE. See NATIONAL MUSEUM OF IRELAND, Dublin City, County Dublin

NATIONAL MUSEUM OF DECORATIVE ARTS & HISTORY. See NATIONAL MUSEUM OF IRELAND, Dublin, County Dublin

NATIONAL MUSEUM OF IRELAND, Dublin City, County Dublin

NATIONAL MUSEUM OF NATURAL HISTORY. See NATIONAL MUSEUM OF IRELAND, Dublin City, County Dublin

NORTHERN IRELAND ASSEMBLY LIBRARY, Belfast, County Antrim

NORTHERN IRELAND HOUSING EXECUTIVE – LIBRARY INFORMATION SERVICES, Belfast, County Antrim

POETRY IRELAND/ÉIGSE ÉIREANN, Dublin City, County Dublin

REPRESENTATIVE CHURCH BODY LIBRARY, Dublin City, County Dublin

ROYAL COLLEGE OF PHYSICIANS OF IRELAND, Dublin City, County Dublin. See HERITAGE CENTRE, ROYAL COLLEGE OF PHYSICIANS OF IRELAND, Dublin City, County Dublin

ROYAL DUBLIN SOCIETY, Dublin City, County Dublin

ROYAL IRISH ACADEMY, Dublin City, County Dublin

ROYAL SOCIETY OF ANTIQUARIES OF IRELAND, Dublin City, County Dublin

ULSTER-AMERICAN FOLK PARK, Omagh, County Tyrone

ULSTER FOLK AND TRANSPORT MUSEUM, Holywood, County Down

ULSTER MUSEUM LIBRARY, Belfast, County Antrim. See ULSTER FOLK AND TRANSPORT MUSEUM, Holywood, County Down

WORTH LIBRARY, Dublin City, County Dublin. See THE EDWARD WORTH LIBRARY (1733), Dublin City, County Dublin

Map of Ireland from S. Lewis, *Atlas of the Counties of Ireland* (London 1837)

COUNTY ANTRIM

INCLUDES BELFAST

LIBRARIES NI HERITAGE COLLECTION, BALLYMENA

The Heritage Collection
Ballymena Central Library
5 Pat's Brae
BALLYMENA, COUNTY ANTRIM, BT43 5AX
Northern Ireland

TELEPHONE: (028) 2563 3960
E-mail: localstudies.neelb@librariesni.org.uk
Website: www.librariesni.org.uk

HOURS
M–Th, 09:30–20:00, F–Sa, 09:30–17:00

ACCESS AND SERVICES
Visitors are welcome. Disabled Access. The collection is non-circulating, reference only. Microfilm reader/printers are available. Due to heavy demand for microfilm readers, booking is advisable for this service. Public Access Terminals with internet access are freely available for all Libraries NI members. Fees apply to photocopies, microfilm reader and IT printouts. ID is required on registering. Heritage staff will assist and advise users seeking genealogical information.

CONTACT
Mary Bradley, Heritage Services Manager.
E-mail: mary.bradley@librariesni.org.uk

DESCRIPTION
Established by the North-Eastern Education and Library Board in the late 1970s and now part of Libraries NI, the library's policy has been to collect material on all aspects of life in County Antrim and County Londonderry.

HOLDINGS
The Heritage Collection in Ballymena library holds a reference collection covering all aspects of life in County Antrim and County Londonderry and includes: large indexed photographic collection, large scale photographs of Langford Lodge, online

newspaper index, selection of specialised and antiquarian books for family history research, including street directories, volumes of Griffith's Valuation for County Antrim and County Londonderry, 1851Census for parishes in Kilconway, Glenarm and Massereene baronies, Gravestone Inscriptions and Grand Jury Presentments for county Antrim administration prior to 1898. The collection additionally includes historical maps and Ordnance Survey Parish Memoirs which describe parishes in the 1830s, complementing the 1830s edition of the 6 inch maps.

School registers for over 80 schools in Counties Antrim and Londonderry (mainly post 1945 but some date from 1870s).

Microfilm sources include:

    Local and regional newspapers;
    Books of Survey and Distribution for Antrim and Derry (post 1641 rebellion);
    1831 Census for County Londonderry;
    Manor of Sal Minute books 1830s–60s (Magherafelt);
    Board of Guardian Minutes (Workhouse);
    Ella Young papers b. 1867–1956 – poet born in Fenagh near Ballymena

LOCATION
In town centre (walk along Mill Street and turn left at junction). Heritage unit is on first floor. Public car parks nearby.

LIBRARIES NI HERITAGE COLLECTION, BALLYMONEY LIBRARY

Ballymoney Library
Rodden Foot, Queen Street
BALLYMONEY, COUNTY ANTRIM, BT53 6JB
Northern Ireland

TELEPHONE: (028) 2766 3589/Fax: (028) 2766 3589
E-mail: ballymoney.library@librariesni.org.uk
Website: www.librariesni.org.uk

HOURS
M–Th, 09:30–20:00, F–Sa, 09:30–17:00

ACCESS AND SERVICES
Visitors are welcome. Disabled Access facilities. The collection is non borrowable, reference only. Microfilm reader/printer to view *Ballymoney Free Press*, January 1870–December 1934 and *Ballymoney Times*, 1989–2009. Public Access Terminals with internet access are freely available for all Libraries NI members. Fees apply to photocopies, microfilm reader and IT printouts. Membership of library is open to anyone living, working or studying in the area. ID is required on registering.

CONTACT
Mary Bradley, Heritage Services Manager.
E-mail: mary.bradley@librariesni.org.uk

DESCRIPTION
Small branch library with two special collections, the George Shiels Collection and the Ballymoney Special Collection.

HOLDINGS
The Shiels Collection comprises plays, books, typescripts, cards, correspondence and photographs of the playwright (1886–1949), whose work was often performed at the Abbey Theatre, Dublin.

The Ballymoney Special Collection contains titles of Ballymoney interest, purchased through bequests left to the people of Ballymoney in the 1800s.

LOCATION
Town centre-parking to rear of library.

NORTH-EASTERN EDUCATION AND LIBRARY BOARD – LIBRARY SERVICE HEADQUARTERS

In April 2009, the 5 Education and Library Boards of Northern Ireland were reorganised and consolidated into one library authority for the whole of Northern Ireland, with Headquarters located at:

Libraries NI
Unit 3a,
The Sidings Office Park,
Antrim Road,
LISBURN, COUNTY ANTRIM, BT28 3RG
Northern Ireland

For further information, *see* listing for LIBRARIES NI under Lisburn in this guide or see website at www.librariesni.org.uk.

BELFAST CENTRAL LIBRARY

Royal Avenue
BELFAST, BT1 1EA
Northern Ireland

TELEPHONE: (028) 9050 9150; FAX: (028) 9033 2819
E-mail: belb.info@ni-libraries.net
Website: www.librariesni.org.uk

HOURS
M–Th, 09:00–20:00; F, 09:00–17:30; Sa, 09:00–16:30

ACCESS AND SERVICES
Belfast Central Library is open to all, with one membership card valid for all libraries in Northern Ireland. There is free internet access for all Northern Ireland public library members with a charge of £2.00 per half hour for non-members; ID is required. Membership is open to anyone living, working or studying in the area. Temporary residents or visitors can register to join Libraries NI using identification for their holiday/temporary address. Visitors from England and Wales can join Libraries NI using their home library card as id. The library is accessible for people with disabilities. It offers a café and public toilets. General lending services and computer facilities are available on the ground floor. This floor also houses the Newspaper library, accessed by a separate entrance on Library Street. Information and Business material is available on the first floor, mainly from closed stacks.

Heritage and Music material is available on the second floor, again with material held in closed stacks. Computerised, printed and a few card catalogues give access to stock. Photocopying and microform prints are available for a fee. The Northern Ireland Music Archive can be viewed in the Music library and the Digital Film Archive is available in the lending library on the ground floor.

CONTACT
Mandy Bryson, Business Manager
Sheena Gamble, Area Manager
Patricia Walker, Heritage Manager

DESCRIPTION
Belfast Central Library, opened in 1888, is a major research, reference and lending library. It is part of Libraries NI, which operate another 96 branch libraries throughout Northern Ireland. In addition to maintaining a strong general collection it holds several major research collections, including the deposit collection of UK patents and the largest newspaper collection in Northern Ireland. In addition, the library maintains significant collections of periodicals, maps, microforms, music scores, pamphlets, photographs, postcards, music recordings, theatre materials and government documents for Northern Ireland, the Republic of Ireland and the UK. Special collections include the 10,000 volume Natural History Collection and a rare book collection, which includes incunabula (fifteenth century printed books) and pre-1701 English printed books. Local material includes a pamphlet collection, the Fine Press Collection, including a complete run of Cuala Press, and the Irish Collection. The last of these is the largest in Northern Ireland, anchored by the 4,000-volume Francis Joseph Bigger Collection.

The Bigger Collection is complemented by the Bigger Archive, with 10,000 items of archaeological, historical and biographical interest. This archive also includes a significant body of correspondence with notable local, national and international figures. Bigger (1863–1926), the grandson of United Irishman David Bigger, was a successful lawyer and member of the Gaelic League who assembled an impressive collection of books, pamphlets and bound manuscripts of Irish historical, archaeological and antiquarian interest. Frederic Bigger, the collector's brother, donated the collection in 1927, and a catalogue of 3,000 entries was published in 1930.

Other major Irish holdings include some 800 pre-1851 Belfast imprints, an extensive collection of printed maps of Ireland and several author collections, including books and manuscripts, e.g. Forrest Reid, Amanda McKittrick Ros, Lynn Doyle and Sam Thompson. Complementing the Irish Collection is the Newspaper Collection, which contains virtually complete runs of the *Belfast Telegraph, News Letter, Irish News* and *Northern Whig*, plus extensive holdings of provincial papers from Ireland, north and south. The library has a newspaper cuttings index covering the eighteenth and nineteenth centuries that may provide a short cut to finding information in the papers. The library does not offer genealogical services *per se*, but its holdings in this area are extensive and staff are willing to assist researchers as far as possible. Online resources available to members include Ancestry.com, and staff will demonstrate its use. *See* separate listing below for more details on the BELFAST, ULSTER AND IRISH STUDIES department located in BELFAST CENTRAL LIBRARY.

LOCATION
City centre, a few blocks north of Belfast City Hall. Public car parks nearby.

BELFAST, ULSTER AND IRISH STUDIES, BELFAST CENTRAL LIBRARY
See LIBRARIES NI HERITAGE COLLECTION, BELFAST CENTRAL LIBRARY

BUSINESS INFORMATION SERVICES AND EURO INFO CENTRE
See INVEST NORTHERN IRELAND, Belfast

DIOCESAN LIBRARY OF DOWN, DROMORE AND CONNOR

Note: This Church of Ireland library no longer exists. Books were split between the Representative Church Body Library, Dublin, and the Armagh Public Library, Armagh. Some manuscript material was sent to the Public Record Office of Northern Ireland, Belfast.

DOWN AND CONNOR DIOCESAN ARCHIVES

73a Somerton Road
BELFAST, BT15 4DJ
Northern Ireland

TELEPHONE: (028) 9077 6185

HOURS
By appointment

ACCESS AND SERVICES
Privately funded archives of the Roman Catholic Diocese of Down and Connor, which includes Belfast. Advance notice required. Apply to Archivist. Photocopying available for a fee.

CONTACT
Diocesan Archivist

DESCRIPTION
Archives for the largest Roman Catholic diocese in Northern Ireland, which historically embraces Belfast, County Antrim, most of County Down and the Liberties of Coleraine in County Londonderry.

HOLDINGS
Houses the official records of the Roman Catholic see of Down and Connor. Of special interest are the correspondence files of various bishops of the diocese dating back to 1803. Nineteenth-century materials sparse.

LOCATION
In the Fortwilliam section of north-east Belfast, between Antrim Road and Shore Road.

EDGEHILL THEOLOGICAL COLLEGE

9 Lennoxvale
BELFAST, BT9 5BY
Northern Ireland

TELEPHONE: (028) 9068 6935; FAX: (028) 9068 7204
E-mail: librarian@edgehillcollege.org
Website: www.edgehillcollege.org

HOURS
Term time: M–F, 09:00–17:00
Vacation period: by appointment

ACCESS AND SERVICES
Theological library primarily for the faculty and students of this Methodist college.
Visitors welcome but restrictions may apply. Photocopying available for a fee.

CONTACT
Dr Stephen Edgar, College Librarian

DESCRIPTION
Private religious library run by the Methodist Church in Ireland.

HOLDINGS
Library of over 13,000 catalogued volumes, with special emphasis on Methodism
and theology. Includes some rare material. Collection also includes considerable
material on Pastoral Theology, Irish/Northern Irish history, 'the Troubles', and
Reconciliation Studies. Note: some older material has been transferred to the
WESLEY HISTORICAL SOCIETY IN IRELAND, Belfast.

LOCATION
3.5 acre campus located about 1.5 miles south of the city centre, between Malone
Road and Stranmillis Road, near Stranmillis University College and Queen's
University.

GAMBLE LIBRARY
See UNION THEOLOGICAL COLLEGE, Belfast

GENERAL REGISTER OFFICE

Northern Ireland Statistics and Research Agency
Oxford House, 49–55 Chichester Street
BELFAST, BT1 4HL
Northern Ireland

TELEPHONE: 0300 200 7890;
(if calling from outside Northern Ireland (028) 9151 3101); FAX: (028) 9047 5746
E-mail: gro.nisra@dfpni.gov.uk (certificate, public searech room or genealogical
enquiries); groreg.nisra@dfpni.gov.uk (adoption, marriage, civil partnership, death
and name change enquiries); grostats.nisra@dfpni.gov.uk (statistical queries)
Website: www.nidirect.gov.uk/gro

HOURS
M–F, 09:30–16:00 (telephones open from 09:00–16:45); closed public holidays

ACCESS AND SERVICES
Open to the general public, but application forms required. Disabled access facilities. General searches and index searches may be made by any member of the public over 16 years of age. Fees charged for searches and extracts. Current fees:

full certified birth, death, marriage and adoption or civil partnership certificates, £15.00; short birth or adoption certificate, £15.00; priority certificate £35.00; general assisted searches, £35.00 per hour; index searches, £14.00 (up to six hours or part thereof). First two verifications included in fee and further verifications £4.00 each.

The GRO now offers an online certificate ordering service (www.nidirect.gov.uk/gro). The following public search facilities are available for anyone interested in tracing ancestors (note: children cannot be admitted to the search room):

Assisted searches. General search of records assisted by members of GRO staff for any period of years and any number of entries. Appointments are available in one hour slots.

Index search. Volumes of indexes are available for searching with limited verification of entries by staff.

Note: To book the above services, telephone 0300 200 7890; if calling from outside Northern Ireland (028) 9151 3101), e-mail: gro.nisea@dfpni.gov.uk. Appointments should be made in advance. Access may be gained if the facility is not fully booked, however to guarantee that a place will be available prebooking is advised.

CONTACT
Customer Services Manager

DESCRIPTION
The GRO is part of the Northern Ireland Statistics and Research Agency and is primarily concerned with the administration of the registration of births, deaths and marriages. The main records held are statutory registers of births, deaths, marriages, still births and adoptions. The registers themselves are not open to inspection, but the information from them is supplied in the form of certificates. The GRO, formally established in 1922 following partition, stores vital records of Northern Ireland for issue of certified copies to the public. Birth, death and Roman Catholic marriage registrations date from 1864 to present; non-Roman Catholic marriages date from 1845 to present; adoptions date from 1931 to present; still-births date from 1961 to present (not open to the general public). Civil partnerships registered in Northern Ireland from December 2005, Second World War death indexes from 1939 to 1945.

HOLDINGS
The GRO holds paper indexes for births from 1864 onwards, deaths from 1922 onwards and Roman Catholic marriages from 1864 to present and non-Roman Catholic marriages from 1845 to present. It holds computerised indexes for births from 1864 onwards, deaths from 1864 onwards and marriages from 1845 onwards.

LOCATION
City centre, on the street extending from City Hall to Law Courts and Waterfront Hall.

INVEST NORTHERN IRELAND – BUSINESS INFORMATION CENTRE & ENTERPRISE EUROPE NETWORK

Bedford Square, Bedford Street
BELFAST, BT2 7ES
Northern Ireland

TELEPHONE: (028) 9069 8135
E-mail: bic@investni.com
Website: www.investni.com

HOURS
M, 13:00–17:00; Tu–F, 09:00–17:00

ACCESS AND SERVICES
Visitors welcome by appointment. Disabled access facilities. Business information resources and services available to any Northern Ireland company/individual with market research requirements. Focus on electronic information services and databases. The team can help clients find:

> Market Research on key markets worldwide
> Country Intelligence
> Data on potential or existing clients
> Competitor information
> Sourcing of materials and equipment
> Tender Opportunities
> Business Opportunities
> Information about EU policy, programmes or legislation

CONTACT
Information Officer

DESCRIPTION
Invest Northern Ireland offers businesses and entrepreneurs access to commercial market research and business intelligence through its Business Information Centre. The Enterprise Europe Network team helps businesses successfully operate within the European Union and beyond. Requests for information can be made by phone, e-mail or in person.

HOLDINGS
The Business Information Centre primarily uses electronic resources, but it does maintain a small reference collection of printed sources and industry journals. Strengths of the collection include market analysis and company data.

LOCATION
Belfast city centre.

LAND & PROPERTY SERVICES
ARCHIVE OF ORDNANCE SURVEY OF NORTHERN IRELAND®
MAPPING & PHOTOGRAPHY

Colby House, Stranmillis Court
BELFAST, BT9 5BJ
Northern Ireland

TELEPHONE: (028) 9025 5743; FAX: (028) 9025 5700
E-mail: oldmaps@dfpni.gov.uk
Website: http://maps.osni.gov.uk/

HOURS
M–F, 09:15–16:30; closed public and bank holidays

ACCESS AND SERVICES
The OSNI® Archive Service provides access to a wide range of Northern Ireland historical material dating back to the 1830s for mapping and 1959 for aerial photographs. The Archive is open to the public by appointment only. To make an appointment please telephone (028) 9025 5743 or e-mail oldmaps@dfpni.gov.uk. A search fee applies, in addition to any mapping or photographic materials that you may wish to purchase. For current cost of maps please see the website http://maps.osni.gov.uk/ the price list can be found under Tools/Pricelist. Wheelchair friendly.

CONTACT
Drew Ferris, Archive Mapping

DESCRIPTION
Land & Property Services (LPS) is an executive agency within Department of Finance and Personnel for Northern Ireland. Ordnance Survey of Northern Ireland (OSNI®) was subsumed into LPS in 2008. The Archive Service is located in Colby House, Stranmillis, Belfast, the former headquarters of OSNI®.

HOLDINGS
The archive houses significant holdings of maps and aerial photographs and films: 6 inch scale series maps, 1830–1900; 6 and 25 inch scale series maps, 1830–1900; 6 and 25 inch scale series maps, 1900–50; Irish Grid maps 1959–present; aerial films 1959–present. The archive also houses many original copies of the earlier county series maps.

You can also access/purchase some of the OSNI Historical Archive online at http://maps.osni.gov.uk/ by clicking on Digital Products followed by OSNI® Historical Map Tiles.

The OSNI Historical Archive provides geo-referenced raster data for over 20,000 historical maps dating from 1835 to the 1960s, enabling digital access to maps that are of significant cultural and social value. Used in conjunction with the Historical Points of Interest dataset the archive provides a unique information and educational resource.

LOCATION
Colby House is located in Stranmillis Court, off Stranmillis Road, about 1.5 miles south of city centre, near Stranmillis University College. The building is wheel-chair friendly.

LIBRARIES NI HERITAGE COLLECTION, BELFAST CENTRAL LIBRARY

Belfast, Ulster and Irish Studies,
Belfast Central Library
Royal Avenue
BELFAST, BT1 1EA
Northern Ireland

TELEPHONE: (028) 9050 9199; Fax: (028) 9032 2819
E-mail: buis.belb@librariesni.org.uk
Website: www.librariesni.org.uk

HOURS
M–Th, 09.00–20:00; F, 09:00–17:30; Sa, 09:00–16:30

ACCESS AND SERVICES
Belfast, Ulster and Irish Studies is located on the second floor of Belfast Central
library. The Newspaper library is on the ground floor of the same building with a
separate entrance at the rear of the building. (See main entry for BELFAST
CENTRAL LIBRARY for other services). Visits to the department are welcomed from
groups, societies and schools. Staff are also available to give talks outside of library
premises. There is always a display or exhibition in the reading room, sometimes
accompanied by a talk. The library does not offer genealogical services *per se*, but its
holdings in this area are extensive and staff will assist as far as possible.

CONTACT
Catherine Morrow, Hertiage Services Manager.
E-mail: catherine.morrow@ librariesni.org.uk
Eileen McVerry, Hertiage Services Manager.
E-mail: eileen.mcverry@ librariesni.org.uk

DESCRIPTION
The Belfast, Ulster and Irish Studies Collection is the largest in Northern Ireland,
anchored by the Francis Joseph Bigger Collection. *See also* BELFAST CENTRAL
LIBRARY entry.

HOLDINGS
As well as a book stock of over 60,000 volumes, Belfast, Ulster and Irish Studies has
a significant collection of historic and current journals. Complete runs are held of
journals such as the *Ulster Journal of Archaeology, Capuchin Annual* and the *Belfast
Health Journal*. There is also an extensive collection of Belfast and Ulster directories
and Thom's directory for Dublin. A notable collection of eighteenth and nineteenth
century pamphlets covering such important events as the famine, the Irish land war
and the Act of Union is also held. Irish Manuscripts Commission publications have
been collected for many years.
    A selection of school and electoral registers are available to consult.
    Government publications are held for both Northern Ireland and the Republic
of Ireland from 1922. The collection includes the publications of the Irish
parliament prior to 1800, plus a selection of local acts, departmental publications
and reports from the nineteenth century.
    The department has a fine collection of maps, both contemporary and
antiquarian. Various Ordnance Survey series are held from the 1830s onwards.

Specialist maps cover a diverse range of topics from coal mines to the railway system in the nineteenth century.

A large photograph collection focuses on Belfast with images of the Belfast gasworks, docks and the inner city of the 1970s. There are also photographs of other areas of Ireland. The Lawrence collection is available on microfilm.

A picture postcard collection covers Ireland with views of famous locations in each county. There are also postcards on cinemas, transport and political leaders.

The archive collection contains 100,000 items of correspondence and manuscripts. The F.J. Bigger archive forms the largest part of the collection, covering such subjects as archaeology and the United Irishmen. Literary archives of note include the work of well known writers such as Sam Thompson and Lynn Doyle.

Currently around 75 daily, weekly and Sunday newspapers covering all of Ireland are subscribed to. The historical collection, housed in the newspaper library, contains over 7,000 volumes of newspapers and approximately 7,000 microfilm reels.

LOCATION
Second Floor of Belfast Central Library, city centre, a few blocks north of Belfast City Hall. Public car parks nearby.

LINEN HALL LIBRARY

17 Donegall Square North
BELFAST, BT1 5GB
Northern Ireland

TELEPHONE: (028) 9032 1707; FAX: (028) 9043 8586
E-mail: info@linenhall.com
Website: www.linenhall.com

HOURS
M–F, 09:30–17:30; Sa, 09:30–16:00

ACCESS AND SERVICES
Independent subscribing research library with some public funding. Open to the public free of charge for reference services. Advance notice for research use advised. Borrowing privileges restricted to members. General stacks and modern Irish interest material are open access; otherwise stacks are closed access. Access to research resources in the Northern Ireland Political Literature Collection requires a written letter of introduction from a university or research institute. Disabled access facilities. Houses the city's largest general lending collection at one location. Photocopying and microform prints available for a fee. Laptops and cameras can be used by arrangement. Immediate membership available. Leaflets for membership and for collections available. Other publications include the annual report and library newsletter. See also John Killen, *History of the Linen Hall Library* (Belfast, 1990).

CONTACT
John Killen, Librarian

DESCRIPTION
The Linen Hall Library was founded in 1788 as the Belfast Reading Society and is the oldest library in Belfast. It is also the last surviving subscribing library in Ireland. The library recently opened a spacious and attractive addition to its historic nineteenth century headquarters, formerly a warehouse in the linen district.

HOLDINGS
The library houses more than 250,000 volumes, 75,000 pamphlets, plus significant
holdings of periodicals, newspapers, manuscripts, maps, microforms, photographs,
films and recordings. It maintains a general lending and reference collection, the
latter being especially strong in genealogy, heraldry, history and travel. Its great
strength, however, is the Irish and Local Studies Collection, with particularly strong
material on Belfast and Counties Antrim and Down. The library seeks to collect in
all Irish interest areas. The Northern Ireland Political Literature Collection,
1968–present, contains some 350,000 items relating to the 'Troubles', including
runs of about 2,000 periodical titles, 11,500 books, 5,000 posters, 55,000
photographs, significant archives and extensive ephemera. The Genealogical
Collection includes some 5,000 volumes, mainly of Ulster interest and Scottish and
American connections, plus army, church and educational lists. Other significant
collections include the Kennedy Collection of Ulster Poetry, the Theatre and
Performing Arts Archive, the Belfast Printed Books Collection 1697–present, the
Michael McLaverty Literary Archive, the Irish Postcard Collection and the Michael
Williams Collection, which contains a first edition of James Joyce's *Ulysses*.

LOCATION
Iconic city centre entrance, facing the front of Belfast City Hall.

METHODIST HISTORICAL SOCIETY OF IRELAND

Edgehill College
9 Lennoxvale
BELFAST, BT9 5BY
Northern Ireland

TELEPHONE: (028) 9068 6934
E-mail: archives@irishmethodist.org

HOURS
W–Th, 09:00–12:00

ACCESS AND SERVICES
Appointment in advance with Archivist advisable. Photocopying facilities available
on request. Alphabetical name, geographical and keyword card catalogues to
periodicals and journals available offsite for consultation. Shelf list in manuscript
detailing archival holdings also available.

CONTACT
Rev Robin P. Roddie, Honorary Archivist: archives@irishmethodist.org

DESCRIPTION
The Methodist Historical Society of Ireland administers and maintains an archive
and reading room in Belfast with a comprehensive and unrivalled collection of works
on or relating to Methodism in Ireland. It was founded in 1926 to promote the
study of the Methodist Church in Ireland.

HOLDINGS
The collection comprises over 12,000 items and is particularly strong in the works of
John and Charles Wesley and Adam Clark. It contains extensive runs of Methodist
journals and periodicals, including the *Irish Evangelist* (1859–83), the *Christian*

Advocate (1883–1923), the *Irish Christian Advocate* (1923–71) and the *Methodist Newsletter* (1973–present). Other series include the Dublin edition of the *Methodist Magazine* (1801–23) and the *Primitive Wesleyan Methodist Magazine* (1823–45), which was unique to Ireland. The collection also includes a range of original and printed manuscript materials. These comprise the archives of the Methodist Historical Society of Ireland from 1926 onwards, original diaries and journals of Irish preachers such as Rev Adam Averell (1754–1847), founder of the Irish Primitive Wesleyans in 1818, a complete series of minutes of the Irish Conference from 1752, Methodist church registers, photographs and other ephemera relating to Methodism in Ireland. The archive holds substantial holdings of local church records, including baptismal and marriage records. Of major interest is the 'Register of Irish Methodist Ministers' with lists of appointments and biographical information.

LOCATION
South Belfast, close to Malone Road.

NORTHERN IRELAND ASSEMBLY LIBRARY

Parliament Buildings, Stormont
BELFAST, BT4 3XX
Northern Ireland

TELEPHONE: (028) 9052 1250; FAX: (028) 9052 1922
E-mail: library@niassembly.gov.uk

HOURS
M–F, 09:00–17:00 (and until half hour after completion of Assembly sittings if after 16:30)

ACCESS AND SERVICES
Usually limited to members and staff of the Northern Ireland Assembly and to government personnel. Referrals made to other appropriate sources. Some exceptions may be made. Appointment required. Apply in writing to Librarian, preferably with sponsorship of an academic institution. Short extracts may be copied. Loans may not be made to visitors.

CONTACT
Stephen Browne, Principal Librarian. E-mail: Stephen.browne@niassembly.gov.uk

DESCRIPTION
Established in 1921 to serve members and staff of the Parliament of Northern Ireland, and from 1973 the Northern Ireland Assembly.

HOLDINGS
The collection includes some 12,500 books, 70,000 official publications, 150 journals, 2,000 microforms and three photograph albums. In addition to collecting Northern Ireland official publications and legislation, the library focuses on Irish history and Northern Ireland history, government and politics. The Northern Ireland Collection emphasises public administration, ethnic/religious conflict and constitutional law. Collections of special note include a collection of eighteenth century and earlier historical and topographical materials, eighteenth century

journals, acts of parliament and other Irish parliamentary material. There is also access to about 45 electronic services, both online and CD-ROM.

LOCATION
Parliament Buildings, Stormont, east of Belfast city centre. Approach from either Massey Avenue or the Upper Newtownards Road. Limited parking available.

NORTHERN IRELAND HOUSING EXECUTIVE – LIBRARY INFORMATION SERVICES

The Housing Centre
2 Adelaide Street
BELFAST, BT2 8PB
Northern Ireland

TELEPHONE: (028) 9031 8022; FAX: (028) 9031 8024
E-mail: library@nihe.gov.uk
Website: www.nihe.gov.uk

HOURS
M–Th, 10:00–17:00; F, 10:00–16:00

ACCESS AND SERVICES
Library primarily for use of staff. Visitors welcome to consult for reference purposes, but by appointment only. Advance notice required. Laptops permitted. Open stacks. Collection catalogued on computer. Disabled access facilities. Short extracts may be copied. Restricted city centre parking.

CONTACT
Margaret Gibson, Library Information Services Manager. E-mail: margaret.a.gibson@nihe.gov.uk

DESCRIPTION
The Housing Executive administers a vast network of public housing throughout Northern Ireland. Its library serves the reference and research needs of staff.

HOLDINGS
The library's collection includes some 12,000 volumes and pamphlets, plus some 200 periodical titles gathered to meet staff reference and research needs. Special interests include architecture and planning, construction, landscape design, housing, the public sector, management, finance and the social sciences, especially sociology. The library also archives Housing Executive publications.

LOCATION
City centre.

ORDNANCE SURVEY OF NORTHERN IRELAND
See LAND & PROPERTY SERVICES, ARCHIVE OF ORDNANCE SURVEY OF NORTHERN IRELAND® MAPPING & PHOTOGRAPHY, Belfast

POLICE MUSEUM

PSNI Headquarters
'Brooklyn', 65 Knock Road
BELFAST, BT5 6LE
Northern Ireland

TELEPHONE: (020) 90 650 222, ext. 22499
E-mail: museum@psni.police.uk
Website: www.psni.police.uk/museum

HOURS
M–F, 10:00–13.00, 14:00–16:30

ACCESS AND SERVICES
Visitors welcome, but prior appointment preferred. Parking for disabled available
and wheelchair access to some public areas. Brochure/leaflet and guide to the
collection available. Study space can be made available. Groups should book in
advance. A genealogical search service is available for constabulary service records,
1822–1922. Museum may also be viewed on the internet.

CONTACT
Hugh Forrester, Curator

DESCRIPTION
The museum includes displays of uniforms and equipment, photographs and
memorabilia relating to the Irish Constabulary since its formation in 1822. The prefix
'Royal' was added in 1867 and in 1922 the Royal Ulster Constabulary was created. In
November 2001, the RUC became the Police Service of Northern Ireland (PSNI).

HOLDINGS
The museum houses a unique collection of material ranging over the 200 years of
organised policing in Ireland. The collection contains an extensive range of uniforms
and associated 'appointments', firearms, medals, badges and trophies and other
material relating generally to policing. There is an archive of photographic material
and documents dating back to the early nineteenth century. The museum also
includes a reference library and research facility containing personnel records of the
early constabulary.

LOCATION
East Belfast, off Upper Newtownards Road.

PRESBYTERIAN HISTORICAL SOCIETY OF IRELAND (PHSI)

26 College Green
BELFAST, BT7 1LN
Northern Ireland

TELEPHONE: (028) 9072 7330
E-mail: phsilibrarian@pcinet.org
Website: www.presbyterianhistoryireland.org

HOURS
Tu–W, 09:30–13:00, 13:30–16:30; Th, 09:30–13:00

ACCESS AND SERVICES
Visitors welcome, no appointment necessary but you can do so if preferred and all
non-members must register. Ground floor premises are fully accessible for those with
a disability. Microfilming viewing facilities (but not microfilm print-outs);
photocopying and scanning available for a small fee. Tours and talks are also offered.
Publications include: *A History of Congregations in the Presbyterian Church in Ireland,
1610–2011* (now only available online on PHSI website to Members and to
Associate Members); *Fasti of the General Assembly of the Presbyterian Church in
Ireland 1840–1910, and of the Seceder Ministers Ordained or Installed in Ireland
1746–1948;* and booklets on a range of topics such as Orangeism, Revival and
Communion Tokens and on the lives of prominent Presbyterian ministers such as
Sinclair Kelburn and the 1798 Rebellion and Francis Makemie, the founder of
Presbyterianism in America.

CONTACT
Librarian and Assistant Secretary

DESCRIPTION
The Presbyterian Historical Society of Ireland was created in 1906 to promote
public awareness of the history of the Presbyterian Churches in Ireland. It is largely
supported by the Presbyterian Church in Ireland.

HOLDINGS
The Society possesses a library of some 12,000 books and pamphlets. These are
mainly concerned with ecclesiastical history and in particular Presbyterian history.
The collection includes a large number of congregational histories. A microfilm copy
of *The Witness*, a Presbyterian newspaper covering the period 1874 –1941, is also
available for consultation, as are the printed minutes of the General Synod of Ulster
from 1691–1838, and of the General Assembly beginning in 1840.

Manuscript material includes session minutes, baptisms and marriages for
individual churches as well as some Presbytery minutes. These include session
accounts for Armagh Presbyterian Church, 1707–32, session minutes for Aghadowey
Presbyterian Church, 1702–61, and baptisms, 1726–1815, and marriages, 1727–92,
with gaps, for Cullybackey (Cunningham Memorial) Presbyterian Church. The *Guide
to Church Records* produced by the Public Record Office of Northern Ireland (Belfast,
1994) and available on the Record Office website indicates which congregational
records are available at the Presbyterian Historical Society. The Society also has a
duplicate set of the microfilm copies of Presbyterian Church registers held by PRONI
covering the vast majority of Presbyterian congregations in Ireland.

Of particular interest is the large amount of biographical data on Presbyterian
ministers. This material can be accessed through a card index, while there are also
handwritten and printed *fasti* providing information on clergymen. The Society also
holds many individual manuscripts, sermons, photographs of churches and ministers
and personal papers of Presbyterian ministers. These include some of the papers of
the most distinguished nineteenth century Presbyterian minister, the Rev Henry
Cooke, and the correspondence and diaries of the Rev Andrew Weir, Presbyterian
missionary to China from 1893–1933.

LOCATION
At the junction of College Green and Rugby Road beside Union Theological College
and near to Queen's University, Belfast. Easily accessible by bus (Metro 7A or 7B) or
by rail (Botanic rail station).

PUBLIC RECORD OFFICE OF NORTHERN IRELAND (PRONI)

2 Titanic Boulevard
Titanic Quarter
BELFAST, BT3 9HQ
Northern Ireland

TELEPHONE: (028) 9053 4800; FAX: (028) 9053 4900
E-mail: proni@dcalni.gov.uk
Website: www.proni.gov.uk

HOURS
M–W, F, 09:00–16:45; Th, 09:00–20:45
DOCUMENT ORDERING TIMES: M–W, F, 09:00–16:15; Th, 10:00–20:15

ACCESS AND SERVICES
PRONI is part of the Department of Culture, Arts and Leisure (DCAL), and open to the general public. Exhibitions, displays and artwork are free to visit without registering. Photographic ID is required for first time users to register before they can view the archives. Advance notice is required for group visits but not for individuals. All public areas are accessible to those with a disability, and there is provision of a lift, Braille signage throughout, PCs with adjustable font size, a loop hearing system and adjustable tables and chairs available. Laptops are permitted at selected points within the Reading Room and there is free WiFi in all public areas including the café.

For a fee, photocopying services are available, usually carried out by staff. There is also a self-service digital camera for public use. Staff are happy to advise on any aspect of the service or facilities.

For queries about our opening hours, etc, please see website. Though PRONI is the major resource for genealogical information in Northern Ireland, it cannot provide a comprehensive research service. However, it can undertake paid searches in response to specific requests for information and staff on site will give guidance to visitors. Records of government departments, courts, local authorities and other public bodies not yet open to the public are subject to the Freedom of Information Act (2000). This provides general access rights but also includes provisions that may exempt information from release for extended periods – for example, sensitive personal data. Applications for access should be made in writing.

CONTACT
FOI/Access Requests: Access to Information Unit
Written and e-mail enquiries: Enquiries Unit
Group visits: Reader Services

DESCRIPTION
PRONI was established in 1923 following partition and opened in 1924 as the official repository for public records in Northern Ireland; however, it also houses an expansive collection of private records.

HOLDINGS
PRONI has more than 53 kilometres of shelves filled with records. The bulk of its public records deal with Northern Ireland since the early 1920s, but some go back as far as the eighteenth century, while the nineteenth and twentieth are well represented. The archive also includes documents from private sources, some dating back to the

fourteenth century, with strong holdings of material from the 1600s. PRONI's
holdings can be divided into a number of categories: *Public Records*, which includes
tithe applotment records, valuation books and maps, Poor Law records and school
records: *Private Archives* which includes church records (available in the Self Service
Microfilm area), landed estate records, business records, solicitors' records, records of
private individuals and families, and photographs. See website for full details.

WEBSITE: There is no single guidebook to the records of PRONI but the fully
searchable *Electronic Catalogue* (e-CATNI), with over 1.5 million individual entries,
is available onsite and on the PRONI website. This is freely available 24/7 and will
permit research to be carried out at home at a time convenient to the researcher.
Also on the PRONI website are professionally written introductions to the major
private collections. Most relate to the archives of the great landed estates, but there
are some introductions to business records, including the shipbuilding firm, Harland
and Wolff. There are introductions to government and non-departmental records,
such as the Ministry/Department of Education. There is a complete Guide to
Church records of all churches in the north of Ireland with a reference number and
covering dates for those records that have been microfilmed by PRONI. The website
includes copies of PRONI's information leaflets that describe the content of different
types of records and how to access them, including tracing family trees, local history
and on different topics such as the Famine, the Act of Union and the Titanic.
   There are several useful online web resources, for example: the *Ulster Covenant*
lists the name, address and place of signing of almost half a million people who
signed the Covenant in 1912 (there is also a feature that allows you to view the page
where the actual signature occurs); the pre-1840 *Freeholders Registers*, lists people
who were entitled to vote, or who actually voted, at elections with images of the
pages on which the name occurs; *Street Directories*; for Belfast and Ulster date from
1809 to the 1980s (not a complete series) which give names, occupations and
addresses of inhabitants; *Will indexes* from 1858 to *c.* 1945, giving details of next of
kin and effects; *Name search* contains names and information gathered from indexes
to books that no longer exist and also include the coroners' index of inquests,
1872–1920. In terms of social media, the Allison photograph collection has been
digitised and is available on the photo-sharing website, Flickr. PRONI also hosts a
YouTube video channel called PRONIonline which includes lectures that have been
filmed.
   Other indexes, guides and information of a general nature, for example, the
annual *Deputy Keeper's Reports* and the *Annual Report and Accounts* can be found on
the PRONI website. A full list of those publications still available appears on the
PRONI website. All of these items and more, may be accessed free of charge.

LOCATION
Located close to the Odyssey Arena, PRONI is a ten minute walk from the city
centre. Metro buses No. 26b and 26c run every ten minutes from Wellington Place.
The Titanic Halt railway station is approximately 15 minutes walk away. Car parks
are available at the Odyssey Arena, the Met College, and on the Queen's Road.

QUEEN'S UNIVERSITY BELFAST LIBRARY

McClay Library
10 College Park
BELFAST, BT7 1LP
Northern Ireland

TELEPHONE: (028) 028 9097 6135
E-mail: library@qub.ac.uk, or use website for contact
Website: www.qub.ac.uk/lib

HOURS
McClay Library
Term time: M–Th, 09:00–21:30; F, 09:00–20:00; Sa, 10:00–17:00; Su, 12:00–17:00
Vacation period: M–Th, 09:00–20:00; F, 09:00–17:00; Sa, 10:00–17:00

Special Collections
Term time: M–Th, 09:00–21:30; F, 09:00–20:00; Sa, 10:00–17:00; Su, 12:00–17:00
Vacation period: M–Th, 09:00–20:00; F, 09:00–17:00; Sa, 10:00–17:00

ACCESS AND SERVICES
Queen's University Belfast Library is a publicly funded academic research library open to the general public for reference purposes where material may not be readily accessed elsewhere. Researchers welcome but intending visitors should register in advance (see: www.qub.ac.uk/directorates/InformationServices/TheLibrary/ TheMcClayLibrary/AccesstotheLibrary/). Laptops permitted. Photocopying restricted. Digital cameras permitted. Digital copies can be provided when photocopying is not permitted; this is a fee based service. The Library, including the Special Collections Department, is wheelchair accessible. All books and journals listed on online catalogue and classified according to Library of Congress classification. Printed guide to manuscript collections available for consultation; guides to manuscript collections may also be accessed electronically from Special Collections Department web pages. See library website: www.qub.ac.uk/lib.

RASCAL
Research and Special Collections Available Locally, hosted by Queen's University Belfast, is a web based directory of special collections available for consultation in Ireland. It provides online access to collection descriptions and contact details to resources held in local libraries, museums and archives. Over 400 collections in almost 70 institutions are listed. The RASCAL Directory is accessible at www.rascal.ac.uk

Queen's University Branch Libraries
Branch libraries are not listed separately in this guide. These are located outside the McClay Library and may be contacted directly as follows:
Biomedical Library, Medical Biology Centre, Lisburn Road, Belfast BT9 7BL. Tel.: (028) 9032 9241, extension 2797/(028) 9026 3913; fax: (028) 9031 5560;
Medical Library, Mulhouse Building, Mulhouse Road, Belfast BT12 6DP. Tel.: (028) 9063 2501.

CONTACT
Elizabeth Traynor, Assistant Director of Information Services
Deirdre Wildy, Head of Special Collections and Archives. Tel.: (028) 9097 6218;
e-mail: d.wildy@qub.ac.uk

DESCRIPTION
Queen's College Belfast was established in Ireland by Queen Victoria in 1845, along
with colleges in Cork and Galway. In 1908 it was elevated to university rank with its
own charter and statutes. Today the university enrols more than 26,000 full and part
time students. Recently two colleges were added to the university: Stranmillis
University College and St Mary's University College. For more information on the
university, see T.W. Moody and J.C. Beckett, *Queen's Belfast* (1959) and B.M.
Walker and A. McCreary, *Degrees of Excellence* (1994).

HOLDINGS
The Library houses the largest collection in Northern Ireland. Queen's Library alone
contains more than 1,000,000 volumes, plus significant holdings of pamphlets,
periodicals and manuscripts. The collection is quite diverse, representing the
teaching and research interests of the curriculum and faculty. The Special Collections
Department houses approximately100,000 volumes, including 20 incunabula,
manuscript collections and the University Archive. Major collections include the
Hibernica Collection, a collection of books and pamphlets relating to the literature,
politics and social history of Ireland; the Percy Collection, the eighteenth century
library of the Church of Ireland Bishop of Dromore; the Bunting Collection,
eighteenth century music manuscripts; the Andrews and Thomson Collections of
early scientific papers; the Somerville and Ross Collection, consisting of diaries,
correspondence and manuscripts; the Hart Collection, comprising the diaries,
personal papers and many personal photographs of Sir Robert Hart, Inspector
General of the Chinese Imperial Maritime Customs, 1863–1908; and the Cardinal
Cahal Daly Collection, the private library of the former Roman Catholic Archbishop
of Armagh and Primate of All Ireland.

LOCATION
One mile south of city centre, near Botanic Gardens and the Ulster Museum.

ST MARY'S UNIVERSITY COLLEGE LIBRARY

191 Falls Road
BELFAST, BT12 6FE
Northern Ireland

TELEPHONE: (028) 9026 8237; FAX: (028) 9033 3719
E-mail: library@stmarys-belfast.ac.uk
Website: www.stmarys-belfast.ac.uk

HOURS
Term time: M–Th, 09:00–09:00; F, 09:00–17:00; Sa, 09:00–13:00
Vacation period: M–F, 09:00–17:00
Closed St Patrick's Day, Easter Week, 12 and 13 July, Christmas–New Year period

ACCESS AND SERVICES
One of two publicly funded university colleges of Queen's University Belfast. Library open to visiting staff and students from other higher education establishments for reference purposes. Open stacks. ID required, as is signing of visitor's book. Disabled access facilities. Library has a printed guide, photocopying facilities and internet access.

CONTACT
Felicity Jones, Librarian. E-mail: f.jones@smucb.ac.uk
Ciaran Crossey, Acquisitions Librarian. E-mail: c.crossey@smucb.ac.uk

DESCRIPTION
St Mary's University College was founded in 1900 by the Dominican Sisters to educate young women for the Roman Catholic school system. In 1985, St Mary's amalgamated with St Joseph's, its male counterpart, to form the present St Mary's University College. While maintaining its independence, the college has a special relationship with Queen's University, which validates St Mary's degrees and gives St Mary's Students full access to Queen's Library resources. The purpose of the college has expanded with the introduction of a BA degree in Liberal Arts and the education and training of teachers for Irish language schools.

HOLDINGS
The collection includes 90,000 items, nearly 100 print journals and provides access to a large range of online journals and a growing collection of eBooks. There is a substantial range of non-book materials and teaching and learning resources. Areas of chief curriculum interest include: education, Irish language, religious education and theology, business studies, European studies, human development, philosophy, physical education, design and technology, English, art, history, geography and science.

LOCATION
One mile west of Belfast city centre, on the Falls Road, close to the Royal Victoria Hospital.

SEAMUS HEANEY LIBRARY
See QUEEN'S UNIVERSITY BELFAST LIBRARY

STRANMILLIS UNIVERSITY COLLEGE LIBRARY

Stranmillis Road
BELFAST, BT9 5DY
Northern Ireland

TELEPHONE: (028) 9038 4310
E-mail: library@stran.ac.uk
Website: www.stran.ac.uk

HOURS
Term time: M–Th, 09:00–21:00; F, 09:00–16:30
Vacation period: M–Th, 09:00–17:00; F, 09:00–16:30

ACCESS AND SERVICES
One of two publicly funded education colleges in Northern Ireland, integrated
academically with Queen's University Belfast. Library open to general public for
reference purposes. Visitors welcome, especially out of term, but borrowing
privileges are restricted. ID useful. Open stacks. Wheelchair access to majority of
Library. Library offers photocopying and microform prints, computerised databases,
finding aids and a printed guides.

CONTACT
Ingrid Mercer, Head of Library and Learning Support Services

DESCRIPTION
Stranmillis was founded in 1922 as a training college for teachers. Today it
concentrates on preparing teachers who work with children of ages three to thirteen;
those who work in early childhood education; and those who work in the health and
leisure sector. Its library supports the learning, teaching and research needs of staff
and students.

HOLDINGS
The collection includes some 80,000 volumes and over 100 print journals with
electronic access to many more. Areas of chief curriculum interest are: primary
education (with its associated curricular subjects), early childhood education, and
health and leisure studies. Among special collections of interest are: the Ulster
Collection of books relating to the northern counties of Ireland, a modest collection
of nineteenth century Irish school books, a microfilm copy of the *Belfast News Letter*
1737–1925 and a microfilm copy of the Lawrence Collection of Irish photographs
1880–1914 (the original is located at the National Library of Ireland, Dublin).

LOCATION
Two miles south of city centre, on Stranmillis Road. Spacious, beautifully
landscaped campus. Parking available by arrangement.

ULSTER AND IRISH STUDIES, BELFAST CENTRAL LIBRARY
See LIBRARIES NI HERITAGE COLLECTION, BELFAST CENTRAL LIBRARY

ULSTER HISTORICAL FOUNDATION

49 Malone Road
BELFAST, BT9 6RY
Northern Ireland

TELEPHONE: (028) 9066 1988; FAX: (028) 9066 1977
E-mail: enquiry@uhf.org.uk
Website: www.ancestryireland.com, www.booksireland.org.uk

HOURS
Visitor's welcome, M–F, 09:30–17:00; appointment preferred for research
consultation service (but not essential)

ACCESS AND SERVICES
A self-sustaining educational not for profit, fee based genealogical research centre
and publisher, open to the public. Research consultancy provided for a fee.
Preliminary search assessments to establish whether research is feasible also carried

out for a charge of £30/US$48. For schedule of research fees, see website (www.ancestryireland.com/research-services/). An initial research report (a specific piece of limited research) costs £99.99, a full research report averages £150–£250. Individual one-to-one consultation at the Foundation's offices, £15 per 15 minute session. The Foundation has undertaken over 13,000 searches for clients throughout the world and each year answers some 2,000 genealogical enquiries. It publishes a wide range of materials, primarily in the areas of Irish, local and family history, and guides to research. For details of UHF's extensive backlist go to: www.booksireland.org.uk.

CONTACT
Fintan Mullan, Executive Director

DESCRIPTION
The Ulster Historical Foundation is the principal genealogical research centre in Ireland, with a concentration on the province of Ulster (six counties of Northern Ireland, plus Counties Cavan, Donegal and Monaghan in the Republic of Ireland). Founded in 1956 to promote interest in Ulster history and genealogy, it provides a professional and comprehensive research service, publishes books and pamphlets and organises annual family history and heritage events. It is a member of the Irish Family History Foundation an island-wide effort to computerise all the major Irish genealogical sources. To this end, it has been at work for years compiling a comprehensive computerised database of genealogical records for Ulster, principally for Counties Antrim and Down, including Belfast. The database is used as a tool, in conjunction with other documentary sources, to provide a comprehensive ancestral research service.

HOLDINGS
The Foundation's database contains: pre-1900 church and civil records 1845–1921 for counties Antrim and Down, including Belfast, plus gravestone transcripts for most of Northern Ireland and calendars of flax growers in Ireland in 1796. It also houses a collection of more than13,000 family history reports, which it has been compiling since 1956.

LOCATION
In the University Quarter, on a main thoroughfare (Malone Road), approximately a quarter-mile from Queen's University Belfast.

ULSTER MUSEUM LIBRARY
The Library is now housed at the Ulster Museum's sister institution, the Ulster Folk and Transport Museum. See separate entry for the ULSTER MUSEUM LIBRARY under Hollywood, County Down.

UNION THEOLOGICAL COLLEGE – GAMBLE LIBRARY

108 Botanic Avenue
BELFAST, BT7 1JT
Northern Ireland

TELEPHONE: (028) 9020 5093
E-mail: librarian@union.ac.uk
Website: www.union.ac.uk/library

HOURS (for visitors)
M–F, 09:00–16:00; closed Easter Week, Twelfth Fortnight (July) and Christmas–New Year period (two weeks)

ACCESS AND SERVICES
Visitors welcome; advance notice preferred. Borrowing privileges available to members, who may join for a current fee of £30 per year. Card catalogue represents approximately 35 per cent of book collection; computer catalogue for books received since 1990, and many earlier. Photocopying available for a fee. The college publishes an annual calendar and a students' handbook.

CONTACT
David Kerry, Librarian

DESCRIPTION
Union Theological College was established by the Presbyterian Church in Ireland. The library supports the work of the faculty, students of the college and ministers.

HOLDINGS
The library houses more than 65,000 books, with a heavy emphasis on theology and Irish church history. A separate collection of rare books features works on theology and church history. Special collections of note include the Magee College Pamphlets Collection and the Assembly's College Pamphlets Collection.

LOCATION
One mile south of Belfast city centre, in the Queen's University quarter.

UNIVERSITY OF ULSTER LIBRARY, BELFAST CAMPUS

York Street
BELFAST, BT15 1ED
Northern Ireland

TELEPHONE: (028) 9536 7268; FAX: (028) 9536 7278
E-mail: m.khorshidian@ulster.ac.uk
Website: library.ulster.ac.uk

HOURS
Term time: M–Th, 08:45–22:00; F, 08:45–18:00; Sa, 10:00–17:00
Vacation period: M–Th, 08:45–17:00; F, 08:45–16:00

ACCESS AND SERVICES
Visitors welcome but ID required. Disabled access facilities, see http://library.ulster.ac.uk/info/disabilities/access.php. Borrowing privileges not extended to visitors unless part of Inspire or SCONUL Access schemes. Entire University of Ulster library system shares a common catalogue database, available free from library website. Visitors may also wish to consult RASCAL website at www.rascal.ac.uk, a web based gateway to research and special collections in Northern Ireland.

CONTACT
Marion Khorshidian, Campus Library Manager

DESCRIPTION
The Belfast campus originated as a technical college in 1849 and was established as a university campus in 1984. It is traditionally considered the home of the School of Art and Design but other subjects are taught on campus including humanities, business and management, mainly at undergraduate level. The campus is part of the four-campus University of Ulster system, which includes Coleraine (County Londonderry), Jordanstown (County Antrim), and Magee, Derry (County Londonderry).

HOLDINGS
The library contains some 65,000 volumes and more than 90,000 slides in support of the campus's curriculum, with strengths in the areas of fine art, design, graphics, fashion, textiles, ceramics, jewellery, metalwork, architecture, film, photography and print-making. It also provides access to over 21,000 online electronic journals and e-books through the four-campus University of Ulster Library system. The library holds occasional exhibitions relating to its holdings/interests, e.g. *The Wood Engravings of Robert Gibbings* (1988), *Illustrated by Hugh Thomson, 1860–1920* (1989), *The Dolmen Press, 1951–87* (1991) and *Wendy Dunbar: Book Designer* (1994). An illustrated catalogue was produced for each of these exhibitions. Recent exhibitions have included material from the Derry and Raphoe conservation project, see: www.derryraphoelibrary.org/index.html

LOCATION
City centre, about one mile north of Belfast City Hall. Royal Avenue becomes York Street just past the Belfast Central Library.

WESLEY HISTORICAL SOCIETY IN IRELAND
See METHODIST HISTORICAL SOCIETY OF IRELAND, Belfast

CARRICKFERGUS LIBRARY

2 Joymount Court
CARRICKFERGUS, COUNTY ANTRIM, BT38 7DQ
Northern Ireland

TELEPHONE: (028) 9336 2261; FAX: (028) 9336 2261
E-mail: carrickfergus.library@librariesni.org.uk
Website: www.librariesni.org.uk

HOURS
M–Th, 09:30–20:00; F, Sa, 09:30–17:00

ACCESS AND SERVICES
Visitors welcome. Borrowing privileges available. Disabled access facilities. Free internet access for all Northern Ireland public library members. One membership card valid for all libraries. Charge of £2.00 per half hour for non-members; ID required. Membership in library open to anyone living, working or studying in the area. In addition to the important local history collection in the M'Skimin Room, the Carrickfergus Library offers books, books on CD, childrens' books on CD, class visits, community information, exhibitions, information service, internet, large print books, music-DVDs, newspapers, magazines, storytimes, talks and special events.

CONTACT
Dawn Young, Branch Manager

DESCRIPTION
The library is one of 96 branch libraries plus 2 specialist libraries in the LIBRARIES NI system, headquartered in Lisburn, County Antrim. In addition to the general collection, the Library houses a special local collection named after an eighteenth century historian of Carrickfergus, Samuel McSkimin. *See* description below.

HOLDINGS
The M'Skimin Collection focuses on Carrickfergus and the surrounding area. It contains nearly 1,000 volumes, with a special emphasis on county histories and Irish literature. The collection includes books, journals, maps, microforms, newspapers, including an archive of local newspapers on microfilm (dating back to the late 1800s) and in bound copies for the more recent editions, and newspaper cuttings. The library's general collection exceeds 30,000 volumes.

LOCATION
Close to the town centre and near Carrickfergus Castle, one of the best preserved Norman castles in Ireland. Carrickfergus is situated on the coast just north of Belfast.

UNIVERSITY OF ULSTER LIBRARY, JORDANSTOWN CAMPUS
See below under Newtownabbey, Co. Antrim.

IRISH LINEN CENTRE AND LISBURN MUSEUM LIBRARY

Market Square
LISBURN, COUNTY ANTRIM, BT28 1AG
Northern Ireland

TELEPHONE: (028) 9266 3377; FAX: (028) 9267 2624
E-mail: irishlinencentre@lisburn.gov.uk
Website: www.lisburnmuseum.com

HOURS
Museum: M–Sa, 09:30–17:00; closed public holidays
Library: M–F, 09:30–16:30

ACCESS AND SERVICES
Museum: open to public free of charge. Access for disabled persons. Car parking for disabled badge holders available. Shop and café offsite.
Library: appointment required. There are no lending facilities. Photocopying service possible, subject to discretion of staff officer in charge. No charge for use of study facilities; however, photocopying is chargeable.

CONTACT
Paul Allison, Museum Services Manager. E-mail: Paul.allison@lisburn.gov.uk

DESCRIPTION
The Irish Linen Centre and Lisburn Museum is financed and managed by Lisburn City Council. Its aim is to collect, safeguard and interpret artefacts and information relating to the Irish linen industry and the history of Lisburn and the Lagan Valley,

making them accessible now and preserving them for the future. The Museum's Research Library contains a range of resources in relation to the Museum's main areas of interest, especially textiles and art in relation to linen, and Irish history, particularly the history of Ulster, Lisburn and the Lagan Valley.

HOLDINGS
The library houses some 2,000 books and approximately 20 journals; a collection of nineteenth and twentieth century Ordnance Survey maps for the district; original copies of the two local newspapers, *Lisburn Herald* and *Lisburn Standard* for many years from the 1890s until the 1950s (also a complete microfilm run for the *Lisburn Standard* from which copies can be printed); microfilm copies of the 1901 census schedules for Lisburn and the surrounding district; and a collection of audio and video tapes relating to the museum's areas of interest. In addition, the library houses the collection of the former Lambeg Industrial Research Association, which closed in 1993. LIRA was originally founded in 1919 as the Linen Industry Research Association and the library collection reflects its research work into a range of aspects of flax and linen production. The library comprises over 6,000 books, journals and research reports. The majority of the material was published between 1900 and 1970; there are also some rare books, pamphlets and journals dating from the eighteenth century.

LOCATION
Town centre. Only 300 metres from rail and bus stations. Disabled parking possible at museum and public car parks within 50 metres. There is a 24 hour interactive tourist information point outside the building.

LIBRARIES NI

Unit 3a,
The Sidings Office Park,
Antrim Road,
LISBURN, COUNTY ANTRIM, BT28 3RG
Northern Ireland

TELEPHONE: (028) 3839 3000; Fax: (028) 3839 9440
E-mail: enquiries@librariesni.org.uk
Website: www.librariesni.org.uk.

DESCRIPTION
On April 1, 2009, the five (5) Education and Library Boards of Northern Ireland listed in the 2007 edition of this guide were reorganised and consolidated into one library authority for the whole of Northern Ireland, with Headquarters located in Lisburn, County Antrim. The Northern Ireland Library Authority was established under The Libraries Act (Northern Ireland) 2008 to provide a comprehensive and efficient public library service for persons living, working or studying in Northern Ireland. Libraries NI oversees some 130 libraries throughout Northern Ireland, with a staff of 727 FTE serving a population of some 1,775,003, with registered users totaling nearly 620,000. In addition to 96 branch libraries, 18 public mobiles, 10 housebound mobiles, and 3 spare mobiles, the Authority supports 2 specialist libraries, IRISH AND LOCAL STUDIES LIBRARY, Armagh City, County Armagh, and the CENTRE FOR MIGRATION STUDIES, ULSTER

AMERICAN FOLK PARK, Omagh, County Tyrone. The Authority is required to maintain a collection of library materials relevant to the cultural heritage of Northern Ireland.

CONTACT
Chief Executive: Irene Knox (Based at Unit 3A, The Sidings Office Park, Antrim Road, Lisburn, BT28 3RG)
Director of Business Support: Terry Heron (Based at Libraries NI, Business Support, 2nd Floor, Portadown Library, 24–26 Church Street, Portadown, BT62 3LQ)
Director of Service Delivery: Helen Osborn (Based at 1 Spillars Place, Omagh, Co Tyrone, BT78 1HL)

HOLDINGS
See Heritage member libraries listed in this guide: **County Antrim** (BALLYMENA LIBRARY, BELFAST CENTRAL LIBRARY); **County Armagh** (ARMAGH IRISH AND LOCAL STUDIES LIBRARY, Armagh City); **County Down** (DOWNPATRICK LIBRARY, NEWRY CITY LIBRARY); **County Fermanagh** (ENNISKILLEN LIBRARY); **County Londonderry** (COLERAINE LIBRARY, DERRY CITY CENTRAL LIBRARY); and **County Tyrone** (OMAGH LIBRARY, Omagh; MELLON CENTRE FOR MIGRATION STUDIES, Omagh).

LOCATION
Town Centre.

THE SOCIETY OF FRIENDS LIBRARY

Meeting House, Railway Street
LISBURN, COUNTY ANTRIM, BT28 1XG
Northern Ireland

ACCESS AND SERVICES
The library deals with postal enquiries only.

CONTACT
Librarian

DESCRIPTION
The archive of the Religious Society of Friends in Ulster.

HOLDINGS
The Religious Society of Friends, or Quakers as they are commonly known, kept amazingly detailed records, many of which date back to the nineteenth century. The library in Lisburn holds all the original surviving records of the Ulster Province Meeting and its constituent meetings with the sole exception of the first minute book of the Ulster Province Meeting. This is in the Historical Library of the Religious Society of Friends in Dublin. These minute books begin in 1674. A large amount of additional documentary source material is also available, including, for the Ulster Province/Quarterly Meeting, copies of marriage certificates (1731–86), a Book of Sufferings (1748–1809) and a register of births and burials (1841–58). Material from the local meetings survives for Antrim, Ballyhagen, Cootehill, Grange (near Charlemont), Lisburn, Lurgan and Richhill. For the Lisburn and Lurgan meetings there are minute books from 1675. Of particular interest from the Ballyhagen meeting is a collection of wills with detailed inventories dating from the

late seventeenth and early eighteenth centuries. There are also family lists from *c*. 1680. Copies of these records are available in the Public Record Office of Northern Ireland (T/1062 and MIC/16). A list of the Ulster material, compiled by B.G. Hutton, can be found in the *Guide to Irish Quaker Records, 1654–1860* published by the Irish Manuscripts Commission in 1967.

LOCATION
Town centre.

UNIVERSITY OF ULSTER LIBRARY, JORDANSTOWN CAMPUS

(Sir Derek Birley Library)
Shore Road
NEWTOWNABBEY, COUNTY ANTRIM, BT37 0QB
Northern Ireland

TELEPHONE: (028) 9036 6964; FAX: (028) 9036 6849
E-mail: lj.mills@ulster.ac.uk
Website: www.ulster.ac.uk/library

HOURS
Term time: M–Th, 08:00–22:00; F, 08:00–20:00, Sa, 13:00–17:00; Su, 13:00–17:00
Vacation period: M–Th, 08:45–17:00; F, 08:45–16:00

ACCESS AND SERVICES
Visitors welcome but advance notice preferred. Borrowing privileges and database searching not usually extended to external visitors. Application preferred for access to special collections. Disabled access facilities. University of Ulster shares a common catalogue database. Fees apply for photocopying and microform print services; advance notice preferred. E-resources are only available to registered staff and students.

CONTACT
Laura Mills, Campus Library Manager

DESCRIPTION
The Jordanstown campus is part of the four-campus University of Ulster system, which also includes the Belfast Campus (County Antrim), Coleraine Campus (County Londonderry), and Magee Campus, Derry City (County Londonderry). Jordanstown is the largest of the four campus libraries in the University of Ulster system. In October 2002, the university formally opened the Sir Derek Birley Learning Resources Centre, a state of the art facility with 1,200 study spaces, of which 900 have network connections. There are 380 networked desktop computers available.

HOLDINGS
The library houses a collection of 280,000 volumes, plus significant holdings of journals (2,000 titles), microforms, newspapers, pamphlets and recordings. It also provides access to over 21,000 online electronic journals and e-books through the four-campus University of Ulster Library system. Its special subject areas are business and management, social services, health sciences, informatics and engineering.

Special collections include the Irish Travellers Collection and a collection of radical English language newspapers and journals on microfilm. The library does not house any genealogical sources of note.

LOCATION
Seven miles north of Belfast, along the coast.

COUNTY ARMAGH

ARMAGH ANCESTRY

40 English Street
ARMAGH, BT61 7BA
Northern Ireland

TELEPHONE: (028) 3752 1801; FAX: (028) 3751 0180
E-mail: researcher@armagh.gov.uk; armaghancestry@armagh.gov.uk
Website: www.armagh.co.uk

HOURS
By appointment: details will be taken at any time and replied to by Researcher.

ACCESS AND SERVICES
Visitors welcome but advance notice preferred. Disabled access facilities. The centre
offers fee based, professional genealogical research services. Fees vary depending on
service and time involved.

CONTACT
Genealogical Researcher

DESCRIPTION
Armagh Ancestry is the designated Irish Family History Centre for county Armagh
research. It is currently hoping to create a comprehensive genealogical database for
all county Armagh from a wide variety of sources, including church and state
records, tithe applotment books, Griffith's Valuation, the 1901 census and gravestone
inscriptions. Armagh Ancestry offers a genealogical research service for County
Armagh. Computerisation of genealogical records for County Armagh has been
under way since 1985. Complete records include: all the County Armagh Roman
Catholic registers from the earliest in 1796 up to 1900; civil births, 1864–1921;
marriages, 1845–1921; and many Protestant registers up until 1900. Currently, the
centre is inputting pre-1870 Presbyterian and Church of Ireland (Anglican) Church
registers.

HOLDINGS
The centre offers a small genealogical library with assisted consultation, with special
emphasis on County Armagh. Items of special interest include: computerised
database of County Armagh church and civil records, CD-ROMS of county Armagh

historical sources, the 1864 Griffith's Valuation and the 1823–38 tithe applotment books, 1901 and 1911 Census and many more smaller miscellaneous sources which it has computerised – muster rolls, hearth rolls, rent rolls, misc census from 1740/1766/1770/1821/1826 etc.

ONLINE ACCESS
Many of the centre's Church and civil records are now online at www.rootsireland.ie and customers can conduct self service research; however, it is recommended that customers should still avail of the genealogical expertise of Researchers in Armagh Ancestry.

LOCATION
City centre, within St Patrick's Trian Visitor Complex behind the Tourist Information Centre. Public car parks nearby.

ARMAGH COUNTY MUSEUM

The Mall East
ARMAGH, BT61 9BE
Northern Ireland

TELEPHONE: (028) 3752 3070; FAX: (028) 3752 2631
E-mail: acm.info@nmni.com
Website: www.nmni.com

HOURS
M–F, 10:00–17:00; Sa, 10:00–13:00, 14:00–17:00; closed bank holidays

ACCESS AND SERVICES
Publicly funded Armagh County Museum has a reference library and exhibits which are open to the public free of charge. Library stacks are closed with material produced on request. For access to research collections advance notification by letter or email is preferred. Laptops are permitted and photocopying is available. Only pencils should be used in the research area. Disabled access facilities are available and parking is opposite Museum.

CONTACT
Dr Greer Ramsey

DESCRIPTION
Armagh County Museum is a branch of National Museums Northern Ireland. *See also* ULSTER AMERICAN FOLK PARK, Omagh (County Tyrone); ULSTER FOLK AND TRANSPORT MUSEUM, Holywood (County Down); and ULSTER MUSEUM, Belfast (County Antrim, but library located at UFTM, Holywood). A community museum focusing on County Armagh, it contains one of the finest county collections in Ireland. The museum is housed in a distinctive classical revival building, which first opened in 1834 as a school.

HOLDINGS
Museum holdings include artworks, archaeological objects, local and natural history specimens, textile, railway and military artefact collections. Paintings of note include John Luke's *The Old Callan Bridge* and many works by George Russell (Æ). The library houses approximately 10,000 volumes and 48 linear feet of manuscripts, plus

a collection of photographs. The holdings are especially strong in local history, with important collections of maps and prints. Subject areas include archaeology, history, folk and rural life, fine arts and crafts, natural history, military history and costume relating to County Armagh. Among special collections of note are the TGF Paterson Manuscript Collection (300 bound volumes), including working papers with notes on local families and buildings, a collection of Paterson's journal *Armachiana*, vols 1–24, including Paterson's typed notes with indexes, the journals (7 vols) of William Blacker (1777–1855), including local notes and jottings with an account of the Battle of the Diamond (1795). The Museum also holds manuscripts and illustrated poems of George Russell (Æ, 1867–1935). Of special genealogical interest are the Ordnance Survey maps (1834) for Counties Tyrone and Armagh, a printed copy of Griffith's Valuation for County Armagh and the Paterson Collection.

Plans to digitise *Armachiana* are under way.

LOCATION
The Museum is on the Mall in Armagh.

ARMAGH DIOCESAN ARCHIVES
See CARDINAL TOMÁS Ó FIAICH MEMORIAL LIBRARY AND ARCHIVE, Armagh

ARMAGH OBSERVATORY

College Hill
ARMAGH, BT61 9DG
Northern Ireland

TELEPHONE: (028) 3752 2928; FAX: (028) 3752 7174
E-mail: jmf@srm.ac.uk
Website: star.arm.ac.uk, climate.arm.ac.uk

HOURS
M–F, 09:00–17:00; closed bank holidays

ACCESS AND SERVICES
Publicly funded, non-circulating library and archives open to researchers by appointment; advance notice to Librarian required. Stacks open except for special collections. Collection catalogued on cards; printed catalogue for part of collection also available. Textbook collection of some 3,000 books listed in Microsoft Access database for in-house use. Access to library free, but charges may be made for use of library or services at Librarian's discretion; partial wheel-chair accessibility. See website for activities and programmes.

CONTACT
John McFarland, Librarian. E-mail: jmf@srm.ac.uk

DESCRIPTION
The Armagh Observatory was founded in 1789 by Archbishop Richard Robinson, Church of Ireland Primate, who also founded the Armagh Public Library. It continues to function as an important player in astronomical research, and its library and archives, housed in the observatory's original Georgian mansion, seek to maintain a centralised Northern Ireland collection of astronomical works.

HOLDINGS
The library and archives hold approximately 3,000 books, 5,000 photographs, 200
linear feet of manuscripts, 50 periodical subscriptions and a very strong collection of
some 20,000 journal volumes. In addition to astronomy, the library has strong
holdings in mathematics, physics, astrophysics, climate and climate change. The
archives contain documents relating to the administration of the observatory,
observations, meteorological records, personal papers and astronomical drawings.
Among special collections of significance are: a collection of historical instruments,
the manuscripts of J.L.E. Dreyer, the papers of J.A. Hamilton, the papers of T.R.
Robinson and the T.R. Robinson (1793–1882) Collection of Rare and Antiquarian
Books (200 vols). A more detailed list of holdings can be found on the RASCAL
(Research and Special Collections Available Locally) website: www.rascal.ac.uk.

LOCATION
Close to city centre, in main observatory building. Limited free parking.

ARMAGH PUBLIC LIBRARY

43 Abbey Street
ARMAGH, BT61 7DY
Northern Ireland

TELEPHONE: (028) 3752 3142
E-mail: admin@armaghpubliclibrary.co.uk
Website: armaghpubliclibrary.arm.ac.uk

HOURS
M–F, 10:00–13:00, 14:00–16:00; or by appointment; closed bank holidays

ACCESS AND SERVICES
Independent reference library, open to the public. No fee for casual visits, but
donations appreciated. Fee applies for guided tours as follows: 1–24 people, £2 per
head; 25 or more people, set fee of £50. Disabled access facilities available. Advance
notice for specific research requests preferred. Fees for photocopying services. Pencils
only; laptops and cameras with permission of the Keeper. No bags allowed.
Catalogue accessible via website.

CONTACT
Very Revd Gregory Dunstan, Keeper
Ms Carol Conlin, Assistant Keeper

DESCRIPTION
The Armagh Public Library was founded in 1771 by Archbishop Richard Robinson,
Church of Ireland Primate, who also founded the Armagh Observatory. It is housed
in a late eighteenth century classical revival building.

HOLDINGS
The Library houses some 35,000 volumes, containing some 45,000 titles on
catalogue, including Archbishop Robinson's personal collection of early printed
books on history, canon and civil law, heraldry, literature, medicine, philosophy,
religion, theology and travel. The Robinson collection is fully integrated into the
main collection, which has been enhanced over the past two centuries chiefly by
other clerical collections.

In recent times the Library has concentrated on ecclesiastical history, St Patrick, Jonathan Swift and Armagh City and County. Book highlights include incunabula (fifteenth-century printed books), a 'Breeches Bible' and a first edition of *Gulliver's Travels*, with marginal emendations in Swift's own hand.

The manuscript collection includes medieval and early modern European items, many of Irish interest, especially concerning lands and tithes records. Other collection highlights include: a fine map collection, a collection of engravings known as the Rokeby Collection and Archbishop Marcus Gervais Beresford's collection of Irish artefacts.

LOCATION
Near city centre, close to St Patrick's Church of Ireland Cathedral. Ample free parking available at the Cathedral.

CARDINAL TOMÁS Ó FIAICH MEMORIAL LIBRARY AND ARCHIVE

15 Moy Road
ARMAGH, BT61 7LY
Northern Ireland

TELEPHONE (028) 3752 2981
E-mail: roddy.hegarty@ofiaich.ie
Website: www.ofiaich.ie

HOURS
M–F, 09:30–13:00, 14:00–17:00; closed statutory and bank holidays. Visits outside of these times by prior arrangement.

ACCESS AND SERVICES
Visitors welcome, but advance notice preferred. Disabled access and facilities onsite. Laptops permitted; pencils only. Fees for photocopying services.
Access to the some collections may be restricted or may require the expressed permission of the depositor. The library hosts regular lectures and seminars relating to Irish history, literature and church history. Irish language classes are also held on Wednesday mornings, and Cumann Seanchais Ard Mhacha, The Armagh Diocesan Historical Society, holds its monthly lectures on the first Wednesday evening of the month. Room hire and conference facilities are available on request.

Genealogy: The Library provides a genealogical research service based around the Catholic Church records for the Archdiocese of Armagh. A search fee is charged, details on request.

CONTACT
Roddy Hegarty, Director. E-mail: roddy.hegarty@ofiaich.ie

DESCRIPTION
The Library and Archive is named in memory of Cardinal Tomás Ó Fiaich (1923–90), former archbishop of Armagh and Catholic Primate of All Ireland. It is a free, independent, publicly accessible reference facility opened in 1999. The library specialises in the five principal areas of interest of the late Cardinal: Church history, Irish history both local and national, the Irish Diaspora, Irish language and Irish sport, particularly but not exclusively Gaelic games. The largest single collection housed at the library is the Irish Overseas Archive containing approximately 250,000

documents relating to the Irish in continental Europe since the sixteenth century. This is held in partnership with University College Dublin. It is also the designated archive for the Gaelic Athletic Association in Ulster, and, as an independent repository, has substantial collections relating to the history of the conflict in the north of Ireland over the last half century.

HOLDINGS
The library has a catalogue of c. 30,000 printed volumes and 450 periodical titles, manuscripts, works of art and artefacts. The map collection contains items from the seventeenth to the twentieth century. There are also collections of microfilm, photographs and audio-visual recording.
The core collection of the archive is comprised of the personal library and papers of Cardinal Tomás Ó Fiaich. However, CÓFLA also holds among other items:

The Armagh Catholic Archdiocese papers from 1787–1977;
The Micheline Kerney Walsh papers;
The papers or substantial portions of the papers of Monsignor Denis Faul and Monsignor Raymond Murray;
The papers of Sister Sarah Clarke on prisoners in British Jails 1960s–90s;
The Hill papers relating to Scarman and Widgery Tribunals of inquiry;
The Louis O'Kane Collection, including c. 120 audio recording relation to the Irish War of Independence;
The minute books of the Ulster Council of the GAA 1917–79;
GAA minute books and papers relating to Counties Antrim, Armagh, Cavan, Down, Monaghan and Tyrone;
The minutes of the Ulster Colleges Council of the GAA, 1928–61;
The minutes of the Youth and Sports Council of Northern Ireland, 1962–71;
The minutes of BOL Cumman na hÉireann, Ard Mahacha;
The minutes of Coiste An tUltach 1947–82;
The papers of an tAth. Lorcán Ó Muireadhaigh;
The papers of the Federation for Ulster Local Studies, 1974–2006.

LOCATION
The library is visable from the A29, the Dungannon/Moy Road from Armagh, and is situated to the rear of St Patrick's Catholic cathedral. The main entrance is via the A29 Moy Road, to the left leaving Armagh city. Free parking is available adjacent to the library grounds

ARMAGH RECORDS CENTRE
See CARDINAL TÓMAS Ó FIAICH MEMORIAL LIBRARY AND ARCHIVE, Armagh

IRISH and LOCAL STUDIES LIBRARY
See LIBRARIES NI IRISH and LOCAL STUDIES LIBRARY, ARMAGH

LIBRARIES NI IRISH and LOCAL STUDIES LIBRARY, ARMAGH

Irish and Local Studies Library
39c Abbey Street
ARMAGH, BT61 7EL
Northern Ireland

TELEPHONE: (028) 3752 7851; Fax: (028) 3752 7127
Email: IrishandLocalStudies.selb@librariesni.org.uk
Website: www.librariesni.org.uk

HOURS
M, Tu, F, Sa, 09:30–13:00, 14:00–17:00; W, 14:00–17:00;
Th, 09:30–13:00, 14:00–20:00

ACCESS AND SERVICES
This library is situated in the old Armagh City Hospital complex. Entrance is at the
rear of the car park with access to the library which is on the first floor via stairs or
lift. Visitors are welcome; wheelchair accessible. A selection of material most used is
on open access in the Reading Room; remainder held off site. There are five
reader/printers for viewing microforms, one of which has PC connection allowing
for downloading of material. Photocopying facilities and six PCs with internet access
are available for public use.

CONTACT
Helen Grimes, Heritage Services Manager. E-mail: helen.grimes@librariesni.org.uk

DESCRIPTION
Established by the Southern Education and Library Board in the late 1970s, and
now part of Libraries NI, the library's policy has been to collect material on all
aspects of Irish life and learning from earliest times to the present day.

HOLDINGS
The library holds an extensive collection of books, journals, maps, photographs and
microforms. Its newspaper collection includes local, provincial and national papers as
well as some devoted to specific interests, e.g. *The Irish Builder* and *The Irish Citizen*
(a women's suffrage paper). Its microforms include Board of Guardian minutes for
Armagh, Banbridge, Cookstown and Newry; the 1901 census for County Armagh;
the Linen Hall Collection of political periodicals, 1966–89; reports of the
Commissioners of National Education in Ireland, 1834–1920; a selection of Dublin
Castle records including those on anti-government organisations, 1882–1921; and
some county inspectors' monthly reports for the same period. It also holds the
Francis Crossle manuscripts relating to local families and the history of the Newry
area, plus a collection of eighteenth and early nineteenth century pamphlets devoted
primarily to contemporary economic, political and religious issues.

LOCATION
Near city centre, at old City Hospital site. Entrance from main car park.

QUEEN'S UNIVERSITY BELFAST LIBRARY, ARMAGH CAMPUS

Note: The Armagh campus was closed in August 2005, and its library, including the
extensive private library of Cardinal Cahal Daly, was transferred to Queen's
University Belfast Library.

ROBINSON LIBRARY
See ARMAGH PUBLIC LIBRARY, Armagh

CRAIGAVON MUSEUM SERVICES

Note: The Craigavon Museum Service is currently relocating to the Lough Neagh Discovery Centre on Oxford Island. It is anticipated that the relocation will be completed by May 2014. During this time it is advisable to contact the Museum in advance before visiting.

Lough Neagh Discovery Centre, Oxford Island,
CRAIGAVON, COUNTY ARMAGH, BT66 6NJ
Northern Ireland

TELEPHONE: (028) 3834 1635
E-mail: museum@craigavon.gov.uk
Website: www.craigavon.gov.uk

HOURS
Call to confirm.

ACCESS AND SERVICES
Call to confirm.

CONTACT
David Weir

DESCRIPTION
Craigavon Museum Services reflects the history of the South Lough Neagh area, where the new city of Craigavon is situated, along with the towns of Portadown and Lurgan. The collection is based on the social, economic and industrial heritage of the area, and in particular the local canal systems and inland waterways. The museum runs the Philip B. Wilson Library.

HOLDINGS
The Philip B. Wilson Library houses three main reference collections totalling around 4,000 volumes. Topics included are agriculture, military history, crafts, architecture, transportation and church history. The library also holds the collections of the Ulster Quarterly Meeting of the Religious Society of Friends, which dates from the mid-1600s to the late 1900s and includes obituaries, journals, biographies and travels in ministry. In addition, there is a Methodist book collection containing volumes relating to the history of Methodism in Ireland and the writings and teachings of John Wesley.

LOCATION
Off junction 10 on the MI motorway.

COUNTY CARLOW

CARLOW COUNTY ARCHIVE
See CARLOW LIBRARY SERVICE, Carlow Town

CARLOW LIBRARY SERVICE – INCLUDING THE LOCAL STUDIES COLLECTION AND THE CARLOW COUNTY ARCHIVE

Tullow Street,
CARLOW TOWN, COUNTY CARLOW
Ireland

TELEPHONE: (059) 912 9700; FAX: (059) 914 0548
E-mail: library@carlowcoco.ie
Website: www.carlowlibraries.ie

HOURS
M–F, 09:45–17:30, and Tu, Th, 09:45–19:30; Sa, 09:45–13:00

ACCESS AND SERVICES
Visitors welcome. Membership required for borrowing privileges. ID required for application. Annual charge of €10 for working adult applies. Photocopying services and printing facilities available for a modest fee. Free internet access and WiFi access for library members. A range of online services available. All buildings across the branch network are wheelchair accessible and induction loops available.

CONTACT
Josephine Coyne, County Librarian
Carmel Flahavan, Executive Librarian.
John Shorthall, Executive Librarian.

DESCRIPTION
Carlow County Library operates branches in Carlow, Muine Bheag (Bagenalstown), Tullow and Borris.
   Borris Library is located on the ground floor of a converted old schoolhouse. The building dates from 1832 and was opened as a library service in 2010. This branch is wheelchair accessible.
   Muinebheag (Bagenalstown Library) originally functioned as a courthouse built *c.* 1835. The library has been refurbished and is now wheelchair accessible.

Tullow Library is located on the banks of the river Slaney. Opened in 1995, the library is located on the ground floor and shares the building with the local authority area office. This branch is wheelchair accessible.

Carlow Central Library is located in a converted and extended 3 storey Presentation Convent built *c.* 1899. The branch library is located on the ground floor. Library Headquarters and Administration is located on the second floor. The archives section is located on the second floor. The branch is also wheelchair accessible.

HOLDINGS

The Local Studies Collection: is located on the first floor of the Carlow Central Library. It is open to all from Monday to Friday 09:45–13:00 and from 14:00–17:30. It does not open on Bank Holiday Mondays. Prior appointment is not required except for use of the Microfilm readers. Books either by local authors or with County Carlow Content are available for reference here. The Department holds an extensive newspaper collection on microfilm and/or hard copy. Newspapers include: *Nationalist and Leinster Times,* September 1883–December 2006 on microfilm and from 1981–current issue in hard copy, *Carlow Sentinel,* 1832–1920 on microfilm, *Carlow People,* 1997–current in hard copy, *Carlow Morning Post,* 1818–November 1822, 1828–January 1835 on microfilm, *Carlow Post* from 1853–78 on microfilm. Other titles include: *Carlow Independent,* 1879–June 1882 on microfilm, *Leinster Independent,* 26 December 1834–18 April 1840 on microfilm, *Leinster Reformer,* 1840–41 in hard copy, *Carlow Standard,* 2 January–19 April 1832 on microfilm, *Carlow Vindicator,* 1892 on microfilm, *Carlow Weekly News,* 27 March 1858–24 October, 1863 on microfilm, *Finns Leinster Journal,* 1767–1806 on microfilm, *Leinster Journal,* 1807–1812 on microfilm, *Irish Times,* 1965–August, 2005 on microfilm.

The Local Studies Department also has a wide range of Irish and Local Periodicals which are all available for reference. Titles include *Journal of the Royal Society of Antiquaries of Ireland, Irish Historical Studies, The Irish Sword, Irish Economic and Social History Review* and many more. Locally published titles include Carloviana, a number of annual journals from villages around County Carlow as well as back editions of non-current titles, for instance *Carlow Past and Present.* Maps also form an important part of the Local Studies collection. Holdings include: Down Survey Barony and Civil Parish maps with terriers of County Carlow, 1654, Ordnance Survey 6 inch maps of County Carlow, 1839 and 1879, Ordnance Survey Large scale 5 foot town maps for Carlow, Muinebheag and Tullow 1873, Archaeological Survey maps with index volume of County Carlow (Office of Public Works), 1986, An important collection is the Tyndall collection made up of books from various bequests either by or about John Tyndall, the famous Co. Carlow born scientist.

Genealogical sources held include Indexes to Parish Baptisms and Marriages for Roman Catholic Parishes in County Carlow, tithe applotment books on microfilm and some in hard copy for County Carlow, Griffith's Valuation for County Carlow with some areas of County Laois bordering Carlow in hard copy and the accompanying maps., Census 1901 and Census 1911 for County Carlow on microfilm.

A number of important Directories are also available for reference including *Thom's Directory* dating from some decades of the nineteenth century. The Carlow

Schools Folklore on microfilm from 1937–38 is also in the collection. The Irish Life and Lore Carlow Collection First Series is an interesting recent acquisition. The Local Studies Department also holds a comprehensive Ephemera Collection which includes Domestic and Commercial Property Development brochures from the 1980s and a comprehensive collection of posters and other materials from a range of business, cultural and sporting organisations around County Carlow.

The Carlow County Archive: is situated on the second floor of the Central Library. This Department is not open to the public but all materials can be consulted in the Local Studies area. Prior appointment is necessary for accessing these materials. Major collections here include a comprehensive Local Authorities Archive – Carlow County Council minute Books, 1899–2008, Carlow Urban District Council minute books 1899–1955, Carlow Urban Sanitary Authority minute books, 1882–1938, Labourers' cottages ledgers, rentals and maps. Muinebheag Town Commissioners Minute Books are also held here for the years 1899–1996. A very useful source for mid nineteenth and early twentieth century history are the Carlow Poor Law Union Board of Guardian minute books for the period 1845–1923. Papers of Landed families are another important source and these include the Browne-Clayton papers, Vigors, Burton and Bagot collections. An interesting photographic archive includes the Stephen Nolan collection from the early twentieth century. Various documents and photographs from the Stephen Nolan collection have been digitised and are available for viewing on www.carlowlibraries.ie

LOCATION
Town centre.

CARLOW GENEALOGY PROJECT
Note: Closed since early 2005. Future unknown at time of publication.

COUNTY CAVAN

BAILIEBOROUGH LIBRARY

Market Square
BAILIEBOROUGH, COUNTY CAVAN
Ireland

TELEPHONE: (042) 966 5779
E-mail: bailieborolibrary@hotmail.com; fburke@cavancoco.ie
Website: www.cavanlibrary.ie

HOURS
Monday closed. W, F–Sa, 10:00–13:15, 14:15–17:15; Tu, Th, 10:00–20:30

ACCESS AND SERVICES
Visitors welcome. Free membership. Advance notice preferred but not essential and ID required. Disabled access facilities on ground level, with immediate plans to install a lift to make library fully accessible. No borrowing privileges for non-members. Photocopier available. Free access to internet and computer facilities. Entire collection automated and catalogued. Planned activities throughout the year, including art and creative writing workshops, lectures, exhibitions, readings and annual Children's Book Festival in October.

CONTACT
Fiona Burke, Senior Library Assistant. E-mail: fburke@cavancoco.ie

DESCRIPTION
Former market house converted to a library in 1992. The system is operated by Cavan County Council Library Services.

HOLDINGS
The library houses a book stock of some 9,000 volumes, with a good local history collection, including a copy of Griffith's Valuation for most of County Cavan, and an extensive reference service.

LOCATION
Town centre.

CAVAN COUNTY LIBRARY

Central Library and Heritage Centre
Farnham Street
CAVAN TOWN, COUNTY CAVAN
Ireland

TELEPHONE: (049) 4378500/1; FAX: (049) 432 6987
E-mail: library@cavancoco.ie
Website: www.cavanlibrary.ie

HOURS
M, W, F–Sa, 10:00–13:15; 14:15–17:15; Tu, Th, 10:00–20:30

ACCESS AND SERVICES
Visitors welcome. Disabled access. Photocopiers, microform readers/printers and free internet access available.

CONTACT
Josephine Brady, County Librarian

DESCRIPTION
The library is the central library in the county's 10 library system. Of these, the Cavan is open six days and Cootehill and Bailieboro libraries operate five days per week. The system is operated by Cavan County Council Library Services. Johnston Central library opened in June 2006 The ground floor offers a spacious state of the art Central Library, which includes a local studies section designed to ensure controlled access and long term conservation of the collection. Integral to the new library is an events space measuring more than 65 square metres to cater for art exhibitions, recitals, concerts, dance workshops, lectures and readings The new building is designed to centralise and integrate delivery of key research services. In addition to the Central Library, it accommodates the Local Authority Staff and Elected Members Library, the County Arts Office, the County Heritage Office and the Cavan County Archive. The County Cavan Genealogical Research Centre is also integrated into the new facility, though it will continue to use its existing facility at Cana House for some services (*See* following entry). Tourist information for County Cavan is also be provided as part of the one stop service offered by the new library and heritage centre.

HOLDINGS
The library houses a strong local history collection, approaching 4,000 volumes, including many eighteenth and nineteenth century books on Cavan Town and County Cavan; maps, including the 1835 Ordnance Survey for County Cavan, the Cavan–Leitrim Railway and the south-western section of Farnham Estate; important holdings of social and genealogical concern, including Cavan Assizes, 1807–51, which record individuals charged with crimes and the verdicts rendered; eighteenth and nineteenth century legal documents, such as leases, rentals and wills for County Cavan, account and fee books and inspectors' reports from Bailieboro Model School, 1860s–1900s; minute books for the Board of Guardians (1839–1921) and the Rural District Council (1899–1925); diaries, including the diary of Randal McCollum, Presbyterian minister, Shercock, County Cavan, describing social conditions in Cavan, 1861–71; photographs and postcards; and the correspondence and papers of

various local personages. There is an extensive microfilm and photocopy collection of materials relating to County Cavan, especially rich in family history sources, newspaper holdings and directories. Genealogical sources also include the 1821, 1901 and 1911 censuses, Griffith's Valuation and tithe applotment books. Recently the former Catholic Bishop of Kilmore, Dr Francis J. McKiernan, donated to Cavan County Council his entire book collection, which is particularly strong in the area of local history. The library also acquired the Farnham Archive Collection, which will become available to the public in the near future.

A digitisation project to scan photographs and historical journals is under way.

LOCATION
Town centre. Limited on-street parking available; car parks nearby.

CAVAN GENEALOGY

First Floor
Johnston Central Library
Farnham Street
CAVAN TOWN, COUNTY CAVAN
Ireland

TELEPHONE: (049) 436 1094; FAX: (049) 433 1494
E-mail: cavangenealogy@eircom.net
Website: www.rootsireland.ie

HOURS
M–F, 09:00–17:00; closed Christmas, Easter and public holidays

ACCESS AND SERVICES
Visitors welcome and disabled facilities available. Enquiries also welcome by telephone, fax, e-mail or post. Admission is free but fees are payable for genealogical research.

FEES
Single Search. A search will be made for one or more baptism/birth, marriage, census record or whatever source is requested. Photocopy of the record provided, if available. Fee €25.
Assessment Report. Enquirers can become registered clients for whom an assessment is carried out, which involves thorough examination of database along with research of non-computerised sources in order to discover all information held in the centre regarding their ancestor or ancestors. When assessment is complete, they will receive a report detailing all information that has been located and the fees involved. Fee €95.

CONTACT
Mary Sullivan, Manager
Concepta McGovern, Senior Researcher

DESCRIPTION
Cavan Genealogy (originally named County Cavan Genealogical Research Centre) was established in 1988 to build a database of all sources of a genealogical nature that are known to exist for County Cavan. The centre is the Irish Family History

Foundation's designated family history centre for County Cavan and is part of the IFHF's Online Research Service which can be viewed at www.rootsireland.ie

HOLDINGS

Sources include church baptism, marriage and burial records; state/civil birth, marriage and death records; census records; land records and numerous other sources of a genealogical nature.

LOCATION

Town centre. Limited on-street parking available; car parks nearby.

COUNTY CLARE

CLARE HERITAGE AND GENEALOGICAL CENTRE

Church Street
COROFIN, COUNTY CLARE
Ireland

TELEPHONE: (065) 683 7955; FAX: (065) 683 7540
E-mail: clareheritage@eircom.net; clareheritage@gmail.com
Website: www.clareroots.com

HOURS
M–F, 09:00–17:30

ACCESS AND SERVICES
Clare Heritage is a not for profit, fee based genealogical research centre offering a professional service to persons wishing to trace their Clare ancestry. A fee of €195 (or equivalent) covers a preliminary report and administrative costs and includes an initial search of the source material that the centre holds, e.g. parish registers, land records, Census returns, civil records. Fee of €425 (or equivalent) may be required to complete a full search and covers all expenses and time expended by the centre. Fee will not exceed €425 (or equivalent) without prior consultation and advice as to probability of positive results. Application can be made online with a credit card.

CONTACT
Antoinette O'Brien, Coordinator

DESCRIPTION
The Clare Heritage and Genealogical Research Centre was founded in 1982 by the late Dr Ignatius (Naoise) Cleary. It is a member of the Irish Family History Foundation, the coordinating body for a network of government approved genealogical research centres in the Republic of Ireland and Northern Ireland, which have computerised tens of millions of Irish ancestral records of different types. The Clare centre now holds data on just over 500,000 people born in County Clare during the nineteenth century and into the middle of the twentieth century. Common surnames in County Clare include: McMahon, McNamara, O'Brien, Moloney, Ryan, Kelly, McInerney, O'Connor, Keane, O'Halloran, Hogan, Burke, Murphy, Lynch and Walsh. The main towns and villages include: Ennis, Kilrush, Kilkee, Miltown Malbay, Ennistymon, Ballyvaughan, Corofin, Sixmilebridge,

Newmarket-on-Fergus, Killaloe, Tulla, Scariff, Feakle, Quin, Kilfenora, Lisdoonvarna, Liscannor, Broadford, Kildysart, Mullagh and Quilty.

HOLDINGS
The centre has indexed all available Roman Catholic parish registers (pre-1900 baptismal and marriage records) for the 47 Clare parishes. The age and condition of these records vary from parish to parish; some records date back to 1802. Because civil recording of births, marriages and deaths does not begin until 1864, parish records remain the main source of genealogical data in Ireland. Also available are: all available Church of Ireland records; tithe applotment books, 1820s; Griffith's Valuation, 1855; 1901 census; civil records – marriages and deaths, 1864–1995, and births, 1900–50; New South Wales archives, 1848–69 (6,000 assisted emigrants entries, R. Reid); *Clare Journal*, 1779–1900; birth, marriage and death notices; and tombstone inscriptions from approximately 80 Clare graveyards. Access is also available to: nineteenth century workhouse records; reports on some convict trials; many Clare wills; Ordnance Survey maps showing parish and townland boundaries; and a reference library which includes publications and lists on landed gentry, Irish surnames, histories of County Clare and its parishes and various family histories.

LOCATION
In the village of Corofin, eight miles north of Ennis.

CLARE COUNTY ARCHIVES SERVICE

Áras Contae an Chláir, New Road,
ENNIS, COUNTY CLARE
Ireland

TELEPHONE: (065) 684 6414; FAX: (065) 682 8233
E-mail: archivesrecords@clarecoco.ie
Website: www.clarelibrary.ie/eolas/archives/archives_index

HOURS
By appointment: contact Archivist

ACCESS AND SERVICES
Visitors welcome. Material can be requested and will be made available to researchers through Clare County Library's Local Studies Centre. One day's notice required for production of material. As material is processed and listed it will be made available for public inspection.

CONTACT
Rene Franklin, Archivist

DESCRIPTION
Clare County Archives was established in 1999 and provides an integrated cultural and information service to researchers at home and abroad. The service seeks to maintain the highest preservation standards possible for the collections in its care while seeking to maximise public knowledge of and access to archives.
The Archives Service is county-wide and in addition to local authority records, it collects other material relating to the county including: private papers; solicitors' papers; architectural drawings, maps and plans; estate papers; photographic collections; and records of academic, social and economic institutions.

HOLDINGS
Local Authority Archives
The service is custodian of a wide range of archival series and includes the records of a number of predecessor groups of the present local government system including the Grand Juries, Poor Law Unions, Rural District Councils and Boards of Public Health and Assistance.

The Archives Service currently holds the archives of Clare County Council, Kilkee Town Commissioners and Kilrush Urban District Council. It contains Board of Guardian minute books for Ennis, Ennistymon, Kilrush and Corofin Unions and Rural District Council minute books for Corofin, Ennis, Ennistymon, Kildysart, Tulla and Scariff Rural District Councils.

Non-Local Authority Archives
Clare County Archives Service is also committed to collecting archival material of private origin thus enriching knowledge of the history of the county. The archives of Our Lady's Hospital, Ennis, were acquired in 2002 in a joint project with the Mid-Western Health Board. The hospital records reveal a microcosm of the social and economic conditions pertaining in Ennis and in County Clare and for this reason the archives are a valuable part of the county's history.

The papers of Roger Casement were transferred to the archives in October 2003. The collection contains mainly correspondence as well as receipts, essays, leaflets and newspaper cuttings. Of particular interest, however, are his letters, which provide us with a glimpse of the Irish-German background to the Easter Rising and Ireland's claim to political independence.

The Griffith Family Papers document the lives of the family of Rev Julius Henry Griffith, who served as Rector of Drumcliffe Union (Killaloe) from 1884. The family lived in the Rectory at 1 Bindon Street in Ennis, County Clare. The papers include correspondence, birth and marriage certificates, financial material, diaries, photographs and press cuttings, and include a family member's eyewitness account of the sinking of the battleship HMS *Victoria* in the Lebanon on 22 June 1893, with the loss of hundreds of lives.

The McMahon Collection contains papers relating to estates in Clare under the management of the Land Agents Michael McMahon and sons. This collection spans from the seventeenth century to the twentieth century and presents significant insight into the tumultuous history of land and land ownership in Ireland while also offering an important genealogical resource containing detailed lists of tenants in the estates in Clare.

The Sampson Estate Papers cover a date span of 1790 to 1970, with the majority of the papers dating from 1920 to 1960. The Sampson family were landowners in Co. Clare from the early nineteenth century. The collection comprises of legal papers which include deeds, leases, conveyances, marriage settlements, wills and correspondence. The majority of the lands referred to relate to Sampson property located in Co. Clare, and concentrated in the baronies of Tulla Upper and Tulla Lower.

The Macnamara photographic collection is a collection of photographs taken by Dr George Unthank Macnamara (1849–1919), of Corofin, between 1890 and 1900. The collection contains a wide variation of images from Clare and Northern India. The County Archives has had these glass plate negatives digitised and are accessible on the Clare Library website.

Recent but not yet processed collections include: A collection of letters written by the Canon Philip Dwyer (Prebend of Dysart and Vicar of Drumcliffe 1864–83), his wife Ann Stather Crowe (the daughter of a prominent local family), daughters and grandchildren to his son William Dwyer in Canada. The letters are written over several decades between 1880 and 1919. They give a vivid portrait of family life of the period, the sadness of families split by emigration , the changing role of women as new opportunities opened up and encounters with or experiences of historic events. In 1883 Philip went with his wife and some of his children to the west coast of Canada. He died in Weston super Mare on October 21, 1905 at the age of 83 after a brief illness.

LOCATION
Access through Local Studies Centre. *See* following entry.

CLARE COUNTY LIBRARY – LOCAL STUDIES CENTRE
The Manse, Harmony Row
ENNIS, COUNTY CLARE
Ireland

TELEPHONE: (065) 684 6271; FAX: (065) 684 2462
E-mail: mailbox@clarelibrary.ie
Website: www.clarelibrary.ie/eolas/library/local-studies/locstudi1.htm

HOURS
M–Th, 10:00–13:00, 14:00–17:30; F, 10:00–13:00, 14:00–20:00; Sa, 10:00–14:00

ACCESS AND SERVICES
Visitors welcome. Disabled access, though public restroom is not wheelchair accessible. Fees for photocopying and microfilm prints. Entire collection catalogued online. In addition, there is a separate, extensive card index (not online) arranged by subject, people and place. Free internet access.

Publications programme of Clare County Library and Clasp Press has issued more than a dozen titles since 1995. These are still available in print and available from Clasp Press, Library Headquarters, Mill Road, Ennis, County Clare. Titles include: *Folklore of Clare, Archaeology of the Burren, The Clare Anthology, The Stranger's Gaze, A Handbook to Lisdoonvarna, The Antiquities of County Clare, Kilrush Union Minute Books, Sable Wings Over the Land, County Clare: a History and Topography, Two Months at Kilkee, Poverty Before the Famine, Memories of an Islander: a Life on Scattery and Beyond* and *Family and Community in Ireland,* 3rd edition.

CONTACT
Local Studies Librarian

DESCRIPTION
The Local Studies Centre is part of Clare County Library and focuses on material of Irish interest in all subject areas, with special reference to County Clare. There is a separate archives department, Clare County Archives Service. *See* preceding entry.

HOLDINGS
The Irish Collection houses books (some 10,000) and periodicals relating to Ireland. A separate Clare Collection (some 3,000 titles) contains newspapers, photographs, manuscripts, microfilm and maps relating specifically to County Clare. The Centre has recently added an Irish Periodicals Collection which contains a wide range of

titles. Journals of specific relevance to Clare include *The North Munster Antiquarian Journal, Dal gCais, The Other Clare, Molua, The Clare Association Yearbook* and *Sliabh Aughty*. Local parish and sporting magazines are also collected. The following local newspapers are available: Dunboyne Collection of newspaper clippings, 1824–73; *Ennis Chronicle and Clare Advertiser*, 1788–1831 (incomplete); *Clare Freeman and Ennis Gazette*, February 1853–January 1884; *Clare Journal and Ennis Advertiser*, 1778–1917 (incomplete); *Limerick Reporter*, 1845–52; *Celtic Times*, 1887; *Clare Champion*, 1903–present; *Clare People*, 1977–80; *County Express*, 1979–present; *Ennis Express*, 1979–82; *Sunday Tribune*, 1983–7; *Irish Times*, 1859–70, 1916–22, 1987–present; *Saturday Record*, July 1898–September 1936; *Clare Independent and Tipperary Catholic Times*, 1877–85. A recent newspaper acquisition is the *Freeman's Journal* (1763–1805). Newspaper holdings are added to each year as resources permit. A new current newspaper, the *Clare People*, was launched in 2005.

The collection of photographs contains approximately 4,000 prints of Clare scenes. The Lawrence Collection (1870–1914) is the largest in the archive. Other collections include the Westropp Collection (1900), the McNamara Collection (1910), Irish Tourist Association Survey (1943), and the Bluett (1940s–60s) and O'Neill (1950s) Collections. Among the special collections are: Schools Folklore Scheme, Twigge Manuscripts; Ordnance Survey field name books; Petworth House Archive (Clare material); Dorothea Lange contact prints; and some estate papers on microfilm. Of special genealogical interest are Griffith's Valuation, the 1901 and 1911 censuses; tithe applotment books; first and second editions of Ordnance Survey 6 inch maps (complete for County Clare) and voter lists. *See also* holdings of CLARE COUNTY ARCHIVES SERVICE. Consult website for a more detailed list of holdings. Two recent microfilm additions are the Church of Ireland parish of Drumcliffe (Ennis) parochial register, 1744–1870 (incomplete) and the old age pension search forms for County Clare from the 1841 and 1851 censuses. Major recent additions to the collection include: a complete set of Roman Catholic parish registers (baptisms and marriages) up to the year 1880. All of County Clare (with the exception of the parish of Kilshanny) is included as well as some incidental neighbouring Galway parishes (www.clarelibrary.ie/eolas/library/local-studies/catholic_parish_records.htm); and the Drumcliff Church of Ireland parish register. Standard Irish historical and bibliographical works are available for consultation in the Centre.

Clare County Library is actively digitising the patrimony of County Clare and making it freely available to all on the internet. Useful links on its website include 'Genealogy', 'Places' and 'History'. The website is a virtual resource which complements the work of the Local Studies Centre and Clare County Library. An 1821 freeholders list of County Clare has been added to the family history resources, particularly valuable as it contains the 'forty-shilling freeholders' who helped elect Daniel O'Connell in Clare in 1828. The 'Donated Material' section of the website has also grown substantially since your 2007 edition, a section of the website where volunteers can contribute to and develop the resources of the website.

LOCATION
Turn left at the end of Abbey Street. Located on the left, beside De Valera Library.

EAST CLARE HERITAGE COMPANY

St Cronan's Church
TUAMGRANEY, COUNTY CLARE
Ireland

TELEPHONE: (061) 921 351, (086) 874 9710
E-mail: eastclareheritage@eircom.net
Website: www.eastclareheritage.com

HOURS
M–F, 10:00–17:00

ACCESS AND SERVICES
Totally voluntary and community based company with charitable status formed in 1989. In 1991 it opened a heritage centre in the oldest church in Ireland still in use. It was built before 964 AD at Tuamgraney, County Clare. Entry fees: adults, €4; children, €2, families, €10.

Centre offers fee based genealogical research service for persons interested in tracing East Clare family roots. Fee of €105 for preliminary search of records and report. In most cases this is all that will be charged. Enquirers notified of any additional costs. Advice freely given on availability of records and possibility of positive results. Applications available through website. The company publishes local histories and newsletters that include genealogical material. Some of the families covered to date in publications are Woods, Reades, Tandys, Logans, Bourchiers, Allens, Tiernans, Huleatts and Bloxams of Mountshannon; Reids, Ringroses, Walnutts and Davises of Scariff; O'Gradys, Bradys, Drews, Parkers and Crottys of Tuamgraney; Goonanes of Whitegate. Six editions, of out of print, *Sliabh Aughty* journal now on line at eastclareheritage.com.

In 2010, Holy Island, in Lough Derg, off Mountshannon, County Clare was finally recognized as one of the foremost centres in Ireland of Celtic learning, teaching and enlightenment and was added to a list of properties submitted to UNESCO for nomination to the World Heritage List.

East Clare Heritage provides boat trips and guided tours to the Holy Island from April to September, seven days a week, weather permitting. First crossing 10:00, last crossing 18:00. Duration of tour: one hour. Rates: adults, €10; children, €5; group rates by appointment.

Traditional music concerts, held in tenth century church every Monday night from April to September.

East Clare Heritage has published to date the following books and journals, most of which still available in print and can be ordered directly from the centre or from Gerard Madden at Scariff, County Clare: *Holy Island, Jewel of the Lough* (1990, reprinted 1997, 2003), €7; *For God or King: the History of Mountshannon County Clare 1742–1992* (1993, reprinted 1997), €20; *The Famine Memorial Park, Tuamgraney County Cleer* (1997); *A History of the Great Hunger in the Scariff Workhouse Union from 1839 to 1853*, €10; *A History of Tuamgraney and Scariff since Earliest Times* (2000), €20; *History of the O'Maddens of Hy-Many* (2004), €15; *History of the O'Grady's of County Limerick and County Clare* (2006), €15; *Sliabh Aughty Ramble, Musings on the Folklore, History, Landscape and Literature of the Sliabh Aughty Region* (2010) €20; *The Old Road, The Writings of Nora T. Goonane Leonard, 1913–2007* (2011) €10; and 14 editions of an annual historical journal called *Sliabh Aughty*, containing numerous articles on genealogy and local history, average price €8; DVD on history, folklore, culture and traditions of North-East Clare also available, €20.

CONTACT
Gerard Madden, Secretary

DESCRIPTION
East Clare Heritage Company provides a comprehensive family research facility for East Clare and encourages the publication of family history in its annual journal *Sliabh Aughty*. This journal also contains a brief history and the gravestone inscriptions of East Clare graveyards. To date most of the graveyards are indexed. The fifteenth edition of this publication is now being published. The company is headquartered in a church built around 950AD, which is claimed to be the oldest church in continuous use in Ireland, England, Scotland and Wales. This tradition is being maintained and service is held here on the last Sunday of each month throughout the year. The church is built on the site of an earlier monastery founded by St Cronan in the seventh century. The Vikings raided the monastery in 886 and again in 949. Cormac Uí Cillín, the Abbot of Tuamgraney, rebuilt the church and erected a round tower prior to his death in 964. Although no trace of the round tower remains, it has the distinction of being the earliest for which there is a written record. Brian Boru, High King of Ireland (1002–14), repaired the round tower and repaired and enlarged the church. The building operates as a visitor centre during the summer months. It also houses a folk museum.

Dr Edward McLysaght, Ireland's foremost family historian, is interred in the grounds of the church. Tuamgraney is also the home town of the novelist Edna O'Brien.

HOLDINGS
In addition to gravestone inscriptions noted above, the company has access to all the standard genealogical reference sources for East Clare, including: Griffith's Valuation ; tithe applotment books; church and civil records; the 1901 census; Ordnance Survey maps; school registers; numerous deeds and other legal documents. It also has a number of family histories and continues to compile information on families with East Clare connections.

LOCATION
Near the western edge of Lough Derg in County Clare, a 40 minute drive from Shannon Airport.

COUNTY CORK

BANTRY HOUSE

BANTRY, COUNTY CORK
Ireland

TELEPHONE: (027) 50047; FAX: (027) 50795
E-mail: info@bantryhouse.com
Website: www.bantryhouse.com

HOURS
April–October: daily, 10:00–18:00

ACCESS AND SERVICES
Open to the public for an admission charge. Fee schedule: House and garden, €11 per person (accompanied children up to 14 years of age who are not part of a school group admitted free); students and seniors, €8; groups of 20 or more, €7; school groups, €6; admission to gardens only, €5. Admission to house and grounds free to residents. Accommodation available (consult website). Archive has been deposited at the Boole Library, University College Cork.

CONTACT
Bantry House: Shelswell-White Family
Archives: Carol Quinn, Archivist, University College Cork. E-mail: libraryarchives@ucc.ie

DESCRIPTION
Bantry House has been in the possession of the White family since 1739 and was the seat of the four Earls of Bantry (1816–91). The house contains furniture, paintings and other *objets d'art* collected for the most part by the Second Earl of Bantry, who was also responsible for laying out the formal gardens.

HOLDINGS
This archive contains the formal records of the legal, financial and general administration of Bantry House and Estate, and also the more personal records relating to the lives and personalities of the White family who have lived in Bantry House for over 200 years. These documents contain much invaluable social information about the White family and the circles in which they moved, as well as records relating to the tenants who occupied and worked the estate. For further

details, consult UCC Library website http://booleweb.ucc.ie/index.php?pageID=261

LOCATION
In Bantry Town, overlooking Bantry Bay, 60 miles south-west of Cork City.

CORK CITY AND COUNTY ARCHIVES (formerly Cork Archives Institute)

Seamus Murphy Building
33A Great William O'Brien Street
CORK CITY
Ireland

TELEPHONE: (021) 4505 876; FAX: (021) 4505 887
E-mail: archivist@corkcity.ie
Website: www.corkarchives.ie

HOURS
By appointment only Tu–F, 10:00–17:00

ACCESS AND SERVICES
Reading room is open by appointment only, with at least one week's notice if possible. Application form for permission to read records is available in PDF format on the Archives website. Photocopying service available. Research service available. Fully wheelchair accessible.

CONTACT
Brian McGee; Timothy O'Connor

DESCRIPTION
Cork City and County Archives is the official repository for the local archives of Cork City and County and it is co-funded by Cork City Council, Cork County Council and University College Cork. The Archives acquires, preserves and makes available records from local government, and also from local private sources such as societies, businesses, families and individuals. Contents are related mainly, but not exclusively, to the Cork area and consist of records, manuscripts, maps plans and drawings, photographs and other archives that have been selected for permanent preservation.

HOLDINGS
The Archives preserves a very large collection of unique archival material that is of both local and national importance, mainly covering the period 1600–1990. Collections include: Board of Guardians records for most of the Poor Law Unions in the Cork area, 1839–1924 (except Fermoy and Schull), with detailed inmate records available for Cork, Midleton, Kinsale, Bandon, Macroom and Youghal union workhouses ; burial records from 15 cemeteries including the major St Joseph's Cemetery in Cork City, c. 1876–1947; property tax valuation lists 1880s–1970s recording owners and occupiers of properties in Cork; Electoral Registers 1957–82; the records of a number of national schools including the Cork Model School, 1865–1982; solicitor and landed estate collections containing large numbers of personal legal documents and deeds, c1600–1970 ; religious institution records including Princes Street Presbyterian Congregation 1717–1860, Society of Friends (Quaker) records for Cork and Munster, c. 1650–1909; hundreds of collections of personal, family and business records, and clubs and societies. The Archives has

placed a number of documents online including an 1845 postal directory for Cork City and a cemetery register for Old Kilcully Cemetery, 1931–1974, and will be placing more items online in the future. For information see the website www.corkarchives.ie

LOCATION
In the north part of Cork City, a 15–20 minute walk from the city centre. On street public disk parking only. No. 3 bus service from the city centre stops at the nearby Watercourse Road. There are currently 12 buses per day within relevant hours.

CORK CITY ANCESTRAL PROJECT

Note: Cork City Ancestral Project is run under the auspices of Cork County Library. For further information, please contact Karen Riordan at: corkancestry@corkcoco.ie. At the time of this publication, Cork City Ancestral was not carrying out research.

CORK CITY LIBRARIES

Headquarters (City Library)
57–61 Grand Parade
CORK CITY
Ireland

TELEPHONE: (021) 492 4900; FAX: (021) 427 5684
E-mail: libraries@corkcity.ie
Website: www.corkcitylibraries.ie/

HOURS
M–Sa, 10:00–17:30

ACCESS AND SERVICES
Visitors welcome. No membership required for use of reference or information facilities: these services provided free of charge except photocopying. Borrower's card available for a fee for persons living in or working in Cork city and county. Photocopying, fax and public internet workstations available. Exhibitions a regular feature in Central Library and at all local libraries. Cork City Libraries hosts a number of national exhibitions and also exhibitions involving local organisations and groups.

CONTACT
Liam Ronayne, Cork City Librarian
Eamonn Kirwan, Senior Executive Librarian, Central Services;
Peggy Barrett, Executive Librarian, Reference Library;
Kieran Burke, Executive Librarian, Cork Local Studies;
Kitty Buckley, Executive Librarian, Rory Gallagher Music Library

DESCRIPTION
Cork City Libraries, the library service of Cork City Council, is a resource for all of the people of Cork: a resource for children and young people, a resource for life and learning, a resource for culture and the imagination.

The City Library, situated on the Grand Parade, houses Adult Lending services, the Children's Library, Rory Gallagher Music Library, Reference Library and Cork

Local Studies Library. Library members can borrow books, audio books on tape and CD, sound recordings of plays, poetry, prose and language learning tapes and CDs. Music Library members can also borrow music on cassette and CD. The City Library is open six days per week including lunchtime.

Cork City Libraries' catalogue of books, CDs and other items in stock is available on the internet at: www.corkcitylibraries.ie. Internet access is available to members of the public at a nominal charge in the City Library and six local libraries. The 'Cork Past and Present' website features digitised images, plans and maps, the history of Patrick Street, bilingual list of street names and place names and much more. Users can access 'Cork Past and Present' at www.corkpastandpresent.ie.

The Council also provides a network of six local libraries around the city – three on the north side of the city, in Hollyhill, Blackpool, and Mayfield (where the library is named after Frank O'Connor), and three on the south side, in Douglas, Tory Top (Ballyphehane), and Bishopstown.

HOLDINGS
The reference library houses 38,000 books, including directories, encyclopaedias, government publications, yearbooks and dictionaries, Irish interest material, journals, periodicals and Sunday and daily newspapers. Access to the newspaper and journal collection is enhanced by an index, created and added to on a daily basis by library staff, and by online information from databases and the internet and CD-ROMs. The Cork Local Studies Library contains some 6,100 books on the history, geography, antiquities, archaeology, folklore and culture of Cork city and county. The collection also contains microfilm, a comprehensive local newspaper archive, journals, periodicals, manuscripts, maps and photographs.

The Rory Gallagher Music Library has a stock of 22,000 CDs, DVDs, and tapes, in addition to 20,000 vinyl records (not on open access), 2,900 scores and 4,000 books on music subjects. The collection caters for all musical tastes including classical, jazz, light opera, folk, choral, military band music, rock and popular. Audio art tapes, including plays, poetry, prose and audio books, are available. Free membership of the music library is available for registered visually impaired citizens. Listening facilities are available in the library. The lending library contains 58,000 adult books and 16,000 children's books.

LOCATION
On Grand Parade in the city centre.

CORK COUNTY LIBRARY

Library Headquarters, Carrigrohane Road
CORK CITY
Ireland

TELEPHONE: (021) 454 6499
E-mail: corkcountylibrary@corkcoco.ie
Website: www.corkcoco.ie
Twitter: http://twitter.com/corkcolibrary

HOURS
Reference/Local Studies Department: M–F, 09:00–17:30; closed bank holidays
Lending Department: M–F, 09:00–17:30; closed bank holidays

ACCESS AND SERVICES
Reference/Local Studies Department: Visitors welcome; appointment recommended for those wishing to avail of microfilm viewers. Advice and guidance on research resources available; telephone enquiries welcome. Public internet workstations available.
Check website for opening hours and services available at each branch library.

CONTACT
Richard Forrest
Kieran Wyse

DESCRIPTION
The headquarters of Cork County Library provides a public library service throughout the county via a network of 27 branches and five mobile libraries. The Local Studies Department offers a wide range of resources reflecting a broad definition of Cork local studies, which includes areas such as local history, natural history, social studies, planning and genealogy. The department's collection reflects an understanding of local history as encompassing all aspects of life in County Cork, past and present.

HOLDINGS
There is a large collection of printed books in the Local Studies Collection and the Irish Studies Collection. Microfilm holdings include 1901 census returns (Cork City and County), tithe applotment books (Cork) and nineteenth and twentieth century Cork newspapers. Other holdings include Griffith's Valuation for Cork City and County.

Primary Sources for Cork Local Studies
Cork County Library's Local Studies Collection includes a number of primary and secondary sources that are key resources for those engaged in local history and genealogical research. In most cases, these resources are available only for consultation at the Model Farm Road Reference Department. Sources are divided into two categories:

Land Tenure and Occupancy
Civil Survey, 1654: survives only for the Barony of Muskerry and for Cork. Provides a description of parishes, quality of soils and names of landed proprietors. Published by the Irish Manuscripts Commission (IMC) in 1942.
Census of Ireland, 1659: This document, edited by Seamus Pender and published by the IMC in 1939, under the headings of County, Baronies and Parishes, gives the names of townlands, tituladoes or principal residents and population figures.
Book of Survey and Distribution, c. 1670: records details of distribution of forfeited lands under the Acts of Settlement and Explanation and gives the names of the landed proprietors in 1641 and 1670. A facsimile copy is held by the library.
Tithe applotment books: comprise a survey of the titheable land in each parish and were compiled between 1823 and 1838. They list only land occupiers; labourers and other landless rural residents are not recorded. In some instances, they include occupiers of small plots on the edges of towns. Microfilm copies of the tithe applotment books for County Cork are held by the library. An index of surnames for each parish is the only finding aid.

Primary Valuation of Tenements (Griffith's Valuation), *c.* 1850: a popular source for local historians and genealogists, these volumes list occupiers of land and houses with acreage in the case of land and valuation in the case of both land and houses. They are published by barony and are further subdivided by parish and townland. A surname index identifying those listed and the townland and parish of occupancy is the principal finding aid. A complete set of the printed volumes is available for reference at the County Library Local Studies Department.

Devon Commission Report: the report of the Commissioners of Inquiry into the state of the law and practice in respect of the occupation of land in Ireland, with minutes of evidence, was published in 1845. A microfiche copy is available at the library.

Miscellaneous
1901 census: the earliest Irish census for which the original household returns survive. It is an invaluable source for the family and social historian. It is arranged by District Electoral Divisions and by townlands or streets within these divisions. The 1901 census returns for Cork City and County are held on microfilm at the County Library (Cork City Library holds microfilm copies of the only other complete census, that of 1911). A fragment of the 1851 census for County Cork survives and covers an area around Kilworth in north-east Cork. Cork County Library holds a copy of the surviving returns.

Census data: though the original returns do not survive, the statistical data derived from censuses from 1813 onwards are accessible and are a useful source of information. The 1871 census statistics for County Cork, for example, give the comparative population figures for each townland and parish in the county for 1841, 1851, 1861 and 1871. These can be used to illustrate the effects of the Famine and emigration at townland and parish level. Cork County Library holds copies of these from 1851 onwards.

Schools Manuscripts Folklore Collection: this collection of material was collected for the Irish Folklore Commission from 1937 to 1939 through the national schools. The material included consists of local folklore and historical traditions collected by schoolchildren from their parents, grandparents and neighbours and written up in copybooks. The quality and value of the material varies from school to school, but it is nevertheless a fascinating and valuable record. The collection for County Cork is available on microfilm at the Reference Department.

A.E. Casey, (compiler), *O'Kief, Coshe Mang, Slieve Lougher and Upper Blackwater in Ireland* (15 vols, 1952–71): this unique compilation of original sources, newspaper abstracts and other records contains a wealth of useful material, relating primarily to the Blackwater Valley and north Cork region, but also relating to the county at large. Care should be taken in using it, as much of the material was transcribed and is prone to errors in transcription.

Irish Tourist Association (ITA) files for County Cork: around 1939, the ITA commissioned researchers to compile files of local historical material at town and parish level that would be of interest to visitors. Each file contains a synopsis of local history, local tourist attractions, local industries and so forth. Much of the material is copied from secondary sources, but some original material is included. The manuscript collection is accompanied by a collection of 269 photographs, mostly of historic buildings.

LOCATION
Western suburbs of the city.

CORK PUBLIC MUSEUM (MÚSAEM POIBLÍ CHORCAÍ)

Fitzgerald Park
CORK CITY
Ireland

TELEPHONE: (021) 427 0679; FAX: (021) 427 0931
E-mail: museum@corkcity.ie
Website: www.corkcity.ie

HOURS
M–F, 11:00–13:00, 14:15–17:00; Sa, 11:00–13:00, 14:15–16:00; Su, 15:00–17:00
(April–September only); Closed bank holiday weekends.

ACCESS AND SERVICES
Visitors welcome. Admission free. Museum offers exhibitions and programmes to
the public. Exhibition themes include prehistory Cork and Cork crafts, including
Cork glassware and silverware. The museum also houses an important archives
collection anchored by the Michael Collins Collection. A project to create a
computer database of the museum's collections has been completed and to date over
26,000 objects have been input. Work to create a database of digital images of the
museum's collections is under way. The museum now holds a large archive covering
the 1916–21 War of Independence period, with particular emphasis on County
Cork native Michael Collins and on Thomas MacCurtain and Terence MacSwiney,
first and second Republican Lord Mayors of Cork (both died in office – MacSwiney
by hunger strike in Brixton Prison; MacCurtain killed by police).

CONTACT
Curator

DESCRIPTION
Cork Public Museum has been preserving and exhibiting the region's cultural
heritage since 1910. Recently it expanded its exhibition and storage areas. It is
funded by Cork City Council.

HOLDINGS
The museum houses artefacts and archival material that document the history,
archaeology and industrial life of Cork City and the surrounding area. Of special
interest is the museum's collection of the correspondence of Michael Collins,
donated in July 2000 by Mr Peter Barry, former TD and Minister for Foreign
Affairs. The correspondence between Michael Collins and Kitty Kiernan forms the
largest body of the collection. The collection also contains letters from Harry
Boland, another leading figure in the fight for independence, a friend of Collins and
unsuccessful suitor of Kiernan. There are a small number of letters to Collins from
various individuals, from Collins to Cumann na mBan and to Kiernan from other
individuals.

LOCATION
Fitzgerald Park, off Western Road, along the River Lee.

NATIONAL UNIVERSITY OF IRELAND, CORK (UCC) – BOOLE LIBRARY

University College Cork, College Road
CORK CITY
Ireland

TELEPHONE: (021) 490 2281; FAX: (021) 427 3428
E-mail: library@ucc.ie
Website: booleweb.ucc.ie

HOURS
Consult website for full details of opening hours.
First term
Reading: M–Th, 08:30–21:45; F, 08:30–20:45; Sa, 10:00–12:45
Second and third terms
Reading: M–Th, 08:30–22:15; F, 08:30–21:15; Sa (second term only),
10:00–17:45; Sa (third term only), 10:00–21:45; Su (March–May only),
10:00–17:45
Vacation period (July–mid-September)
Lending: M–F, 09:15–16:15; reading: M–F, 08:30–16:15; Sa, 10:00–12:45

ACCESS AND SERVICES
Visitors admitted at Librarian's discretion. Annual membership fee for borrowing
privileges. Disabled access facilities. Photocopying and microform prints available for
a fee. Internet access available. Leaflets and booklets describing services available.
Consult website for special regulations governing external users and user fees.
External readers may choose to: (a) consult library collection; (b) use information
services; and (c) borrow library material. Eligibility: (a) graduates of UCC; (b)
members of Graduates Associations of some Irish universities; (c) persons engaged in
scholarly research who are not eligible to use the library through membership of the
College.
    For access to special collections and archives, *see* separate entry below.
    Brookfield Health Sciences Library is located opposite security desk and next to
nursing and midwifery studies reception desk within the Brookfield complex. It is
on two floors (ground floor and lower ground) and houses the main nursing and
midwifery collections for UCC. Along with the Nursing and Midwifery Studies
Collection, Brookfield Library holds the Clinical Therapies, Epidemiology and
Public Health, Pharmacy and General Practice Collections.
    The Medical Library, located at Cork University Hospital, is jointly funded by
UCC and the Southern Health Board. Staff and students of UCC, as well as
healthcare professionals working in the University Hospital, St Finbarr's Hospital
and Erinville Hospital, may consult in, and borrow from, the Medical Library. Other
healthcare professionals may apply to Librarian for consultation or borrowing
facilities as external readers, on payment of appropriate fee. One fee covers the Boole
Library, the Medical Library and the Brookfield Health Sciences Library.

CONTACT
Information desk. Telephone: (021) 490 2794; e-mail: informationdesk@ucc.ie

DESCRIPTION
The Boole Library is the main library for University College Cork, part of the
National University of Ireland system that also includes campuses in Dublin,

Galway, Limerick and Maynooth. Its first purpose is to serve the university by 'supporting study, teaching and research as efficiently as possible'. The Boole Library brings together in one large centre many sources of information not readily available elsewhere in Munster. They include books, periodicals, audiovisual materials, a European Community Documentation Centre, online searching and inter-library loans, together with the professional expertise to interpret the collections to its users. The Boole Library is named after George Boole, first Professor of Mathematics at Queen's College, Cork (now UCC). He developed Boolean algebra, which led to the creation of computer science.

HOLDINGS
Subjects of concentration include: humanities, law, medicine (CUH), medicine (UCC), official publications, European Documentation Centre, science and social sciences. The library houses a collection of 600,000 books, 4,000 periodicals (including national and foreign newspapers), an expanding collection of electronic resources covering all disciplines, the European Documentation Centre, which receives most of the basic documents of the European Communities and those of some international organisations, all Irish Government publications, a representative collection of British official publications, tapes, LPs, CDs, videos and slides. Special collections and archives are treated separately: *See* following entry.

LOCATION
The university is located one mile west of city centre. Follow signs to the library.

NATIONAL UNIVERSITY OF IRELAND, CORK (UCC) – SPECIAL COLLECTIONS AND ARCHIVES

Boole Library, University College Cork
CORK CITY
Ireland

TELEPHONE: (021) 490 2282 (Special Collections), (021) 490 3132 (Archives)
E-mail: specialcollections@ucc.ie (Special Collections); libraryarchives@ucc.ie (Archives)

WEBSITE: http://booleweb.ucc.ie/index.php?pageID=38 (Special Collections); http://booleweb.ucc.ie/index.php?pageID=238 (Archives)

HOURS
Special Collections
Term time: M–F, 09:30–16:45
Vacation period (July–September): M–F, 09:30–16:15
Please telephone or e-mail to make arrangements at least 24 hours prior to arrival.
Archives
By appointment only
Term time: M–F, 09:30–12:45, 14:15–16:45
Vacation period (July–September): M–F, 09:30–12:30, 14:15–16:15

ACCESS AND SERVICES
Visitors welcome but advance notice and ID required. See http://booleweb.ucc.ie/index.php?pageID=27. Wheelchair access. Pencils only; laptop facilities available. Photocopying and microfilm printing facilities available by

arrangement with Special Collections Librarian (or Archivist for archival material) and are subject to copyright and other restrictions. All material is for consultation only and may not be removed from the library. Printed and electronic guides available, viz. *Special Collections Boole Library University College Cork: an Introduction*; *Primary Sources for Medieval Studies in the Boole Library Special Collections*; *Sources for Seventeenth to Nineteenth Centuries Historical Studies in the Boole Library Special Collections*. The library's website gives detailed descriptions of holdings.

CONTACT
Crónán Ó Doibhlin, Sub-Librarian, Head of Division
Carol Quinn, Archivist
Emer Twomey, Archivist.

DESCRIPTION
Special collections of the Boole Library consist of primary source materials in a variety of formats (book, manuscript, map, newspaper, microform, electronic) which support research and teaching in the humanities and social sciences, spanning all periods from classical and early Christian to modern, with a particular emphasis on Ireland (especially Munster) and the Irish diaspora. Private libraries donated by individuals are sometimes maintained as discrete units by special arrangement. Since 1997 the section has acquired archival collections relating primarily, but not exclusively, to Munster families and businesses. The Boole Library Archives Service is an active repository, collecting and administering archival collections generated from outside of UCC which complement the research and teaching needs of University College Cork.

HOLDINGS
Holdings include archives, books, manuscripts, facsimiles of manuscripts, maps, microforms, newspapers, pamphlets, journals, theses, photographs and recordings. These collections are divided into three main categories: manuscripts, printed books and archives. For more detailed information, consult website.

Manuscripts
Highlights from the Manuscript Collections include Gaelic manuscripts, divided into two main series. (1) the Tórna Collection, containing manuscripts which belonged to Professor Tadhg Ó Donnchadha, Professor of Irish at University College Cork, 1916–44, and catalogued by Professor Pádraigh de Brún of the Dublin Institute for Advanced Studies, Clár Lámhscríbhinní Gaeilge Choláiste Ollscoile Chorcaí: Cnuasach Thórna (TR 017 DEBR). Tórna manuscripts are identified numerically with a 'T' prefix. (2) Other Gaelic Manuscript Collections consists of over 200 manuscripts purchased by or donated to the library. Seventy-seven of these belonged to Professor James E.H. Murphy, Professor of Irish at Trinity College Dublin, 1896–1919. A catalogue of this collection has been compiled by Dr Breandán Ó Conchúir, Department of Modern Irish at University College Cork, and published by the Dublin Institute for Advanced Studies (1991), Clár Lámhscríbhinní Gaeilge Choláiste Ollscoile Chorcaí: Cnuasach Uí Mhurchú (TR 017 OCON). Most of the remainder belonged to Canon Power, lecturer in and later Professor of Archaeology at University College Cork, 1915–32. The catalogue of these and the other Gaelic manuscripts in the collection has been prepared by Dr Breandán Ó Conchúir and is currently in press. A list is available at the enquiry desk

in the research room. Non-Gaelic manuscripts are grouped as 'manuscripts in English and/or bilingual'. These include the papers of various eminent professors, Tadhg Ó Donnchadha (Tórna), and Cormac Ó Cuilleanáin, and reflect part of the intellectual history of the college; they constitute a large portion of this collection. Collection guides are available for consultation at the enquiry desk in the Research Room. Please note that Tórna's papers are entirely independent of the Tórna Collection. Also included in this category are documents belonging to and relating to individuals or enterprises, e.g. William O'Brien and Kinsale Manorial Records. An archival finding list is available for the William O'Brien papers; all access is through the list at the enquiry desk in the Research Room and requires 24 hours' notice for retrieval.

The Manuscript Collection also includes several manuscript estate maps, music scores and minor manuscripts from the Middle East and Far East. In addition, there are manuscripts on microfilm, which include a large collection of manuscripts of Gaelic and historical interest, such as the Gaelic manuscripts in the Royal Irish Academy, the Folklore Collections at University College Dublin, manuscripts in the National Archives, Public Records Offices in London and Belfast and other institutions in Ireland and abroad. List of holdings is available at the enquiry desk. Of special genealogical interest are microfilm copies of Petty's parish maps for most of Munster, the originals of which are in the National Library of Ireland; the 1901 census returns for most of Munster; and all published censuses up to and including 1911. There was no census between 1901 and 1911. The Special Collections Department does not have the 1911 census returns: but it does have nineteenth century published censuses. Twentieth century published censuses from 1926 (there was no census in 1921) are held by the Official Publications Section in the Boole Library. (Owing to a one hundred year embargo on census returns after 1911 no access will be allowed to the returns in the National Archives, Dublin.) Holdings of manuscripts in facsimile are quite extensive. Among these are: *the Book of Kells*, *Book of Durrow* and *Book of Lindisfarne*; those published by the Irish Manuscripts Commission and the Royal Irish Academy; the *Domesday Book*; the *Utrecht Psalter*; and several Books of Hours. Early English manuscripts in facsimile series are also available, as are modern manuscript facsimiles, including the works of John Milton and James Joyce and the letters of Paul Valéry.

Printed Books

Major collections of printed books include: Pre-1850 Books – some 13,000 books and pamphlets published before 1850. St Fin Barre's Cathedral Library, which consists of some 3,000 books and pamphlets, mostly pre-1850, of theological, political and general interest; the Tórna Collection of books and journals belonging to the late Professor Tadhg Ó Donnchadha, which forms the nucleus of a research collection for Celtic studies; Munster Printing – a collection of books, pamphlets and ephemera printed in Munster irrespective of date.

Special collections of individual donors include the Arnold Bax Collection of Memorabilia. Bax (1883–1953) was Master of the King's Musick, 1941–53. This collection consists of a small number of his own compositions, a portion of his library, some of his letters and some personal effects. Other collections include the de Courcy Ireland Collection, containing a wide range of books, periodicals and ephemera dealing with maritime history and travel, acquired from Dr John de Courcy Ireland (1911–present); and the Friedlander Collection, named in memory of Elizabeth Friedlander (1903–84), German artist and designer who lived in

Kinsale, County Cork, and designed covers for Penguin books, the Nonesuch Press and many other prestigious publishing houses during her long life. Within this collection are books from Penguin and other publishers on a wide variety of subjects, including book design, layout, calligraphy and the arts, and printing in general. These books and some of her papers were donated to University College Cork by Mr Gerald Goldberg. Another collection of importance is the Ó Ríordáin Collection.

Archives Service
Major archival collections include: Attic Press/Róisín Conroy Collection, generated and collected by Róisín Conroy as co-founder and publisher of Attic Press and as an activist in the Irish Women's Movement; family papers belonging to the Grehan family; estate collections – Bantry House Collection; Seward Estate, Youghal, County Cork; Ryan of Inch Family Papers; political papers – Thomas MacDonagh Collection, Neville Keery Papers (unprocessed); literary papers – collections relating to Frank O'Connor and Sean O'Faolain; Nancy McCarthy and Daniel Corkery. Other collections include the Peters Photographic Collection (World War II), Papers of George Boole, Papers of Daniel Corkery, Murphys Brewery Archives, Woodford Bourne Collection and the Seán Ó Riada Collection. Please note that access to unprocessed collections is not permitted. UCC Library also maintains the official Frank O'Connor website www.frankoconnor.ie

LOCATION
Special Collections and Archives are in the basement level (floor Q-1) of the Boole Library, situated in the centre of UCC camps. Maps and other visitor information are accessible here www.ucc.ie/en/visitors/maps/

MALLOW HERITAGE CENTRE

27–28 Bank Place
MALLOW, COUNTY CORK
Ireland

TELEPHONE: (022) 50302; FAX: (022) 20276
E-mail: mallowhc@eircom.net and mallowheritagecentre@gmail.com
Website: www.mallowheritagecentre.com

HOURS
M–Th, 10:30–13:00, 14:00–16:00; F, 10:30–13:00; closed religious and bank holidays

ACCESS AND SERVICES
Fee based organisation offering genealogical research services to those interested in tracing their roots in County Cork, especially in East and North Cork. Enquiries welcome. Application form can be found on the centre's website. Initial search fee of €65.00 (or equivalent) per family must accompany applications. Priority/next day search, €90; single search, €40. Delay of four weeks can be expected for a reply to an initial enquiry. Chief surnames in rural Cork include: McCarthy, O'Callaghan, McAuliffe, Fitzgerald, Sullivan, Murphy, Walsh, O'Connor and O'Connell.

CONTACT
Susanna Russell

DESCRIPTION
Mallow Heritage Centre is the designated heritage centre for the Diocese of Cloyne.
It is a member of the Irish Family History Foundation, the coordinating body for a
network of government approved genealogical research centres in the Republic of
Ireland and in Northern Ireland, which have computerised tens of millions of Irish
ancestral records of different types. It is also a member of the Irish Genealogical
Project.

HOLDINGS
The centre holds baptismal and marriage records for 46 out of the 120 parishes
within the County of Cork, totalling 1,000,000 entries on its database, the third
largest record database in Ireland. Main records include: Roman Catholic baptismal
and marriage records, a few dating from 1757, and Church of Ireland records for the
North Cork area only, the earliest dating from 1730. A variety of the main
genealogical sources are currently being computerised and tombstones from several
cemeteries have been transcribed.

LOCATION
On the main Cork to Limerick Road, half an hour's drive north of Cork City. The
Heritage Centre is next to the Hibernian Hotel, just west of the town centre.

COUNTY DONEGAL

DONEGAL ARCHAEOLOGICAL SURVEY
See DONEGAL COUNTY MUSEUM, Letterkenny

DONEGAL COUNTY LIBRARY

Donegal County Library Headquarters
Rosemount
LETTERKENNY, COUNTY DONEGAL
Ireland

TELEPHONE: (074) 91 21968; FAX: (074) 91 21740
E-mail: central@donegallibrary.ie
Website: www.donegallibrary.ie

Central Library
Oliver Plunkett Road
LETTERKENNY, COUNTY DONEGAL
Ireland

TELEPHONE: (074) 912 4950; FAX: (074) 912 4950
E-mail: central@donegallibrary.ie
Website: www.donegallibrary.ie

HOURS
M, Tu, W, F, 10:30–17:30; Th, 13:00–20:00; Sa, 10:30–13:00

ACCESS AND SERVICES
Visitors welcome. Disabled access. Photocopying, printouts from the internet and microfilm reader available for a modest fee. Public internet access in Central Library and all other service points, WIFI in main branches. All library holdings, including local material, is available online at www.donegallibrary.ie.

CONTACT
Executive Librarian, Central Library. Telephone: (074) 912 4950; fax: (074) 912 4950

DESCRIPTION
Main library of the county's network, with library administration located at Rosemount, close to the Central Library in Letterkenny.

HOLDINGS
The library houses more than 70,000 volumes, with access to the system's some
350,000 volumes, including significant holdings of early printed books (some 300
pre-1851 volumes). The Local Studies collection based in the Central Library
consists of a wealth of resources for people wishing to research their family history,
such as the 1901 and 1911 Census returns on microfilm, local papers dating back to
the early nineteenth century on microfilm, Griffith's Valuation of County Donegal,
cemetery listings and passenger lists, to name but a few. Local authors collections
include: Patrick MacGill, Peadar O'Donnell, Seumas MacManus and John Kells
Ingram. These collections consist mostly of printed editions of their works, plus a
small amount of original papers and illustrative matter. Some of these Local Studies
resources can be accessed online via the www.askaboutireland.ie website. The
Collection of Personal Papers includes: Cathal Ó Searcaigh's personal archive –
manuscripts of his poetry and other writings, original editions of his published work
in monograph and journal form, videos and tapes of his broadcast work, and other
relevant papers and materials are deposited with Donegal County Library and the
County Archive in Lifford. Cathal Ó Searcaigh's own library of poetry and other
literature is housed in his house *Dámhlann an Ghleanna* in Mín a'Leagha, Gort
a'Choirce, is catalogued by Donegal County Library and maintained by Donegal
County Library *in situ*. Details of all library holdings can be accessed via the library
catalogue on the www.donegallibrary.ie website.

LOCATION
Housed in three storey building on the corner of Lower Main Street and Oliver
Plunkett Road, in the town centre.

DONEGAL COUNTY MUSEUM

High Road
LETTERKENNY, COUNTY DONEGAL
Ireland

TELEPHONE: (074) 912 4613
E-mail: museum@donegalcoco.ie
Website: www.donegal.ie

HOURS
M–F, 10:00–12:30, 13:00–16:30; Sa, 13:00–16:30

ACCESS AND SERVICES
Visitors welcome, but at least two weeks' advance notice required if a researcher
desires to view a particular artefact or group of artefacts. Access also depends on
availability of staff. ID required. Admission Free. Wheelchair access. Fax and
photocopying services available. Museum contains two exhibition galleries: one for
temporary exhibitions, the other for permanent exhibition telling the story of
Donegal from the Stone Age to the twentieth century. Collections catalogued
manually and electronically.

CONTACT
Curator or Assistant Curator

DESCRIPTION
Donegal County Museum was first opened to the public in 1987 and is housed in
what was once the Warden's house of the Letterkenny Workhouse, built in the
1840s. The role of the museum is to collect, record, preserve, communicate and
display for the use and enjoyment of the widest community possible the material
evidence and associated information of the history of Donegal.

HOLDINGS
The museum develops and cares for a comprehensive collection of over 8,000
original artefacts relating to the County of Donegal in the areas of archaeology,
geology, natural history, social and political history and folklife. It also houses the
archives of the Donegal Archaeological Survey, consisting of maps, plans, drawings,
slides and files relating to the Survey. The Survey was published in book form and
contains a description of the field antiquities of County Donegal from the
Mesolithic period to the seventeenth century.

North West Film Archive
This is unique digital collection of film archive material on Donegal and Derry. It
contains over 90 hours of programmes, documentaries, feature films, shorts and
news footage from some of the major televisions channels as well as Super 8 amateur
film and home video dating back over 60 years. The archive is available for viewing
free of charge.

Donegal Islands Digital Archive
This is a unique digital collection of archive material relating to the islands of
County Donegal. The archive provides free public access to over 23 hours of film,
television and video in the form of 94 separate items such as newsreels, television
news and documentaries and home movies. It also contains over 14 hours of radio
documentaries and news items. Material has been provided to this archive by RTE,
BBC, UTV, TG4, TV3, Radio na Gaeltachta, Sky TV, INA, Gael Linn, independent
film and radio producers and donators of family footage. The audio and visual material
contained in this archive gives an understanding of the social history of the offshore
islands of County Donegal from the 1950s to the present day. The collection captures
the relocation of some communities to the mainland, the struggle to maintain and
improve basic services and the unique cultural heritage of the County's islands.

LOCATION
Signposted in Letterkenny, a five minute walk from the town centre or bus station.

DONEGAL COUNTY ARCHIVES SERVICE

Donegal County Council
Three Rivers Centre
LIFFORD, COUNTY DONEGAL
Ireland

TELEPHONE: (074) 917 2490; FAX: (074) 914 2290
E-mail: archivist@donegalcoco.ie
Website: www.donegal.ie/dcc/arts/archive.htm

HOURS
M–F, 09:00–12:30, 13:15–16:30

ACCESS AND SERVICES
Public access by advance appointment only, by arrangement with Archivist. Service offers small permanent exhibition area with regularly changing exhibitions; research room; photocopying facilities; occasional joint exhibitions with other organisations; lectures and talks; liaison with local schools; and events for Heritage Week (last week in August or first week in September) and other local festivals.

CONTACT
Niamh Brennan, Archivist. E-mail: archivist@donegalcoco.ie

DESCRIPTION
Donegal County Archives holds the archives of Donegal County Council, its predecessor bodies, schools, railways and private historical collections of local interest. The priorities of the service include the listing and conservation of archival materials to make them accessible to the public, and the general development of the Archives Service.

HOLDINGS
Poor Law Unions
Donegal County Council has some of the finest surviving local archives in Ireland, including one of the nation's best county collections of records of Boards of Guardians of the Poor Law Unions in the county. The principal function of the Boards of Guardians was to supervise and run workhouses where the destitute were accommodated. Workhouses in Donegal were in Letterkenny, Ballyshannon, Stranorlar, Dunfanaghy, Carndonagh (run by the Inishowen Board), Donegal, Glenties and Milford. The collection includes:

> an almost complete set of minute books, c. 1840–c. 1923, for all Poor Law Unions in the county except Donegal Town (where minutes only survive for the years 1914–23);
> a considerable number of indoor relief registers and workhouse admission and discharge registers, which give very detailed information about destitute persons entering or leaving the workhouses, covering:
> Dunfanaghy Poor Law Union, 1891–1915,
> Glenties Poor Law Union, 1851–1922 (incomplete),
> Inishowen Poor Law Union, 1844–59, 1899–1911,
> Letterkenny Poor Law Union, 1864–78,
> Milford Poor Law Union, 1855–1922;
> outdoor relief registers for Letterkenny Union, 1855–99, and Milford Union, 1847–99;
> minute books for the dispensaries at Killygordon and Stranorlar, 1852–99;
> other records, including records of deaths for Milford (1899–1917) and Letterkenny Unions (1910–21), and some financial and administrative correspondence and documentation for some of the unions.

Grand Jury
The Archives Service holds significant records relating to the Grand Jury of Donegal, a local authority responsible for services including making and repair of roads and bridges, construction of courthouses, levying for support of district hospitals, schools and prisons. The Grand Jury's administrative functions were taken over by the newly established Donegal County Council in 1899. Grand Jury records include: 34 volumes of Spring and Summer and Lent Assizes 1754–1898 (with many gaps in years); accounts and correspondence, 1816–1901; and a Grand Jury map, 1801.

Rural District Councils

The Rural District Councils were set up under the 1898 Local Government (Ireland) Act. Functions included local housing, sewerage, water and public health services. They were abolished in 1925. Records include minutes of meetings for the councils of:

> Ballyshannon (19 volumes of minutes, 1899–1925);
> Donegal (11 volumes of minutes, 1914–25);
> Dunfanaghy (volumes of minutes for the period 1899–1918 and 13 folders of correspondence, 1909–18);
> Glenties (14 volumes of minutes, 1899–1925);
> Inishowen (13 volumes of minutes, 1899–1925);
> Letterkenny (18 volumes of minutes, 1899–1925);
> Londonderry No. 2 (volumes of minutes, 1899–1925);
> Milford (26 volumes of minutes, 1899–1925);
> Strabane No. 2 (15 volumes of minutes, 1899–1922);
> Stranorlar (8 volumes of minutes, 1899–1925).

Donegal County Council, 1899–present

Records of the County Council, formed under the 1899 Local Government Act, and still in existence today, include:

> minutes including Committee minutes, 1899–1975 (77 volumes);
> County Manager's Orders, 1942–75;
> finance material including abstracts of accounts, secretary's statements and General Ledgers, 1914–67;
> motor tax registers, 1903–23, 1951–92;
> housing records including housing of 'working classes' and 'labourers': plans, correspondence, reports etc, 1890–1940;
> County Library archives, including reports and minutes of meetings, 1928–87;
> electoral material, including registers of electors from the county, summaries of registers, 1920s–80s (incomplete);
> notices of elections, correspondence, 1920s–80s;
> local and general election campaigning material, generally from the 1970s;
> planning: applications, registers and development plans, 1934–72;
> environmental services, plans and maps;
> roads: plans, drawings and maps;
> legal deeds.

Private Records

Records of administration for landed estates include: some rentals and maps for the Murray Stewart Estate, Killybegs and other areas in South-West Donegal, 1749–1880; administrative records and maps for the Cochranes of Redcastle and Edward Harvey of Ballyliffin Estate, both in Inishowen, c. 1860–1900, and one Harvey rental, c. 1900 including lands at Inch; the Hamiltons of Fintown, 1818–49, and the Boytons and Montgomerys of Convoy, 1890s–1920s.

Other privately acquired archives include the papers of: Irish speaking poet Cathal Ó Searcaigh and the manuscripts of other local authors; papers relating to the history and culture of Donegal in the nineteenth and twentieth centuries, collected by Fr Patrick Gallagher of the Donegal Historical Society; and the historical lecture notes taken by Dr Maureen Wall. Also included are photographs of various towns;

oral history interviews; and archives relating to the Groves of Castle Grove House, Letterkenny.

School Records

Pupil registers and roll books for public elementary/primary or 'national' schools, *c.* 1880–*c.* 1990 are available for 80 schools (some no longer in existence), including schools at Dunfanaghy, Donegal, Mountcharles, Lettermacaward, Burtonport, Dunkineely, Fintown, Letterkenny, Buncrana, Ballyshannon, Ramelton, Fanad, Newtowncunningham, Creeslough, Churchill, Bunbeg, Kilmacrenan, Liscooley and Ray. The archive also holds rollbooks, registers and financial and administrative papers relating to the Lifford Endowed (Secondary) Schools.

Petty Sessions

Very rare court records (19 vols) for local petty sessions, mainly at Ballyshannon 1828–55. These include:

> Registry of Criminal Proceedings at Ballyshannon Petty Sessions, 1828–48, 1849–51, 1851–53 – details include date, informant's name and address, name and residence of person charged, offence (e.g. 'waylaying and assault', 'entering his orchard and stealing apples', 'stealing three bricks'); witnesses sworn; and determination (e.g. 'fined', 'committed to gaol');
> Registry of Civil Proceedings at Ballyshannon Petty Sessions, 1828–48, 1848–50, 1851–56 – details include date; complainant's name and address; defendant's name and address; complaint (e.g. 'non payment of county cess', 'having a quantity of flax on the public road', 'wilfully driving your mare into his grazing land'); witnesses sworn; and adjudication (e.g. 'dismissed', 'no appearance', 'postponed', 'settled', 'fined');
> Registry of Summons issued from Ballyshannon Petty Sessions, 1828–33, 1831–9, 1833–7, 1844–8, 1848–50 – details include name and address of complainant; name of person summoned; date; offence (e.g. 'assault and forcibly carrying away turf', 'house breaking'); and decision (e.g. 'dismissed', 'no jurisdiction', 'conviction', 'fined').

Railways

The railways of Donegal were closed down by 1960. The Archives Service holds some of the records relating to the railways, including:

> Letterkenny and Lough Swilly railway records: accounts, personnel documents (with restricted access);
> West Donegal Railway Drawings (1880);
> Finn Valley Railway plans (1860);
> prints of Great Northern Railway Company (1956–60);
> prints of Lough Swilly Railway trains (1951–9);
> prints of Letterkenny and Burtonport Extension Railway (1951–9);
> prints of trains, stations and lines of County Donegal Railways Joint Committee (1951–61);
> bye-laws, accounts, legal documents, timetables, leaflets and tickets, 1880–1960;
> posters and flyers relating to railways, *c.* 1900–50.

LOCATION
First floor, Three Rivers Centre.

LIFFORD OLD COURTHOUSE

The Diamond
LIFFORD, COUNTY DONEGAL
Ireland

TELEPHONE: (074) 914 1733; FAX: (074) 914 1228
E-mail: liffordoldcourthouse@gmail.com
Website: www.liffordoldcourthouse.com

HOURS
M–F, 09:30–14:00 (hours may be subject to change during summer months)

ACCESS AND SERVICES
Visitors welcome; admission fee for exhibitions. Fees: adults, €5.80; children, €2.90;
students and seniors, €3.85; families, €14.40. Advance notice required for large
groups. Late openings can be arranged in advance. Tours organised outside of
normal opening hours are usually for groups only.

Guided 'live' tours are available Monday–Friday from 10:00–16:00, with the last
tour leaving at 15:00, but in the winter months our guides may be out on school
visits so please ring in advance to confirm availability of a tour guide or if you wish
to book a guided tour outside of these times. Note a 'family' admission is 2 adults
and 2 children. There are also special group rates for groups of 10 or more.

The Courthouse Bistro situated in the historic Courtroom open 09:30–14:00,
Monday to Friday. It also cater outside of normal opening hours for conferences and
parties. Free brochures available.

CONTACT
Gillian Graham, Manager

DESCRIPTION
The old courthouse was built in 1746 by Dublin architect Michael Priestly and
functioned as a courthouse until 1938. It was restored and reopened as a heritage
centre in 1994. Visit the prisoners and inmates held in the original underground
cells and lunatic asylum. Lifford was also the administrative centre for the
Plantation. The building is believed to have been built on the foundation of Lifford
Castle, a sixteenth and seventeenth century O'Donnell stronghold.

HOLDINGS
The courthouse houses the Rupert Coughlan Collection of documents, manuscripts
and charts on the O'Donnell family and chieftains; and historic local artefacts,
letters and photographs relating to the old courthouse and gaol. The building houses
the Lifford branch of the County Donegal Library Service.

LOCATION
Located in the Diamond, Lifford, one mile west of Strabane, County Tyrone, and 14
miles from Derry City.

DONEGAL ANCESTRY

Note: Donegal Ancestry Centre closed at the end of 2010. The genealogy service, however, is continuing to operate under Donegal Ancestry Ltd. The database is now available online and the site is hosted by the Irish Family History Foundation at: www.rootsireland.ie. The index can be searched freely and there is an option to conduct an all-Ireland or a specified County search and the user has an option either to purchase or view relevant records at a cost of five Euro per record. Clients who feel they require further assistance can contact Joan Patton at info@donegalancestry.com. If clients can provide sufficient information, Ms. Patton will be happy to assess the feasibility of conducting further research. An assessment fee of €20.00 is required, (the currency exchange rate can be checked at www.xe.com) – this fee will be discounted from any further research that may be commissioned.

CONTACT
Joan Patton, Donegal Ancestry Ltd, C/o Mr John Coyle, Donegal Ancestry Chairman, Brookwood, Killycreen, Ramelton, Co Donegal, Ireland

COUNTY DOWN

LIBRARIES NI HERITAGE COLLECTION, DOWNPATRICK

The Heritage Gallery
Downpatrick Library
Market Street
DOWNPATRICK, COUNTY DOWN, BT30 6LZ
Northern Ireland

TELEPHONE: (028) 4461 1448; Fax: (028) 4461 1444
E-mail: localstudies.down@librariesni.org.uk
Website: www.librariesni.org.uk

HOURS
M, Tu, Th, 09:30–20:00; W, F, 09:30–17:00; Sa, 10:00–17:00

ACCESS AND SERVICES
Visitors are welcome. The gallery is wheelchair accessible. The collection is non-circulating, reference only. Microfilm reader/printers are available. Due to heavy demand for microfilm readers, booking is advisable for this service. Public Access Terminals with internet access are freely available for all Libraries NI members. Fees apply to photocopies, microfilm reader and IT printouts. Membership of library is open to anyone living, working or studying in the area. ID is required on registering. Heritage staff will assist and advise users seeking genealogical information.

CONTACT
Joan Magee, Heritage Services Manager. E-mail: joan.magee@librariesni.org.uk

DESCRIPTION
Originally formed as part of the South Eastern Education and Library Board's Local Studies Department in Ballynahinch, County Down, the collection was transferred to the Heritage Gallery in Downpatrick Library following the consolidation of Northern Ireland Libraries in 2009.

HOLDINGS
The Heritage Gallery in Downpatrick library holds a reference collection covering all aspects of life in County Down and includes: postcards and photographs; journals; newspaper cuttings; local and regional newspapers on microfilm and a selection of specialised and antiquarian books for family history research, including street

directories, volumes of Griffith's Valuation, gravestone inscriptions, Ireland's memorial records and Grand Jury Records of the county administration prior to 1898. These and Grand Warrants contain information about work ordered to be done by the Grand Jury on roads, bridges and jails and about constabulary duties in the counties. The Collection additionally includes historical maps as well as ordnance survey parish memoirs which describe parishes in the 1830s, complementing the 1830s edition of the 6 inch maps.

Libraries NI Online Resources
Libraries NI customers have access to 'Online Resources' on the library website.

Ancestry Library Edition is an online genealogical collection accessible on the Libraries NI website to library members at any library in Northern Ireland. This resource is available only from the Libraries NI network and is not accessible to members from their home computers. The Ancestry Library Edition collection has approximately thousands of databases and billions of indexed names from key collections spanning the fourteenth century to present day enabling customers to search for vital information about their ancestors.

The 'JSTOR Ireland Collection' is fully searchable, consists of the digital content of journals and other material relating to Ireland, and will be of great interest to anyone researching Irish history, genealogy, archaeology, literature etc. Most of the material included was published in the eighteenth, nineteenth and twentieth centuries.

The DIPPAM web resource is a virtual library of sources relating to the history of modern Ireland and its global diaspora. Documenting Ireland: Parliament, People and Migration (DIPPAM) is a collaboration project between Queen's University Belfast, The University of Ulster, The Mellon Centre for Migration Studies, Omagh, and Libraries NI, and has been funded by the Arts and Humanities Research Council. DIPPAM may be of particular interest to people involved in research the history of their locality or family, and for use in school history projects. It includes three searchable databases: Enhanced British Parliamentary Papers on Ireland (EPPI) – which comprises scans of over 15,000 official publications relating to all aspects of Irish affairs during the period of the Act of Union, 1800–1922, including bills, reports, royal commissions of inquiry and the published census returns. It is a rich source for the social history of Ireland, as well as for statistics and evidence relating to population, emigration, famine, crime and political movements: The Irish Emigration Database (IED) is made up of documents relating to Irish emigration since the eighteenth century, mainly to North America, and mostly drawn from archives in Northern Ireland and from private collections. The documents include emigrant letters, newspaper extracts, shipping advertisements, family papers and extracts from relevant publications and Voices of Migration and Return (VMR) is an oral history archive of over 90 life-narrative interviews conducted with emigrants and return-emigrants from the province of Ulster, collected between 2004 and 2008. The study participants represent a range of geographical origins within Ulster, class backgrounds and religious identities.

LOCATION
By Bus: Get off the bus at the bus station. Walk toward the centre of the town up Market Street. Downpatrick library is situated on 79 Market Street approx 1 min from bus station.

By Car: From Belfast, follow the A7. At the roundabout take the 2nd exit onto Bridge Street. Continue onto Church Street, turn left onto English Street, and turn right onto Market Street. The library is on the right. From Clough follow the A25 into Downpatrick town centre.

ULSTER FOLK AND TRANSPORT MUSEUM

Cultra
HOLYWOOD, COUNTY DOWN, BT18 0EU
Northern Ireland

TELEPHONE: (028) 9042 8428; FAX: (028) 9042 8728
E-mail: uftm@nidex.com
Website: www.uftm.org.uk, www.magni.org.uk

HOURS
March–June: M–F, 10:00–17:00; Sa, 10:00–18:00; Su, 11:00–18:00
July–September: M–F, 10:00–18:00; Sa, 10:00–18:00; Su, 11:00–18:00
October–February: M–F, 10:00–16:00; Sa, 10:00–17:00; Su, 11:00–17:00
Closed for several days at Christmas

ACCESS AND SERVICES
Museum
Open to general public. Separate admission charges to Folk Museum and Transport Museum (adults, £5; children (5–16 years), £3; reduced rates for seniors, students, families, groups, etc; children under five free). Combined visit to both Folk Museum and Transport Museum: adults, £6.50; children, £3.50. Disabled access to most of site. Museum publishes a wide range of material, including the journal *Ulster Folklife*, exhibition catalogues, educational study packs and worksheets for schools.

Library and Archive
Appointment required. Library offers reference assistance, photocopying, microfilm reader/printer, photographic reproductions and database searching.

CONTACT
Roger Dixon, Librarian

DESCRIPTION
The museum occupies 177 acres just east of Belfast in northern County Down. It is devoted to preserving the ways things were in the north of Ireland, especially around the turn of the twentieth century. While your primary purpose in visiting the museum may be to conduct research in its library and archives, it would be worthwhile to take time to explore the Folk Museum's exhibitions and reconstructed farms, houses, workshops, mills, schools, churches and other facilities that take you back in time. The Transport Museum also offers an array of distractions, from old railway engines and cars to the modern De Lorean automobile, which was manufactured in Belfast. The museum is part of the Museums and Galleries of Northern Ireland (MAGNI) service, which also includes the Ulster American Folk Park, Omagh, County Tyrone; the Ulster Museum, Belfast; and its branch, the Armagh County Museum, Armagh. The museum has been voted Irish Museum of the Year and ranks among Ireland's most important cultural, educational and tourist facilities.

HOLDINGS

The library and archive collections support the various interests of the museum, especially folk life, social history and transport. The book collection, which exceeds 25,000 volumes, and an extensive range of periodicals, are available for reference purposes only. The archive boasts an extensive collection of photographs from the late nineteenth century to the present. The largest collection of photographs is the 70,000 item archive of Harland and Wolff Ltd, which records the shipping activity of the company from 1895 to the mid-1980s. Harland and Wolff built the Titanic, and the museum's archive houses what is probably the world's largest and most important collection of photographic negatives and ship plans relating to this ill fated liner and other famous ships built by the yard. The museum also houses Ireland's largest collection of Lloyd's shipping and yacht registers along with an extensive collection of sound recordings documenting stories, language, music, customs, beliefs and traditions, including the BBC (Northern Ireland) Archive and the tape recorded survey of Hiberno-English. The most important recent addition is the Living Linen Archive, which has recorded the knowledge and experience of people associated with the linen industry. The museum also maintains an Ulster Dialect Archive, and has compiled an Ulster Dictionary onto a computer database. The Library also houses the Ulster Museum Library and Archive Collection. See immediately below.

LOCATION

About ten miles east of Belfast on the A2 Belfast to Bangor Road, 2.5 miles outside Holywood.

THE ULSTER MUSEUM LIBRARY

Ulster Folk and Transport Museum
Cultra
HOLYWOOD, COUNTY DOWN, BT18 0EU
Northern Ireland

HOURS

By appointment

ACCESS AND SERVICES

The book and archive collection is designed primarily for the use of the Ulster Museum staff but limited access is available to the public by appointment. The image collection is principally available through the Museum's website but personal inquiries are welcome. Contact: Michelle Ashmore, Picture Library Manager.

CONTACT

Roger Dixon, Librarian, National Museums Northern Ireland

DESCRIPTION

The Library is intended primarily to serve the needs of the the staff of the Ulster Museum, located in Belfast, near Queen's University. The intention is to merge the Ulster Museum library with that of the Ulster Folk and Transport Museum to provide improved public access supported by a joint catalogue and new storage facilities.

HOLDINGS
The Library houses an extensive book and periodical collection relating to the
Museum's areas of interest. Subjects covered include Irish history and typography,
the natural sciences, art and archaeology.
The image archive includes the photographic collections of Welch, Hogg and
Bigger and extends to some 45,000 items.
The small archive collection relates principally to the natural sciences and
includes the manuscripts of the botanist John Templeton [1766 to1825].

LOCATION
About ten miles east of Belfast on the A2 Belfast to Bangor Road, 2.5 miles outside
Holywood.

DIOCESAN ARCHIVE, DROMORE (Roman Catholic)

44 Armagh Road
NEWRY, COUNTY DOWN, BT35 6PN
Northern Ireland

TELEPHONE: (028) 3026 2444; FAX: (028) 3026 0496
E-mail: bishopofdromore@btinternet.com
Website: www.dromorediocese.org

HOURS
By appointment

ACCESS AND SERVICES
Enquiries welcome, but advance notice required. Researchers asked to know exactly
what they are looking for, as archive not fully processed.

CONTACT
Most Rev John McAreavey

DESCRIPTION
Small Roman Catholic diocesan archive. The Diocese of Dromore is part of the
ecclesiastical province of Armagh and includes portions of Counties Down, Armagh
and Antrim.

HOLDINGS
The archive comprises the written materials handed down by diocesan bishops from
approximately 1850. The volume of material is very uneven, however. The archive is
in the process of being reorganised following its removal from the Bishop's House
while this was being refurbished.

LOCATION
Bishop's House, Newry.

LIBRARIES NI HERITAGE COLLECTION, NEWRY CITY

Newry City Library
79 Hill Street
NEWRY, COUNTY DOWN, BT34 1DG
Northern Ireland

TELEPHONE: (028) 3026 4683; Fax: 028 3026 4683
E-mail: newry.library@librariesni.org.uk
Website www.librariesni.org.uk

HOURS
M, Tu, Th, 09:30–20:00; W, 09:30–17:00, F, 09:30–18:00, Sa, 09:30–17:00

DESCRIPTION
Part of the Libraries NI Heritage Collection program, created following the consolidation of Northern Ireland Libraries in April 2009.

ACCESS AND SERVICES
Visitors are welcome. The collection is wheelchair accessible. The collection is non-lending, reference only. Microfilm reader/printers are available. Due to heavy demand for microfilm readers, booking is advisable for this service. Public Access Terminals with internet access are freely available for all Libraries NI members. Fees apply to photocopies, microfilm reader and IT printouts. Membership of library is open to anyone living, working or studying in the area. ID is required on registering.

CONTACT
Joan Magee, Heritage Services Manager. E-mail: joan.magee@librariesni.org.uk

HOLDINGS
The Heritage Collection in Newry City Library holds a reference collection which includes books on Irish history, local studies and family history. Also available are historical maps of Co. Down covering the County series (1830s to 1930s) and a selection of local newspapers on microfilm which can be viewed on the reader-printers.

Libraries NI Online Resources
Libraries NI customers have access to 'Online Resources' on the library website.

Ancestry Library Edition is an online genealogical collection accessible on the Libraries NI website to library members at any library in Northern Ireland. This resource is available only from the Libraries NI network and is not accessible to members from their home computers. The Ancestry Library Edition collection has approximately thousands of databases and billions of indexed names from key collections spanning the fourteenth century to present day enabling customers to search for vital information about their ancestors.

The 'JSTOR Ireland Collection' is fully searchable, consists of the digital content of journals and other material relating to Ireland, and will be of great interest to anyone researching Irish history, genealogy, archaeology, literature etc. Most of the material included was published in the eighteenth, nineteenth and twentieth centuries.

The DIPPAM web resource is a virtual library of sources relating to the history of modern Ireland and its global diaspora. Documenting Ireland: Parliament, People and Migration (DIPPAM) is a collaboration project between Queen's University Belfast, The University of Ulster, The Mellon Centre for Migration Studies, Omagh, and Libraries NI, and has been funded by the Arts and Humanities Research Council. DIPPAM may be of particular interest to people involved in research the history of their locality or family, and for use in school history projects. It includes three searchable databases: Enhanced British Parliamentary Papers on Ireland (EPPI) – which comprises scans of over 15,000 official publications relating to all aspects of Irish affairs during the period of the Act of Union, 1800–1922, including bills, reports, royal commissions of inquiry and the published census returns. It is a rich source for the social history of Ireland, as well as for statistics and evidence relating to population, emigration, famine, crime and political movements: The Irish Emigration Database (IED) is made up of documents relating to Irish emigration since the eighteenth century, mainly to North America, and mostly drawn from archives in Northern Ireland and from private collections. The documents include emigrant letters, newspaper extracts, shipping advertisements, family papers and extracts from relevant publications and Voices of Migration and Return (VMR) is an oral history archive of over 90 life-narrative interviews conducted with emigrants and return-emigrants from the province of Ulster, collected between 2004 and 2008. The study participants represent a range of geographical origins within Ulster, class backgrounds and religious identities.

LOCATION
Newry city centre.

NEWTOWNARDS BRANCH LIBRARY

Queen's Hall, Regent Street
NEWTOWNARDS, COUNTY DOWN, BT23 4AB
Northern Ireland

TELEPHONE/FAX: (028) 9081 4732
E-mail: info@seelb.org.uk
Website: www.seelb.org.uk

HOURS
M–W, 09:30–20:00; Th, 10:00–17:00; F, 09:30–17:00; Sa 10:00–16:00

ACCESS AND SERVICES
Visitors welcome, but ID required. Borrowing privileges for visitors may be restricted. Consult Librarian. Disabled access. Photocopying and fax services available. Free internet access for all Northern Ireland public library members. One membership card valid for all libraries. Charge of £1.50 per half hour for non-members; ID required. Membership of the library open to anyone living, working or studying in the area.

CONTACT
Elizabeth Consiglia, Branch Library Manager
Irene Costley, Branch Library Manager

DESCRIPTION
The library is one of 96 branch libraries plus 2 specialist libraries in the LIBRARIES NI system, headquartered in Lisburn, County Antrim.

HOLDINGS
Houses a collection of more than 20,000 volumes, with access to the system's larger collection, including online resources. Modest local studies collection focusing on Newtownards and North County Down.

LOCATION
Town centre.

COUNTY DUBLIN

AN CHARTLANN MHÍLEATA/THE MILITARY ARCHIVES

Cathal Brugha Barracks
Rathmines
DUBLIN 6
Ireland

TELEPHONE: (01) 804 6457; FAX: (01) 804 6237
E-mail: militaryarchives@defenceforces.ie
Website: www.militaryarchives.ie

HOURS
Tu–Th, 10:00–16:00; closed public holidays and Defence Forces commemorations and Christmas–New Year period (annual file release).

ACCESS AND SERVICES
By appointment only. ID and advance notice by phone or email required. Access limited to eight persons at a time. Limited disabled access facilities. Lockers available. No catering facilities onsite. Laptops permitted; pencils only. Digital Photography with permission only.

CONTACT
Officer in Charge/Duty Archivist

DESCRIPTION
The Military Archives is the place of deposit for the records of the Department of Defence, the Defence Forces and the Army Pensions Board. The function of the archives is to collect, preserve and make available the documentary heritage of the Department of Defence and the Irish Defence Forces from the formation of Óglaigh na hÉireann (the Irish Volunteers) in November 1913 to the present day, inclusive of overseas service with United Nations, NATO and EU peace support operations since 1958.

HOLDINGS
The archive houses approximately 35,000 linear shelf feet of archival material, including departmental files, military documents, records and some related photographic, audio and visual material. Major collections include the Bureau of Military History (1913–21), which includes 1,773 witness statements, 334 sets of

contemporaneous documents, photographs (including action sites of the 1916 Easter Rising), press cuttings and voice recordings; Collins papers 1919–22; liaison documents (From Truce to British evacuation); Civil War operations, intelligence and radio reports; internment camp and prison administration records 1922–4; captured documents (IRA) 1922–4; the army crisis 1924; military mission to the United States 1926–7; emergency defence plans 1939–46; military intelligence (G2) files 1939–46; Office of the Controller of Censorship files; internment camp records for the 1939–46 period; Department of Defence files from 1922 up to the 1960s; Air Corps and Naval Service material and records. Other collections of special interest include bound volumes of *An tÓglach* (1918–33) and *An Cosantóir* (1940–2002 + digital version 2003 and index up to 2009), plus other military periodicals and newspapers; the National Army Census, 1922; records and history of units that served overseas on United Nations peacekeeping missions; and approximately 1,000 personal papers collections.

LOCATION
At Cathal Brugha Barracks, Rathmines, Dublin 6, off the main Rathmines Road, adjacent to St Mary's College, approximately two kilometres from the city centre on the south side of the Liffey. Served by buses 14A or 15 from the city centre. Parking available on advance notification and provision of photo ID.

ASSOCIATION OF PROFESSIONAL GENEALOGISTS IN IRELAND

Honorary Secretary
30 Harlech Crescent
Clonskeagh
DUBLIN 14
Ireland

E-mail: info@apgi.ie
Website: www.apgi.ie

DESCRIPTION
APGI is an association of individual professional genealogical researchers who subscribe to a strict code of practice. APGI acts as a regulating body to maintain high standards among its members and to protect the interests of clients. Since the 1980s APGI Members have served as consultants at the Genealogical Office and continued in that role when the service transferred to the National Library of Ireland. Since 2003 APGI Members have also staffed the National Archives of Ireland Genealogy Advisory Service. Both services have been highly commended by LDS (Church of Jesus Christ of the Latter Day Saints). Future restructuring in both institutions may alter APGI's role in their genealogy advisory services. There are currently 28 members, all of whom are accredited by an independent board of assessors. Some offer special areas of interest, e.g. 'research within Ulster only'. A brochure listing members and their addresses with telephone numbers, e-mail addresses and websites, where applicable, is available through the Honorary Secretary or through the website. Fees apply for research undertaken at the request of clients.

AUSTIN CLARKE LIBRARY
See POETRY IRELAND/ÉIGSE ÉIREANN, Dublin

BLACKROCK LIBRARY, Michael Smurfit Graduate School of Business
See UNIVERSITY COLLEGE DUBLIN LIBRARY, Dublin

CENTRAL CATHOLIC LIBRARY

74 Merrion Square
DUBLIN 2
Ireland

TELEPHONE: (01) 676 1264
E-mail: catholiclibrary@imagine.ie
Website: www.catholiclibrary.ie

HOURS
M–F, 11:00–18:00; Sa, 11:00–17:30

ACCESS AND SERVICES
Visitors and enquiries welcome, but advance notice preferred. Membership fees
apply: general public, €25 per year; students and seniors, €10. No disabled access
facilities. Open and closed collections; closed collection accessible only on request.
Sheaf and card catalogues available. Printed catalogue of older books available.
Photocopying (excludes early printed books) available for a fee at Librarian's
discretion. Staff carry out any photocopying. Laptops and photography permitted
with Librarian's approval. Series of four lectures held each spring and autumn.
Copies of library brochures available on request. Borrowing privileges limited to
members. Library regularly holds book sales.

CONTACT
Teresa Whitington, Librarian

DESCRIPTION
The library is a voluntary subscription library founded by Fr Stephen Brown, SJ in
1922 to provide reading matter and reference services on church and religious affairs.
It is entirely self-funded, relying on membership fees, donations and bequests.

HOLDINGS
The collection totals some 76,500 volumes, including 360 journal titles, dealing
with all branches of human knowledge with which religion is concerned. It also
includes pamphlets. Though its focus is Catholic, the library's holdings vary widely
and include an important reference collection. Closed collections include: the Art
Library – a small archive dealing with the work of the Academy of Christian Art, a
collection on European art, including Celtic art, and a non-European art collection
donated by Sir John Galvin, a member of the board of the Chester Beatty Library;
the Irish Room – journals, books on Irish history and nineteenth century Irish
fiction; the Leo Room – sociology, politics and international affairs; the Carnegie
Collection – philosophy, religion and sociology (many dealing with non-Catholic
and non-Christian traditions); the Periodicals Collection; and some 1,200 older
printed books (1541–1850), mostly of a Catholic interest. Among the reference
books are several standard works on genealogy.

LOCATION
Nearly halfway along the south side of Merrion Square from the Upper Merrion
Street end. The south side is the side running from Upper Merrion Street to Upper

Mount Street and the Pepper Canister Church (St Stephen's). Bus 7 stops about five minutes' walk from the library. From the north side of the city, bus 13 stops nearby. The library is a ten minute walk from Pearse DART station.

CENTRAL LIBRARY
See DUBLIN CITY PUBLIC LIBRARIES, Dublin

CENTRE FOR DUBLIN AND IRISH STUDIES
See DUBLIN AND IRISH COLLECTIONS, Dublin

CHESTER BEATTY LIBRARY

Dublin Castle
DUBLIN 2
Ireland

TELEPHONE: (01) 407 0750; FAX: (01) 407 0760
E-mail: info@cbl.ie
Website: www.cbl.ie

HOURS
Exhibitions
May–September: M–F, 10:00–17:00
October–April: Tu–F, 10:00–17:00
All year: Sa, 11:00–17:00, Su, 13:00–17.00
Closed Good Friday, 24–26 December, 1 January and public holiday Mondays.
Research
Reading Room reference: M–F, 10:00–13:00, 14:15–17:00
Access to manuscript collections: by written arrangement, M–F, 10:00–13:00, 14:15–16:30

ACCESS AND SERVICES
Free admission to exhibition galleries. Access to Reading Room by appointment. Photocopier and microfilm reader available. Online access to reference and early printed book collections available at https://opac.cbl.ie/. Laptops permitted; pencils only; gloves may be required for use in the Reading Room. Photography not permitted. Photographs, microfilms, transparencies and digital images to order.

CONTACT
Reference Library: Celine Ward, Reference Librarian. E-mail: reference@cbl.ie
Manuscript research: write to Director or Specialist Curator (consult website for details)
Members of the Chester Beatty Library: Mary Dowling. E-mail: mdowling@cbl.ie
Photographic services: Sinead Ward. E-mail: photographicservices@cbl.ie

DESCRIPTION
The library was formed by the American born mining engineer and philanthropist Chester Beatty (1875–1968), who moved his priceless collections of artworks, manuscripts and illustrated printed books to Dublin in 1950. The library relocated to its current premises in 1999. Beatty bequeathed his library to a trust for the benefit of the public. It is now supported by the Government of Ireland. The library

boasts a state of the art exhibition gallery in a modern addition to the renovated and redesigned eighteenth century clock tower building in the grounds of Dublin Castle. Facilities include a restaurant, gift and bookshop, audiovisual presentations, roof garden, wheelchair access and baby changing facilities. Free brochures are available in ten languages, and in Braille. The Chester Beatty Library is a 'must see' even if you have no plans to research its rich collections. The exhibitions alone are worth a visit. The Chester Beatty Library was named European Museum of the Year 2002.

HOLDINGS
The library houses one of the world's finest collections of manuscripts, prints, icons, paintings, early printed books and *objets d'art*, with special strengths in the areas of the Middle East and Asia. Items from the collection date back to 2700 BC. Among the highlights of the collection are: Egyptian papyrus texts, exceptional early Biblical papyri, illuminated copies of the Koran, the Bible and European medieval and renaissance manuscripts.

LOCATION
In the garden behind the main buildings of Dublin Castle, off Dame Street. There is also an entrance on Ship Street. It is a ten minute walk from Trinity College. The library is on bus routes 13, 16, 19 and 123 (from O'Connell Street).

DUBLIN AND IRISH COLLECTIONS

Dublin City Library and Archive
138–144 Pearse Street
DUBLIN 2
Ireland

TELEPHONE: (01) 674 4999; FAX: (01) 674 4879
E-mail: dublinstudies@dublincity.ie
Website: www.dublincity.ie/RecreationandCulture/libraries/Heritage%20
and%20History/Collections/Pages/index.aspx

HOURS
M–Th, 10:00–20:00; F–Sa, 10:00–17:00; closed bank holidays, including Saturdays of bank holiday weekends

ACCESS AND SERVICES
The Dublin and Irish Collections and Dublin City Archives share facilities at Dublin City Library and Archive. Visitors welcome. The library is intended for serious students and researchers as well as the general public. Facilities include the Research Reading Room, conference rooms and exhibition rooms. All readers need a reference readers' ticket to use the collections. Readers need to bring personal photographic ID and tickets will be issued without delay. No admission fees. Fees charged for photocopying and photography. Facilities provided for laptops; pencils only. No photography in Research Reading Room or in collections. Part of library catalogue accessible online. All items published before 1801 included in the English Short Title Catalogue (ESTC). Parts of collection accessible through printed *Catalogue of the Library of Sir John T. Gilbert* (Dublin, 1918) – available as an ebook on www.openlibrary.org and on card catalogue in Research Reading Room. Conferences, seminars and single lectures held regularly. Information can be found on the website.

The Library has compiled and published a *Directory of Dublin for 1738* (Dublin, 2000). This replicates the eighteenth century directories, but information drawn from legal recognisances, parish cess books, newspaper advertising and other sources. Laid out in alphabetical order by surname, in street order and by occupation or trade, and accompanied by fold out map based on maps of the period. This has proved quite useful for family and historical research. Annual lecture held in January to commemorate the life and works of Sir John T. Gilbert, and first eight of these lectures published as separate booklets. All publications available for purchase through website.

CONTACT
Máire Kennedy, Divisional Librarian. E-mail: maire.kennedy@dublincity.ie

DESCRIPTION
The Dublin and Irish Collections houses the special collections of the city's public library system, most especially the valuable collection of books on early Dublin contained in the library of Sir John T. Gilbert, the Dix Collection, the Yeats Collection, the Swift Collection and the Dublin and Irish Collections. It also houses one of the strongest genealogical collections in Ireland.

HOLDINGS
The Dublin Collection
The Dublin Collection comprises a number of special collections relating to Dublin and Dubliners. New material is acquired as it becomes available, including second hand and antiquarian books, newspapers, periodicals, photographs, maps, prints, drawings, theatre programmes, playbills, posters, ballad sheets, audiovisual materials and ephemera, as resources allow. The collection includes the following special collections:

The Gilbert Library: The most extensive of the special collections, the Gilbert Library is made up of the manuscripts, books and other printed materials collected by Sir John T. Gilbert (1829–98), historian and archivist. The collection reflects Gilbert's interest in the social, political and cultural history of Ireland, particularly of Dublin. Notable features include early Dublin newspapers, fine Dublin bookbindings of the eighteenth century, Dublin almanacs and directories. Of special interest are the manuscripts of the municipal records of the city of Dublin and records of the Dublin guilds. A printed catalogue of the Gilbert Library compiled by Douglas Hyde and D.J. O'Donoghue is available. John T. Gilbert's many original historical works and his edited volumes are prominent in the library. He is perhaps best known for his three volume *History of the City of Dublin*. He compiled and edited the *Calendar of Ancient Records of the Corporation of Dublin*, the first seven volumes of which were published during his lifetime. His widow (the novelist Rosa Mulholland) continued the work, and 19 volumes of the *Calendar* were published from 1889 to 1944. The *Calendar* comprises a record of the muniments in the possession of Dublin City Council and is an extremely valuable source for the history of the city;

The Dix Collection: The gift of Irish bibliographer E.R. McClintock Dix, this collection contains some 700 Dublin and Irish imprints, mainly from the seventeenth and eighteenth centuries, and a number of eighteenth century fine bindings;

The Yeats Collection: This consists mainly of first editions of Yeats works, including those from the Dun Emer Press founded by Lilly and Lolly Yeats.

The Swift Collection: Consisting of books, manuscripts, periodicals and ephemera, this contains an extensive collection of rare and valuable items and is growing annually.

The Directories Collection: This is one of the most heavily used collections and includes an almost complete set of Dublin directories from 1751 to the present. Specific holdings include: *Watson's Almanack*, 1729–1837; *Wilson's Dublin Directories*, 1751–3; 1761–1837; *Pettigrew and Oulton's Dublin Directories*, 1834–47; *Thom's Irish Almanac and Official Directories*, 1844–present. The early directories, from 1751 to 1833, are in surname order only, and from 1834 street listings are available as well as the name sequence. *Pigot's Directory of Ireland 1822–4* on microfiche is the earliest directory in the collection to cover all of Ireland, followed by *Slater's Directory of Ireland*, published in the years 1846, 1856, 1870, 1881 and 1894. The 1894 edition has a very useful general directory of private residents of Ireland.

The Newspaper Collection: The newspaper collection covers a range of titles published from the 1700s to the present. The early Dublin newspapers, including rare and some unique items dating from 1700 to 1750, form an important part of the collection. Current and recent issues of the newspapers are not available for viewing for a period of six months, as all newspapers are sent out for binding. The Irish Times digital archive is available free online and the library has subscribed to Irishnewsarchive.com, so newspaper articles may be accessed free, to be printed or downloaded. (Daily newspapers are available for reading in the Business Information Centre, Dublin City Public Libraries – Central Library, Ilac Centre, Dublin 1.)

The Family History Collection

The library has a strong collection of source materials for family history. These include: Griffith's Valuation 1847–64, held on microfiche and covering 32 counties – it can also be consulted for free on www.askaboutireland.ie; tithe applotment books 1823–38, held on microfilm and covering 32 counties; Ordnance Survey first edition 6 inch maps; Ordnance Survey letters, held in typescript copies and arranged by county. The library holds a full set of census returns for 1901 and 1911 on microfilm for Dublin City and County; they are still used in addition to the census online. Church of Ireland registers of Dublin parishes from the Representative Church Body Library, Dublin, have been microfilmed and purchased for the library. Many date from the seventeenth to the end of the nineteenth century. Selected Dublin parish registers were published in book form and are held in the library:

> those of St John's, Dublin, 1619–99, baptisms, marriages, burials; St Michan's, Dublin, 1636–85, baptisms, marriages, burials; St Catherine's, Dublin, 1636–1715, baptisms, marriages, burials; Monkstown, County Dublin, 1669–1786, baptisms, burials; St Nicholas Without, 1694–1739, baptisms, marriages, burials; St Andrew's, St Anne's, St Audoen's, St Bride's, 1632–1800, marriages; St Marie's, St Luke's, St Catherine's, St Werburgh's, 1627–1800, marriages; St Patrick's, 1677–1800, baptisms, marriages, burials; the register of the parish of St Thomas, Dublin, 1750–91, edited by Raymond Refaussé, Representative Church Body Library, 1994. A Microsoft

Access database in the Research Reading Room of baptisms, marriages and burials from Dublin parishes, containing some 160,000 records. These records have been digitised and can be viewed in the Research Reading Room. They also form part of the website www.irishgenealogy.ie Also available are: the registers of the French Conformed Churches of St Patrick and St Mary, Dublin (1893); and a set of Huguenot records relating to Ireland on microfiche. There are a number of publications that may be of special interest to genealogists. These include: shipping indexes of persons who left Ireland for America during the nineteenth century; *The Famine Immigrants 1846–51*, covering those arriving at the port of New York during the Famine; *Memorials of the Dead*, a series of volumes compiled by Richard Flatman, and another series by Brian Cantwell listing gravestone inscriptions in cemeteries in Dublin, Wicklow and Wexford (these are not published but are available in bound typescripts); and *First World War Memorial Records*, published in 1923 in eight volumes listing the Irish soldiers who died in World War I, these records are included in the CD ROM *Soldiers died in the Great War 1914–1919*, also available. The names are in alphabetical order. Other helpful standard reference sources include: *Who's Who* (1897–1998 is available on CD-ROM), *Burke's and Lodge's Peerages*; biographical dictionaries; indexes to wills (published indexes compiled before the destruction of the Public Record Office); *King's Inns Admission Papers*; *Alumni Dublinensis*, containing a list of students of Trinity College Dublin from 1593 to 1860; Civil Survey for Dublin and other counties, seventeenth century; and *Palmer's Index to The Times 1790–1905* on CD-ROM. There are also General Register Office indexes to births, marriages and deaths (on microfilm from the Church of Jesus Christ of LDS) 1864 to the 1950s, with some gaps, and marriages from 1845; microfilm copies (from the LDS) of cemetery records from Deansgrange and Mount Jerome cemeteries.

The Irish Collection
The Irish Collection is made up of about 90,000 items: books and other materials relating to Ireland, by Irish authors, or in the Irish language. A comprehensive collection of material of Irish interest published outside Ireland is also available, as well as a considerable amount of material of genealogical interest. This general collection gives a national context to the Dublin special collections.

LOCATION
The library is situated on Pearse Street, two blocks eastwards from Pearse DART station. Bus: 1, 2, 3, 50, 56/a, 77/a stop across the street.

DUBLIN CITY ARCHIVES
(*See also* IRISH THEATRE ARCHIVE, Dublin)

138–144 Pearse Street
DUBLIN 2
Ireland

TELEPHONE: (01) 674 4996/7; FAX: (01) 674 4879
E-mail: cityarchives@dublincity.ie
Website: www.dublincity.ie

HOURS
M–Th, 10:00–20:00; F–Sa, 10:00–17:00; closed Sundays, bank holidays and bank
holiday weekends

ACCESS AND SERVICES
Visitors welcome. ID required to facilitate registration on first visit. Disabled access
facilities. Laptops permitted; pencils only. Photocopying and microform prints
available for a fee. Publications specifically relating to the holdings of the archives
include: Sir John T. and Lady Gilbert (eds), *Calendar of Ancient Records of Dublin*,
19 vols (Dublin, 1889–1944); Mary Clark, *The Book of Maps of the Dublin City
Surveyors* (Dublin, 1983); Niall McCullough, *A Vision of the City: Dublin and the
Wide Streets Commissioners* (Dublin, 1991); Philomena Connolly and Geoffrey
Martin, *The Dublin Guild Merchant Roll* (Dublin, 1992); Mary Clark and Raymond
Refaussé, *Directory of Historic Dublin Guilds* (Dublin, 1993); Mary Clark and
Gráinne Doran, *Serving the City: the Dublin City Managers and Town Clerks* (Dublin,
1996); Colm Lennon and James Murray, *The Dublin City Franchise Roll* (Dublin,
1998); and Jane Ohlmeyer and Éamonn Ó Ciardha, *The Irish Statute Staple Books*
(Dublin, 1998).

CONTACT
Mary Clark, City Archivist

DESCRIPTION
Dublin City Archives houses the historic records of the municipal government of
Dublin from the twelfth century to the present. On 1 January 2002 Dublin
Corporation changed its name to Dublin City Council.

HOLDINGS
The Dublin City Archives contain a wealth of published and unpublished records,
including City Council and committee minutes, account books, correspondence,
reports, court records, charity petitions, title deeds, maps and plans, photographs
and drawings, all of which document the development of Dublin over eight
centuries. Among the principal civic collections are: royal charters of the city of
Dublin, 1171–1727; medieval cartularies, including two important bound
manuscripts, one written on vellum, the *White Book of Dublin* (also known as the
Liber Albus) and the *Chain Book of Dublin*; Dublin City assembly rolls, 1447–1841;
Board of Dublin Aldermen, 1567–1841; journals of sheriffs and commons,
1746–1841; Tholsell Court of Dublin, sixteenth–eighteenth centuries; Dublin city
treasurer's accounts, 1540–1841; freedom records, 1468–1918; City Surveyor's
maps, 1695–1928; minutes and reports of Dublin City Council, 1841–present;
photographic collection, including Liffey Bridges and North Strand bombing;
records of Dublin Corporation departments, nineteenth and twentieth century.

Private collections held include: Irish Theatre Archive; Royal Dublin Fusiliers Association Archive; Dublin City Archaeological Archvie; Dublin City Sports Archive.

LOCATION
The archives are situated on Pearse Street, two blocks eastwards from Pearse DART station. Bus 3 from O'Connell Street to Ringsend stops across the street.

DUBLIN CITY PUBLIC LIBRARIES AND ARCHIVE

Library Headquarters
138–144 Pearse Street
DUBLIN 2
Ireland

TELEPHONE: (01) 674 4800; FAX: (01) 674 4879
E-mail: dublinpubliclibraries@dublincity.ie
Website: www.dublincitylibraries.ie

HOURS
See separate listings for DUBLIN AND IRISH COLLECTIONS (above), DUBLIN CITY PUBLIC LIBRARIES – CENTRAL LIBRARY (below), DUBLIN CITY ARCHIVES (above) and the IRISH THEATRE ARCHIVE (below). Call or visit website for hours of branch libraries listed below. Library Headquarters is not open to visitors.

CONTACT
Margaret Hayes, City Librarian

DESCRIPTION
The Headquarters Library is responsible for the overall administration of library services in a network of 31 libraries and service points. These include: Ballyfermot Library (tel. (01) 626 9324/5); Ballymun Library (tel. (01) 842 1890); Cabra Library (tel. (01) 869 1414); Central Library (tel. (01) 873 4333); Charleville Mall Library (tel. (01) 874 9619); Coolock Library (tel. (01) 847 7781); Dolphin's Barn Library (tele. (01) 454 0681); Donaghmede Library (tel. (01) 848 2833); Drumcondra Library, tel. (01) 837 7206); Finglas Library (tel. (01) 834 4906); Inchicore Library (tel. (01) 453 3793); Kevin Street Library (tel. (01) 475 3794); Marino Library (tel. (01) 833 6297); Pembroke Library (tel. (01) 668 9575); Phibsborough Library (telephone (01) 830 4341); Raheny Library (tel. (01) 831 5521); Rathmines Library (tel. (01) 497 3539); Ringsend Library (tel. (01) 668 0063); Terenure Library (tel. (01) 490 7035); Walkinstown Library (tel. (01) 455 8159); Mobile Libraries (tel. (01) 869 1415); and City Archives (tel (01) 674 4999).

HOLDINGS
See separate listings for DUBLIN AND IRISH COLLECTIONS (above), DUBLIN CITY PUBLIC LIBRARIES – CENTRAL LIBRARY (below), DUBLIN CITY ARCHIVES (above) and the IRISH THEATRE ARCHIVE (below).

Digital Projects Section
Dublin City Public Libraries established a Digital Projects Section in January 2010 to progress work on the Dublin City Council Photographic Collection. The objective is to digitise images relating to the history of Dublin and its people and make them freely accessible online for research purposes.

The collection primarily consists of approximately 500,000 images taken by official Dublin Corporation/Dublin City Council photographers over the period 1955–to date. The Collection offers a fascinating and previously unseen insight into the social, cultural and political history of Dublin in the second half of the twentieth century.

Image galleries based on the Collection can be viewed at: www.dublincitypubliclibraries.com/

LOCATION
Headquarters is situated on Pearse Street, two blocks eastwards from Pearse DART station. Bus 3 from O'Connell Street to Ringsend stops across the street.

DUBLIN CITY PUBLIC LIBRARIES – CENTRAL LIBRARY

Ilac Centre, Henry Street
DUBLIN 1
Ireland

TELEPHONE: (01) 873 4333; FAX: (01) 872 1451
E-mail: centrallibrary@dublincity.ie
Website: www.dublincitylibraries.ie

HOURS
M–Th, 10:00–20:00; F, Sa, 10:00–17:00

ACCESS AND SERVICES
Open to the public. Facilities include: Internet access, photocopying, online catalogue, Wi-FI access, study spaces and access to online educational resources for children. Programming activities include music recitals, author readings, language exchanges, bi-annual start your own business series. Storytelling for mothers and toddlers and for young children take place on a weekly basis. For those wishing to borrow material, full membership is available on production of ID and proof of address. Visitors are welcome to use all other facilities but will need a reference card to use the Internet facilities. This is available on production of ID. Services and Internet facilities are available free of charge. Photocopying and printing is available at 20 cent per page. Accessible for library visitors using wheelchair and hearing loops installed at customer desks.

CONTACT
Bernadette Cogan, Divisional Librarian. E-mail: bernadette.cogan@dublincity.ie

DESCRIPTION
The Central Library delivers lending services for adults and children, a music library, an Open Learning Centre and Business Information service. Located within a shopping centre in Dublin's city centre, the Central Library received over half a million visits in 2011.

HOLDINGS
Business Information Centre
The Business Information Centre is a reference service and a key information source for those starting a business or conducting research. It holds sample business plans, journals and newspapers, company information, market research and financial markets information and national and international statistics. It also offers reference

books, national and international directories, journals, databases, newspaper cuttings and an extensive collection of company reports.

The Open Learning Centre
This offers a wide range of self-learning opportunities in language and computers. Online and CD language learning is available in 123 languages. Courses are available in ECDL 5, basic computer skills, wordprocessing, spreadsheets, databases and use of the internet. All courses must be booked in advance and a certificate is awarded to students who complete 50 hours of study using the learning facilities. The centre also facilitates conversation exchange in Italian, Spanish, French, German, Irish, Japanese and Russian. There is also a multilingual language exchange.

Music Library
The Music Library is a valuable resource for anyone with an interest in music. The library offers a lending and reference service, including music CDs, cassettes and videos for lending. It also stocks literature on all aspects of music, sheet music including vocal scores, songbooks, tutor books and orchestral sets. In addition, the library provides listening facilities for leisure or study purposes and a wide range of music periodicals. A number of computer databases have been produced including a tracks index, a sheet music index and databases of music and choral societies in Dublin.

LOCATION
In the Ilac Shopping Centre, between Henry Street and Parnell Street, in the city centre.

CREGAN LIBRARY
See ST PATRICK'S COLLEGE – CREGAN LIBRARY, Dublin

DUBLIN CITY UNIVERSITY LIBRARY
Dublin City University
DUBLIN 9
Ireland

TELEPHONE: (01) 700 5212; FAX: (01) 700 5010
E-mail: library@dcu.ie
Website: www.library.dcu.ie

HOURS
Semester time: M–Th, 08:30 – 22:00; Fri, 08:30–16:45 with full service; 16:45–21:00 study only; Sa, 09:30–17:00
Outside of semester: consult library website

ACCESS AND SERVICES
The Library welcomes visitors as part of a number of library membership and access schemes. Please consult the 'Information for Visitors' page on the library's website for full details. The Library building is accessible for persons with a disability. All locally held print material can be found by using the library's online catalogue, accessible via the website. The library also provides access to an extensive collection of online information resources including full text journals, newspapers and research databases. DCU research theses and staff publications can be accessed via the library's institutional repository called 'DORAS'.

Users can avail of photocopying/printing/scanning facilities, read microforms, watch DVDs and access the internet.

CONTACT
Paul Sheehan, Director of Library Services. Tel. (01) 700 5211;
e-mail: paul.sheehan@dcu.ie
Ellen Breen, Sub-Librarian, Information and Public Services.
Tel. (01) 700 5210; e-mail: ellen.breen@dcu.ie
Miriam Corcoran, Sub-Librarian, Collection and System Services.
Tel. (01) 700 8732; e-mail: miriam.corcoran@dcu.ie

DESCRIPTION
Dublin City University was established as the National Institute of Higher Education, Dublin, in 1980, to respond to the challenges being set for higher education by rapidly diversifying industrial and business sectors in Ireland and in the European Union. It gained university status in 1989. The university currently enrols more than 11,000 students. In 2000, it opened its new state of the art library building, designed to facilitate all forms of research and learning. The university's linked colleges include St Patrick's College, Drumcondra (SPD) and Mater Dei Institute (MDI) of Education and more recently, All Hallow's College Drumcondra. Each college has its own library, but SPD and MDI share a library management system with DCU Library. *See* separate listing for ST PATRICK'S COLLEGE.

HOLDINGS
The library's collection contains approximately 111,160 print volumes and 395 print journal subscriptions. The library provides access to over 60,000 e-journals and over 100 research databases. The collections support the academic programmes offered by DCU and the research needs of its faculty and research centre staff. DCU comprises four faculties: Business; Engineering and Computing; Humanities and Social Sciences and Science and Health.

LOCATION
The University is located on an 85 acre campus in the northern suburbs of Dublin, near Glasnevin cemetery and the Botanic Gardens. It is served by buses 4, 9, 13, 105, 11, 116, 46X, 58X, 77B.

DUBLIN COUNTY ARCHIVES
See FINGAL COUNTY ARCHIVES, Dublin

DUBLIN DIOCESAN ARCHIVES

Holy Cross Diocesan Centre
Clonliffe Road,
DUBLIN 3
Ireland

TELEPHONE: (01) 837 9253, extension 183; FAX: (01) 836 8393
E-mail: archives@dublindiocese.ie (this e-mail address is protected from spam and requires Javascript enabled)
Website: www.archives.dublindiocese.ie

HOURS
M–F, 09:30–13:00, 14:00–16:45; closed religious and bank holidays; appointment essential to guarantee access to collections: contact Diocesan Archivist

ACCESS AND SERVICES
Visitors welcome; appointment in advance highly recommended. Please contact Diocesan Archivist. Pencils only; laptops and digital cameras permitted with Archivist's permission. Photocopying by staff only. Wheelchair accessible.

CONTACT
Noelle Dowling, Diocesan Archivist

DESCRIPTION
The Dublin Diocesan Archives exists to preserve the records of the Roman Catholic Archdiocese of Dublin and has operated as an archival repository on a full time basis since 1984. The Diocesan Archives has three functions:

to preserve the records of central diocesan administration;
to provide services to the secretariats and agencies at Archbishop's House and to the clergy and the laity of the Archdiocese of Dublin;
to make the archives of the Archdiocese of Dublin available to researchers.

HOLDINGS
The Archive contains the papers of the Roman Catholic Archbishops of Dublin from c. 1750 to 1972, including those of Ireland' first Cardinal, Paul Cullen (1852–78). Also available are the papers of +Daniel Murray (1823–52); Cardinal Edward McCabe (1878–85); +William Walsh (1885–1921); +Edward Byrne (1921–40); +John Charles McQuaid (1940–72). The information in the collections relates mainly to Irish political and social history but information can also be found on many of the English speaking Dioceses throughout the world.

Other collections include the surviving papers of the Catholic Association and Repeal association (1806–47); papers of +Bartholomew Woodlock, Rector of the Catholic University of Ireland (1861–79); papers of Canon Francis Gleeson, First World War Chaplain; records of Holy Cross College (1867–1946); Minutes of Bishops' Meetings 1829–49; 1882.

Only three sets of parish registers, up to 1900, are held in the Archives. These are from St Catherine's, Meath Street, St Audoen's, High Street and SS. Michael and John's, Exchange Street. Searches can be carried out by the Archivist for a fee. Those wishing to view the registers onsite are most welcome to do so free of charge. All other Parish Registers are maintained in their own churches and researchers need to contact them directly regarding access.

LOCATION
Holy Cross Diocesan Centre is based in the grounds of the former Archdiocesan Seminary, Holy Cross College. Visitors should enter the campus via the main entrance on Clonliffe Road and follow the signs directing them to the Diocesan Centre. The 3, 11, 11A, 13, 13A, 16, 16A, 33 and 41 buses from the city centre stop on Lower Drumcondra Road, approximately 5 minutes walk to the Archives. Trains on the Dublin–Maynooth (Sligo) line stop at Drumcondra Station on Lower Drumcondra Road. Free parking available to visitors on the College grounds.

DUBLIN UNIVERSITY
See TRINITY COLLEGE DUBLIN

DÚN LAOGHAIRE LIBRARY
See DÚN LAOGHAIRE LIBRARY – LOCAL HISTORY DEPARTMENT, Dún Laoghaire, Co. Dublin.

DÚN LAOGHAIRE-RATHDOWN HERITAGE CENTRE
The Courtyard, Marlay Park
Rathfarnham
DUBLIN 16
Ireland

TELEPHONE: DLR Heritage and Genealogy (01) 495 4485; Marlay Park, Rathfarnham (01) 205 4700
E-mail: heritage@dlrcoco.ie; DLR Co. Council, Marine Road, Dun Laoghaire, Co. Dublin: cmalone@dlrcoco.ie

HOURS
Heritage and Genealogy Office: Tu, 09:00–17:00; W, 09:00–13:00, or by special arrangement. Manger Catherine Malone will be happy to arrange a meeting with visitors unable to call at appointed times. Please see contact information below.

ACCESS AND SERVICES
Dún Laoghaire-Rathdown Heritage Centre offers a fee based, partial genealogical service to persons wishing to trace their roots in South County Dublin. In addition, the centre holds a large collection of archival material covering area's archaeology, geology and ecology, with illustrations, photographs and maps, plus files on area's maritime history. Fees vary depending on amount of time and research required. Typically, initial enquiry receives reply within two weeks. Visitors welcome and given immediate service. Publications include: *In the Mind's Eye: Memories of Dun Laoghaire*; *Dalkey: St Begnet's Graveyard*; and *Dalkey: Medieval Manor and Seaport*. Permanent exhibition Marlay House: 'Evie Hone 1894–1955, Painter and Stained Glass Artist.' Hone resided in the Courtyard at Marlay when she was working on some of her most famous works. The Permanent Exhibition, now housed in her former studio, was researched and collated by Catherine Malone.

CONTACT
For DLR Heritage and Genealogy: Catherine Malone, Manager.
E-mail: cmalone@dlrcoco.ie;
For Dun Laoghaire Rathdown Co. Council, Marine Road, Dun Laoghaire, Co. Dublin: Tim Carey, Heritage Officer, Tel: (01) 203 4700; E-mail: tcarey@dlrcoco.ie

DESCRIPTION
Dún Laoghaire-Rathdown Heritage Centre is the Irish Family History Foundation's designated genealogical centre for South County Dublin. IFHF is the coordinating body for a network of government approved genealogical research centres in the Republic of Ireland and in Northern Ireland that have computerised tens of millions of Irish ancestral records of different types. The centre focuses on Roman Catholic and Church of Ireland parish registers for South County Dublin. The area covered

by this centre now lies in the hinterland of Dublin city but was, in the nineteenth century, a collection of rural towns and villages. The centre's archival holdings are an important research source for the history of this area. Chief surnames of South Dublin include: Byrne, Doyle, Kelly, Murphy, Kavanagh, O'Neill, O'Brien, O'Connor, O'Farrell and O'Toole.

HOLDINGS
The centre has computerised over 145,000 records. The main records include: Roman Catholic records (baptismal and marriage) 1755–1900; Church of Ireland records, which include burial records as well as baptismal and marriage records, starting in 1694; and Presbyterian records that date from 1843. Also computerised are the pre-1900 gravestone inscriptions at the extensive Deansgrange Cemetery (from 1868) and St Begnet's Cemetery in Dalkey. The Centre has compiled an inventory of war memorials, listing all wars memorialised in the Dún Laoghaire-Rathdown area, and has also collated the names of the men from area who fought in World War I. Main towns in the Dún Laoghaire-Rathdown Heritage Centre's area include: Booterstown, Cabinteely, Dundrum, Dún Laoghaire (formerly Kingstown), Blackrock, Dalkey, Glasthule, Monkstown and Donnybrook.

Computerised Parish Records:

Roman Catholic Records
Ballybrack: Baptisms 1829–1900; Blackrock: Baptisms 1854–1900; Booterstown: Baptisms 1824–1900, Marriages 1712–1916; Cabinteely: Baptisms 1862–1900; Dalkey: Baptisms 1861–1900; Dundrum: Baptisms 1854–1900, Marriages 1861–1900; Glasthule: Baptisms1863–1900, Marriages, 1860–1900; Kingstown/Dun Laoghaire: Baptisms 1755–1900, Marriages 1755–1900; Monkstown: Baptisms 1855–1900, Marriages 1865–1900.

Church of Ireland Records
Ballybrack: Baptisms 1829–1900; Booterstown: Baptisms 1824–1900; Carysford: Baptisms 1851–91; Dalkey: Baptisms 1877–1900; Donnybrook: Baptisms 1712–1900, Marriages 1712–1900; Dun Laoghaire (Mariners Church): Baptisms 1843–1900, Marriages 1712–1916; Glenageary (St Paul's): Baptisms 1829–64; Kilternan (Holy Trinity): Baptisms 1817–93, Marriages 1890–1900, Burials 1817–1900; Killiney Baptisms 1861–1900, Marriages 1817–66; Newscastle Lyons: Baptisms 1768–1847, Marriages 1773–1859, Burials 1776–1847; South Dublin Union: Baptisms 1846–97.

Dun Laoghaire Rathdown Inventory of War Memorials

Photographic records of War Memorials covering all wars as follows:

> Memorial buildings, gardens, stained glass windows, stone, marble and brass plaques, honouring those who fought and died in all conflicts 1800–1945. *Inventory: Army, Air Officers and Soldiers, born or resident in Dun Laoghaire, formerly known as Kingstown, who died in WWI; Record of Naval and Mercantile Marine who died in WWI.*

Other Sources:
> History of family names – partial collection
> Local History publications, various books, DVD and CDs

Maps
Ordnance Survey maps, original, South Co Dublin only.
Exhibition panels – covering aspects of local history

Titles
Early and Late Christian Monuments
Did you know? (some less known facts on local history)
Quarrymen Dun Laoghaire Rathdown 1816–1940s.
The Kingstown/Dun Laoghaire Regatta 1825–2004.
Marconi-Guglielmo Marconi's Kingstown Experiment.
Local Writer's/Poet's –
Work and background information

LOCATION
Bus 16 from O'Connell Street stops at the main gate.

FINGAL COUNTY ARCHIVES
See under SWORDS, COUNTY DUBLIN

FINGAL COUNTY LIBRARIES—LOCAL STUDIES DEPARTMENT
See under SWORDS, COUNTY DUBLIN

FINGAL GENEALOGY
See under SWORDS, COUNTY DUBLIN

FRANCISCAN LIBRARY
See under KILLINEY, COUNTY DUBLIN

THE FRIENDS' HISTORICAL LIBRARY
See HISTORICAL LIBRARY, RELIGIOUS SOCIETY OF FRIENDS, Dublin

THE GAA MUSEUM
(Gaelic Athletic Association)

St Joseph's Avenue
Croke Park
DUBLIN 3
Ireland

TELEPHONE: (01) 819 2300; FAX: (01) 819 2324; tour bookings, (01) 819 2374.
E-mail: info@crokepark.ie
Website: www.crokepark.ie

HOURS
M–Sa, 09:30–17:00; Sundays and bank holidays, 12:00–17:00; Café: M–Sa,
10:00–16:00; Sun, 12:00–16:00
Closed 1 January, Good Friday, eve of All Ireland hurling and football finals, 24–27
and 31 December. On match days the museum is open to Cusack Stand ticket
holders only and regular museum admission rates apply.

ACCESS AND SERVICES
Located under Cusack Stand in Croke Park. Access via St Joseph's Avenue off Clonliffe Road. Group bookings welcome. Guided tours of Croke Park Stadium depart daily, except on match days, from museum. For up-to-date information on stadium tour times, consult website. Museum is self-guided and includes a 'test your skills in hurling and gaelic football' games area. Facilities include gift shop, café, toilets, baby changing facilities and ample car parking. Disabled access.

CONTACT
Mark Dorman, Museum Director. E-mail: mdorman@crokepark.ie
Joanne Clarke, Museum Curator. E-Mail: jclarke@crokepark.ie
Mark Reynolds, Museum Archivist. E-Mail: mreynolds@crokepark.ie

DESCRIPTION
The GAA Museum was established to commemorate, recognise and celebrate the GAA's enormous contribution to Irish sporting, cultural and social life since its foundation in 1884. Located under the Cusack Stand of GAA headquarters at Croke Park, the museum is open daily throughout the year. The museum traces the birth and growth of the GAA at home and abroad and its unique role in the national movement and cultural revival in Ireland. It houses a vast collection, including hurleys, jerseys, trophies, medals, programmes, publications and banners that illustrate the development of Gaelic games from ancient times to the present day. First opened in September 1998, in 2010 the museum unveiled an exciting refurbishment which includes a new Café, temporary exhibition space, updated match footage, a new interactive games area and a magnificent new trophy display. The revamped GAA Museum was officially launched in April 2010 in the presence of GAA stars including footballers Sean Kavanagh (Tyrone) and Kieron Donaghy (Kerry) and Cork hurler Aisaike Ó hAilpín.

HOLDINGS
The museum houses a vast collection of sports memorabilia, including hurleys, jerseys, trophies, medals, programmes and photographs. On permanent display is the original All Ireland Football Championship trophy, the Sam Maguire (1928) and the original All Ireland Hurling Championship trophy, the Liam MacCarthy (1923). Medal collections belonging to legendary players such as Christy Ring, Jack Lynch, Jimmy Doyle, Noel Skehan and Peter McDermott are also on display. The GAA Museum has an extensive archive collection consisting of a range of artefacts including programmes, yearbooks, annuals, medals, photographs, posters, tickets and various GAA related memorabilia. The Archives, a department of the GAA Museum, was formed in 2007. The GAA Archives is committed to fostering and promoting a culture of research and enquiry into the rich history of the GAA, its members and the contribution made by the Association to the social, political and cultural life of Ireland. The mission of the GAA Archive is to identify and preserve collections of archives, papers and manuscripts that record the values, culture and history of the Association, Gaelic Games and individuals who have contributed to the Association. The core function of the GAA Archives is the curatorship of the historical records and archives of the Association, and of those collections of private individuals who have made an outstanding contribution to the Association. These documents are acquired and preserved to help document the history of the Association, both in Ireland and abroad.

LOCATION
In Croke Park, Drumcondra, on the north side of the Liffey, *en route* to Dublin
Airport. It is located under the Cusack Stand, which is accessible via St Joseph's
Avenue, just off Clonliffe Road. It is a 15 minute walk from O'Connell Street (city
centre). Buses from O'Connell Street are: 3, 11, 11A, 16, 16A, 123; bus 51A runs
from Lower Abbey Street to Clonliffe Road. By rail, the museum is a 15 minute
walk from Connolly station; it is less than ten minutes from Drumcondra station.

GARDA MUSEUM/ARCHIVES

Record Tower
Dublin Castle
DUBLIN 2
Ireland

TELEPHONE: (01) 666 9998; FAX: (01) 666 9992
E-mail: museum@garda.ie
Website: www.garda.ie (follow links to 'Historical Society')

HOURS
M–F, 10:00–16:00

ACCESS AND SERVICES
Visitors welcome but advance notice preferred, especially for use of archives or
library. No admission charge. Disabled access facilities, but only to ground floor.
Pencils only when using original material. Laptops and photography permitted.
Printed finding aids available.

CONTACT
Sergeant Paul E. Maher, Archivist. E-mail: museum@garda.ie

DESCRIPTION
An Garda Síochána Museum/Archives collects and preserves archival material and
artefacts relating not only to An Garda Síochána, but also to the Irish Constabulary,
the Royal Irish Constabulary and the Dublin Metropolitan Police. It serves both as a
support service within the Police Force, with a primary responsibility to provide a
records management service, and as an outreach resource for the general public.

HOLDINGS
The Historical Library houses a collection of police related publications, including
monthly Garda publications from 1922 to the present. The book collection numbers
approximately 1,000 catalogued bound volumes. The archives contain photographs,
sound recordings and documents outlining the history and development of policing
in Ireland in the nineteenth and twentieth centuries. The sound recordings are of
retired RIC/DMP and Garda members. In addition to documenting policing in
Ireland, the collection seeks to document the impact of Irish policing on the English
speaking world and the British colonies. Of special interest is the large genealogical
collection on policing from 1822 to 1922. The archives also contain the Dublin
Metropolitan Police personnel register for the period 1836–1925.

LOCATION
The museum/archive is located at the Record Tower of Dublin Castle, off Dame Street, next to City Hall and diagonally opposite Christchurch Cathedral. There is also an entrance on Ship Street.

GENEALOGICAL OFFICE
See NATIONAL LIBRARY OF IRELAND – OFFICE OF CHIEF HERALD, Dublin

GENERAL REGISTER OFFICE

Note: The General Register Office was relocated from Joyce House, 8–11 Lombard Street East, Dublin 2 to Government Offices, Convent Road, Roscommon, on 11 April 2005. *See* current listing under Roscommon Town, County Roscommon, for details.

The Research Room, however, continues to be located in Dublin, relocated from Joyce House to:

General Register Office
Block 7 Floor 3
Irish Life Centre
Lower Abbey Street
DUBLIN 1

Opening hours: M–F, 09:30–16:30; closed bank holidays. Contact Declan Roche, Manager, Research Room.

GILBERT LIBRARY
See DUBLIN AND IRISH COLLECTIONS, Dublin

GRAND LODGE OF FREEMASONS OF IRELAND: LIBRARY, ARCHIVES AND MUSEUM

Freemasons' Hall
17 Molesworth Street
DUBLIN 2
Ireland

TELEPHONE: (01) 676 1337; FAX: (01) 662 5101
E-mail: hayesr@freemason.ie
Website: www.irish-freemasons.org

HOURS
Museum: M–F, 09:30–17:00
Library and Archive: by appointment

ACCESS AND SERVICES
Visitors welcome, but by appointment only; advance notice and ID required. Disabled access to Library. Laptops permitted; pencils only. No access charges to library. Printed finding aids available. Computer catalogue for the 12,000 volume book collection. Descriptive lists available for some correspondence files and minute

books. General readers may consult all published works, while only members may borrow books. See holdings for further restrictions. Records prior to 1975 available to the general public, but Grand Secretary's permission required for access to post 1975 material. Records of current Lodges and other Masonic bodies deposited with the archives may only be consulted with permission of bodies concerned. Photocopying available but with some restrictions.

CONTACT
Librarian and Archivist

DESCRIPTION
The Library, Archives and Museum of the Grand Lodge of Ireland serves as the repository for the history of Irish Freemasonry in Ireland and abroad. The purpose of the library/archives is to collect, preserve and exhibit items and information relating to the development of the Masonic Order from c. 1725. The collection is funded by the Grand Lodge, and acquisitions come primarily as gifts from members and the public.

HOLDINGS
The collection houses approximately 12,000 volumes. The Chetwode Crawley Library contains books printed between 1527 and 1851 and these volumes can be neither lent nor photocopied. Books printed since 1851 form the modern section and members may borrow recently published books or older books from this section that are available in duplicate. The library contains books on all Grand Lodges, organised geographically. The archives, consisting of some 800 boxes of material, house the records of the Governing Bodies of the Order, as well as representative collections from Lodges and Chapters. Membership registers date from 1760 and the correspondence files date from the 1820s. The latter include some 100,000 pieces from the Secretaries of Lodges in Ireland and around the world to the Grand Secretary. Pre-1975 records of the Girls and Boys schools and other charities supported by the Masons are available for research, but with restrictions.

LOCATION
City centre, opposite Buswell's Hotel, near Kildare Street, close to the National Library and the National Museum.

GUINNESS ARCHIVE

Guinness Storehouse,
St James's Gate
DUBLIN 8
Ireland

TELEPHONE: (01) 471 4557
E-mail: guinness.archives@diageo.com
Website: www.guinness-storehouse.com/en/Archive.aspx

HOURS
By appointment only, M–F, 09:30–17:00

ACCESS AND SERVICES
Visitors welcome by appointment. Disabled access. Laptops permitted; pencils only.

Limited photocopying available for a fee. Access may be restricted to parts of the collection that are uncatalogued at the discretion of the Archivist.

CONTACT
Eibhlin Roche, Guinness Archive Manager

DESCRIPTION
The Guinness Archive is a treasure chest preserving over 250 years of Guinness company and brand history and is the only corporate Archive fully open to the public in Ireland. It serves as an information resource for Diageo globally as well as the researching public.

HOLDINGS
The collection represents the Guinness company's history in Ireland from 1759 to the present day, including activities of its Irish subsidiaries. The majority of records document the transactions of the departments at St James's Gate Brewery.

Brewing material (GDB/BR) documents the brewing of Guinness, principally at St James's Gate Brewery, and is either in ledger or file form. The earliest brewing ledger dates from 1798. Brewing ledgers record details of daily brews throughout nineteenth century to mid twentieth century in the form of saccharometer books, brewhouse daily statements, storehouse books, vathouse books, sampling books etc. From the twentieth century brewing files were also kept by the Head Brewer and senior brewing management to document all aspects of the brewing process and production of Guinness.

Company material (GDB/CO), mostly in the form of files, includes the records of the governing Board, its Directors and the Company Secretary's department. The principal records of the Board are the Board minutes that began at the company's incorporation (1886), board orders (directions issued on all aspects of business to be followed by all within the Brewery), board endorsements (recommendations issued), annual reports. The executive Directors of the Board held senior management positions and received reports on all aspects of the Brewery's business – management committees, personnel, operations, external affairs, trade, brewery history. Other functions covered by this category include the Company Secretary's Department. The Company Secretary's Department began principally as a trade department, managing trade in Ireland and with overseas markets, but by the 1940s it dealt almost exclusively with matters of corporate governance and legal issues.

Distribution material, (GDB/DB) mostly in file form, documents transportation of GUINNESS Stout by road, rail and sea to customers in Ireland and abroad. The cooperage, and its successor the keg department, are also covered here. The transportation records document all modes of Brewery transport including: horses, motor vehicles, barges and shipping. The cooperage, and later kegging records, document the manufacture of these containers, and their use for the transport of GUINNESS Stout. This series also includes minutes books of the Regular Dublin Coopers Society.

Engineering material (GDB/EN05) is in the form of files, maps, plans and drawings, and documents the work of the Brewery's engineering functions, from individual engineers in the nineteenth century, to the work of the Engineer's Department in the twentieth century. Activities documented include: Brewery building and maintenance projects, installation, maintenance and design of Brewery machinery, Terenure Housing Scheme.

Guinness family material (GDB/GU) contains any material connected with

individual members of the Guinness family in their capacity as private citizens. The
Guinness Archive holds only a very small selection of material in this category as the
Guinness Family maintain their own family records. This series consists mainly of
photographs.

Marketing material documents (GDB/MK) the marketing activities by the
company in Ireland, in particular advertising and merchandising. A wide variety of
media are covered from paper-based materials in the form of departmental files and
advertising posters to Audio-visual materials such as photographs and film, and
artefacts in the form of memorabilia. The collection of GUINNESS memorabilia
dates from 1930s to present day, and includes ceramics such as original Carlton
Ware pieces, clothing samples, showcards, waiters trays, tin signs, and calendars. This
series also documents a limited collection of overseas advertising in the United
Kingdom (GPR/MK) and overseas (GOL/MK).

Personnel, (GDB/PE) is one of the largest single categories within the collection,
it covers employment within the Brewery, from individual employment files to
personnel management and policies. Although some ledgers are included, most
material is in file form. Personnel covers management policy and administration of the
entire Brewery workforce, which in its peak numbered over 5000. This category gives a
unique insight into the working conditions within the Brewery for all levels of staff.

Packaging (GDB/PK) series is mainly in the form of packaging samples, either
in paper or artefact form, such as labels, cardboard boxes, and bottles and cans. The
samples record the evolution of GUINNESS branded packaging, for markets
supplied from the St James's Gate Brewery, from the nineteenth century to the
present day. Most of the samples were destined for the Irish market, although a small
number of items represent packaging used in overseas markets prior to the 1960s.

Raw materials (GDB/RM) records the purchase and management of raw materials
within the Brewery, used in the production of GUINNESS Stout, primarily: barley,
water, hops and yeast. The records are in the form of both files and ledgers.

Activities recorded include: the operation and management of the company's
Hop Farms in England, maltings and raw materials departments; barley and hop
purchases; disposal of spent hops, grains, and yeast, left over from the brewing
process.

Trade (GDB/SA) documents the supply of GUINNESS Stout, from the St
James's Gate Brewery. The records cover the management of trade for the different
markets supplied from St James's Gate, from Ireland to countries overseas. All the
trade in overseas markets was managed from Dublin until the twentieth century. In
the twentieth century, the management of overseas trade began to change. As new
GUINNESS breweries were established overseas, and new subsidiaries were formed
to handle brewing and marketing for overseas markets, the St James's Gate Brewery
became less involved in the marketing and supply of overseas markets.

After the opening of the Park Royal Brewery in London in 1936, responsibility for
the supply of the British market was gradually transferred from Dublin to Park
Royal. The management of supply and marketing in overseas markets was transferred
to a new subsidiary, Guinness Exports Limited (GEL). A new drive to establish
overseas operations began in the early 1960s and in 1963, 'Guinness Overseas
Limited' (GOL) was formed. GOL was responsible for brewing of Guinness
overseas, shares in other brewing companies overseas and brewing exports for
overseas. Records concerning trade in overseas markets outside of Great Britain and
Europe, do not reach beyond the 1940s. Even after the establishment of GEL, the St

James's Gate Brewery retained direct control of trade in European markets, until the early 1960s.

A large proportion of the records are in ledger form, although there is also a large body of file-based material. Activities documented include sales of Guinness, trade with customers, use of the distribution network for supply, market research conducted by sales representatives and early overseas travellers.

LOCATION
The Guinness Archive is located in Guinness Storehouse at St James's Gate.

HERITAGE CENTRE, ROYAL COLLEGE OF PHYSICIANS OF IRELAND

6 Kildare Street
DUBLIN 2
Ireland

TELEPHONE: (01) 669 8817; Fax: (01) 639 4821
E-mail: heritagecentre@rcpi.ie
Website: www.rcpi.ie/heritagecentre
Blog: www.rcpilibrary.blogspot.com

HOURS
M–F, 10:00–13:00, 14:00–16:00, by appointment

ACCESS AND SERVICE
Reading room, open by appointment only. Full wheelchair access. Laptops and pencils permitted in the reading room, also digital cameras with permission from staff. Genealogical Research Service available at a nominal charge.
Copying charges: photocopies – 25c per sheet, minimum charge €1; digital images €2.50 per image, minimum charge €5; CDs – €5 per CD; postage – Ireland €3, worldwide €6.

CONTACT
Harriet Wheelock, Archivist

DESCRIPTION
The Royal College of Physicians of Ireland (RCPI) was founded in 1654, and is Ireland's oldest post-graduate medical education Institution. The mission of RCPI is to develop and maintain the highest professional standards in medicine.
The Heritage Centre is located in RCPI's historic home on Kildare Street, and constitutes; Dun's Library, the archive collections, the heritage collections and the genealogical research collections. The aim of the Heritage Centre is to become a centre for excellence for research, study and public outreach on the history of medicine and medical education in Ireland.

Tours of the Kildare Street building can be arranged through the Heritage Centre. The building is also open on set days during the year as part of national cultural and heritage events. The Heritage Centre has a number of books for sale on the history of the College, and the history of medicine in Ireland. These books can be purchased directly from the Heritage Centre or online via www.rcpi.ie/HeritageCentre/Pages/bookshop.aspx

COLLECTIONS

Dun's Library was founded in 1713 with the personal bequest of the library of Sir Patrick Dun to the College. The library now contains approximately 30,000 books, journals and pamphlets dating from the fifteenth century to the present time. Until 1960 the library was a medical library for the Members and Fellows of RCPI. Since the 1960s the focus of Dun's Library has become the history of medicine in Ireland. Aside from the College's own collections, the key collections include the Churchill Collection of Obstetrical and Gynaecological works, the Kirkpatrick Collection on Irish Medical History and the Travers Collection of fine works on medicine, history, science and theology. Dun's Library also holds two substantial collections of pamphlets on Irish medicine and medical history, and a large number of medical journals, both Irish and international, some of which are unique in Ireland. Dun's Library is currently undergoing a major e-cataloguing project. The new online catalogue can be accessed through the Heritage Centre website.

The Archive contains both the records of RCPI itself and a number of donated collections relating to the history of medicine in Ireland, including the records of hospitals and other medical institutions and the papers of Irish medics and medical historians. In 2009 the archive undertook a 21 month Wellcome Trust funded cataloguing project. A full e-catalogue of the archive material is now available through the Heritage Centre website. The main collections are the records of the Royal College of Physicians of Ireland (1667 onwards), Dun's Trust Estates in County Waterford (1696–1960), Saint Ultan's Hospital (1900–89), Kathleen Lynn's Diaries (1916–55), Sir Patrick Dun's Hospital (1800–1989), Sir Dominic Corrigan's Papers (1795–1880), T P C Kirkpatrick Archive (c. 1800–1954), Westmoreland Lock Hospital (1792–1922), Royal National Hospital for Consumption for Ireland (1891–1967), Medico-Philosophical Society (1756–1939), Royal Academy of Medicine in Ireland (1882 onwards) and Apothecaries Hall of Ireland (1745–2006).

Genealogical Collections. The Heritage Centre holds a number of sources for those trying to trace Irish medical ancestors, notably the Kirkpatrick index (a biographical index of over 10,000 Irish doctors from the earliest times to the 1950s) and a full set of the Medical Directories and Registers. Several of the archival collections can also be useful in tracing professional careers, including the hospital records, RCPI's register of Licentiates, Members and Fellows and the registers of Apothecaries Hall. The Heritage Centre also holds a digital copy of the roll of Licentiates of the Royal College of Surgeons from 1828–1983. All the genealogical material can be consulted in the reading room, or a search can be commissioned from the Heritage Centre, at a nominal charge.

Heritage Collections. RCPI's heritage collections are made up of material from a number of sources. They include silverware, furniture and other items which form part of RCPI's history, as well as an impressive collection of portraits of former RCPI Presidents, and other medical luminaries. Also included in this area is an interesting collection of medical instruments dating from the eighteenth, nineteenth and twentieth centuries. There are also a number of artefacts which have been donated with other collections, such as the wooden tray carved by Countess Markievicz, which forms part of the Saint Ultan's Hospital archive.

LOCATION

Located in the heart of Dublin, on Kildare Street, next to the National Library of Ireland and Trinity College Dublin.

HISTORICAL LIBRARY, RELIGIOUS SOCIETY OF FRIENDS IN IRELAND

Quaker House
Stocking Lane
DUBLIN 16
Ireland

TELEPHONE: (01) 499 8006
E-mail: qhist@eircom.net
Website: www.quakers.ie

HOURS
Th, 11:00–13:00

ACCESS AND SERVICES
The Library welcomes visitors during its opening hours. Prior notice by e-mail with details of field of interest can be helpful in view of the short official opening time. All Library staff are part-time voluntary workers. Photocopier and microfilm reader are available. A donation of €10 per reader is requested. Brief replies to e-mail, postal or phone enquiries are made free of charge. A fee of €30 or more is payable in advance for more substantial genealogical work.

CONTACT
Christopher Moriarty, Curator. E-mail: cmoriarty4@gmail.com

DESCRIPTION
Friends Historical Library, Dublin (cited either as FHLD or DFHL) is the depository for manuscript material relating to Quakers in Ireland. Records begin in the 1660s. The library also holds a substantial collection of printed books and pamphlets from the mid-seventeenth century onwards together with personal manuscripts and artefacts.

HOLDINGS
The collection is centred on the minutes and family records of the national meetings of the Society in Ireland and of local meetings in the provinces of Leinster, Munster and Connaught, together with microfilm of the records of Ulster Quakers from originals held in Lisburn or the Public Records Office of Northern Ireland. The library also holds a substantial collection of printed books and pamphlets from the mid-seventeenth century onwards together with personal correspondence, diaries, vocal recordings, pictures and artefacts. Searchable databases include details of births, marriages, deaths and disownments up to the mid-nineteenth century, and of 'removals' of individuals from one meeting to another. A manuscript of genealogies of the principal Quaker families is in the process of digitisation.
The holdings of printed books and pamphlets, diaries and correspondence are indexed in a comprehensive database of more than 40,000 entries. These provide a wealth of information on such major concerns as education, the slave trade, famine relief, care of the mentally ill, temperance, peace, prison reform, refugees and commercial interests.

LOCATION
The Library is part of the Quaker House Dublin/Bloomfield complex on Stocking Lane in the south suburbs of Dublin. For details see www.quakers-in-ireland.ie/contact/

THE HONORABLE SOCIETY OF KING'S INNS

Henrietta Street
DUBLIN 1
Ireland

TELEPHONE: (01) 878 2119; FAX: (01) 874 4846
E-mail: library@kingsinns.ie
Website: www.kingsinns.ie

HOURS
By appointment

ACCESS AND SERVICES
Visitors welcome, but by appointment only; advance notice, references and ID required. No disabled access facilities. Laptops permitted; pencils only. Charges for genealogical and other research undertaken vary by category of user. Registered members of the society (Category A) exempted from search fees but pay reduced photocopying and facsimile charges and normal postage charges. Academics (Category B) may be charged a search fee depending on length of time involved in search, and pay a slightly higher charge for photocopying and facsimile services and normal charges for postage. All others granted permission to use the library facilities (Category C) required to pay minimum fee of €30.00 per search plus normal charges for photocopying, facsimiles and postage. Photocopying carried out by staff; 12c per page surcharge for all users. Consult library staff for fee schedule.

Publications available at the library for consultation include: Wanda Ryan-Smolin (cataloguer), *King's Inns Portraits*, Daire Hogan, *The Honorable Society of King's Inns* and various accession lists. Visitors may purchase *King's Inns Barristers 1868–2004*, price €30. Several leaflets, including *Library Guide* and *How to Find Irish Cases*, are available free of charge.

CONTACT
Jonathan Armstrong, Librarian. E-mail: jonathan.armstrong@kingsinns.ie

DESCRIPTION
The library was founded in 1787. The society itself dates from 1541. King's Inns trains students wishing to become barristers (lawyers), and the focus of its collection is on the law, with history, literature, classics, biography, typography, science and natural history also well represented.

HOLDINGS
In addition to its book collection, the library houses architectural drawings, art and artefacts, manuscripts, maps, microforms, newspapers and pamphlets. Of special interest are the holdings of: British parliamentary papers; Irish appeals to the House of Lords; the pamphlet collection; the papers of John Patrick Prendergast, Irish language manuscripts and rentals under the 1849 Encumbered Estates Act. Of special genealogical interest are the King's Inns admission papers, 1607–1867 (abstracts published by Irish Manuscripts Commission), plus a printed copy of Griffith's Valuation and a collection of Ordnance Survey maps.

LOCATION
Off Bolton Street, almost directly opposite Dublin Institute of Technology Bolton Street, on the north side of the Liffey, west of Parnell Square. King's Inns can also be approached via Constitution Hill, opposite Broadstone Bus Garage.

IRISH ARCHITECTURAL ARCHIVE

45 Merrion Square
DUBLIN 2
Ireland

TELEPHONE: (01) 663 3040; FAX: (01) 663 3041
E-mail: info@iarc.ie
Website: www.iarc.ie

HOURS
Tu–F, 10:00–17:00

ACCESS AND SERVICES
Visitors and enquiries welcome. No appointment necessary. Readers required to register when using the archive for the first time. Disabled access facilities. Laptops permitted; pencils only. Photocopying available for a fee of 40c–80c; photographic prints, €25–€140, depending on size and nature of print required. Computer catalogue. See D. Griffin and S. Lincoln, *Drawings from the Irish Architectural Archive* (Dublin, 1993). See website for updated lists of collections.
Archive premises contain a reading room (seating approximately 20 readers), a lecture room, meeting rooms and an exhibition gallery.

CONTACT
Colum O'Riordan, Archive Administrator

DESCRIPTION
The Irish Architectural Archive is a charitable company established in 1976 to collect, preserve and make available the records of Ireland's architectural heritage. The archive is a non-confrontational body, which does not involve itself in any way in matters of planning or conservation controversy. The archive also pursues an active publications policy and outreach programme, including exhibitions to bring the riches of its collections to as wide an audience as possible.

HOLDINGS
The Irish Architectural Archive collects, preserves and makes available records of every type relating to the architecture of Ireland. The holdings date from the 1690s to date and comprise in excess of 400,000 architectural drawings, 400,000 photographs, 25,000 items of printed matter and several dozen architectural models. The collections include information, primary or secondary, on every notable Irish architect, on every important Irish building period or style and on most significant holdings in the 32 counties of Ireland. Major collections include: AAI Collection, ABK Collection, Archer Estate Collection, Ashlin and Coleman Collection, Boyd Barrett Murphy O'Connor Collection, Burgage Collection, Rudolf Maximillian Butler Collection, W.H. Byrne & Son Collection, Wilfred Cantwell Collection, Charleville Forest Collection, Costello Murray Beaumont Collection, Cullen and Co. Collection, C.P. Curran Collection, Dublin Artisans Dwellings Co. Collection, Emo Court Collection, Peter and Mary Doyle Collection, Desmond FitzGerald Collection, Charles Geoghan Collection, Arthur Gibney & Partners Architects Collection, Group 91 Archive, Guinness Drawings Collection, Brian Hogan & Associates Architects Collection, Alan Hope Collection, Richard Hurley & Associates Collection, Brendan Jeffers Collection, Alfred Jones Biographical Index, Paul Keogh Architects Collection, Robin Mandal Architects Collection, McCurdy

and Mitchell Collection, McDonnell & Dixon Collection, Raymond McGrath Collection, Dr Edward McParland Collection, Munden and Purcell Collection, Desmond Rea O'Kelly Collection, Donal O'Neill Flanagan Collection, Patterson Kempster Shortall Collection, Fleming Rasmusen Collection, Anthony Reddy Associates Collection, Fred Rogerson Collection, RIAI Archives, RIAI Murray Collection, Royal (Collins) Barracks Collection, Royal Institute of the Architects of Ireland Archives, Robinson Keefe and Devane Collection, Scott Tallon Walker Collection, Michael Scott Collection, Sibthorpe Collection, Stephenson Gibney Collection, Townley Hall Collection, Derek Tynan Architects Collection, Tyndall Hogan Hurley Collection and the Workhouse Collection.

The archive's photograph collection is one of the largest in Ireland. Aside from ongoing photographic survey work carried out by the archive, photographic collections include Automobile Association Photographs, BKS Aerial Photographs, Aodhagán Brioscú. Collection, Buildings of Ireland Photographs, Edward Cassidy Collection, Maurice Craig Collection, Alec R. Day ARPS Collection, J.V. Downes Slide Collection, Hugh Doran Collection, Kieran Clendinning Collection, Green Studio Collection, Thomas Gunn Collection, Paddy Healy Collection and the Westropp Albums.

LOCATION
Halfway along the eastern side of Merrion Square, the largest of the terraced houses. Bus 7 stops about five minutes' walk away. From the north side of the city, bus 13 stops near the archive. It is a ten minute walk from Pearse DART station and from St Stephen's Green LUAS stop.

IRISH FILM INSTITUTE

6 Eustace Street
DUBLIN 2
Ireland

TELEPHONE: (01) 679 5744; FAX: (01) 677 8755
E-mail: see contact
Website: www.irishfilm.ie

OPENING HOURS
Moving image collections viewing: M–F, 10:30–13:00, 14:15–17:30
Tiernan MacBride Library: M, Th, 14:00–17:30; Tu, 10:30–13:00, 14:00–17:30; W, 10:30–13:00, 14:00–17:30 (late opening until 19:00 by appointment)

ACCESS AND SERVICES
Visitors and enquiries welcome. Appointment necessary for paper archive and for viewing but not for access to library during opening hours. The Library can also be visited outside opening hours by appointment. Booking should be made with IFI Irish Film Archive staff by phone or email at least 48 hours in advance. Archive staff must be informed of cancellations at least 24 hours in advance of appointment. Information relating to film, tape, stills, posters and library holdings held on computer database. Archive staff facilitate public enquiries relating to content of any aspect of collections. Access to collections may be restricted owing to donor stipulations or preservation concerns. Tiernan MacBride Library accessible for reference purposes only, but all materials may be photocopied. Use and access

charges apply. There is wheelchair access to the library which also has viewing facilities for certain moving image formats. Please check with the Archive Access officer regarding this.

Access charges for Moving Image collections: viewing: €8.00 per hour or per title, €13 per half day (€25 per day), €100 per week.

Access charges to Tiernan MacBride Library are: students, €1.50 per visit; general public, €2 per visit. Annual Library and Archive Membership is available at €15 for students and €20 for the general public. This allows unlimited visits to the Tiernan MacBride Library for one year, one free archive viewing, and a discounted viewing rate subsequently.

The IFI is based in a converted seventeenth century Quaker Meeting House. It comprises 3 cinemas, a Film/book shop, a Café Bar and is wheel chair accessible. Free WiFi is available for customers of the Café bar.

CONTACT
Kasandra O'Connell, Head of IFI Irish Film Archive.
For general queries, e-mail: koconnell@irishfilm.ie
Raelene Casey, Moving Image Access Officer.
For moving image queries, e-mail: rcasey@irishfilm.ie
Fiona Rigney, Library & Document Archivist.
For image, Library and document queries, e-mail: frigney@irishfilm.ie

DESCRIPTION
The IFI Irish Film Archive is part of the Irish Film Institute, Ireland's national cultural institute for film. The National Film Institute was established in the early 1940s under the direction of the Roman Catholic Archbishop for Dublin, John Charles McQuaid. McQuaid felt it was important that the Church was actively involved in the production and distribution of film thus ensuring the morality of the nation was protected. His main point of reference was *The Vigilianti Cura* (1936) issued by Pope Pius XI, which stressed the importance of the Catholic Church's involvement in all aspects of motion pictures. To this end the National Film Institute not only maintained a distributing library of film but was also involved in the production of safety, health and educational films in the 1940s and '50s. Although NFI film production ceased in the 1960s, the distributing library continued until the 1980s. In the mid -1980s, when the decision was made to set up an Archive section of the IFI (as it was now called), it was natural that the library holdings would form the core of the embryonic archive and consequently titles of Irish interest were isolated. This core collection has developed over the last 2 decades into a comprehensive resource for researchers; it endeavours to reflect all aspects of indigenous film production since the Lumiere Brothers' cameraman Alexander Promio first visited Dublin in 1897.

In 1986 recognising the need to protect Ireland's moving image heritage the Irish Film Institute established what has become the national film collection: the IFI Irish Film Archive. Since its inception the Archive's mission has been to acquire, preserve and make available Ireland's moving image heritage and related materials. It has built up a collection of approximately 27,000 cans of film, and 15,000 tapes predominantly made in or about Ireland, or by Irish producers abroad. A complementary collection of documents, posters, images are held in the Paper Collection and the Tiernan MacBride library holds a wealth of published material on Irish and international cinema. These collections are held in custom-built, climate-controlled vaults at the IFI premises in Temple Bar, designed especially for viewers' access and long-term preservation.

HOLDINGS
The Archive collection is a unique cultural and historical resource reflecting indigenous film production from 1897 to the present day. The changing landscape of the Irish nation has been captured alongside changing attitudes, customs and social conditions. Amateur films, newsreels, sporting and social events are preserved alongside feature films and documentaries. The work of such luminaries as John Boorman, Neil Jordan and Jim Sheridan is held with films made within local communities and by amateur filmmakers. The most important social, political and historical events of the last century are represented, enriching our understanding of this period and enabling us to connect with our past. The material safe-guarded by the Archive is a vivid and tangible document of Ireland's past and present and chronicles the development of modern Ireland at a time of unprecedented change. The IFI works hard to ensure that this rich resource is shared with the public and there is an extensive programme of Archive screenings, on site, regionally and internationally; it also provides Archive material for inclusion in documentaries exploring Ireland's culture and history and publish key titles from the Archive collection on DVD.

The IFI Irish Film Archive is the only Irish member of FIAF (International Federation of Film Archives)

Online Resources
The Archive collections can be partially searched via TCD Irish film online: www.tcd.ie/irishfilm; some examples of titles from the collection can be viewed at European Film Treasures: www.europafilmtreasures.eu; Some collection level descriptions can be viewed at Irish Archives Resource: www.iar.ie; DVDs of selected titles from the collections can be purchased online at: www.ifi.ie/shop

IFI IRISH FILM ARCHIVE COLLECTIONS

The IFI Irish Film Archive collections can be divided into 3 categories, the Library collection, the Paper Archive and the Moving Image collections.

The Tiernan MacBride Library is the most comprehensive collection of film related publications in Ireland. It is named after one of the founding fathers of the Irish film industry. Its holdings include:

The Book Collection. It contains over 3,000 books covering all aspects of national and international cinema including production, scriptwriting, acting, theory, genre and criticism. New books are acquired on a monthly basis, and suggestions are welcomed on future purchases. We invite colleges to submit their reading lists so that all students can be catered for.

The Journal Collection. The Library contains a range of film related national and international periodicals, both critical and production-based. Periodicals in the collection include *Cahiers du Cinema, Cineaste, Daily Cinema, Empire, Film Quarterly, In Camera, In Production, Kinematograph Weekly, Premiere, Screen International, Variety, Sight and Sound, American Cinematographer, Screen, Vertigo, Film Ireland*, and many more.

The Clippings Collection. The Clippings Collection is a unique resource consisting of Irish film-related media clippings from national and international newspapers, magazines and journals, arranged and indexed by subject, film or personality. Topics covered include feature film, documentary, animation, shorts, actors, directors, production companies, broadcasting, representations of Irish people, Northern Ireland, the travelling community, censorship, television, legislation, and the Irish Film Institute itself. Files of newspaper clippings on Irish film production are maintained and updated on a daily basis.

The Paper Archive Collection. Stored in climate-controlled vaults, the Paper Archive offers primary source material on the history of film in Ireland. Material includes scripts, shot lists, stills, storyboards, correspondence, posters, brochures. Notable collections include the papers of directors Neil Jordan and Tiernan MacBride, producer Lord Killanin, set designer Josie MacAvin, production company Hell's Kitchen and the Horgan Picture Theatre, Youghal, Co. Cork. The stills and poster collections include nearly 8,000 images in a variety of formats. Researchers can access the paper collection by appointment.

Moving Image Collections. The IFI Irish Film Archive holds one of the largest collections of film and film related materials in the world. The Archive is built on a core of Irish films which were produced or acquired for distribution by the National Film Institute. Since then the collection has grown with over 500 individuals or organisations who were eager to see films preserved and centralised in a national archive depositing material. The collection, which exists in a number of different formats, can be described under a series of subject and type headings. The earliest films in the collection were filmed by the Lumiere Brothers in Dublin and Belfast in 1897. Recent acquisitions come in via delivery agreements with the IFB and BAI. The following list is intended as a broad introduction to the major elements of the moving image collection.

Feature Films: an increasingly comprehensive collection of independently produced Irish feature films. The Archive also holds Irish theme feature films produced by non-Irish production companies.

Shorts: collection of short (less than 40 minutes) fiction films includes student films; independent fictions; early works of feature film -makers.

Government Information films: non-fiction films produced by various government departments examining health, public safety, savings, education, agriculture, issues relating to Northern Ireland etc.

Travelogues/tourist promotional films: non-fiction works produced by Bord Failte and by commercial organisations designed to attract tourists to Ireland or a particular location or amenity.

Sports films: All Ireland football and hurling finals 1940s - 60s produced by the National Film Institute for the G.A.A.; training films etc.

Educational/informational films: Films were produced by, among others, semi-state bodies, educational institutions, corporate bodies. Many of the films were distributed, or produced and distributed by the National Film Institute between

1940s and 1980s to schools and colleges throughout the country. Subjects include agriculture; rural modernisation; immunisation; industry; savings; health and safety; hygiene etc.

Documentaries: The Archive holds a broad collection of pre-RTE documentaries of political and sociological significance.

Newsreels: The Archive holds representative material from all but one of the indigenously produced Irish cinema newsreel series and a selection of issues from foreign newsreel Irish editions (e.g. *Universal Irish News, Movietone Irish Edition).* The earliest home-produced newsreel material is from the Irish Events newsreel (1917–19) and the most recent, the Gael Linn *Amharc Eireann* series (1956- 1964). Commercials: collection includes early cinema advertisements; collections of individual producers and production companies (e.g. Vincent Corcoran; Tiernan MacBride); complete collections of leading Irish advertising agencies.
Missionary Films: films produced by Irish religious orders to promote work of Irish missionaries abroad.

Animations: a small but representative collection of animated films includes early experiments in photographic animation, Irish language cartoons etc.

Amateur non-fiction films: Films of personal or public events produced by amateurs. The collections include 'home movies'; films of community activities such as Corpus Christi Processions, village fairs, work outings and military parades; and films of events of historical significance.

Amateur fiction films: short edited fiction films made, largely by the Irish Film Society, for public but not theatrical exhibition.

For preservation and access purposes the moving image collection is divided as follows:

> Master Collection - Unique or best quality copies of titles held, exists as prints negatives and in some cases broadcast quality tapes. Access to the master collection is undertaken only for cataloguing or duplication purpose. Viewing Collection – Second or multiple copies of titles held in the master collection. Exists as broadcast quality tape and film prints. Access is provided.

> Reference collection: VHS/DVD Collection – a large collection of Irish Fiction and non-fiction a films on VHS/DVD. This collection is invaluable for research and reference purposes and is used by programme makers, students and the general public alike.

LOCATION
The IFI is located just off Dame Street in the Temple Bar area of Dublin, a five minute walk from Trinity College. Its location is sign-posted at the junction of Dame Street and Eustace Street.

IRISH JESUIT ARCHIVES

35 Lower Leeson Street
DUBLIN 2
Ireland

TELEPHONE: (01) 775 8569
E-mail: archives@jesuit.ie
Flickr: www.flickr.com/photos/jesuitsireland/collections/
Irish Archives Resource: www.iar.ie/

HOURS
M–F, 10:00–13:00, 14:00–16:30

ACCESS AND SERVICES
Access by advance appointment only. Laptops permitted; pencils only. No
photocopier, microfilm/microfiche reader/printer. Digital photography is at the
discretion of the Archivist. Printed finding aids available.

CONTACT
Fergus O'Donoghue, SJ, Province Archivist; and Damien Burke, Assistant Archivist

DESCRIPTION
The Irish Jesuit Archives are the official repository for the records of the Irish Jesuits
from the sixteenth to the twenty-first centuries. They are part of the central
administration of the Irish Jesuit Province, though located some distance from the
Provincialate.

HOLDINGS
The bulk of papers relate to individual Jesuits, Jesuit administration, sermon and
retreat notes and sodalities. The MacErlean Transcripts, which cover the years from
1527 to 1774, include documents relating to ministries in Ireland and abroad. Other
material includes:

> Irish Colleges: Lisbon, Poitiers, Rome, Salamanca, Santiago de Compostela,
> Seville;
> Irish Missions: Australia, Hong Kong, Isle of Man, Zambia;
> Jesuit Chaplains: Emigrants in Britain, WWI, WWII;
> Education: Belvedere College, Clongowes Wood College, Coláiste Iognáid
> Galway, Crescent College Limerick, Gonzaga College, Mungret College, St
> Declan's, St Stanislaus College Tullabeg, Catholic University, University
> College Dublin;
> Jesuit Residences: Dromore, Emo Court, Gardiner Street, John Austin
> House, Killiney Castle, Leeson Street, Loyola House, Manresa House,
> Milltown Park, Rathfarnham Castle, Tullabeg, and University Hall.

The archive contains many photographs, but the photographs of Fr. Frank Browne,
SJ are held at Gonzaga College, Sandford Road, Dublin 6. Contact Fr. Eddie
O'Donnell, SJ.

LOCATION
Close to the city centre, a five minute walk from the south-eastern corner of St
Stephen's Green. Entrance by 37 Lower Leeson Street.

IRISH JEWISH MUSEUM

3–4 Walworth Road
South Circular Road
DUBLIN 8
Ireland

TELEPHONE: Mobile: 08570 67357 or (01) 453 1797 (during opening hours)
E-mail: museum@jewishireland.org
Website: www.theirishjewishmuseum.org

HOURS
May–September: Su, Tu, Th, 11:00–15:30
October–April: Su, 10:30–14:30

ACCESS AND SERVICES
Visitors welcome. No admission charge. Access to manuscripts and photographs
requires Curator's permission. Adult and school tours available by request.
Wheelchair accessible lower floor only.

CONTACT
Curator

DESCRIPTION
The museum seeks to document the religious, historical and cultural life of the
Jewish people in Ireland, most especially the communities of Belfast, Cork, Derry,
Dublin, Limerick and Waterford. Though the collection focuses on the past 150
years, there have been Jews in Ireland since 1492. The museum is located in a
former synagogue, which consisted of two adjoining terraced houses. The original
synagogue, with all its fittings, can be viewed upstairs. The home of Rabbi Isaac
Herzog, first Chief Rabbi of Ireland and father of Dr Chaim Herzog (1918–97), the
Irish born President of Israel, is nearby. President Herzog officially opened the
Museum on 20 June 1985 during a state visit to Ireland. The fictional boyhood
home of Leopold Bloom, the hero of Joyce's *Ulysses*, is also close by, at 52 Upper
Clanbrassil Street. There are some 1,400 Jews living in Ireland today: 1,200 in the
south, 200 in the north.

HOLDINGS
The Jewish Museum contains a substantial collection of memorabilia relating to
Ireland's Jewish communities, whose commercial and social life is documented in
photographs, paintings and other displays. A feature of particular interest is a
kitchen depicting a typical Sabbath/Festival meal setting in Jewish home at the turn
of the twentieth century. The museum also contains a collection of material on
Judaism in general. The museum has access to some genealogical material in its
archives and can advise in this regard. An expansion is planned to increase the
exhibition area and offer greater access to the library and archives

LOCATION
In Portobello, off Victoria Street, just south of the city centre, an area that once had
a sizeable Jewish population. Buses include: 16, 19 and 122 to Victoria Street, South
Circular Road and 14, 15, 65 and 83 to Lennox Street, off South Richmond Street.

IRISH THEATRE ARCHIVE

Dublin City Library and Archive
138–144 Pearse Street
DUBLIN 2
Ireland

TELEPHONE: (01) 674 4996/4997; FAX: (01) 674 4879
E-mail: cityarchives@dublincity.ie
Website: www.dublincity.ie

HOURS
M–Th, 10:00–20:00; F–Sa, 10:00–17:00

ACCESS AND SERVICES
Visitors welcome. ID required to facilitate registration on first visit. Disabled access facilities. Laptops permitted; pencils only. Photocopying and microfilm prints available for a fee. No borrowing privileges permitted. Publication: *Prompts: Bulletin of the Irish Theatre Archive.*

CONTACT
Mary Clark, Honorary Archivist

DESCRIPTION
The Irish Theatre Archive is operated by Dublin City Council under the auspices of Dublin City Archives. Its mission is to collect and preserve materials relating to the history of theatre in Ireland.

HOLDINGS
The archive houses an impressive array of materials relating to theatre in Ireland. Types of material include: programmes, posters, photographs, press cuttings, prompt books, costume and stage designs, together with plays in typescript and manuscript. Theatre collections include: An Damer; Cork Theatre Company; Dublin Masque Theatre Guild; Dublin Theatre Festival; Gaiety Theatre, Dublin; Irish Theatre Company; Olympia Theatre, Dublin; Rough Magic Theatre Company; Brendan Smith Academy; Theatre Royal, Dublin; and Storytellers Theatre Compnay, Dublin. There are also the collections of actors, costumiers and designers, including: P.J. Bourke, Eddie Cooke, Ursula Doyle, Donald Finlay, James N. Healy, Eddie Johnston, Nora Lever, Micheál Mac Liammóir, Dennis Noble, Jimmy O'Dea, Shelah Richards, Cecil Sheridan, Patrick McLarnon and Vernon Hayden.

LOCATION
On Pearse Street, two blocks eastwards from Pearse DART station. Bus 3 from O'Connell Street to Ringsend stops across the street.

IRISH TRADITIONAL MUSIC ARCHIVE

73 Merrion Square
DUBLIN 2
Ireland

TELEPHONE: (01) 661 9699; FAX: (01) 662 4585
E-mail: donations@itma.ie; sales@itma.ie
Website: www.itma.ie

HOURS
M-F, 10:00–17:00, one Sat. each month (see www.itma.ie); closed Christmas–New Year period and bank holidays

ACCESS AND SERVICES
Visitors welcome. No appointment needed for general visit; registration on first visit; no access charge. Limited disabled access facilities. Printed materials, sound recordings and images catalogued and indexed on in-house opac and web opac; online digital library of sound recordings, printed items, manuscripts and images; non-circulating collection. Listening, viewing and reading facilities; photocopying, digitising and faxing available for a fee; supervised digital photography permitted; laptops permitted; free WiFi. Monthly e-mail newsletter; bi-monthly listing of recent publications and acquisitions in Irish traditional music; facebook, Twitter and other social media; digital material accessible via online portals. ITMA sells books, CDs and DVDs published by itself or by its partners at its premises and online.

CONTACT
The Secretary

DESCRIPTION
ITMA was established in 1987 as a multimedia reference and resource archive for the collection, preservation, organisation and dissemination of the traditional song, music and dance of Ireland. It is a public, not-for-profit institution supported by the Arts Council of Ireland, the Arts Council of Northern Ireland and private donations. It publishes books, CDs and DVDs in its own right and in partnership with others, and is involved in broadcasting partnerships. It engages in an active programme of field and studio recording. ITMA holds the largest collection in existence of the materials of Irish traditional music.

HOLDINGS
ITMA collects comprehensively and broadly all materials, including sound recordings, printed items, images and born-digital items, for the appreciation and study of Irish traditional music. Collections encompass the island of Ireland, the Irish diaspora, especially in Britain and North America, and other performers of Irish traditional music throughout the world. A representative collection of traditional music of other countries is also held.

The collection includes 30,000 sound recordings, 33,000 printed items, 25,000 visual items, 2,200 online digital items, 9,000 melodies in digital form, and manuscripts.

LOCATION
Merrion Square South in south central Dublin. Well serviced by public transport. Meter parking is available on Merrion Square.

THE JESUIT LIBRARY

Milltown Park
Sandford Road
DUBLIN 6
Ireland

TELEPHONE: (01) 218 0285
E-mail: jeslib@eircom.net
Online catalogue: www.jesuitlibrary.ie
Website: www.milltown-institute.ie

HOURS
M–F, 09:00–17:00

ACCESS AND SERVICES
Visitors welcome, but by appointment. Advance notice and references required.
Library services leased on annual basis to Milltown Institute of Theology and
Philosophy, a third level college located in the same building. See website above.
Books may be borrowed by members of the Jesuit order and by registered students
and staff of the Institute of Theology and Philosophy. Photocopying services
available.

CONTACT
Mary Glennon, Acting Librarian

DESCRIPTION
The Jesuit Library, Milltown Park, is the library of the Irish Province of the Society
of Jesus. It is a private library specialising in theology (including scripture and
spirituality) and philosophy.

HOLDINGS
The library houses a collection of some 140,000 bound volumes, which mainly
cover theology, church history, philosophy, the human sciences, scripture and Irish
material. It is strongest in theology, scripture, patristic studies, spirituality and
medieval and modern European philosophy. It receives more than 265 current
periodicals, the principal areas covered being theology, church history, scripture,
spirituality and philosophy. The library also contains a collection of rare and Irish
books. Access to the Irish Collection is strictly closed.

LOCATION
In Milltown, south-west of Donnybrook, about two miles south-east of St Stephen's
Green through Ranelagh. From city centre or Lower Baggot Street, take buses 11, 44
or 61 to bus stop 855 at Sandford Road junction with Belmont Avenue. Luas stops:
Cowper.

MACBRIDE LIBRARY (TIERNAN MACBRIDE LIBRARY)
See IRISH FILM INSTITUTE, Dublin

MARSH'S LIBRARY

St Patrick's Close
DUBLIN 8
Ireland

TELEPHONE: (01) 454 3511; FAX: (01) 454 3511
E-mail: keeper@marshlibrary.ie
Website: www.marshlibrary.ie
Facebook: Archbishop Marsh's Library

HOURS
M, W–F, 10:00–13:00, 14:00–17:00; Sa, 10:30–13:00

ACCESS AND SERVICES
Visitors welcome. Admission fees: general public, €2.50; students and seniors, €1.50; children free. Researchers admitted free but required to make application in advance to the Keeper of the Library. Consult website for details. No disabled access facilities but special arrangements can be made for researchhers; laptops permitted; pencils only.

Marsh's Library offers impressive exhibitions programme; catalogues available for purchase, if still in print. Consult website for listing.

An excellent introduction to the library is Muriel McCarthy's *Marsh's Library, Dublin: All Graduates and Gentlemen* (Dublin, 2003).

CONTACT
Dr Jason McElligott, Keeper of the Library

DESCRIPTION
Marsh's Library was founded in 1701 by the deeply scholarly Narcissus Marsh, Archbishop of Dublin. The first public library in Ireland, it contains more than 25,000 volumes, largely reflecting its founder's sophisticated interest in the full spectrum of seventeenth century knowledge. The library remains virtually the same as it was 300 years ago, and it is one of the cultural treasures of Ireland, used by luminaries from Jonathan Swift to James Joyce. It is mentioned in *Ulysses*. Some modern physical additions have been made to the library, including a conservation bindery and seminar room, but without altering the appearance of the original library space. Visitors to Marsh's Library can step three centuries back in time.

HOLDINGS
The library was built on four major acquisitions. The first was the 10,000 volume personal library of Bishop Stillingfleet, covering a variety of subjects, including travel, science, mathematics, history, medicine, lexicography and witchcraft. The Stillingfleet Collection occupies the first gallery. The second acquisition was the library of a French Huguenot medical doctor, Elias Bouhéreau. These books are housed in the main reading room. The third collection was the library of Archbishop Marsh himself. Marsh was particularly interested in science, mathematics and music, but he was also interested in oriental languages and rabbinical and medieval writers. He collected books in Hebrew, Arabic, Turkish and Russian. The fourth major collection was bequeathed to the library in 1745 by Bishop Stearne, whose collecting interests closely paralleled those of Stillingfleet, Marsh and Bouhéreau. Exhibitions at Marsh's Library have drawn heavily on the collection's rich holdings. The library also houses early manuscripts and printed books in the Irish language.

In 2009 the exquisite library of Benjamin Guinness, 4th Earl of Iveagh was donated by his family to Marsh's Library. This collection is particularly strong in seventeenth and eighteenth-century Irish books, but it also contains a number of much earlier items (including a thirteenth century manuscript history of Ireland), and an impressive array of modern literature. This collection is housed in Farmleigh House in the Phoenix Park and is administered for Marsh's Library by the Office of Public Works.

The library has embraced digital media and uses Facebook on a daily basis to post images of items in its collection. It is also digitising and making available manuscripts from its collections on its website

LOCATION
Discreetly tucked away behind St Patrick's Cathedral. Entry is through a stone archway in St Patrick's Close. It is near the National Archives, within easy walking distance (10–15 minutes) of St Stephen's Green.

MATER DEI INSTITUTE OF EDUCATION LIBRARY
See DUBLIN CITY UNIVERSITY LIBRARY

THE MILITARY ARCHIVES
See AN CHARTLANN MHÍLEATA/THE MILITARY ARCHIVES, Dublin

MILLTOWN PARK LIBRARY
See THE JESUIT LIBRARY, Dublin

NATIONAL ARCHIVES OF IRELAND

Bishop Street
DUBLIN 8
Ireland

TELEPHONE: (01) 407 2300; FAX: (01) 407 2333
E-mail: mail@nationalarchives.ie
Website: www.nationalarchives.ie

HOURS
M–F: 10:00–17:00; closed New Year's Day, St Patrick's Day, Good Friday, Easter Monday, 25–26 December (consult website), bank and public holidays, and for 3 days in early December each year (consult website).

ACCESS AND SERVICES
Visitors welcome; disabled access facilities; photographic ID and reader's ticket required (reader's ticket can be applied for on day of first visit); no access charge; laptops permitted; pencils only; photocopies and microform printouts available for a modest fee. There are 23 microform readers in Bishop Street, including eight reader/printers, available on a first come, first served basis. The NAI publishes *Reports of the Director* and *Reports of the National Archives Advisory Council*. Also available are helpful leaflets, including *Reading Room Information* (2007), *Some Facts*

about the National Archives (2010) and *Sources for Family History and Genealogy* (2010). All leaflets are also printed in Irish.
For up to date research guides and information consult website; especially helpful for genealogical researchers. Website also offers access to online exhibitions, e.g. the 2007 'The Theft of the Irish "Crown Jewels"', click on 'News' section. More recent additions include 1901 and 1911 census returns (www.census.nationalarchives.ie/), Anglo-Irish Treaty (http://treaty.nationalarchives.ie/) and Chief Secretary's Office Registered Papers (www.csorp.nationalarchives.ie/).

CONTACT
Director

DESCRIPTION
The National Archives was formally established in 1988 with the amalgamation of the Public Record Office of Ireland and the State Paper Office. It is a government agency, open free of charge to the public.

HOLDINGS
The National Archives is the official depository for the records of the Irish government. All government departments and state agencies, including the courts, are required to deposit their papers with the National Archives.

Records of modern government departments
The Taoiseach (formerly President of the Executive Council), including government minutes and associated files; Agriculture (originally the Department of Agriculture and Technical Instruction) and successors; Education, including records of the Commissioners of National Education, the Commissioners of Intermediate Education and Department of Education successors; Energy (formerly part of the Department of Industry and Commerce); Environment, including records of the Local Government Board and records of the Department of Local Government and Public Health; Finance, Foreign Affairs (formerly the Department of External Affairs), including records of embassies and consulates in other countries; Gaeltacht (originally part of the Department of Lands); Health and successors (formerly part of the Department of Local Government and Public Health); Industry and Commerce, including records of the Department of Supplies; Justice (originally the Department of Home Affairs) and successors; Labour (formerly part of the Department of Industry and Commerce); the Marine and predecessors, including record of the Commissioners of Fisheries and Department of Fisheries; Social Welfare (formerly part of the Department of Industry and Commerce and the Department of Local Government and Public Health); Tourism, Transport and Communications (formerly part of the Department of Industry and Commerce, the pre-1922 Post Office and the Department of Posts and Telegraphs) and successors.

Note: the Military Archives at Cathal Brugha Barracks, Rathmines, Dublin 6, holds records of the Department of Defence, the Army Pensions Board and the Defence Forces and the Bureau of Military History, including records relating to persons active in the War of Independence, the formation of the IRA and Defence Forces personnel. *See first entry under Dublin,* AN CHARTLANN MHÍLEATA/THE MILITARY ARCHIVES.

Records of other modern government offices and state agencies
Office of the Attorney General; Office of the Film Censor, including the Censorship

of Films Appeals Board; Office of the Commissioners of Charitable Donations and Bequests for Ireland; Companies Registration Office, including dissolved companies files; Office of the Comptroller and Auditor General; Fair Trade Commission; Office of the Governor General; Labour Court; Land Settlement Commission; Met Éireann; Ordnance Survey, including original manuscript mapping records; Patents Office; Office of the Secretary to the President; Office of Public Works, including property management and architectural records; Registry of Friendly Societies; Mercantile Marine Office, including crew lists and shipping agreements; Valuation Office and Boundary Survey, including Griffith's Valuation and various land and property valuation records; Office of the Registrar General, comprising census records, particularly 1901 and 1911 census for all of Ireland (now available online at www.census.nationalarchives.ie/): prison administration records, including prison registers.

Records of Dáil Éireann administration, 1919–22
Records of the Dáil Éireann departments of government, 1919–22, including records of the Dáil Éireann Courts (Winding Up) Commission and the Dáil Éireann Department of Local Government.

Records of offices of the British administration in Ireland whose functions abolished in 1922 or whose functions became defunct thereafter
Chief Secretary's Office, including Registered Papers, Outrage Papers, State of the Country Papers, Official Papers and Rebellion Papers; and records of its constituent departments: the Convict Department, including nineteenth century Transportation Registers, Prisoners' Petitions and Convict Reference Files; the Privy Council Office and the Chief Crown Solicitor's Office.
Board of Health, comprising Cholera Papers; Church Temporalities Commission, comprising tithe applotment books; Famine Relief Commission; Customs and Excise; Government Prisons Office and General Prisons Board, comprising records of prison administration and including records of convicts sentenced to penal servitude; Quit Rent Office, comprising records relating to the management of crown estates.

Court and testamentary records
Supreme Court; Court of Criminal Appeal; Central Criminal Court; High Court; High Court Probate Office (formerly the Principal Probate Registry) and District Probate Registries, including wills, grants of probate and of letters of administration; Circuit Court; County Courts; Grand Juries; District Courts; Petty Sessions Courts; Incumbered Estates Court, Landed Estates Court, Chancery Land Judges Court, including rentals; Chancery, consisting of sixteenth and seventeenth century pleadings; plea rolls, fourteenth and fifteenth centuries.

Records of baptisms, marriages and burials
Church of Ireland registers of baptisms, marriages and burials, comprising some surviving original records of a small number of parishes and microfilms of other parishes located mainly in dioceses of the south and west of Ireland.

Record transcripts calendars and abstracts
Transcripts, calendars, abstracts and indexes to original archives destroyed in the former Public Record Office of Ireland building at the Four Courts, including Irish Record Commission calendars of court records, thirteenth to nineteenth centuries;

Ferguson extracts from Exchequer records, thirteenth to eighteenth centuries; Lodge abstracts from Chancery patent rolls, seventeenth century; collections of genealogical abstracts by Betham, Crosslé, Groves, Grove-White, and Thrift, mostly seventeenth to nineteenth centuries.

Other records:
Records accessioned under agreement from harbour boards, health boards, hospitals, schools, charities, trade unions, business firms, solicitors' offices, estate offices and private individuals.

Note: some archives are not stored in the Bishop Street building and are produced in Bishop Street Reading Room the day after ordering. These include the following: some Departmental archives; some court archives; wills, 1900–74; administration papers, 1900–74; Schedules of Assets (Principal Registry), 1922–74; archives salvaged in 1922 (in part); Companies Registration Office; national school salary books; Office of Public Works (part); Quit Rent Office; Royal Hospital Kilmainham; shipping agreements and crew lists, post-1922; business records; hospital records (available only with prior permission). It is advisable to telephone several days in advance to check on exact position of archives to be consulted, as the above location list is subject to change.

Archives on microfilm:
The following archives are available only on microfilm:

Belturbet Corporation Records
Betham's Abstracts
Board of Guardians: Minute Books
Board of Guardians: Registers of Admission and Discharge
Census 1851: Dublin, Heads of Households
Census 1901
Census 1911
Census nineteenth century: Surviving portions of 1821, 1831, 1841, 1851
Census Search Forms
Chief Secretary's Office, Convict Department: Convict Reference Files, 1835–56 (transportees only)
Chief Secretary's Office, Convict Department: Free Settlers' Papers, 1828–52
Chief Secretary's Office, Convict Department: Prisoners' Petitions and Cases
Chief Secretary's Office, Convict Department: State Prisoners' Petitions
Chief Secretary's Office, Convict Department: Transportation Registers
Chief Secretary's Office: Rebellion Papers
Church of Ireland Parish Registers
Church of Ireland records
Church of Ireland: Reports of Searches in Parish Registers
Colonial Office records of Irish Government in Dublin Castle, 1872–1926 (originals in NA, U.K., Ref: CO 904)
Court of Chancery: Bill Books, 1633–1850
Courts Service: Petty Sessions: Dog Licence Registers (CS/PS/2/1–1164)
Courts Service: Petty Sessions: Order Books (CS/PS/1/1–11720)
Courts Service: Petty Sessions: Order Books (Miscellaneous) (CS/PS/3/1 –204)

Crossle Genealogical Abstracts
Dublin Metropolitan Police
Elphin Diocesan Census 1749
Equity Exchequer: Bill Books, 1674–1850
Grove White Transcripts
LEC Rentals (O'Brien)
Lodge, Records of the Rolls and other documents
National Education Commission: National School Applications for Grants,
c. 1832–90 (Carlow–Cork)
National Education Commission: National School Registers/Roll Books
Ordnance Survey Name Books (Placenames) (Antrim–Meath)
Ordnance Survey, 6 inch maps
Pembroke Estate Letters 97/46/1/2/8
Post Office Archives, Irish Minute indexes
Prison Registers
PROI, Deputy Keeper's Reports, 1–59
Royal Hospital Kilmainham (NA, U.K.)
Royal Irish Constabulary (NA, U.K.)
Shipping Records, 1863–1921
State Papers, Register of Convicts on Ships, 1851–3
Survey and Distribution, Books of
T series, including some M and D series
Testamentary, Calendars of Grants of Probate and Letters of Administration
1951–1952
Testamentary, Calendars of Grants of Probate and Letters of Administration,
1858–1920
Testamentary, Irish Will Registers and Administration Registers
Testamentary, Prerogative Court Indexes Books
Testamentary, Will Books
Thom's Directories 1844–1958
Thrift Abstracts
Tithe Applotment Books
Tithe Applotment Books: Northern Ireland
Valuation Office, Primary Valuation Books
Valuation Office: Field Books
Valuation Office: House Books (5.0001–5.4254)
Valuation Office: Miscellaneous Books (OLX.1–OLX.170)
Valuation Office: Quarto Books (7.0001–7.0088)
Valuation Office: Tenure Books (6.0002–6.0466)
Wicklow Gaol Prison Registers

LOCATION
A few blocks west of St Stephen's Green and south of Dublin Castle, near St Patrick's
Cathedral. The National Archives is on the west end of Bishop Street, at the corner
of Bride Street.

NATIONAL GALLERY OF IRELAND RESEARCH SERVICES

Merrion Square West
DUBLIN 2
Ireland

TELEPHONE: (01) 663 3546; FAX: (01) 661 5372
E-mail: see contact
Website: www.nationalgallery.ie

HOURS
M–F, 10:00–17:00; closed Christmas, Easter and bank holidays
ESB Centre for the Study of Irish Art is open Tuesday – Thursday, 10:00–17:00;
closed Christmas, Easter and bank holidays
Note: Prints and Drawings Study Room is open Tuesday–Friday, 10:00–13:00,
14:00–17:00; closed Christmas, Easter and bank holidays

ACCESS AND SERVICES:
For Fine Art Library, NGI Archive, ESB Centre for the Study of Irish Art, Yeats
Archive and Diageo Prints and Drawings Study Room: All Visitors are welcome, but
access to the Diego Prints and Drawings Study Room, archive collections and library
special collections is by appointment only. Advance notice can be made by phone, e-
mail or in writing. Wheelchair access. Laptops permitted. Photocopying facilities
available.

CONTACT
NGI Archives: Leah Benson, Archivist. E-mail: library@ngi.ie
Diageo Prints and Drawings Study Room: Anne Hodge, Curator of Prints and
Drawings. E-mail: ahodge@ngi.ie
ESB Centre for the Study of Irish Art: Donal Maguire, CSIA Administrator. E-mail:
csia@ngi.ie
Art Library: Andrea Lydon, Librarian. E-mail: library@ngi.ie
Yeats Archive: Pauline Swords, Yeats Archivist. E-mail: yeats@ngi.ie

DESCRIPTION
The National Gallery is Ireland's major museum of art and holds the national
collection of European and Irish fine art which includes some 15,000 paintings,
sculptures, works on paper and objets d'art dating from the early thirteenth century
through to the mid-twentieth century. The collection boasts an impressive range of
masterpieces by artists from the major European schools of art whilst also featuring
the world's most comprehensive collection of Irish art. Admission to the Gallery is
free. The Gallery also holds an extensive research collection which is a significant
resource for anyone interested in researching art and its associated disciplines. Rich
and varied, these resources relate to the national and international development of
the visual arts from the middle ages onwards. The collections are regularly consulted
by artists, students, scholars and academics, art dealers and collectors and members
of the public. Further information is available on the research section of the Gallery's
website www.nationalgallery.ie/Research. NGI PORTICO, which lists the Gallery's
bibliographic holdings and provides general information on archive collections, can
be accessed at http://portico.nationalgallery.ie/. NGI DORAS, which provides access
to high-quality digital images, accompanied by catalogue entries and related

information to selected items from the Gallery's archive and library special collections, can be accessed at http://doras.nationalgallery.ie/

HOLDINGS

Art Library

The Art Library comprises over 70,000 publications relating to art from the fifteenth century to the present day. The collection primarily covers paintings, drawings, watercolours, prints and sculpture in the Western European artistic tradition. Art and artists that feature in the Gallery's collection are especially well represented whilst publications on American, African, Asian and Australasian art also feature. Monographs, catalogue raisonnés, exhibition catalogues and collection catalogues from museums and galleries throughout the world are available to researchers. The Library also holds the most comprehensive collection of art auction catalogues in Ireland, covering sales of European art dating from late eighteenth century onwards. Over 200 journal titles are represented in the collection and recently received journals are available for consultation in the Library reading room. The Library has an extensive reference collection as well as access to a number of useful online resources. Many of the publications in the Library's special collection, which includes rare and antiquarian books, art treatises, illustrated books, pamphlets, early exhibition and sales catalogues, are unique to this collection. The Library also holds all NGI publications dating from the first catalogue published in 1864.

Diageo Prints and Drawings Study Room

The Study Room provides researchers and the general public with supervised access to the National Gallery of Ireland's wide-ranging collection of prints and drawings. Works range from simple pencil sketches, preparatory studies for paintings, finished landscape watercolours, portraits in all media and architectural and topographical drawings. Highlights include Irish and British landscape and old master drawings from the Italian, French and Dutch schools.

ESB Centre for the Study of Irish Art

The ESB Centre for the Study of Irish Art facilitates study and research into Irish art. Its library and archive collection documents the country's rich artistic legacy from early Celtic art to the present. It is an essential resource for anyone interested in the visual arts in Ireland. The holdings include a library of publications on Irish art, as well as a rare and illustrated book collection. Current periodicals are also available as well as older journals that covered the arts in Ireland. Major Irish auctioneers are represented along with other auction and sales catalogues that document the Irish art trade since the late eighteenth century. The CSIA also provides access to a selection of useful online resources. In addition to this it holds an important archive collection relating to Irish artists and art organisations. Also available is a collection of artist folders, which hold a variety of ephemera relating to individual artists, and a large collection of gallery folders containing material produced by the many commercial galleries, art societies, clubs and institutions that have existed in Ireland over the past 300 years.

NGI Archives

The Archives contain the official records of the institution, reflecting the history of the gallery from the 1850s to the present day. They are a valuable source for those interested in the development of the institution since its foundation and its involvement in Irish cultural affairs.

Yeats Archive

The Yeats Archive consists of a prestigious collection of material donated to the National Gallery of Ireland by Anne Yeats in 1996 and several additional collections acquired since. These collections relate to Jack B. Yeats and members of his extended family.

Sir Denis Mahon Library and Archive

Sir Denis Mahon was a collector and scholar of the Italian baroque. The library collection covers art from classical times onwards. Italian art is strongly represented particularly the baroque period while British, Dutch, French and Spanish art also feature prominently. The library collection includes many rare and antiquarian volumes which are regarded as key sources in the study of European, particularly Italian, art. The library also boasts several large bound volumes of Carracci and Guercino prints together with a stack of loose engravings. In addition there are artists' monographs, catalogue raisonnés, exhibition catalogues, sales catalogues, journals, conference proceedings, guide books and pamphlets published between the sixteenth-century and the present day. The archive collection consists of a vast accumulation of correspondence and academic notes relating to collections and individual works of art, in particular Italian art and artists. A substantial *fototeca* of photographs, prints and glass plate negatives is of significant research value.

LOCATION

At the northern end of Merrion Square West, near Clare Street, next to Leinster House (the seat of the Irish parliament). The library is located near the main entrance, one flight down. There is also an entrance on Clare Street to the new Millennium Wing of the National Gallery where the Diageo Prints and Drawings Study Room, Centre for the Study of Irish Art and Yeats Archive are located. **Note:** the Gallery's Merrion Square entrance is closed during ongoing renovations, and it is unlikely to reopen until late 2014. Currently the only public access into the Gallery is via the Clare Street entrance.

NATIONAL LIBRARY OF IRELAND

Kildare Street
DUBLIN 2
Ireland

OFFICE OF THE CHIEF HERALD

2–3 Kildare Street
DUBLIN 2

NATIONAL PHOTOGRAPHIC ARCHIVE

Meeting House Square, Temple Bar
DUBLIN 2
Ireland

TELEPHONE: (01) 603 0200; (01) 603 0373 (appointments); FAX: (01) 661 2523
E-mail: info@nli.ie; npaoffice@nli.ie (Reading Room appointments)
Website: www.nli.ie

HOURS
Main Reading Room: M–W, 09:30–19:45; Th–F, 09:30–16:45; Sa, 09:30–12:45;
closed Christmas, Easter and public holidays
Manuscripts Reading Room: M–W, 09:30–19:45; Th–F, 09:30–16:45; Sa,
09:30–12:45; closed Christmas, Easter and public holidays
Genealogy Advisory Service: M–W, 09:30–17:00; Th–F, 09:30–16:45; Sa,
09:30–12:45

National Photographic Archive
Exhibitions: M–Sa, 10:00 to 16:45; Su, noon to 16:45
Reading Room: Strictly by prior appointment only, Tu–W, 10:00–13:00;
Th, 10:00–13:00 and 14:30–16:30

ACCESS
Visitors welcome; photo ID required to access print and visual collections and
manuscripts. Advance notice for group visits required. Non-circulating collection.
Advance ordering system in place – full details can be found on the website. Certain
collections or partial collections are held offsite and must be ordered by Wednesday
for delivery on the subsequent Friday. Wheelchair access. Pencils only; laptops
permitted. Photocopying available for a fee, with restrictions for age and condition
of material and for copyright. Digital photography permitted with the same
restrictions – no fee applies. Library website carries information on exhibitions
programme. Published histories of the library include, *The National Library of
Ireland: One Hundred and Twenty Five Years* (Dublin, 2002); Noel Kissane (ed.),
Treasures from the National Library of Ireland (Drogheda, 1994); Noel Kissane, *The
National Library of Ireland* (Dublin, 1984), vol. 42 of Irish Heritage series; Patrick
Henchy, *The National Library of Ireland, 1941–1976* (Dublin, 1986) and Gerard
Long, 'The Foundation of the National Library of Ireland, 1836–1877', in *Long
Room* 36 (1991), 41–58. A full listing of the Library's publications can be found on
website. Online catalogue holds records of greater part of printed books collection;
prints, drawings and photographs (some 35,000 of which have digitised images
attached); and manuscripts catalogued since 1990. The online *Sources* database
contains over 180,000 catalogue records for Irish manuscripts, and for articles in Irish
periodicals, including the National Library's manuscripts catalogued up to the 1980s.
Also online are detailed special lists of some 170 manuscript collections (including 60
landed estate archives), indexes to a number of key photographic collections and the
newspaper database, listing the Library's newspaper holdings. In 2004, the inaugural
event in library's new exhibition area was the acclaimed *James Joyce and Ulysses at the
National Library of Ireland*. It is succeeded by *Yeats: The Life and Work of William
Butler Yeats*, which can also be visited online. The multimedia exhibition, *Discover
Your National Library*, has a rotating schedule of linked temporary exhibitions,
drawing on the riches of our collections and is located at 2 Kildare Street and online.

CONTACT
Fiona Ross, Director
Katherine McSharry, Head of Services
Catherine Fahy, Keeper – Printed Collections
Colette O'Flaherty, Keeper – Archival Collections and Chief Herald
Elizabeth Kirwan, Curator – National Photographic Archive

DESCRIPTION
The National Library is Ireland's major public research library and aims to collect, preserve, promote and make accessible the documentary and intellectual record of the life of Ireland and to contribute to the provision of access to the larger universe of recorded knowledge. To this end it seeks to build a comprehensive collection documenting the history and culture and life of Ireland. The Library's holdings constitute the most outstanding collection of Irish documentary material in the world.

In 1943, the Library took responsibility on behalf of the State for matters relating to heraldry in Ireland. The Office of the Chief Herald of Ireland, formerly the Office of the Ulster King of Arms, has functioned as part of the Library since that date.

Since 1998, the Library's photographic collections have been housed in the National Photographic Archive in the Temple Bar area of Dublin. In 2004, a new exhibition facility in the main Kildare Street building was opened to the public, together with a café and seminar room.

HOLDINGS
The National Library houses a collection of some 1,000,000 printed books, including pamphlets; approximately 63,000 linear feet of manuscripts; some 150,000 maps, either in print or manuscript form; about 2,500 current periodical titles; around 10,000 reels of microforms; 300 current newspaper titles, plus complete files of many non-current titles; over four million photographs, held in the National Photographic Archive; and some 90,000 prints and drawings. Library collections focus on Irish history and society, including the Irish diaspora. Major collections are described in detail on the Library website. These include numerous literary manuscript collections, such as the papers of William Butler Yeats, the James Joyce collection, the papers of Roddy Doyle, Brian Friel, Edna O'Brien, Sean O'Casey and Colm Tóibín, and most recently the Seamus Heaney literary archive. The Library's history holdings are second to none and include the papers of a number of family estates dating back as far as the sixteenth century. Among the more notable of the landed estate archives are: Castletown (County Laois), Clements (Leitrim and Donegal), Clonbrock (Galway), Coolattin (Wicklow), De Vesci (Laois), Doneraile (Cork), Headford (Meath), Inchiquin (Clare), Lismore (Waterford), Monteagle (Limerick), O'Hara (Sligo), Ormond (Tipperary and Kilkenny), Powerscourt (Wicklow), Prior-Wandesforde (Kilkenny), Wicklow (Wicklow) and Leslie (Monaghan). Estate archives contain the records of estate administration by landlords and their agents and generally include leases, rentals, accounts, correspondence and maps.

Of special genealogical interest are the microfilm copies of almost all Catholic parish registers from their respective start dates to 1880. The list of parish registers on microfilm can be consulted on the website. The Library does not provide copies of, or transcriptions from, registers but readers may use the self-service facilities. Original registers are generally in the custody of the parish priest. Also of interest to genealogists are the holdings of newspapers, trade and social directories, and many published works of family and local history. Other relevant material includes the annual printed Army Lists, Royal Irish Constabulary publications, and various other records of trades and professions. As research progresses, the appendices to nineteenth century parliamentary reports may prove useful and, of course, the archives of the former landed estates are of unique value as genealogical and local studies sources. The Library also offers a range of online services including access to a number of subscription websites on the topics of genealogy, history and literature. The Library's Genealogy Service is designed to assist those who wish to research their family history in Ireland and is available free of charge to all personal callers to the Library. The service is operated by experienced staff who will advise on research methodology and sources. Guides to using the Library's genealogical resources, especially for the novice genealogist, are available on the website.

The Office of the Chief Herald (formerly the Office of the Ulster King of Arms) became part of the Library in 1943. The Chief Herald has responsibility for the granting and confirming of coats of arms to individuals and corporate bodies. All arms granted are recorded in the Register of Arms, maintained since the foundation of the Office in 1552. Information regarding the application process leading to a Grant or Confirmation of Arms can be obtained by contacting the Office of the Chief Herald. The archives of the Office of the Ulster King of Arms, including a large collection of Irish heraldic and genealogical manuscripts, are held as a distinct collection – the Genealogical Office or G.O. Manuscripts.

The National Photographic Archive houses some 4.5m photographs, most of which are Irish, dating from the 1840s to the present. The oldest photographs in the collection are from the collections of wealthy amateurs, while the late nineteenth and twentieth century holdings were generated largely by commercial firms.

Photographic formats include daguerreotypes, ambrotypes, tintypes, stereoscopic pairs, glass plate negatives, various formats of prints, 4x5 inch and 2x2 inch negatives, and also albums. The bulk of the subject matter ranges from portraits to topographical views, nineteenth century tourist views, and to twentieth century photojournalism. The Independent Newspapers (Ireland) Collection (1912–97), a gift, comprises the largest collection at approximately 4.3m items. Other large photo collections include the Lawrence, Poole, Eason and Valentine collections, created by the postcard and portrait studios that operated in the towns and cities of Ireland at the turn of the twentieth century. The Clonbrock collection of some 3,500 glass plate negatives from 1860 to 1930 provides an important record of life on a landed estate. The Keogh collection (330 glass plate negatives) includes important images of political figures and events in Dublin during the period 1915–30. Other notable collections include Morgan (aerial photographs of Ireland during the mid-1950s), Wiltshire (Dublin 1951–70), O'Dea (Irish railways 1937–66), and Clarke (Dublin 1897–1904).

LOCATION
National Library of Ireland/Office of the Chief Herald
Dublin city centre, adjacent to Leinster House (the seat of the Irish parliament) and to the National Museum of Ireland, close to Trinity College Dublin.

National Photographic Archive
In the Temple Bar area of Dublin, close to the Gallery of Photography, the Irish Film Institute, the Dublin Institute of Technology School of Photography, and Filmbase. Download http://dublinculturetrail.ie for a live GPS-activated map.

NATIONAL MUSEUM OF IRELAND

Museum of Country Life, Turlough Park
CASTLEBAR, COUNTY MAYO
Ireland

Museum of Decorative Arts and History, Collins Barracks, Benburb Street
DUBLIN 7

Museum of Archaeology, Kildare Street
DUBLIN 2

Museum of Natural History, Merrion Street
DUBLIN 2

Castlebar site
TELEPHONE: (094) 903 1755; FAX: (094) 903 1628
E-mail: tpark@museum.ie
Website: www.museum.ie

Dublin sites
TELEPHONE: (01) 677 7444; FAX: (01) 677 7450
E-mail: marketing@museum.ie
Website: www.museum.ie

HOURS
Museums (all): Tu–Sa, 10:00–17:00; Su, 14:00–17:00; closed Monday (including
bank holidays), Good Friday, Christmas Day; for further information see
www.museum.ie
Archives: by appointment
Facebook: National Museum of Ireland
Twitter: NMIreland

ACCESS AND SERVICES
Access to archives by appointment only. Contact Archivist or Librarian. Access to or
information on the collections may be made by appointment using the 'Contact us'
facility on the Museum's website www.museum.ie. Events and activities for people of
all ages. Admission for self-guided visits free; public guided tours available – for
more information see www.museum.ie; Groups must book tours in advance. Rates
for Dublin sites available from the Education and Outreach Department. Bookings
office: opening hours: Tu–F, 10:00–13:00. Castlebar site: telephone (094) 903 1751,
fax (094) 903 1498, e-mail educationtph@museum.ie; Dublin sites: telephone (01)
648 6453, fax (01) 679 1025, e-mail bookings@museum.ie. For information on
current and forthcoming temporary exhibitions contact the Marketing Department
(details above). For Castlebar site, telephone (094) 903 1773; fax (094) 903 1583.

WHEELCHAIR ACCESS
Collins Barracks and Turlough Park are fully wheelchair accessible.
Kildare Street – Ground floor exhibitions, shop, café and toilets are wheelchair
accessible.
Merrion Street – Ground floor exhibitions and toilet are wheelchair accessible.

CONTACT
Librarian for access to archives; marketing for all other enquiries. For collections, use the 'Contact us' facility on the Museum's website.

DESCRIPTION
The National Museum of Ireland houses the nation's artefacts dating back to 7,000 BC. The museum is based in four sites as outlined below.

National Museum of Ireland – Decorative Arts and History
Collins Barracks could be said to be the National Museum of Ireland's largest Irish artefact, having had a unique history all its own in another life. It now completes the picture for the National Museum in Dublin and joins the two already famous buildings in the museum's possession. On display are silver, ceramics, glassware, weaponry, furniture, folklife, clothing, jewellery, coins and medals. All of these are displayed with imagination in innovative and contemporary galleries, which entice the visitor to go further, look harder and examine more closely.

Don't miss the *Curator's Choice* exhibition where, amongst other treasures, there is an ancient Japanese ceremonial bell, which dates back over 2000 years. *What's in Store?* gives you the chance to get behind the scenes and explore a working museum collection. Over 16,000 artefacts are on display in this fantastic visible storage area, which allows you access to the reserve collections for the first time in the history of the National Museum. The double-height *Out of Storage* gallery also provides a fascinating opportunity to view artefacts that were previously held in storage.

Other new approaches to exhibiting major collections in these magnificent buildings include the permanent exhibitions *Irish Silver, Irish Period Furniture, The Way We Wore – 250 Years of Irish Clothing & Jewellery*, and *Airgead – A Thousand Years of Irish Coins & Currency*. While you're with us in Collins Barracks, come and see the work of one of the most influential designers and architects of the twentieth century, Irish-born *Eileen Gray* and *The Easter Rising: Understanding 1916* exhibition, which examines the decade of disturbance between 1913 and 1923, from the Dublin Lockout, through the Easter Rising to the end of the Civil War. The *Soldiers & Chiefs* exhibition traces Ireland's military history from 1550 into the twenty-first century. Original artefacts, such as the Stokes Tapastry, letters, replicas and interactives show how soldiering and war have affected the lives of Irish people over the centuries. Broken down into three themes, Soldiers & Chiefs looks at Irish soldiers at home, Irish soldiers abroad, and Irish soldiers in the twenty-first century. For information on temporary exhibitions see www.museum.ie.

National Museum of Ireland – Natural History
Opened in 1857 as the museum of the Royal Dublin Society, the Natural History Museum has developed as a cabinet style zoological museum with animals from all over the world. Over 150 Years later exhibitions in this museum have changed little, adding to the charm and rarity of this national treasure.

Recent conservation work has improved access for visitors and provided new learning opportunities, including the Discovery Zone where visitors can handle taxidermy and open drawers to see what is lurking inside. The Reading Area at first floor level is a great place to rest and settle down with a good book. The traditional exhibition style and furnishings are unchanged. Familiar favourites include skeletons of 11,000 year old giant deer, Spoticus the giraffe and whale skeletons suspended from the roof. Exhibits cover the *Irish Fauna* at ground floor level and *Mammals of the World* on the first floor. The history of collecting extends over two centuries has resulted in a rich variety of animals, many of which are now endangered or extinct. We apologise that the upper levels of the museum are not accessible at present. This requires funding for a conservation and access plan. For further information see www.museum.ie.

National Museum of Ireland – Archaeology
Opened in 1890, the National Museum of Ireland – Archaeology, Kildare Street displays artefacts dating from 7000 BC to the twentieth century.

The Irish archaeological collections include *The Treasury*, featuring outstanding examples of Celtic and Medieval art such as the famous Ardagh Chalice, the Tara Brooch and the Derrynaflan Hoard. Within the exhibition the second gallery is devoted to an early medieval Book of Psalms known as the Faddan More Psalter. This manuscript, which dates to approximately AD 800, was discovered by chance in a Co. Tipperary bog in 2006. *Ór – Ireland's Gold* features the finest collection of prehistoric gold artefacts in Europe, while *Prehistoric Ireland* introduces the visitor to the everyday culture of prehistory. *Viking Age Ireland* focuses on Irish archaeology from 800–1200 AD. *Medieval Ireland 1150–1550* explores life in later medieval Ireland: meet the nobles who go to war, the common people who work and the clergy who pray in galleries entitled 'Power', 'Work' and 'Prayer'.

The building is also home to the exhibition *Ancient Egypt*, which explores this mysterious and multi-faceted civilisation.

Kingship & Sacrifice is a fascinating exhibition centred on a number of recently-found bog bodies of Iron Age date. Displayed along with other bog finds from the Museum's collections, it offers you an opportunity to come 'face to face' with your ancient ancestors.

National Museum of Ireland – Country Life
Set in modern exhibition Galleries in the spectacular grounds of Turlough Park House and surrounded by magnificent gardens and artificial lake (known as a Turlough in Irish), visitors are invited to experience traditions of rural life throughout Ireland from 1850–1950 in the award-winning Museum of Country Life.

Fascinating artefacts, which are drawn from the National Folklife Collection, deal with domestic life, agriculture, fishing and hunting, clothing and textiles, furniture and fittings, trades and crafts, transport, calendar customs, leisure and religion. Interactive displays and screens, actual video footage of traditions we are fast losing are featured alongside handcrafted harvest knots and wickerwork, spinning wheels and boats, clothing and artefacts from the islands and hand operated machinery our grandparents used.

Explore the Museum's collections through the Education and Outreach programmes, which include guided tours, workshops and demonstrations, 'Behind the Scenes' tours, lectures, handling sessions plus activity sheets for children and families. Outreach visits can be arranged through the Education and Outreach Department.

The Irish Farmers' Association Millennium Library and Archive is located in Turlough Park House and is a centre for study and research for national and international scholars.

HOLDINGS
As a designated place of deposit under the National Archives Act (1986), the archives house the official historical papers of the National Museum of Ireland, 1877 to present and relevant collections of private papers.
The library collection reflects the work of the curatorial divisions of the Museum and also holds a comprehensive collection of exhibition catalogues, Irish auction catalogues and the annual reports of other museums and cultural institutions.

LOCATION
The National Museum of Ireland – Country Life is located eight kilometres east of Castlebar on the N5.
The National Museum of Ireland – Decorative Arts and History can be found three kilometres west of Dublin city centre along the north quays.
The National Museum of Ireland – Archaeology is in the city centre, near Leinster House (the seat of the Irish parliament).
The National Museum of Ireland – Natural History is located in Dublin city centre, parallel to Kildare Street.

NATIONAL PHOTOGRAPHIC ARCHIVE
See under NATIONAL LIBRARY OF IRELAND

NATIONAL UNIVERSITY OF IRELAND, DUBLIN
See UNIVERSITY COLLEGE DUBLIN

Note: UCD is part of the National University of Ireland system, but it petitioned the Irish government successfully to keep its familiar name, i.e. UCD, so its full title is now University College Dublin, National University of Ireland.

OFFICE OF THE CHIEF HERALD/GENEALOGICAL OFFICE
See under NATIONAL LIBRARY OF IRELAND

ORDNANCE SURVEY OF IRELAND
Note: Archives transferred to NATIONAL ARCHIVES OF IRELAND, Dublin

PEARSE STREET LIBRARY
See DUBLIN AND IRISH COLLECTIONS, Dublin

POETRY IRELAND/ÉIGSE ÉIREANN

32 Kildare St
DUBLIN 2
Ireland

TELEPHONE: (01) 678 9815; FAX: (01) 678 9782
E-mail: poetry@iol.ie
Website: www.poetryireland.ie

HOURS
For Library: By appointment only. Normal Office hours.

ACCESS AND SERVICES
Members and Visitors welcome. Advance notice and ID required. No fees; laptops permitted.

CONTACT
Joseph Woods, Director

DESCRIPTION
Library sponsored by Poetry Ireland, a not for profit organisation founded to promote and support poets and poetry in Ireland. Poetry Ireland aims to provide as much information and resources for both new and established poets as possible. It covers everything from assessments and writers workshops to readings, copyright and general enquiries. It also provides a countrywide reading programme and administers the Writers in Schools, Writers in Residence and Writers in Libraries Schemes.

HOLDINGS
Poetry Ireland owns the Austin Clarke Collection, consisting of more than 5,000 volumes of poetry, prose, criticism and drama, most of which came from the poet's private library. The Clarke Collection is now housed at UCD Special Collections on long term loan. The Poetry Ireland Library also contains a significant amount of material that belonged to Irish poet and UCD lecturer John Jordan, and to Dutch critic Tanya Touwen. The Jordan Collection of some 2,000 volumes of poetry, prose, criticism and fiction is also housed in Special Collections, UCD. A full listing of these collections is available through the Poetry Ireland website and UCD website. Visitors to these collections can be refered via Poetry Ireland. Poetry Ireland retains a small working library of some 3,000 volumes of poetry books, anthologies and journals that is available to the public for research and reading purposes by appointment. In addition, the Library continues to receive small collections, including the Angela Greene Collection and the Anthony O'Neill collection.

LOCATION
City centre, near the National Library of Ireland and the National Museum of Ireland.

THE QUAKER LIBRARY
See HISTORICAL LIBRARY, RELIGIOUS SOCIETY OF FRIENDS, Dublin

REGISTRY OF DEEDS

Henrietta Street
DUBLIN 1
Ireland

TELEPHONE (01) 670 7500; Fax (01) 871 6536
E-mail: bernie.casey@prai.ie
Website: www.webmaster@prai.ie

Note: *See also* LAND REGISTRY OFFICES:
Chancery Street, Dublin 7; telephone (01) 670 7500
Cork Road, Waterford; telephone (01) 670 7500
Golf Links Road, Roscommon; telephone (01) 670 7500

HOURS:
M–F, 10:00–16:30

ACCESS AND SERVICES
Visitors welcome. Registry provides a variety of services for the public, including registration of deeds, searching facilities (official searches/public searches), copy facilities, copy memorial and genealogical services. In order to carry out a search, the Registry requires:

Names of all parties to the Deed
Date of Deed
The situation of the premises, e.g. Street or Townland and location, e.g. Town or County

Fees for the service:

Official Search: €20.00 for each name, for each property, for each county for each period of 10 years or part thereof.
Search by members of the public: €2.00 for each name, for each county, for each period of 10 years or part thereof.
Copy Memorial/Copy Application Form: €20.00.
General Search: No fee for members of the public attending the office against all indexes prior to 1969. After 1970, records are Online.
Plain copy of microfilm of memorial/application form €1.00 per page.

CONTACT
Bernie Casey. E-mail: bernie.casey@prai.ie

DESCRIPTION
The Registry of Deeds provides a system of voluntary registration of deeds and conveyances dating back to 1708 affecting land. The system is based on a grantors' index, e.g. persons who dispose of an interest in a property. In the case of property disposed after death, the deceased's executor is the grantor and the executor's name and not the name of the deceased person will appear in the names index. A deed and memorial (synopsis of deed) is required for registration. Once registered, the deed is returned to the lodging party and the memorial is retained by the Registry of Deeds. Only memorials/application forms are retained by this Registry. Maps are not retained by the Registry of Deeds.

HOLDINGS
Documents retained in the Registry of Deeds include: memorials (1708–30/04/2008
(microfilmed 1930–present), transcripts (1708–1960, incomplete), abstracts
(1833–1969), names index or index of grantors and lands index (1708–1946). A
memorial is the synopsis of an original deed, with information on the names of all
parties to the deed, location of the property and details of the type of transaction. A
transcript is the handwritten/typed copy of the memorial. An abstract is the
summary of the memorial, containing the name of the grantor, grantee, description
of property and type of deed. The names index is the index of names of the persons
who have disposed of an interest in the property. The lands index is an index of all
transactions compiled in order of the names of the townland/street affected. On
01/05/2008 Application Forms replaced memorials and contain the lodging party,
Grantor, Grantee and description of property.

LOCATION
King's Inns, just off Bolton Street, almost directly opposite Dublin Institute of
Technology Bolton Street, on the north side of the Liffey, west of Parnell Square.
The registry can also be approached via Constitution Hill, opposite Broadstone Bus
Garage. The Luas red line stops at the Four Courts, approximately 600 metres away
via Church Street.

REPRESENTATIVE CHURCH BODY LIBRARY

Braemor Park, Churchtown
DUBLIN 14
Ireland

TELEPHONE: (01) 492 3979; FAX: (01) 492 4770
E-mail: library@ireland.anglican.org
Website: www.library.ireland.anglican.org

HOURS
M–F, 09:30–13:00, 14:00–17:00

ACCESS AND SERVICES
Visitors welcome, but advance notice preferred. No disabled access facilities. Laptops
permitted; pencils only. Fees for photocopying. Of special genealogical and historical
interest are a series of nine parish registers published by the library. These include:
registers edited by Raymond Refaussé for the Parish of St Thomas, Dublin, 1750–91
and for Church of St Thomas, Lisnagarvey, County Antrim, 1637–46; by Colin
Thomas for the Cathedral Church of St Columb, Derry, 1703–32 and 1732–75; by
Susan Hood for the Holy Trinity Church, Cork, 1643–68; by James Mills for the
Parish of St John the Evangelist, Dublin, 1619–99 (the oldest extant parish registers
in Ireland); by Suzanne Pegley for the Parish of Leixlip, County Kildare, 1667–1778;
by Herbert Wood for the Parish of St Catherine, Dublin, 1636–1715; and by Brigid
Clesham for the Parish of St Nicholas, Galway, 1792–1840; by Raymond Gillespie
& Alison O'Keeffe for the Parish of Shankill, Belfast, 1745–61; by J.H. Bernard &
Raymond Refaussé for St Patrick's Cathdral, Dulbin, 1677–1869; by Alicia St Leger
for St Fin Barre's Cathedral, Cork, 1753–1804. Also of interest: Raymond Refaussé
(ed.) *A Library on the Move: Twenty-Five Years of the Representative Church Body
Library in Churchtown* (1995); *A Handlist of Church of Ireland Parish Registers in the
Representative Church Body Library* (1996); and *A Handlist of Church of Ireland Vestry*

Minute Books in the Representative Church Body Library (1996). In the Texts and Calendars series, published by Four Courts Press in association with the Representative Church Body Library, there are five titles currently available: Raymond Gillespie (ed.), *The Vestry Records of the Parish of St John the Evangelist, Dublin, 1595–1658*; Raymond Gillespie (ed.), *The Vestry Records of the Parishes of St Catherine and St James, Dublin, 1657–1692*; Maighread Ni Mhurchadha (ed.), *The Vestry Records of the United Parishs of Finglas, St Margaret's, Artane and the Ward, 1657–1758*: Adrian Empy (ed.), *Te Proctors' Accounts of the Parish Church of St Werburgh, Dublin, 1481–1627*;W.J.R. Wallace (ed.), *The Vestry Records of the Parishes of St Bride, St Michael le Pole and St Stephen, 1662–1742* For price and ordering information, contact Representative Church Body Library by mail, e-mail, phone or fax.

CONTACT
Raymond Refaussé, Librarian and Archivist

DESCRIPTION
The library was founded in 1931 and has been developed as the theological and reference library of the Church of Ireland and as the Church of Ireland's principal repository for its archives and manuscripts. It seeks to collect any printed, archival and manuscript material that is produced by or related to the Church of Ireland. The library is owned and funded by the Church of Ireland and is managed by the Library and Archives Committee of the Representative Church Body, which is the perpetual trustee for the real and movable property of the Church of Ireland.

HOLDINGS
The library houses some 40,000 volumes, focusing on theology and history, plus architectural records, archives and manuscripts, microforms, pamphlets, photographs and recordings. Major archival collections include: Church of Ireland archives chiefly for the Republic of Ireland, representing more than 1030 parishes, mainly in Counties Carlow, Clare, Cork, Dublin, Galway, Kerry, Kildare, Kilkenny, Mayo, Meath, Westmeath and Wicklow; the records of 20 dioceses; the records of 20 cathedrals, especially Christ Church and St Patrick's in Dublin, St Canice's in Kilkenny and St Brigid's in Kildare. The archives also house medieval and early modern manuscripts, the records of the General Synod and the Representative Church Body, 1870–present, and the records of societies and organisations related to the Church of Ireland including schools, educational societies, missionary organisations and clerical groups from the eighteenth to the twentieth century. In addition, the collection includes miscellaneous ecclesiastical manuscripts, such as the papers of bishops, clergy and laity, correspondence, diaries, research notes and writings, scrapbooks, photographs and transcripts of non-extant Church of Ireland records from the seventeenth to the twentieth century. Also of interest are: the microfilms of church records in other custodies from the seventeenth to the twentieth centuries; photographs of Church buildings, clergy, laity and church plate; and an oral history collection. *See also* the NATIONAL ARCHIVES OF IRELAND, Dublin, and the Public Record Office of Northern Ireland, Belfast, for additional parish registers. Some original parish records are still in the custody of local clergy.

LOCATION
Adjacent to the Church of Ireland Theological Institute in Churchtown in the southern suburbs of Dublin. Take bus 14 from D'Olier Street (city centre) to Mount Carmel Hospital (Braemor Park). The library is opposite 33 Braemor Park.

ROYAL COLLEGE OF PHYSICIANS OF IRELAND
See HERITAGE CENTRE, ROYAL COLLEGE OF PHYSICIANS OF IRELAND,
Dublin

ROYAL DUBLIN SOCIETY LIBRARY
Ballsbridge
DUBLIN 4
Ireland

TELEPHONE: (01) 668 0866; FAX: (01) 660 4014
E-mail: library@rds.ie
Website: www.rds.ie

HOURS
Reading area and issue desk: M, Tu, F; 10:00–17:00; W, Th, 10:00–18:00; closed
public and bank holidays and Christmas–New Year period.

ACCESS AND SERVICES
A facility for Members of the Society with access provided to *Bona fide* researchers
by appointment. Membership of the Society is open to all, subject to normal
application and election procedures. Annual fee structure applies, with local, regional
and overseas rates.

A 'Guest Readers Ticket' is available for those who need long-term access to the
collections, for which a nominal charge applies. A letter of introduction acceptable
to the Library Director must first be provided. If access to one or two items over one
or two visits is required, no charge will be levied.

Library catalogue and further details online at: www.rds.ie/library. Card
catalogue exists for scientific publications. Photocopying service operates through
library desk. Laptops permitted and free WIFI available.

CONTACT
Joanna Quinn, Foundation and Library Director. Tel.: (01) 240 7299;   e-
mail: joanna.quinn@rds.ie.
Gerard Whelan, Librarian. Tel.: (01) 240 7256; E-mail: gerard.whelan@rds.ie
Natasha Serne, Special Collections Cataloguer. Tel.: (01) 240 7288;
e-mail: natasha.serne@rds.ie
Library Desk, Tel.: (01) 240 7254; e-mail: librarydesk@rds.ie

DESCRIPTION
The Dublin Society was founded in 1731 (it became 'Royal' in 1820) for the
improvement of 'husbandry' (agriculture), 'manufactures' and other 'useful arts and
sciences'. One of the newly formed society's first acts was to establish a library. This
became one of the most significant collections in Ireland, going on to form the
nucleus of the National Library of Ireland collection when that body was established
in 1877. The Society retained many of its scientific collections of books and
journals, which it continued to collect. The science collection developed through a
publication exchange programme with many institutions and like minded societies
across the world.

HOLDINGS
The general library contains over 200,000 volumes including over 4,000 relating to Ireland, many of them old and rare. There are 6,000 works and pamphlets on all branches of agricultural science including some 1,500 items of equestrian interest. These works form one of the most important collections on agriculture in the country. Of special research interest, the library contains the records of the Royal Dublin Society. These are in manuscript form dating from its foundation and in printed annual volumes since 1764. The diverse activities and interests the Society pursued are recorded through the minutes of its meetings and its publications. The society acted as an intermediary for distributing funds that were awarded as premiums, provided by the Irish Parliament prior to the Act of Union (1801) and afterwards from the British Parliament. It was through the Society's many endeavours that leading institutions of the State came into being, including the National Museum, the National Museum of Natural History, the Botanic Gardens, the National Veterinary College, the National Library and the National College of Art and Design.

LOCATION
Royal Dublin Society headquarters is in Ballsbridge Dublin 4, approximately 2 miles south east of Dublin city centre, on the Merrion Road. The Library is accessed through the members' entrance. Visitors can travel on buses 4, 7, 8, 45, 47. Two DART stations (Lansdowne Road and Sandymount) are within a ten to fifteen minute walk of the RDS.

ROYAL IRISH ACADEMY

19 Dawson Street
DUBLIN 2
Ireland

TELEPHONE: (01) 676 2570/4222; FAX: (01) 676 2346
E-mail: library@ria.ie
Website: www.ria.ie

HOURS
M–Th, 10:00–17:30; F, 10:00–17:00; closed public and bank holidays, Easter Tuesday, Christmas–New Year period and two weeks in May/June for cleaning and checking of stock.

ACCESS AND SERVICES
See www.ria.ie/library/access—services.aspx
Visitors welcome; registration required. Wheelchair accessible. Registration forms available online at www.ria.ie/library/catalogue/open or can be requested by telephone, fax, post or e-mail. Completed forms accompanied by a letter of introduction from an Academy member or the faculty of a university together with valid ID, student card or passport should be presented. Reader's ticket issued for initial period of one year on payment of €15. Holders of a valid ALCID (Academic Libraries Cooperating in Ireland) card may gain automatic access to the library and are not required to pay a fee. Laptops permitted; pencils only. Gloves issued for use of vellum manuscripts, drawings and rare items. Library offers ongoing exhibitions

programme and participates in Academy's celebrated publications and lecture programmes. Access to exhibitions free of charge.

Entire print collection catalogued online. Five online catalogues accessible on website are: Main (books, articles, maps); Manuscripts; Periodicals; Prints, Drawings and Artefacts; Photographs. *Catalogue of Irish Manuscripts in the Royal Irish Academy* (28 fascicles, 1926–70) available for purchase from the Dublin Institute for Advanced Studies.

Groups are welcome for tours and classes (contact library@ria.ie).

CONTACT
Siobhán Fitzpatrick, Librarian. E-mail: s.fitzpatrick@ria.ie
Bernadette Cunningham, Deputy Librarian. E-mail: b.cunningham@ria.ie
Petra Schnabel, Deputy Librarian. E-mail: p.schnabel@ria.ie

DESCRIPTION
The Royal Irish Academy was founded in 1785 as a society for 'promoting the study of science, polite literature and antiquities'. Anchored by its celebrated library, the Academy promotes the sciences and the humanities through publications, lectures, conferences and cooperative programmes with other institutions. Currently, for example, it is working with the Department of Foreign Affairs on the multi-volume publication of a major series of historical documents charting the development of Irish diplomacy and foreign policy since 1919. The Royal Irish Academy also sponsors research on the *Irish Historic Towns Atlas*, the *Dictionary of Medieval Latin from Celtic Sources*, the *Dictionary of Irish Biography* and *Foclóir na Nua-Ghaeilge*. For a downloadable tour of the Academy and the library click *Take a tour* on the homepage www.ria.ie or www.ria.ie/library/inside-no—19-dawson-street.aspx.

HOLDINGS
The library houses an extraordinary manuscript and book collection, plus important holdings of artefacts, drawings, journals (approximately 7,000 titles), maps, pamphlets (50,000), photographs, antiquarian drawings, portraits and recordings. Its collection of over 2,000 manuscripts includes many of the oldest and most treasured original documents of Irish cultural history. These include the *Cathach*, or *Psalter of St Columba*, the oldest surviving Irish manuscript, written in Latin *c.* 560–630 AD; the *Stowe Missal*, the oldest extant mass book of the early Irish Church, *c.* 792–803 AD; the *Book of the Dun Cow*, the oldest extant literary manuscript in the Irish language, before 1106 AD; and the *Annals of the Four Masters*, written between 1632 and 1636 in Irish, chronicling Irish history from earliest times to 1616. Over 60 of the most important early Irish manuscripts are accessible online via the Irish Script On Screen website with which the Academy library is cooperating on an ongoing basis (www.isos.dias.ie). The library houses the largest collection of Irish language manuscripts anywhere, plus important medieval and early modern manuscripts in Latin, French and English. It contains important modern manuscript material. Of especial interest are the nineteenth-century Ordnance Survey collections; the De La Ponce papers relating to members of the Irish Brigade in France, and important genealogical papers including those of Marquess MacSwiney and H.A.S. Upton. The library also houses the papers of individual members, including those of its founder, Lord Charlemont. These collections are augmented by continuing donations and by purchase as funds permit. Acquisitions since 2000 include the extensive Dublin Unitarian Church archive; the Caldwell papers (seventeenth–nineteenth century) relating to the family of Andrew Caldwell (1733–1808), MP and Academy member;

Charlemont correspondence relating to the Volunteers in Armagh (1780s–1790s), and a music manuscript connected with Tom Moore, poet, author and composer, whose library collection was donated to the Academy in 1855. The Printed Book Collection of more than 100,000 volumes includes the 35,000 item Charles Haliday Pamphlet Collection, the Celtic Studies library of Osborn Bergin, Rev Richard Kirwan's Collection of early scientific works, a collection of early Irish imprints, over 7,000 antiquarian drawings, and an Irish and international journal collection. The library is constantly augmenting the documentation of the collections in order to facilitate researchers. Collection descriptions in respect of manuscripts, drawings and print and photographic collections are regularly uploaded to the Special Collections feature on the website www.ria.ie/library/special-collections.aspx. Collection-level descriptions are also input to the RASCAL database (www.rascal.ie). Thumbnails of the antiquarian drawings are accessible on the Prints, Drawings and Artefacts catalogue.

Much of the cataloguing and conservation programme was funded by an Atlantic Philanthropies grant (2002), by Heritage Council grants, the Esmé Mitchell Trust and private funders.

The Doegen Irish dialect recordings (1928–31) were digitised and are accessible at http://dho.ie/doegen, a PRTLI IV-funded project. These recordings are also accessible on Europeana (www.europeana.eu/portal/) through which other collections are being made available, e.g. T.J. Westropp's photographs of Dublin after the 1916 Rebellion – these are also accessible on the library's Photographs catalogue. The library manages the Irish History Online project, providing an important resource for historians (http://irishhistoryonline.ie/).

SELECT BIBLIOGRAPHY
Bernadette Cunningham and Siobhán Fitzpatrick (eds), *Treasures of the Royal Irish Academy library* (Dublin, 2009). ISBN: 978-1-904890-54-6; Bernadette Cunningham and Sarah Gearty, *Mapping urban Ireland: an exhibition of historical maps of Irish cities and towns, 3 August, 2010–20 May, 2011* (Dublin, 2010). ISBN: 978-1-904890-73-7; Sophie Evans, *From Cromwell to cholera: a history of Ireland from the pamphlet collection of Charles Haliday: an exhibition at the Royal Irish Academy, autumn 2011–spring 2012* (Dublin, 2011). ISBN: 978-1-904890-85-0; Siobhán Fitzpatrick (ed.), *My gentle harp: Moore's Irish melodies, 1808–2008* [exhibition at the Royal Irish Academy, 16 June–29 August, 2008] (Dublin, 2008). ISBN: 978-1-904890-52-2; Róisín Jones and Martin Steer (eds), *Darwin, Praeger and the Clare Island Surveys* [exhibition at the Royal Irish Academy, 23 July–14 December, 2009] (Dublin, 2009). ISBN: 978-1-904890-560.

LOCATION
Nestled between St Ann's Church and the Mansion House (the Lord Mayor's residence) on Dawson Street, one block west of the National Library of Ireland, close to the north side of St Stephen's Green.

ROYAL SOCIETY OF ANTIQUARIES OF IRELAND

63 Merrion Square
DUBLIN 2
Ireland

TELEPHONE: (01) 676 1749.
E-mail: rsai@rsai.ie
Website: www.rsai.ie

HOURS
M–F, 10:00–12:00, 14:00–16:30; closed Christmas–New Year period, Easter period
and bank holidays

ACCESS AND SERVICES
Visitors welcome, but advance notice appreciated. Staff happy to answer queries by
post or e-mail. No disabled access facilities. Wifi available; laptops permitted; pencils
only. Special permission from council to view Du Noyer sketches but not to view
photograph copies and catalogue of Du Noyer collection. Photocopies cost 25–35c
per sheet, post extra. The society publishes the *Journal of the Royal Society of
Antiquaries of Ireland*, free to members, otherwise cost varies with subscription rate
annually (contact office for details). The lecture theatre, garden and function rooms
with a self catering kitchen are available for hire (contact office for details).

CONTACT
Donal Fenlon, Librarian. E-mail: library1@rsai.ie

DESCRIPTION
The society was founded in 1849 'to preserve, examine and illustrate all
Ancient Monuments and Memorials of the Arts, Manners and Customs of the past,
as connected with the Antiquities, Language, Literature and History of Ireland'. To
this end, it sponsors lectures, talks and excursions and publishes a journal. It also
maintains a research library, open to the public and free to members.

HOLDINGS
The library houses a collection of around 5000 books and pamphlets on Irish
history, see website for catalogue (www.rsai.ie click on library)
The main subjects covered are local history, Dublin history and Archaeology. It also
has a fine photographic collection with around 20000 scanned images, including a
photographic survey (mainly of archaeological sites of interest in Ireland but also UK
architecture, archaeology and some continental European images) done by members
during the period 1870–1910. A collection of glass slides called Darkest Dublin,
made during a survey of the poor areas of Dublin in 1913 is a part of the larger
photographic collection. Other important collections are around 3000 sketches by
Georges Du Noyer and manuscript notes by Elrington Ball for his History of
County Dublin. There are many historical and archaeological journals for most of
Ireland and many from the UK. The Society's journal is available to view online at
www.jstor.org. In addition there are papers of Leask, Roe, Lord Walter FitzGerald,
Elrington Ball and the archives of the RSAI. There are some sketch books of Graves,
Miller-Robertson collection and Coughlin collection of drawings. Also there is a
collection of gravestone rubbings done on cloth with charcoal. On closed access is a
run of archaeology journals from institutions and societies around Europe.

LOCATION
Merrion Square South, around 10 doors up from the Upper Mount Street end.

ST PATRICK'S COLLEGE – CREGAN LIBRARY
St Patrick's College, Drumcondra
DUBLIN 9
Ireland

TELEPHONE: (01) 884 2170
E-mail: info.library@spd.ie
Website: www.spd.dcu.ie/library

HOURS
Term time: M–Th, 10:00–22:00; F, 10:00–17:00; Sa, 10:00–13:00
Vacation period: M–F, 10:00–13:00, 14:00–17:00

ACCESS AND SERVICES
Members of the public wishing to read in library may do so on application at issue desk. Borrowing privileges not available. General enquiries should be made to information desk. St Patrick's College shares integrated online public access catalogue (OPAC) with Dublin City University and The Mater Dei Institute of Education, the first system in Ireland to provide full web search facilities in both English and Irish. Catalogues provide single search point for over 350,000 book titles. Photocopy cards of various values on sale in both library and resource centre and may be used in both places. Reader/printer available for reading and copying microfilm and microfiche. All special collections non-circulating and may be consulted only in library. Some collections, e.g. Belvedere House Library, may be visited only by arrangement with Librarian.

CONTACT
Orla Nic Aodha, Librarian. E-mail: orla.nicaodha@spd.dcu.ie

DESCRIPTION
St Patrick's College was founded in 1875. In 1883 it was officially recognised as a denominational teacher training college and in that year moved from 2 Drumcondra Road to the historic Belvedere House, whose core dates to the seventeenth century. The library building is mid-eighteenth century on its present campus. From its beginnings until 1999, the college was administered by the Vincentian community, a Roman Catholic religious order. It is now administered by a lay president. While St Patrick's College maintains an independent and separate identity, it has been a college of Dublin City University since 1993 and all its courses are accredited by DCU. Current enrolment is approximately 2,500 students.

HOLDINGS
The college library contains over 190,000 books and 550 journals as well as microfiche, microfilm and other materials. The collection is a balanced one for a humanities college, with particular strengths in Celtic and Irish languages and literature and in Irish history. Special collections include: Belvedere House Library, the old Vincentian community library, which includes collections of publications by former students and faculty members, some of whom are quite famous; the Dolmen Press and Three Candles Press Collections; a collection of pre-1880 publications;

rare children's books, including Irish, e.g. Patricia Lynch; the Padraic Colum Collection of printed material; the Gaelic League Collection, including letters written to Henry Morris, a member of the Gaelic League and a graduate of the college; the P.W. Joyce Collection (in development); and a small collection of books from the library of Fr Donal Cregan CM, a distinguished historical scholar, a president of the college (1957–76) and a leading innovator in Irish education of his time. The collection is housed in Belvedere House Library and the library is named in his honour. The library also boasts the largest collection of Irish textbooks in the nation, arguably its most important special collection. More recently the library has begun actively collecting Abbey Theatre plays.

Note: several of these special collections are currently uncatalogued.

The library hold a wide range of material in Irish and English from the eighteenth and nineteenth centuries including four Irish manuscripts. A full description of the contents of the manuscripts is available in Studia Hibernica Vol.1 1961. They are indexed as Lámhscríbhinní I, II, III, IV. They contain mostly religious or devotional material although also include other poems and prose texts. LS III was digitized by the Dublin Institute of Advanced Studies as part of the Irish Script on Screen (ISOS) project in 2011 and can be view online (www.isos.dias.ie). Work to digitize the remaining three is on-going.

LOCATION
On the N1, two miles north of the centre of Dublin City and nine miles south of Dublin Airport. The area is well serviced by public transport. Frequent buses from the city include 3, 11, 16 and 41. Drumcondra station is within walking distance. The college has good parking facilities.

TIERNAN MACBRIDE LIBRARY
See IRISH FILM ARCHIVE OF THE IRISH FILM INSTITUTE, Dublin

TRINITY COLLEGE LIBRARY

College Street
DUBLIN 2
Ireland

TELEPHONE: (01) 896 1657; FAX: (01) 896 3774
E-mail: consult staff directory on website
Website: www.tcd.ie/library

HOURS
Visitor areas (including Long Room and Book of Kells exhibition):
M–Sa, 09:30–17:00; Su (May–September), 09:30–16:30; Su (October–April) 12:00–16:30; bank holidays (October–April), 12:30–16:30
Reading Rooms: Consult website for details of opening hours
Department of Manuscripts: see separate entry below
Department of Early Printed Books and Special Collections: see separate entry below
Berkeley/Lecky/Ussher Library (Reading Rooms and collections for arts, humanities, social sciences, business, music and nursing): Consult website for opening hours
Hamilton Science and Engineering Library: Consult website for opening hours
Map Library: Consult website for opening hours

ACCESS AND SERVICES
Website provides details of services, access arrangements for visiting researches and
links to the catalogues. Included are details for the Library Shop and services
available for tourists. Library serves both heritage visitors and readers.

Heritage Visitors
Access to the Old Library exhibition area, Manuscripts Treasury and the Long Room
is open to the public on payment of an admission fee. The main chamber of the Old
Library, the Long Room, is nearly 65 metres in length and houses around 200,000
of the library's oldest books. In 1860 the roof was raised according to plans by
architects Deane and Woodward, to allow construction of the present barrel vaulted
ceiling and gallery bookcases. Marble busts are placed down either side. This
collection began in 1743 when 14 busts were commissioned from the sculptor Peter
Scheemakers. Other sculptors represented are Simon Vierpyl, Patrick Cunningham,
John van Nost and Louis Francois Roubiliac, whose bust of the writer Jonathan
Swift is one of the finest in the collection. The harp on exhibition, constructed from
oak and willow with brass strings, is the oldest to survive from Ireland and probably
dates from the fifteenth century. As an emblem of early bardic society, this is the
harp that appears on Irish coins. The attribution to Brian Boru, High King of
Ireland (d. 1014), is legendary. One of the dozen or so remaining copies of the 1916
Proclamation of the Irish Republic is on display.
     Changing exhibitions of printed books and manuscripts from the library's
collections are mounted in the Long Room. The *Book of Kells*, on display in the
Treasury, was written around the year 800 AD and is one of the most beautifully
illuminated manuscripts in the world. It contains the four gospels, preceded by
prefaces, summaries and canon tables or concordances of gospel passages. It is
written on vellum and contains a Latin text of the gospels in insular majuscule script
accompanied by magnificent and intricate whole pages of decoration with smaller
painted decorations appearing throughout the text. The manuscript has been on
display in the Old Library since the nineteenth century. Accompanying the *Book of
Kells* in the display are other manuscripts such as the *Book of Armagh*, the *Book of
Durrow*, the *Book of Mulling* and the *Book of Dimma*.
     The library shop offers a wide range of books, gifts and Trinity merchandise.

Reading Rooms
All members (staff and students) of the university are admitted to the Reading
Rooms on production of their Trinity College identity card. Other readers will be
admitted to use the library's collections (without borrowing rights) for study and
research provided they satisfy the conditions of one of the variety of schemes or cross
higher education institutional arrangements listed on the library's website or can
demonstrate that Trinity is a library of last resort for their material. During busy
periods access restrictions may apply. For instance, admissions may be confined to
Saturdays only. Access to the Special Collections Department (manuscripts and
maps) will normally only be permitted by prior arrangement with the heads of
departments concerned. If intending researchers are unclear about procedures, it
would be advisable to contact the library prior to visiting. *See* separate entries below
for Trinity College Library – Department of Early Printed Books and Trinity College
Library – Manuscripts Department.

CONTACT
Anne-Marie Diffley, Visitor Services. Telephone: (01) 896 2320; fax: (01) 896 2690
Jessie Kurtz, Acting Librarian
Trevor Peare, Keeper (Readers' Services)

DESCRIPTION
Trinity College, the single constituent college of the University of Dublin, was
founded by Queen Elizabeth I in 1592 and so celebrated its first quatercentenary in
1992. It is the oldest university in Ireland and one of the older universities of
Western Europe. Based on the general pattern of the ancient colleges at Oxford and
Cambridge, Trinity has a main campus extending over 40 acres in a unique site in
the heart of the city.

As a university library, the library serves the needs of the college's population of
15,000 undergraduate and postgraduate students and academic staff. As a research
library of international standing its rare and unique materials are consulted by
scholars from all parts of the world.

Several of the library buildings are architecturally significant: six are located on
the college campus. The Old Library, completed in 1732, contains the Department
of Manuscripts, the Department of Early Printed Books and Special Collections, as
well as the Long Room, the Library Shop, the Exhibition Gallery and Manuscripts
Treasury. The Berkeley/Lecky/Ussher complex (1967, 1974 and 2003) consists of
three units operating as a single library. The complex contains the main
administrative offices, the Reading Rooms and collections for arts, humanities, social
sciences, business and nursing as well as closed access stacks. The complex also
houses the Glucksman Map Library and Conservation Department.

HOLDINGS
The Library's history dates back to the establishment of the College in 1592. Today
it has five million printed volumes with extensive collections of journals, more than
half a million maps and very large collections of manuscripts and music reflecting
over four hundred years of academic development. More recently, it has established a
collection of 30,000 electronic journals and 250,000 electronic books. It is the
largest library in Ireland and has been a legal deposit library for Ireland and the
United Kingdom since 1801. The Library continues to add to its collections through
purchases, private donations, acquisitions and as a library of legal deposit.

LOCATION
City centre, entrance opposite the Bank of Ireland building, formerly the home of
the pre-1801 Irish parliament.

TRINITY COLLEGE LIBRARY – DEPARTMENT OF EARLY PRINTED BOOKS

College Street
DUBLIN 2
Ireland

TELEPHONE: (01) 896 1172
E-mail: epbooks@tcd.ie
Website: www.tcd.ie/library/epb

HOURS
Term time: M, Th, F, 10:00–17:00; Tu, W, 10:00–20:00; Sa, 10:00–13:00
Vacation period: M–F, 10:00–5:00; Sa, 10:00–13:00

ACCESS AND SERVICES
See TRINITY COLLEGE LIBRARY, Dublin for general guidelines for library use. Department's holdings may be read only in Early Printed Books Reading Room, where priority is given to readers using this material. Special guidelines in force for handling material in Reading Room, which includes use of laptops and pencils only. Books from other reading rooms may only be transferred with special permission.

There is a printed catalogue known as the *Catalogus librorum impressorum qui in Bibliotheca Collegii Sacrosanctae et Individuae Trinitatis ... juxta Dublin, adservantur.* Dublinii: E Typographeo Academico, 1864–87. 9 vols (vol. 9 = supplement). A digitised version of it is available online on the Library website. It represents the Library's holdings up to the 1880s. It is continued by the guardbook Accessions Catalogue which records material acquired up to 1963. Most of this catalogue has in recent years been converted to electronic format, with financial support from the Mellon Foundation. Material catalogued since 1963 is available online and mostly contains a high level of detail, such as entries for printers and publishers, illustrators, papermakers, binders and provenance.

CONTACT
Dr Lydia Ferguson, Assistant Librarian, Early Printed Books. E-mail: lydia.ferguson@tcd.ie

HOLDINGS
The Department of Early Printed Books and Special Collections houses some 500,000 pre-1920 volumes, plus some modern collections. The early library collection reflected the academic interests of the university in theology and religious controversy, classical literature, law, mathematics and natural philosophy. Among the early collections of note acquired by the library were those of Archbishop James Ussher (10,000 vols) in 1662, the Butler family (1,400 vols) in the late eighteenth century and the Dutch Fagel family (20,000 vols) in 1802. In 1801 the library became a legal deposit library for United Kingdom publications. Until the late nineteenth century, accessioning policies were very conservative and only those items judged to be of academic merit or suitable religious tenor were catalogued. A consistent and active purchasing programme for antiquarian materials did not begin until the 1960s, when a separate Department of Early Printed Books was set up, but it has made up for many of the earlier deficiencies in the collection. While the department maintains a good representation of very early printing from all over Continental Europe, the focus is on imprints from North-West Europe, with

considerable strengths in works printed in France and the Low Countries from the sixteenth to the eighteenth centuries and, above all, in Irish and English works. Political history is another area of strength, especially the Netherlands, 1580–1780; the English Civil War; the Fronde; England 1680–90 and the 1720s; England and Ireland, 1780–1820 (where the printed works are enhanced by the Nicholas Robinson Collection of caricatures); the French Revolution, 1789–1800 (about 12,000 items); Ireland and England in the nineteenth century.

One of the library's great strengths is in English language drama from 1660 to the present. Holdings of authors educated at Trinity College Dublin, such as Congreve, Farquhar and Goldsmith, are particularly good. French drama holdings are good, with particular strength in the seventeenth century. There are minor collections of Dutch, German and Spanish drama. Poetry in English is strong, especially for the period 1710–40, including much Swiftiana. Popular verse is represented in the J.D. White Ballads (900 items, c. 1860–90). Eighteenth and nineteenth century English fiction, once an area of weakness, has been strengthened in recent years and there is also a significant amount of seventeenth and eighteenth century French fiction. Classical literature is present in quantity from the incunabula period on.

In 2005, the Department took in a bequest of ca 10,500 early children's books, the Pollard Collection, with mainly British and Irish imprints, dating from the seventeenth to the early twentieth century. Nearly 1,500 titles have been added to this collection since it was acquired.

Not surprisingly, theology and religious controversy are among the strongest areas in the Library's collection, with an especially good collection of Bibles. There are about 1,200 Reformation tracts printed before 1545. Coverage of Anglican theology is excellent for the entire period and that of Roman Catholic theology is surprisingly good up to the end of the seventeenth century, reasonable for the eighteenth century and now improving for the nineteenth century. There is some Quaker and Presbyterian material.

The department also boasts significant holdings of pre-1830 maps, including most of the major atlases, the oldest being an edition of Ptolemy's *Cosmographia* of 1490. Ortelius, Mercator and Blaeu are well represented. In addition there are some 2,000 sheet maps printed before 1790. Ordnance Survey maps from the 1830s to the present can be found in the Map Library. There is a good collection of early mathematical books, including Euclid's *Opus elementorum* (1482), plus good holdings in geology, physics, chemistry, medicine, botany, engineering and architecture. There is a small amount of seventeenth century music and a fair collection of Handel's operas. The bulk of the early music, however, dates from the 1760s to the 1820s and came from Townley Hall in County Louth. There are more than 1,600 items from this period, including more recent purchases. Other early music collections are those of Ebenezer Prout (3,500 items) and the Strollers, an amateur *Singverein* (1,900 items). There is also music from the College Choral Society and College Chapel. Irish and English law is held in considerable quantity from the earliest editions and more recently editions of French customary law and *mémoires* have been collected.

For the post-1901 holdings there is a collection of recruiting posters issued in Ireland during World War I, the Samuels Collection of subversive ephemera taken up by the Royal Irish Constabulary (1914–21), the Cuala Press Archives, the personal library of James Stephens and Irish nationalist and radical newspapers, 1901–30.

Digitization of the library collections is still at an early stage but the following collections have been photographed and will shortly be available for consultation through the Library's Digital Collections website: the Robinson Collection of caricatures, the Samuels Collection of ephemera and the J.D. White Collection of nineteenth-century ballads.

LOCATION
East Pavilion of the Old Library building with access from the entrance hall of the Berkeley Library. Lifts are available for wheelchair access.

TRINITY COLLEGE LIBRARY – MANUSCRIPTS & ARCHIVES RESEARCH LIBRARY (M&ARL)

College Street
DUBLIN 2
Ireland

TELEPHONE: (01) 896 1189
E-mail: mscripts@tcd.ie
Website: www.tcd.ie/Library/manuscripts/index.php

HOURS
M–F, 10:00–17:00; Sa, 10:00–13:00

ACCESS AND SERVICES
See TRINITY COLLEGE LIBRARY, Dublin for general guidelines for library use. Manuscript readers should first obtain reader's ticket from Berkeley Library and permission to consult manuscripts should be applied for in advance to Keeper of Manuscripts. The department offers photography services. The M&ARL Online Catalogue (MARLOC), which is still in development, is available at http://marloc.library.tcd.ie/calmview/. Published guides include T.K. Abbott, *Catalogue of the Manuscripts in the Library of Trinity College, Dublin* (Dublin and London, 1900), a general catalogue of accessions to 1900. Introductory leaflet available throughout the library. Sectional language catalogues have appeared in print, including T.K. Abbott and E.J. Gwynn, *Catalogue of the Irish Manuscripts in the Library of Trinity College, Dublin* (Dublin, 1921) and Marvin L. Colker, *A Descriptive Catalogue of the Mediaeval and Renaissance Latin Manuscripts in the Library of Trinity College Dublin* (Scholar Press for Trinity College Library, 1991); idem, *Supplement One* (Dublin 2008). Peter Fox (ed.), *Treasures of the Library, Trinity College Dublin* (Dublin, 1986) discusses some of the library's major holdings. See also Bernard Meehan, 'Manuscript Accessions in Trinity College Library Dublin, 1982–2003, Part I', *Long Room* 48 (2003), 38–55.

CONTACT
Keeper of Manuscripts

HOLDINGS
Major collections include: Greek and Egyptian papyri; corpus of medieval manuscripts, largely from the collection of James Ussher (d. 1656), but also including the library's greatest treasures: the *Book of Kells* (*c*. 800), *Book of Durrow* (*c*. 675), *Book of Armagh* (807), *Book of Dimma* (eighth century), *Book of Mulling* (eighth century), Matthew Paris's *Life of St Alban* (thirteenth century) and the *Fagel*

Missal (fifteenth century); a collection of medieval Irish-language manuscripts including the Annals of Ulster. Also of great significance are: college muniments, sixteenth–twentieth century; Roman inquisitorial records, sixteenth–twentieth century; depositions of 1641 (fully searchable digital edition at http://1641.tcd.ie/); 1798 Rebellion papers; and the archives of the Royal Zoological Society of Ireland, 1836–*c*. 1953. Family and private paper collections include those of: William King (1650–1729), Archbishop of Dublin; Thomas Parnell (1679–1718), poet; Earls of Donoughmore, sixteenth–twentieth century; Wynne family of Hazlewood, County Sligo and Glendalough, County Wicklow, eighteenth–twentieth century; Elvery family of Carrickmines and Foxrock, County Dublin, nineteenth–twentieth century; Sir William Rowan Hamilton (1805–65), mathematician and astronomer; Michael Davitt (1846–1906), author and politician; John Dillon (1851–1927), politician; Robert Erskine Childers (1870–1922), author and politician; Liam de Roiste (1882–1959); politician and author; John Millington Synge (1871–1909), poet and dramatist; Susan Mitchell (1866–1926), poet and editor; Thomas Bodkin (1887–1961), art historian and gallery director; Thomas MacGreevy (1893–1967), poet and gallery director; Denis Johnston (1901–84), playwright and journalist; Jennifer Johnston, novelist (born 1930); Frank Gallagher (1898–1962), journalist; Joseph Campbell (1879–1944), poet; James Stephens (1880–1950), author; Máirtín Ó Cadhain (1906–70), writer in Irish; George MacBeth (1932–93), poet and novelist; John Banville (1945–present), novelist; Samuel Beckett (1906–89), author; Herbert Butler (1900–91), essayist; Gerald Barry (1952–present), composer; John B. Keane (1928–2002), author; Tom Murphy (1935–present), playwright; Lilliput Press, Dublin archives 1984–2004; Gerard Victory (1921–95), composer and broadcaster; St John Ervine (1881–1971), writer, novelist, playwright (papers, manuscripts and correspondence); Eiléan Ní Chuilleanáin, poet (born 1942); Risteárd Ó Glaisne (1927–2003), writer and Irish language activist (papers, manuscripts and correspondence); and James Wilson (1922–2005), composer (papers, scores and correspondence).

LOCATION
Old Library, with entry via the library shop and the Long Room.

UCD ARCHIVES

James Joyce Library
University College Dublin
Belfield
DUBLIN 4
Ireland

TELEPHONE: (01) 716 7555; FAX: (01) 716 1146
E-mail: archives@ucd.ie
Website: www.ucd.ie/archives

HOURS
M–Th, 10:00–17:00

ACCESS AND SERVICES
Visitors welcome, but by appointment only. Advance notice required. Disabled access facilities. Laptops permitted; pencils only. Collections not available unless

catalogued. Fees for photocopying, microform print and digital imaging services. Website gives best current indication of holdings and is updated regularly. Some modern paper collections available online on the Irish Virtual Research Library and Archive: ivrla.ucd.ie/ivrla/home. UCD-OFM Franciscan A MSS available online on the Irish Script on Screen website: www.isos.dias.ie.

CONTACT
Duty Archivist

DESCRIPTION
UCD Archives mainly houses the deposited private collections of papers of public figures, such as politicians, presidents, and public servants; the official papers of the university and its predecessors; and the significant holdings of modern, early modern and medieval collections transferred from the FRANCISCAN LIBRARY KILLINEY under the terms of the UCD-OFM Agreement. Though it occupies space in the UCD James Joyce Library, UCD Archives is a separate administrative unit within the UCD School of History and Archives.

HOLDINGS
The collections overwhelmingly date from the independence period (1921–present) and relate to the political, cultural and economic development of modern Ireland. Major collections include papers of Frank Aiken, Todd Andrews, Kevin Barry, Ernest Blythe, Colonel Dan Bryan, Michael Collins, John A. Costello, Conor Cruise O'Brien, the Cumann na nGaedheal and Fine Gael parties, George Gavan Duffy, the Fianna Fáil party, Desmond FitzGerald, Garret FitzGerald, Michael Hayes, T.M. Healy, Dr P.J. Hillery, Sighle Humphreys, Hugh Kennedy, Tom Kettle, Sean Lester, Denis McCullough, Sean MacEntee, Sean Mac Eoin, Patrick McGilligan, Eoin MacNeill, Josephine MacNeill, Mary MacSwiney, Terence MacSwiney, Michael MacWhite, Richard Mulcahy, Donnchadh Ó Briain, Daniel O'Connell, Kathleen O'Connell, Cearbhall Ó Dálaigh, Diarmuid Ó hEigeartaigh, Dan O'Herlihy, Ernie O'Malley, Alfred O'Rahilly, The O'Rahilly, Desmond Ryan, Dr James Ryan, Moss Twomey, Eamon de Valera and T.K. Whitaker.

Other collections include the records of predecessor institutions of the university, including the Catholic University of Ireland, 1854–1911; the Royal College of Science for Ireland, 1867–1926; the Museum of Irish Industry, 1846–7; Albert Agricultural College, 1838–1926; and the Royal Veterinary College of Ireland, 1900–60.

UCD Archives holds collections transferred from the FRANCISCAN LIBRARY, KILLINEY under the terms of the UCD-OFM Partnership. These include 'A' Manuscripts, Irish language manuscripts such as the *Martyrology of Tallaght* (fragment of the *Book of Leinster*), the *Annals of the Four Masters*, the *Psalter of St Caimin* and the *Liber Hymnoroum* (see Myles Dillon, Canice Mooney OFM and Pádraig de Brún *Catalogue of Irish Manuscripts in the Franciscan Library Killiney* Dublin Institute for Advanced Studies, 1969); B Manuscripts, in languages other than Irish including Latin, English, Italian, Arabic, and Catalan (see Ignatius Fennessy OFM 'The B Manuscripts in the Franciscan Library Killiney' in Benignus Millett and Anthony Lynch *Dún Mhuire Killiney 1945–95 Léann agus Seanchas* Dublin 1995; C Manuscripts containing official and quasi-official letters and papers relating to the Irish Franciscans, seventeenth century; D Manuscripts, mainly papers of Luke Wadding and his contemporaries, seventeenth century.

More recently UCD Archives has acquired collections in support of major research strands within UCD such as the history of sport (archives of the Football Association of Ireland, Leinster Football Association, and Cricket Ireland); and the history of health (archives of An Bord Altranais/The Nursingboard).
UCD Archives also include trade union archives and labour related paper collections deposited through the Irish Labour History Society. These include archives of actors', bakers', coopers', municipal employees', plasterers', shoe and leather workers' and woodworkers' trade unions.

LOCATION
In the James Joyce Library on the main university campus in Belfield, on the south-east side of Dublin, accessible by bus from city centre. *See* directions in following entry.

UNIVERSITY COLLEGE DUBLIN LIBRARY

James Joyce Library
University College Dublin
Belfield
DUBLIN 4
Ireland

TELEPHONE: (01) 716 7583; Fax: (01) 716 7068;
Email: library@ucd.ie;
Website: www.ucd.ie/library

HOURS
Opening hours vary in each Library. Consult the website for up to date information.
www.ucd.ie/library/using_the_library/open_hours/

ACCESS AND SERVICES
There are various arrangements in place for visitors and researchers to gain access to the libraries, and in some circumstances to borrow library materials. One week's access may be given during term with a letter of introduction from a reader's home library. A fee may be required for longer access. Readers should always have their own ID and must show it if requested. Check the Library website for details
www.ucd.ie/library/using_the_library/admission/

CONTACT
James Joyce Library. Tel.: (01) 716 7699 or 7583; e-mail: reader.services@ucd.ie
Blackrock Library (Michael Smurfit Graduate School of Business) University College Dublin, Carysfort Avenue, Blackrock, Co. Dublin. Tel.: (01) 716 8069; e-mail: biclib@ucd.ie
Health Sciences Library University College Dublin, Belfield, Dublin 4. Tel.: +353 (01) 716 6588; e-mail: hsl@ucd.ie
Richview Library, University College Dublin, Clonskeagh Road, Dublin 6. Tel.: (01) 716 2727; e-mail: richview.library@ucd.ie
Veterinary Medicine Library, University College Dublin, Belfield, Dublin 4. Tel.: (01) 716 6208; e-mail: vetlib@ucd.ie

DESCRIPTION
UCD is the largest university institution in Ireland. It traces its origin to the
Catholic University of Ireland, founded in 1854 with John Henry Newman as its
first rector, and has grown from modest beginnings to a seven college institution
with 38 schools. It has over 24,000 students. The Library system includes the
following:

The James Joyce Library supports Arts, Celtic Studies, Human Sciences, Business
(Undergraduate), Law, Science, Agriculture, and Engineering. This Library also
holds: an Official Publications Collection which includes Irish government
publications and a European Documentation Centre (EDC); the Developments
Studies Library and a Confucius Collection. The latter collection is held in UCD
Library on behalf the UCD Confucius Institute for Ireland. The James Joyce Library
is located on four levels of the Library building on the Belfield Campus. This library
uses an automated access system, and valid readers cards are required for admission.

The Health Sciences Library supports diagnostic imaging, health and safety,
medicine, nursing, physiotherapy and performance science, public health and
population science, sports and exercise science, history of medicine and nursing.
This library also uses an automated access system, and valid readers cards are
required for admission.

The Richview Library, located in the School of Architecture and Planning complex
at Richview, Clonskeagh Road, holds collections relating to architecture, landscape
architecture, environmental subjects, urban history and planning. This Library also
provides the UCD Library maps service – with historical Irish maps and large scale
mapping printed from OSI databases; Development plans for every county in
Ireland (both current and superseded versions). Archinfo, the commercial
information service for architectural practices is located in this Library.

The Blackrock Library primarily supports the teaching and research activities of the
UCD Michael Smurfit Graduate Business School. This Library is located about 4
km from the main UCD Campus at Belfield. It maintains a comprehensive and
relevant collection of business resources. This library also uses an automated access
system, and valid readers cards are required for admission.

The Veterinary Medicine Library is situated within the Veterinary Sciences Centre
on the Belfield Campus. This library, the only academic veterinary medicine library
in the Republic of Ireland, holds an extensive collection of databases, books, journals
and audio/visual materials.
It supports the teaching and research activities of the Veterinary Medicine and
Veterinary Nursing Programmes in UCD. Members of the Irish veterinary profession
are welcome to use the Veterinary Medicine Library and its resources.

Special Collections Library, which contains unique book, archival and manuscript
collections, is located on Level 1 of the James Joyce Library. See separate entry below.

HOLDINGS
The library's holdings consist of over 1,000,000 volumes. Almost 80 per cent of the
stock is on open access. An increasing number of electronic resources is being
purchased. Approximately 15,000 purchased monographs and 2,550 donations are
added to the stock each year.

UCD Library is a European Documentation Centre, and a legal deposit library for Irish publications.

Other collections of note include a substantial Maps Collection holding historical, print and online maps; a Theses Collection of all major theses awarded by UCD holding original primary research dating back to 1910; a specialist library for Development Studies, a collection relating to the emergence of the Irish economic boom (Celtic Tiger era in Ireland); Confucius Collection (currently held in UCD Library on behalf the UCD Confucius Institute for Ireland). Special Collections Library incorporates the libraries of older institutions, such as the Royal College of Science of Ireland and the Museum of Irish Industry. This Library also holds the donations and bequests of many former members of the University, those who made their careers as teachers and researchers in UCD and those who pursued careers elsewhere.

Digital repository services

The UCD Library support digital repository services for dissemination of open access publications by university staff as well as for the management of digitised cultural heritage resources and data produced, or consumed, by the UCD community. A new framework for our digital library services is being developed. It will be a successor to the Irish Virtual Research Library and Archive (IVRLA). In 2012, a project was started, in collaboration with UCD Research, to develop interoperability between the Library **Institutional Repository (IR)** and the UCD **Research Management System (RMS)**. The UCD Digital Repository is based on DSpace and provides access to full text articles, working papers, reports, and other staff publications. Based on DSpace, it also provides a means of exporting information to a national open access repository, RIAN, as well as other subject-specific portals.

The **UCD Digital Library,** launched in 2012, is a platform for the dissemination of diverse digital content associated with the University. The major cultural heritage collection is the Irish Virtual Research Library and Archive (IVRLA); additional information includes geographic, quantitative and qualitative data produced or consumed by the UCD community.

LOCATION

Belfield, the main University College Dublin campus is located on a 132 hectare site, 4km south of Dublin city centre. The campus in an attractively landscaped complex of modern architectural buildings, accommodating student residences and numerous leisure and sporting facilities. The UCD Michael Smurfit Graduate School of Business is located on the campus at Blackrock, County Dublin.

UCD is served by a variety of public transport, including: Dublin Bus numbers 2, 3, 11, 17, 39A, 46A, 84 and 145 all provide services to the Belfield campus. The 39A terminates within the Belfield campus, and can be boarded from in the City Centre from College Street. The numbers 2, 3, 11 and 46A can be boarded at O'Connell Street. Several additional *Xpresso* services operate directly to campus during morning and evening peak. For timetable information please visit the Dublin Bus website and search for 'University College Dublin'. Aircoach operates a bus service from Dublin Airport to Leopardstown/Sandyford/Stillorgan which passes UCD. Further details available at www.aircoach.ie

UNIVERSITY COLLEGE DUBLIN LIBRARY – SPECIAL COLLECTIONS

James Joyce Library
University College Dublin
Belfield
DUBLIN 4
Ireland

TELEPHONE: (01) 716 7149; FAX: (01) 716 1148
E-mail: special.collections@ucd.ie
Website: www.ucd.ie/library/finding_information/special/

HOURS
M–F, 10:00–13:00, 14:00–17:00; closed Christmas period, Good Friday and public holidays

ACCESS AND SERVICES
Visitors welcome by appointment. Letter of introduction may be required; students should have letter from supervisor. Access charges: no charge for up to ten working days. For longer periods, users must purchase library admission card from main information desk. All materials must be consulted in the Special Collections Reading Room. Pencils only; laptops and digital photography (subject to constraints of Irish copyright law) welcome; no photocopying permitted or undertaken. Photography and scanning can be arranged for a fee. Most printed material included in library's web catalogue; various finding aids available for manuscript material and staff are happy to advise. See website for further information.

CONTACT
Evelyn Flanagan, Librarian for Special Collections

DESCRIPTION
The Special Collections Department holds books, pamphlets and journal titles printed before 1851 (in addition to some later titles of particular significance or interest). All the library's manuscripts, as well as some maps, photographs, prints and drawings and ephemera, are also located here, as are a number of important personal collections of significant content or provenance.

Printed Collections
The foundation collections are drawn from the libraries of those bodies which ultimately became part of University College Dublin, most notably the Catholic University of Ireland and the Royal College of Science for Ireland. The strengths of the Catholic University library are primarily in philosophy, theology and church history, but there is also significant coverage of Irish literature and the Irish language, history, archaeology and classics. Important individual collections from the Catholic University include those of Archbishops Joseph Dixon (1806–66) and Daniel Murray (1768–1852). The library of the Royal College of Science for Ireland is one of the most comprehensive Victorian science libraries in the UK and Ireland. It contains rare scientific monographs from the seventeenth to the nineteenth centuries and earlier, and complete runs of scientific periodicals which are not to be found in any other Irish library. Many of the items from this collection contain very beautiful plates and illustrations.

Among the collections acquired since the establishment of University College Dublin in 1909, three are particularly notable: the Ó Lochlainn, O'Kelley and

Sweeney Collections. The library of Colm Ó Lochlainn, bibliophile and owner of the Three Candles Press, includes early printings, handsome bindings, broadside and single ballads, songbooks and devotional literature. Francis J. O'Kelly's collection encompasses Irish history, local history and especially Irish printing and printing relating to Ireland from the seventeenth to the nineteenth century, with particular emphasis on pamphlets, many scarce. The bequest of John Lincoln Sweeney constitutes a major modern printed collection and includes English, Anglo-Irish and American literature in fine and early editions, limited editions and signed copies. Other important printed collections include: the Heinrich Zimmer Library (Celtic studies); the Palles Collection (seventeenth and eighteenth century law books); the Curran Collection (literary first editions of James Joyce and of the Irish literary revival); the Tasso Collection deposited by David Nolan; John Manning's collection of children's books, mostly by English authors; the Quinn Collection (works by and about American poet Robert Frost); the Power Collection of rare sixteenth–nineteenth century editions concerning Catholic Ireland; a collection of over 1000 pre-sixteenth–eighteenth century theological and historical books from the Order of Friars Minor (Franciscans).

In addition to this material, Irish publications for children and young adults are collected and kept as an archival collection. One copy of selected Anglo-Irish literary work is acquired and kept in its original condition. These items are available for research use only.

Manuscript Collections
The O'Curry, Morris, Ferriter and Ó Lochlainn Collections include manuscripts relating to Irish history, literature, religion and folklore. These are complemented by the series entitled Additional Irish Manuscripts, consisting of individual manuscripts in Irish; among these is Dubhaltach Mac Firbisigh's *Leabhar na nGenealach*, or *Book of Genealogies* and a transcription with translation of Brian Merriman's *Cúirt an Mheán-Oíche*.

Modern literary papers
These include the papers of poet Patrick Kavanagh, writer Mary Lavin, novelist Maeve Binchy, poet and dramatist Tom McIntyre, and the deposited drafts and proofs of works by dramatist Frank McGuinness. UCD Library Special Collections also holds the literary papers of novelist and biographer Edna O'Brien. In addition, the Constantine Curran Manuscript Collection includes over 400 letters from Irish writers and artists, among them James Joyce, while the Special Collections Department also houses the manuscript for Thomas Hardy's *Return of the Native*. In the Irish language, the collections include the valuable papers of writer Seán Ó Ríordáin, ranging from diaries and correspondence to notebooks and copies of his published columns.

Other material: the Special Collections Department holds the library's first edition (produced between 1833 and 1846) of the Ordnance Survey of Ireland's 6 inch maps of Ireland, in addition to a selection of other historical Irish maps. There is also a small group of music scores by Sir Arnold Bax and 39 eighteenth century watercolours of Irish antiquities, done by or for Gabriel Beranger.

LOCATION
Level one of the James Joyce Library.

VALUATION OFFICE

Irish Life Centre, Lower Abbey Street
DUBLIN 1
Ireland

TELEPHONE: (01) 817 1000; FAX: (01) 817 1190
E-mail: info@valoff.ie
Website: www.valoff.ie

HOURS

M–F, 09:15–16:30 (including lunchtime), closed public holidays

ACCESS AND SERVICES

Visitors welcome. Customer service team provides inspection facilities for members of the public to view all current and archive rating records and maps, provides certified extracts from maps, current valuation certificates, historical valuation certificates from current to those of 1850s, known as backdated certificates, and provisional valuations, required for licensing applications. Team also deals with archival queries, commonly for genealogical research. Fees may apply. Daily research fee after one hour, €15.24, which is the maximum amount payable per day; 63c per sheet for monochrome photocopying; €1.27 per sheet for colour photocopying. Search of current valuation list available through website at no cost. In addition, requests for research and certificates may be made through e-mail address above. A quotation of cost will be supplied and orders may be placed via website using credit cards.

CONTACT

Anne Durkin/ Brendan Robbins

DESCRIPTION

The Valuation Office is the state property valuation agency. The core business of the office is the provision of accurate, up to date valuations of commercial and industrial properties to ratepayers and local authorities as laid down by statute. The office also provides a valuation consultancy service to other government departments, local authorities, health boards and the Revenue Commissioners.

HOLDINGS

The archive contains the original books of surveys carried out in the 1840s, books and maps of Griffith's Valuation from the 1850s, the original rating records and documentation showing revisions up to the current position. Of special interest to genealogists, the archive holds a list of occupiers of property for the 26 counties of the Republic of Ireland dating back to 1846. The following details are held in relation to each property: occupier name, townland, address, description of property, acreage of holding, rateable value and reference to its position on a valuation map. The archive is unique in that it can relate people to a particular property. The valuation maps are archived, so it may be possible to locate the exact position of a house or property of a particular family back to c. 1850.

The Valuation Office also holds valuations lists, valuation notebooks and files, maps, databases, manuals and publications. The valuation lists contain details of the current rateable valuation of commercial properties, hereditaments and tenements, and of the rateable valuation of commercial, domestic and land properties from 1852. (Rates on domestic property were abolished in 1978 and on agricultural land from 1984. Consequently, there has been no need to update these categories.) The valuation lists also contain information on those classes of property which have a rateable valuation but which have been identified by law and by legal decision as not required to pay rates. The lists are grouped geographically, corresponding to local authority areas, with administrative subdivisions in electoral district, townland or ward. Valuation notebooks and files contain a report of the inspection by the valuer of each property that has a rateable valuation placed upon it. Ordnance Survey maps show property boundaries for valuation purposes. Files contain papers, correspondence, briefings, submissions and reports produced in the performance of office functions. The databases – electronic, typed and manuscript – contain information associated with the establishment and revision of rateable valuations. Publications include *Guide to the Valuation Office Ireland*.

LOCATION
Diagonally opposite the Abbey Theatre, two blocks east of O'Connell Street in the city centre.

THE EDWARD WORTH LIBRARY (1733)

Dr Steevens' Hospital
DUBLIN 8
Ireland

TELEPHONE: (01) 635 2215
E-mail: eaboran@tcd.ie
Website: www.edwardworthlibrary.ie

HOURS
M–F, 10:00–16:30 (with lunch break), excepting days when public holidays occur or when the Librarian is on annual leave.

ACCESS AND SERVICES
The Library is a collection of rare books and bindings which the Trustees make accessible to suitably qualified scholars and readers, advised by the Librarian, and in accordance with the terms of a High Court judgment of 1994. While every effort is made to facilitate scholars, particularly those who wish to draw on the Library's excellent resources for the History of Science, Medicine and History of the Book, it should be noted that the Library may only be used where specific required material is not reasonably available elsewhere. Enquiries by post, telephone, or e-mail must be made before any appointment to inspect material can be made. Applicants should expect to be asked for scholarly/character references, likewise for a statement of their research project. Readers are requested to consult the 'Rules of Admission' on the Worth Library website for further details.

The Librarian is keen to develop cordial professional relations with scholars and readers active in the various fields served by the Library. The Librarian is delighted to give guided tours of the Library on request, but appointments must be made in advance so that readers may not be discommoded.

The Library offers an impressive series of web exhibitions. Recent titles include: '*Alchemy and Chemistry at the Worth Library*,' '*Infectious Diseases at the Worth Library*,' and '*Astronomy at the Worth Library*.' It also organises a monthly lecture series and a research fellowship program to encourage use of the Library's special holdings. More information on these programs is available on the Library's website. See also the Library's website for information about its catalogues, which can be searched online. The Librarian, Dr Elizabethanne Boran, has also undertaken the compilation and publication of a scholarly three-volume edition of the correspondence of James Ussher, Archbishop of Armagh (1625–56).

CONTACT
Dr Elizabethanne Boran, Librarian. E-mail: eaboran@tcd.ie

DESCRIPTION
The book-collection assembled by Edward Worth (1678–1733), a notable Dublin physician, is one of the lesser-known treasures of the Dublin's cultural inheritance. It is housed in Dr Steevens' Hospital, an institution of which Worth was a governor and major benefactor. Edward Worth was a physician whose taste in books radiated outwards from his professional concern with medicine. He collected as a man of science, a gentleman, and a connoisseur. Beside medical books, ancient and modern (i.e. eighteenth century), one finds important contributions to the study of related sciences, then philosophy, the classics, history etc. Worth was particularly interested in the book as object: the collection not only holds fine examples of sixteenth-century typography but is also considered to be the best preserved collection of early modern bookbindings in Ireland.

Following Worth's death in January 1733, his fellow governors moved promptly to protect the books bequeathed to them under his will. A room was specially designed and built to accommodate them on the first floor of an as-yet unfinished building. The original book-shelves, cases, glass-panes and other fittings remain as they were in the 1730s.

HOLDINGS
The collection is made up of some 4,400 volumes, the earliest dating from 1475. Most are sumptuously bound in decorated leather or are preserved in original bindings covered with vellum. Approximately one third of the collection is made up of medical and related scientific works, with classics, history, literature, philosophy, reference, and travel accounting for much of the remainder.

Though the collection contains a small number of books which Worth inherited from his father (the Revd John Worth, 1648–88, sometime dean of Saint Patrick's Cathedral), the greatest number of books were bought by Edward Worth himself. Born in Dublin, educated in Oxford and the Netherlands, holding medical degrees from three universities, Worth remains an enigma. Little or nothing is known of his personal life or professional career. The most intimate documents discovered to date are book-auction lists which he carefully studied and upon which his collecting interests and financial commitments can in part be traced. The library, which bears his name, possesses a sizeable collection of these catalogues in their original state, mostly dating from the 1720s. A small collection of nineteenth-century government publications and a growing reference collection are also available to readers.

LOCATION
The Worth Library is located in the renovated and redecorated Dr Steevens' Hospital, which faces the south side of Dublin's main railway terminal, Heuston (former King's Bridge) Station. It is well served by buses from the city centre, and by the Luas tram system.

DÚN LAOGHAIRE LIBRARY – LOCAL HISTORY DEPARTMENT

Lower George's Street
DÚN LAOGHAIRE, COUNTY DUBLIN
Ireland

TELEPHONE: (01) 280 1147
E-mail: localhistory@dlrcoco.ie
Website: www.dlrcoco.ie/library/lhistory.htm

HOURS
M, W, F, Sa, 10:00–13:00, 14:00–17:00; Tu, Th, 13:15–20:00; closed bank holiday
weekends

ACCESS AND SERVICES
The Local History Department is based in the Dún Laoghaire Library, a branch of
the Dún Laoghaire-Rathdown Public Library Service, www.dlrcoco.ie/library [e-mail
libraries@dlrcoco.ie). Visitors welcome. Wheelchair access. Photocopying and
microfilm services available for modest fee. Free internet access, available on five
personal computers, dedicated PC for Local History queries, free Wifi. Exhibitions
mounted on a regular basis. Recent showings include: the Irish Civil War (1997),
the 1848 Rebellion (1998), Dún Laoghaire Before the Railway (1998), Ships in the
Bay (2000) and Ancient Places, Sacred Spaces (2001).

The Local History Department has been contributing for several years to a
digitisation project called www.askaboutireland.ie, hosted by an Comhairle
Leabharlanna, the Library Council. Contributions to date include *Postcards of Dún
Laoghaire-Rathdown*; *Selected Wild Flowers of Dún Laoghaire-Rathdown*; *The Big
Houses of Dún Laoghaire-Rathdown*; and *Transport of Dún Laoghaire Port*. A new
digitisation project is in preparation, entitled, *Then and Now*, a look at how the
landscape, monuments, archaeology, architecture and artefacts of the Dún
Laoghaire-Rathdown area have changed over time. For further information on the
history of the Dún Laoghaire-Rathdown area, contact the Dún Laoghaire Borough
Historical Society, 18 Melifont Avenue, Dún Laoghaire, County Dublin (telephone
+353 1 280 4319). Contact Mairin Cullen, Honorable Secretary, Dún Laoghaire
Borough Historical Society.

CONTACT
Any member of staff

DESCRIPTION
On 1 January 1994 Dublin County Council and the Corporation of Dún Laoghaire
were dissolved and replaced by three new administrative counties, South Dublin,
Dún Laoghaire-Rathdown and Fingal. It is the aim of the Local History Department
to collect, preserve and make available for reference material on the history of the
administrative county.

HOLDINGS
The collection includes directories dating from 1798, Council minutes from 1888,
newspapers from 1819 and surveys and maps from 1730. The department also holds
such genealogical resources as Griffith's Valuation, census returns, 1813–1911 and
tithe applotment books. The photograph collection covers prints and drawings from
the seventeenth century to the present. Highlights include copies of the Lawrence

Collection, the Civil War (Ireland 1922–3) Series and the Dún Laoghaire Harbour Collection.

LOCATION
By rail, take DART to Dún Laoghaire station; the library is a ten minute walk from there. By bus, take bus 7 or 46A from Dublin city centre; 59 from Killiney; 63 from Kilternan; 75 from Tallaght; or 111 from Loughlinstown. No parking available at the library.

DÚN LAOGHAIRE-RATHDOWN HERITAGE CENTRE
Listed under Dublin. The centre moved in April 2006 to Rathfarnham.

FRANCISCAN LIBRARY KILLINEY (FLK)

Dún Mhuire, Seafield Road
KILLINEY, COUNTY DUBLIN
Ireland

TELEPHONE: (01) 282 6760 (Friary), (01) 282 6091, extension 25 (Library); FAX: (01) 282 6993
E-mail: dmkilliney@eircom.net (Friary), ignatiusfen@eircom.net (Library)
Website: www.franciscans.ie (contains information about the provincial library in Killiney), www.isos.dcu.ie (website for Irish Script On Screen from Dublin City University – contains information on Irish manuscripts (MSS A))

HOURS
M–F, 10:00–13:00, 14:30–16:30 (subject to staffing)

ACCESS AND SERVICES
Visitors welcome, but by appointment only. Disabled access facilities. Fees for photocopying, carried out by Librarian. There is a printed catalogue of Irish manuscripts that are now in the care of UCD (*see* above). Some copies of the catalogue of MSS B (other than Irish) published in *Dun Mhuire Killiney 1945–95* still available from Librarian. The book is out of print. Collection catalogued on computer.

CONTACT
Fr Ignatius Fennessy, Information Officer. E-mail: ignatiusfen@eircom.net

DESCRIPTION
Private Franciscan library available to researchers by appointment.

HOLDINGS
The collection includes some 23,000 volumes, 1,000 pamphlets and 250 journal titles dealing primarily with Franciscan studies, the Irish language and Irish history, especially with respect to ecclesiastical and state history. Collections include: the papers of Eamon de Valera, Seán Mac Eoin, Muiris Ó Droighneáin and George Gavan Duffy, and Luke Wadding OFM, all five now in the care of University College Dublin Archives; and a rare book collection that includes 26 incunabula (fifteenth century). The incunabula are also now in the care of UCD. The indexing of the papers of George Gavan Duffy, Seán Mac Eoin, Muiris Ó Droighneáin and Eamon de Valera is now complete.

LOCATION
From Dublin city centre take the DART to Killiney (30 minutes); walk for ten
minutes up Station Road (a hill) and down the other side on Seafield Road, around
corner at bottom of the hill. The entrance is on right hand side, with a green
postbox on the wall and the name Dún Mhuire on an entrance pillar.

FINGAL LOCAL STUDIES AND ARCHIVES

Fingal Local Studies Department
Clonmel House
Forster Way,
SWORDS, COUNTY DUBLIN
Ireland

TELEPHONE: (01) 870 4495; (01) 870 4496
E-mail: Local.Studies@fingalcoco.ie or jacinta.judge@fingalcoco.ie
Website: www.fingalcoco.ie (follow links in Libraries to 'Local Studies')

HOURS
M–F, 10:00–13:00; 14:00–17:00; closed bank holiday Mondays

ACCESS AND SERVICES
Visitors welcome. Photocopying and microfilm print services available for a modest
fee. Local Studies produces publications and exhibits to promote the collection. In
addition to publishing a series of seven different posters of old picture postcards
(relating to the towns of Balbriggan, Howth, Skerries, Rush, Malahide,
Portmarnock, Baldoyle and Sutton), Local Studies has published several books,
including: *Discovering Fingal: a Photographic Tour*, vol. 1 (1997); *Discovering Fingal:
a Photographic Tour*, vol. 2 (2002); *Swords: Monastic Foundation to Modern Town*, by
the Transition Year students of Loreto College, Swords (2001–02); Aine Shields,
Swords in the 19th Century (2003); Sean Lennon, *Dublin Writers and Their Haunts*
(2003); Petra Skyvova, *The Holy Wells of Fingal* (2005) *Fingal through old picture
postcards* (2009), *Fingal Sporting Heroes* (2011); Paul Harris. Fingal Local Studies also
publishes the local history journal 'Fingal Studies'. The two editions to date are
Fingal at War (2010) and *Early Fingal Entrepreneurs* (2011).

CONTACT
Jacinta Judge, Senior Librarian

DESCRIPTION
Part of the Fingal County Libraries system, headquartered at County Hall Main
Street, Swords, County Dublin (telephone (01) 890 5000) under the sponsorship of
Fingal County Council. Fingal County Council was established on 1 January 1994
following the dissolution of Dublin County Council and the Corporation of Dún
Laoghaire and their replacement with three new administrative counties, South
Dublin, Dún Laoghaire-Rathdown and Fingal.

HOLDINGS
Items contained in the collection include: antiquarian and new books covering
standard reference texts, history, topography, ecclesiastical matters, transport,
maritime matters, postal matters and many more; periodicals, including older
standard research titles and those with specific local history interest; prints, focusing

on sketches of the archaeological and architectural views of Fingal; photographs, including copies of the relevant Fingal subjects taken from the primary collections of the National Library of Ireland, with some private photographic material also available; postcards (800 items capturing scenes of Fingal from the early part of the twentieth century); pictures (watercolour, oil and ink drawings by local artists and some original paintings); maps (Ordnance Survey, townland, Down Survey and contemporary development items); videos (copies of videos produced within the Fingal area by various groups); newspapers (bound editions of the *Fingal Independent*, 1994–present, bound editions of the *Freeman's Journal*, 1912–1922 and an excellent collection of newspapers on microfilm, ephemera (material including pamphlets, letters, coins, posters, postal items, memorabilia and curiosities makes up a growing portion of the collection), *Fingal Parish Registers* dating from mid 1700s to 1880 and the *Fingal Oral History Collection*.

LOCATION
Swords Village, Co. Dublin. Swords the county town of Fingal, is located approximately 8 miles north of Dublin City Centre, just west of the Dublin Airport, easily accessible by bus or car. Buses 43, 33, 41 will bring you to the main street in Swords.

Fingal County Archives
2nd Floor Clonmel House,
Forster Way
SWORDS, COUNTY DUBLIN
Ireland

TELEPHONE: (01) 870 4496
E-mail: archives@fingalcoco.ie
Website: www.fingalcoco.ie (follow links in Libraries to 'Archives')

HOURS
M–F, 10:00–13:00, 14:00–16:30

ACCESS AND SERVICES
Visitors welcome. Research facilities provided free of charge. Advance appointment required. In order to facilitate researchers, appointments outside normal hours may be arranged if sufficient notice given. Archives for reference purposes only; materials not available for loan. Access to storage area not permitted. Depending on age and condition of material, photocopying services may be provided. Please note: some records may have to be withdrawn for conservation treatment and may not always be available for consultation.

CONTACT
Archivist

DESCRIPTION
Under the terms of the 1993 Local Government Act, Dublin County Council was replaced by the three new Councils of Fingal, South Dublin and Dún Laoghaire-Rathdown. The archives of Dublin County Council were transferred to Fingal County Archives, which is now located in the Village of Swords, in North County Dublin, near the Dublin Airport. All material relating to the former Dublin County Council and its predecessor bodies including Boards of Guardians and Grand Juries is housed here.

HOLDINGS
Fingal County Archives contains a small number of manuscript Grand Jury minute
books and a more extensive collection of printed Presentment Books for the period
1818–98, when most of the Grand Juries' functions were transferred to the newly
established County Councils. The Grand Juries were responsible for setting up
Boards of Trustees to supervise and maintain the turnpike (toll) roads system. Fingal
County Archives contains the records of a number of these boards for roads leading
out of County Dublin north and south. The collection of records of the Board of
Trustees for the turnpike road between Dublin and Dunleer, County Louth, is one
of the most complete in the country, covering the period 1775–1856. Fingal County
Archives also contains material for the Boards of Guardians and Rural District
Councils of Balrothery, Dublin North, Dublin South and Rathdown and the Rural
District Council of Celbridge.

The Dublin County Council records constitute the largest body of material in
the archives. Dublin County Council was established under the 1898 Local
Government Act. In the early years of its existence its main functions were the
maintenance of roads and mental hospitals and the raising of rates. In 1930 it took
over the functions of the Boards of Guardians and Rural District Councils and as
the century progressed its functions expanded to include the provision of roads,
planning, libraries, community and environmental services. Fingal County Archives
contains a large number of collections dealing with the establishment and provision
of these services. There are also collections of records of some Urban District
Councils and Town Commissioners such as Balbriggan and Howth, and the Dublin
Board of Assistance/Dublin Board of Public Health. Fingal County Archives also
contains a small number of collections of private individuals and organisations
connected with the County of Dublin, including the Fingal Estate Papers, 1685-
–1969, the Butler Estate Papers and a small collection of correspondence belonging
to Miss Brigid Connolly, a member of Cumann na mBan, 1914–36.

LOCATION
Swords Village, Co. Dublin. Swords, the county town of Fingal, is located
approximately 8 miles north of Dublin City Centre, just west of the Dublin Airport,
easily accessible by bus or car. Buses 43, 33, 41 will bring you to the main street in
Swords.

FINGAL GENEALOGY

Swords Historical Society Co Ltd,
Carnegie Library
North St.
SWORDS, COUNTY DUBLIN
Ireland

TELEPHONE: (01) 840 0080
Email: swordsheritage@eircom.net; fingalgenealogy@gmail.com
Website: www.rootsireland.ie; www.swordsheritage.com

HOURS
M–F, 13:00–16:30 or by appointment

ACCESS AND SERVICES

Fingal Genealogy is part of a nationwide network of Genealogy Centres as part of The Irish Family History Foundation Ltd. As its name suggests, the Centre covers the north side of Dublin; Fingal being the old name for same. Clients may access the Centre's records online at: rootsireland.ie or request a search by contacting the Centre directly. Fingal Genealogy also has a small Museum with a collection of photographs and artifacts reflecting aspects of local and national history. Publications currently available include, *Working Life in Fingal–Recollections from North County Dublin*, €6.00; *Swords Voices* (eighteenth in the series published 2011), €6; *Sewn by Candlelight: History of Act of Union & Education in Swords*, €6; *Greatly Benefited, Old Borough School Swords*, €10; *A Hard Auld Station, Musing on St Colmcille's Church*, Swords, €12.00.

CONTACT

Bernadette Marks
Geraldine McGovern

DESCRIPTION

Fingal Genealogy is a member of the Irish Family History Foundation, the coordinating body for a network of government approved genealogical research centres in the Republic of Ireland and in Northern Ireland which have computerised tens of millions of Irish ancestral records of different types. Fingal Genealogy focuses on North County Dublin. Main towns in the area include: Balbriggan, Baldoyle, Balrothery, Balscaden, Blanchardstown, Clontarf, Donabate, Fingal, Lusk, Malahide, Naul, Portmarnock, Rush, Skerries and the 'county town', Swords.

HOLDINGS

Records include: Roman Catholic records, the earliest of which date from 1701; Church of Ireland records from 1705; and census records from as early as 1901. Fingal Genealogy also holds records of interment for all Church of Ireland cemeteries in its area, the earliest being Swords from 1705; vaccination records; school roll books; gravestone inscriptions for some local cemeteries; various trade directories; dog licence records; and 1916 volunteer records.
As part of the Fingal Heritage Network, Fingal Genealogy has access to the knowledge of at least 12 local historians from towns and villages throughout Fingal. Their firsthand knowledge of local names, placenames, and graveyards, can add more to genealogical research.

LOCATION

North of Dublin City, near Dublin Airport and close to several sites of interest, including Newbridge House, Skerries Windmill, Ardgillen Castle, Swords Castle and Malahide Castle.

COUNTY FERMANAGH

LIBRARIES NI HERTITAGE COLLECTION, ENNISKILLEN

Hall's Lane
ENNISKILLEN, COUNTY FERMANAGH, BT74 7DR
Northern Ireland

TELEPHONE: (028) 6632 2886; FAX: (028) 6632 4685
E-mail: Enniskillen.library@librariesni.org.uk
Website: www.librariesni.org.uk

HOURS
M, F, 08:30–17:15; Tu–Th, 08:30–20:00; Sa, 09:00–13:00, 14:00–17:00

ACCESS AND SERVICES
Visitors welcome. Borrowing privileges for visitors may be restricted. Disabled
access. Fees for photocopying, microfilm prints, faxes and e-mail. Only five per cent
of collection catalogued online. Printed finding aids available. Linked to emigration
database of the Ulster American Folk Park.

CONTACT'
Helen Grimes, Heritage Services Manager. E-mail: helen.grimes@librariesni.org.uk

DESCRIPTION
Part of the Northern Ireland Libraries system, covering all Northern Ireland,
Enniskillen is the principal public library in County Fermanagh.

HOLDINGS
The library houses a general educational and recreational collection of some 21,000
books. Its Nawn Collection is one of the best and largest local studies collections at a
public library in all of Ireland. This collection consists of some 30,000 books of Irish
interest, plus prints, periodicals, paintings, photographs and an especially good
collection of some 1,500 printed maps, including copies of County Fermanagh
barony maps, a few county and Ulster maps from 1685, Ordnance Survey 6 inch
maps for Fermanagh and Tyrone (1835, 1859, 1908) and Ordnance Survey grid
maps. Other collections of note include: the W.B. Yeats Collection of some 400
volumes, including a considerable number of first editions; a collection on
Fermanagh author Shan Bullock; the extensive Local Newspaper Collection on
microfilm from 1738 to the present; the Railway History Collection, which consists

of some 200 books, journals and maps on the history and development of railways in Ireland from the mid-1800s to recent times; and the Military History Collection, focusing on Irish regiments, especially the Royal Inniskilling Dragoon Guards and the Royal Inniskilling Fusiliers.

The Genealogy and Heraldry Collection focuses on Irish interests but also covers English and Scottish interests. The collection includes a number of rarities. The man for whom the Nawn Collection is named, Frederick James Nawn, possessed an 'encyclopaedic knowledge of genealogy and family history', and the collection he built as divisional librarian reflects this interest.

Other material includes Griffith's Valuation of County Fermanagh, c. 1862, microfilm copies of all Board of Guardian minute books for Enniskillen, Irvinestown (Lowtherstown) and Lisnaskea Poor Law Union workhouses, c. 1840–94; hearth money rolls, 1660s, muster rolls, militia lists; electoral registers for County Fermanagh, 1978, 1982–6, 1988–9; a microfiche copy of the 1901 census of Ireland and name index for County Fermanagh, plus various other important genealogical sources, including directories, indexes and lists.

Periodicals include: *Familia*, 1987–present; *Irish Genealogical Research Society (Ireland Branch Newsletter)*, 1986–present; *Irish Genealogist*, 1939–present; *Irish Heritage Links*, 1981–90/91; *Irish Links*, 1984–present; *North Irish Roots*, 1984–present; *Ulster Link*, 1987–8 (odd numbers only); and *Ulster Origins*, 1984–8 (5 vols).

The library also has a substantial collection of valuation revision lists for County Fermanagh. The earliest volumes cover the years 1864–5, 1869–70 and 1883–90. The larger section comprising approximately 110 volumes covers the years 1910–30. The lists are bound individually by Poor Law Union, Rural District and Electoral Division with a list of townlands inside each cover. Some volumes are in need of repair and could not be produced to the public.

There is a small collection of records of public elementary schools in County Fermanagh. These are mainly roll books for schools in the Clones area returned by the Public Record Office of Northern Ireland. For Lisroon there are roll books covering the period 1884–1954 (8 vols), Magheraveely, 1908–17 and Roslea, 1921–7. For the public elementary school of Letter in Templecarn parish there is a pupil register for the years 1951–7 bearing PRONI reference SCH 132/1/3. For that school PRONI will have retained the earlier volumes in the series starting in 1865 (SCH 3/1/1–2).

Libraries NI Online Resources

Libraries NI customers have access to 'Online Resources' on the library website.

Ancestry Library Edition is an online genealogical collection accessible on the Libraries NI website to library members at any library in Northern Ireland. This resource is available only from the Libraries NI network and is not accessible to members from their home computers. The Ancestry Library Edition collection has approximately thousands of databases and billions of indexed names from key collections spanning the fourteenth century to present day enabling customers to search for vital information about their ancestors.

The 'JSTOR Ireland Collection' is fully searchable, consists of the digital content of journals and other material relating to Ireland, and will be of great interest to anyone researching Irish history, genealogy, archaeology, literature etc. Most of the material included was published in the eighteenth, nineteenth and twentieth centuries.

The DIPPAM web resource is a virtual library of sources relating to the history of modern Ireland and its global diaspora. Documenting Ireland: Parliament, People and Migration (DIPPAM) is a collaboration project between Queen's University Belfast, The University of Ulster, The Mellon Centre for Migration Studies, Omagh, and Libraries NI, and has been funded by the Arts and Humanities Research Council. DIPPAM may be of particular interest to people involved in research the history of their locality or family, and for use in school history projects. It includes three searchable databases: Enhanced British Parliamentary Papers on Ireland (EPPI) – which comprises scans of over 15,000 official publications relating to all aspects of Irish affairs during the period of the Act of Union, 1800–1922, including bills, reports, royal commissions of inquiry and the published census returns. It is a rich source for the social history of Ireland, as well as for statistics and evidence relating to population, emigration, famine, crime and political movements: The Irish Emigration Database (IED) is made up of documents relating to Irish emigration since the eighteenth century, mainly to North America, and mostly drawn from archives in Northern Ireland and from private collections. The documents include emigrant letters, newspaper extracts, shipping advertisements, family papers and extracts from relevant publications and Voices of Migration and Return (VMR) is an oral history archive of over 90 life-narrative interviews conducted with emigrants and return-emigrants from the province of Ulster, collected between 2004 and 2008. The study participants represent a range of geographical origins within Ulster, class backgrounds and religious identities.

LOCATION
Town centre, at the corner of Hall's Lane and Queen Street, opposite the bridge over the north branch of the River Erne (route to Enniskillen Airport).

COUNTY GALWAY

GALWAY CITY LIBRARY

St Augustine Street
GALWAY
Ireland

TELEPHONE: (091) 561 666
E-mail: info@galwaylibrary.ie
Website: www.galwaylibrary.ie

HOURS
M, 14:00–17:00; Tu–Th, 11:00–20:00; F, 11:00–17:00; Sat, 11:00–17:00; Juvenile
Library closes at 17:00 each day.

ACCESS AND SERVICES
Visitors welcome. Memberships available for modest annual fee, allowing borrowing
privileges. ID required for application and proof of address. Photocopying available
for a fee; computers provided for internet access subject to conditions.

CONTACT
Galway City Library Services: Bernie Kelly, Librarian with overall responsibility for
Galway City Library Services
Public Library: Tom Browne
Juvenile Library: Geraldine Mannion

DESCRIPTION
The largest of the 30 branch libraries in the Galway Library Service.

HOLDINGS
Galway City Library offers a good general collection of educational and recreational
material. The Local History Department and Archives have a separate entry below.

LOCATION
City centre, off Lower Abbeygate Street, one block south-west on William Street
from Eyre Square/Kennedy Park.

GALWAY CITY LIBRARY – LOCAL HISTORY DEPARTMENT AND ARCHIVES

Galway Public Library (County Library Headquarters)
Island House, Cathedral Square
GALWAY
Ireland

TELEPHONE: (091) 562 471; FAX: (091) 565 039
E-mail: info@galwaylibrary.ie; archivist@galwaycoco.ie
Website: www.galwaylibrary.ie

HOURS
M–F, 09:30–13:00, 14:00–17:00

ACCESS AND SERVICES
Visitors are welcome, but it is advisable to make an appointment through the Local History Department by phone or fax, as some material requires use of microform readers, which may have to be reserved in advance. Staff are unable to undertake actual research on behalf of the public; however, advice is given on whether there are records held relevant to a query. Access to archives is by appointment only. Please contact the Archivist at (091) 562 471 or e-mail at archivist@galwaycoco.ie.

CONTACT
Maureen Moran, Deputy County and City Librarian.
E-mail: mamoran@galwaycoco.ie
Patria Mc Walter, Archivist. E-mail: archivist@galwaycoco.ie

DESCRIPTION
The Galway Library Service was established in 1924 as an integral branch of the Galway Local Authority Service. The Headquarters Library houses the main local history collection and archives.

HOLDINGS
This collection includes a comprehensive collection of old local newspapers, Griffith's Valuation, local Board of Guardian minute books, local maps, local historical photographs and the 1901 and 1911 censuses.

There are virtually complete sets of Board of Guardian minutes, *c.* 1840–1922, for the Poor Law Unions of Clifden, Galway, Gort, Loughrea, Mount Bellew and Tuam. There are substantial gaps in the series of Ballinasloe, and for Glenamaddy minutes survive only for the years 1894–5 and 1914–15. There are indoor relief registers for Gort 1914–20 and Tuam 1913–19.

Significant collections of records of administration are available for about a dozen estates, including: Blake Estate, near Tuam, 1666–1934 (including agent's correspondence and land surveys); that of Ffrench of Rahasane, near Loughrea, 1765–1897 (including agents' correspondence and inventory of auctioned items 1830s); that of St George Mansergh, Headford 1775–1853 (including volume of maps and a rent roll giving tenants' names and their holdings); that of O'Kelly of Castle Kelly, Aghrane, Killeroran, 1606–*c.* 1880 (including wills and correspondence as well as marriage settlements).

The Newspaper Collection is of special interest because of its comprehensive coverage of the local area going back to 1823. Holdings (listed chronologically) include: *Galway Weekly Advertiser*, 1823–43; *Tuam Gazette*, 1824; *Western Argus*,

1828–33; *Galway Independent*, 1829–32; *Galway Free Press*, 1832–5; *Galway Patriot*, 1835–9; *Tuam Herald*, 1837–78; *Connacht Journal*, 1839–40; *Galway Vindicator*, 1841–99; *Galway Standard*, 1841–3; *Galway Mercury and Connacht Weekly Advertiser*, 1844–60; *Western Star*, 1845–69; *Galway Packet and Connacht Advocate*, 1852–4; *Galway Express*, 1853–1920; *Warden of Galway*, 1853; *Connacht Patriot and Tuam Advertiser*, 1859–69; *Galway Press*, 1860–61; *Galway American*, 1862–3; *Tuam News*, 1871–3; *Western News and Weekly Examiner*, 1878–92; *Tuam Herald*, 1883–1923; *Connacht People and Ballinasloe Independent*, 1884–6; *Western Advertiser*, 1884–96; *Western Star*, 1888–1902; *Galway Observer*, 1889–1923; *Western News and Galway Guardian*, 1899–1901; *Western News*, 1901–03; *Connacht Champion*, 1904–11; *Western News*, 1905–20; *Loughrea Nationalist*, 1905; *Galway Pilot*, 1905–18; *Connacht Tribune*, 1909–96; *East Galway Democrat*, 1913–21; *Western News and Galway Leader*, 1921–6; *Galway Observer*, 1925–66; *Connacht Sentinel*, 1927–45; *East Galway Democrat*, 1936–49; *Tuam Herald*, 1938–99; *Connacht Sentinel*, 1950–99; and *City Tribune*, 1984–99.

Online Resources

The 1st Edition Ordnance Survey Maps for County Galway are available at www.galwaylibrary.ie

Ordnance Survey Place Name Books for Galway: In 1838, John O'Donovan was commissioned to list the place names of Ireland. For each place name, he listed variations of its name, its Irish form, its translation, its situation, and a brief description. The O'Donovan Place Names of Galway are on the galwaylibrary.ie website.

Lawrence Family Album: The Lawrence Family, of Lisreaghan, also known as Belview, owned extensive land in the east county Galway region in the eighteenth and nineteenth centuries, and founded the village of Lawrencetown. The Album, an important archive, is a wonderful history, pictorial and textual, of the family and the district of Lawrencetown. It is a treasure trove in terms of its value to local history containing so much rich detail on the family, together with late nineteenth century photographs of the village of Lawrencetown, family portraits and interior views of the house. The Album reveals so much about an era and a family which have long since disappeared but which played an important part in the development of the local landscape. This album is now available, in its entirety, on the Ask About Ireland website.

Web sites dealing with Genealogy and Galway's history is a web page that briefly outlines other resources on Galway's history and on genealogy. Clicking the above link will open the web page in a new window. To return to this page simply close the window.

Galway Reader is a website consisting of articles on Galway's history. It was edited by Samuel J. Maguire and was compiled in the 1950s. It is now available online. Clicking the above link will open the web page in a new window. To return to this page simply close the window.

Irish Newspaper Archives is a database of national and regional newspapers from centuries gone by. It includes newspapers from Galway. The database is searchable. It is also possible to browse the collection by newspaper title and date.

A number of books on Galway's history are available online at:
www.galway.net/galwayguide/history/. These books include *History of Lough Corrib*
by William R. Wilde, *History of Galway* by James Hardiman; *Iar Connaught* by
Roderick O'Flaherty, and *Waterways of Galway* by IEI

LOCATION
City centre, across the Salmon Weir Bridge, near the New Cathedral (the Cathedral
of Our Lady Assumed into Heaven).

GALWAY FAMILY HISTORY SOCIETY WEST LTD

St Joseph's Community Centre, Ashe Road, Shantalla
GALWAY
Ireland

TELEPHONE: (091) 860 464; FAX: (091) 860 432
E-mail: galwaywestroots@eircom.net
Website: www.rootsireland.ie

HOURS
M–Th, 10:00–16:00m; F, 10:00–13:00

ACCESS AND SERVICES
By gathering important genealogical sources such as Church and Civil records of
Baptisms/Births, Marriages and Deaths, Census Returns, Property and Burial records
in one place, Galway Family History Society West Ltd. offers a professional
genealogical research service for the Galway West region. Visitors are welcome to
send queries to, or make appointments for research consultations at our office in St
Joseph's Community Centre, Ashe Road Shantallla, Galway. During a consultation,
research queries can be discussed with a researcher and the scope of research to be
conducted can be assessed. Commissioned research is then conducted by our
researchers, using all available and relevant sources; reports and family trees are
compiled based on the findings of the research. The Centre has access to over a
million records for genealogical research. Initial enquiries and applications dealt with
in rotation, with every effort made to deal with applications within four weeks of
receipt. In addition to providing full service for those who wish to have their family
roots traced, the society offers publications for sale including: the journals *Galway
Roots 1–5; Forthill Cemetery; Castlegar Graveyard Inscriptions; Inishbofin through Time
and Tide, Memorial Inscriptions and Related History of Forthill Graveyard, Galway City*
and *The Memorial Inscriptions and Related History of Kiltullagh, Kilimordaly and
Esker Graveyards*. Prices range from €10 to €15 plus postage. Write, phone or e-mail
for exact quotation, including postage costs. Disabled access.

CONTACT
Mary Murray, Coordinator
Siobhan McGuinness, Researcher/Assistant Coordinator

DESCRIPTION
One of the Irish Family History Foundation's two designated family research centres
for Galway, the other being East Galway Family History Society, Woodford. The
main towns and villages in West Galway are: Galway City, Tuam, Clifden,
Oughterard, Athenry and Kinvara. The Aran Islands and Inishbofin are also in this

centre's catchment area. Parishes covered are: Abbeyknockmoy, Annaghadown, Aran Islands, Ardrahan, Athenry, Ballinderreen/Kilcolgan, Ballyconneely, Ballynakill/Letterfrack/ Tullycross, Carraroe, Carna, Castlegar, Claregalway, Clarinbridge, Clifden, Clonbur, Cummer, Donaghpatrick, Dunmore, Galway City, Headford, Inishbofin, Kilconly/Kilbennan, Kilcummin/Oughterard, Kilannin, Killererin, Kinvara, Lackagh, Milltown, Moycullen, Oranmore, Omey/Ballindoon, Rahoon, Rosmuc, Roundstone, Spiddal, and Tuam.

HOLDINGS
The centre has access to the following records containing over 1,000,000 entries in the West Galway area: Roman Catholic, Church of Ireland, Methodist and Presbyterian Church records up to 1900; civil records of births, deaths and marriages from their inception in 1864 up until 1900; elector lists; gravestone inscriptions; indexed directories (*Slater's*, *Pigot's*); parochial censuses (the oldest of which dates from 1821); newspaper obituaries; workhouse census search forms for pension applications; tithe applotment books; Griffith's Valuation (1848–55); 1901 and 1911 censuses; Ordnance Survey maps showing townlands; Certificates of Freedom, Churchings, RIC Pension Records, and Spinning Wheel Entitlements. The centre has also built up an extensive collection of local family history publications.

LOCATION
From Eyre Square take Eglington Street and follow St Francis Street to a set of traffic lights. Turn left and cross the Salmon Weir Bridge to the Roman Catholic Cathedral. Continue on University Road to a set of traffic lights in front of the University (Regional) Hospital. Turn left at the traffic lights onto Newcastle Road. Take the first right, which brings you onto Costello Road and Ashe Road. The centre is located in St Joseph's Community Centre, on the right hand side of the road.

NATIONAL UNIVERSITY OF IRELAND, GALWAY – JAMES HARDIMAN LIBRARY

University Road
GALWAY
Ireland

TELEPHONE: (091) 493 399; FAX: (091) 522 394
E-mail: library@nuigalway.ie
Website: www.library.nuigalway.ie

HOURS
Term time: M–F, 08:30–20:00; Sa, 08:30–17:30; Su, 10:00–17:30. Shorter hours apply during vacation period. Hours differ for Special Collections Department (*see* separate entry below) and for the Medical Library located at University College Hospital.

ACCESS AND SERVICES
Visitors welcome, but advance notice preferred and ID required. External service fees apply for visitors seeking self service to library facilities and for those seeking borrowing privileges. The library also offers a customised information service tailored to the needs of businesses, industry professionals and individuals on a fee paying basis. Fees also apply for photocopying and microform prints. Disabled access. Website updated regularly and contains more detailed information.

CONTACT
John Cox, University Librarian
Trish Finnan, Subject Librarian, Commerce and External Liaison.
Tel: (091) 493 564; e-mail: trish.finnan@nuigalway.ie

DESCRIPTION
The James Hardiman Library supports the teaching and research interests of the
National University of Ireland, Galway, originally founded in 1845 by Queen
Victoria, along with universities in Cork and Belfast. NUI Galway, formerly
University College Galway, is part of the National University of Ireland system,
which includes campuses in Dublin, Cork, Limerick and Maynooth. The Galway
campus has teaching and research interests in the sciences, engineering, law,
commerce, medicine and humanities.

HOLDINGS
The library houses a collection of more than 450,000 volumes, 340,000 e-books,
over 70,000 serials (print and online), a range of electronic information products, a
reference collection of Irish government publications, a European Documentation
Centre, special collections (*see* separate entry below), newspapers, and an audiovisual
collection.

LOCATION
Take N6 into Galway and follow signs for West Galway and Salthill. At junction of
N6 and Newcastle Road, turn left. Take next left turn into campus.

NATIONAL UNIVERSITY OF IRELAND, GALWAY – JAMES HARDIMAN LIBRARY – DEPARTMENT OF SPECIAL COLLECTIONS AND ARCHIVES

University Road
GALWAY, COUNTY GALWAY
Ireland

TELEPHONE: (091) 492 543, (091) 493 636; FAX: (091) 522 394
E-mail: marie.boran@nuigalway.ie, loretto.odonohoe@nuigalway.ie,
kieran.hoare@nuigalway.ie, barry.houlihan@nuigalway.ie .
Website: www.library.nuigalway.ie

HOURS
Term time: M, W–F, 09:00–17:00; Tu, 09:00–21:00
Vacation period: M–F, 09:00–17:00

ACCESS AND SERVICES
Visitors welcome to consult material not available to them in their local repositories,
but advance notice and ID required. Disabled access. Laptops and photography
permitted; pencils only. External service fees for visitors seeking borrowing privileges.
Fees for photocopying and microfilm prints, but photocopying of materials at staff
discretion. Copying of archival material carried out by Archivist, at his discretion.
Some 98 per cent of books in Department of Special Collections catalogued online.
Printed and electronic finding aids available for archival holdings. Collection level
descriptions of all archival collections are available on the website, as are descriptive
lists for some of the collections. Finding aids to archival collections are also available
in the Special Collections Reading Room. Exhibitions of material from the

collections held throughout the year. Free brochures available, including one entitled *Information Service for External Users*. Website updated regularly and contains more detailed information.

CONTACT
Marie Boran, Special Collections Librarian. E-mail: marie.boran@nuigalway.ie
Loretto O'Donohoe, Special Collections Librarian. E-mail:
Loretto.odonohoe@nuigalway.ie
Kieran Hoare, Archivist. E-mail: kieran.hoare@nuigalway.ie
Barry Houlihan, Archivist. E-Mail: barry.houlihan@nuigalway.ie

DESCRIPTION
National University of Ireland, Galway – James Hardiman Library was founded in 1849 and has been developing special collections of both archival and printed material from its inception. Its areas of special interest include: Galway and West of Ireland studies; Irish literature in English; literature and publishing in the Irish language; and local history pertaining to all counties but particularly those in the province of Connacht and County Clare.

HOLDINGS
The Department of Special Collections houses some 40,000 volumes, plus significant holdings of journals, manuscripts, maps, microforms, newspapers, pamphlets, photographs and recordings. Major book collections include: the Bairéad Collection of Irish language material, particularly ephemera from the early days of the Gaelic revival movements; the Cairnes Collection of works on nineteenth century economy and society; the Coen Collection of local and Irish history, plus some religious and devotional material; the Déon Collection of modern French writing, including the publications of the donor, French author Michel Déon; the Delargy Collection of twentieth century Irish and European folklore; the Fanning Collection of Irish archaeology and history; the Freyer Collection of works by and about author Liam O'Flaherty (1896–1984); the Gregory Collection containing virtually all material published by and about Augusta, Lady Gregory (1852–1932), including associated works and biographies; the Hunt Collection of books on twentieth century psychology and related subjects, especially from an American perspective; the Irish Women's Publishing Collection, with a focus on feminist publishers in Ireland since 1980; the Killanin Collection of some 3,500 volumes on twentieth century Irish literature, art and archaeology, plus world politics and horse racing; the St Anthony's Collection of some 20,000 volumes from the library of St Anthony's College in Newcastle, Galway, with a concentration on devotional literature, theology, Irish and Church history and the Henry Library, a collection on long-term loan from the Church of Ireland diocese of Tuam, Killala and Achonry. It includes Anglican church literature, sermons and biblical studies as well as nineteenth century literary and travel collections.

Manuscript and Archive collections of special importance include: The De hÍde Collection of manuscripts gathered by Doughláis de hÍde (Douglas Hyde), founder of the Gaelic League, who collected folklore and music in the Irish language (a selection from the De hÍde manuscript collection now appears in digitised format in the Irish Script On Screen database (www.isos.dias.ie); the Bairéad Collection of papers and correspondence relating to the Gaelic League and related Irish language material; the literary papers of Eoghan Ó Tuairisc; the LSB Manuscripts Collection

of miscellaneous manuscripts on a variety of subjects, some in Irish; the Estate
Papers Collection of material, such as rentals, marriage settlements, estate maps and
household correspondence relating to landed estates, principally in the west of
Ireland; the Revolutionary Ireland Collection of papers pertaining to the period
1914–22 in Ireland, especially County Galway; The Ruairí Ó Brádaigh Collection
and Brendan Duddy collection relate to Northern Ireland from the 1970s–1990s;
the County Galway Collection, which includes the records of the Galway Municipal
Authority dating back to its foundation in 1484; the minute books for Galway
Corporation, Galway Town Commissioners and the Galway Urban District Council;
the Clifden Railway documents and the papers relating to LDF activity in Galway
during World War II; the Academic Papers Collection containing the papers and
books of distinguished faculty members, including John E. Cairnes, Mary Donovan
O'Sullivan and Richard Doherty; the Theatre Archive containing the archives of
Taibhdhearc na Gaillimhe, the Irish theatre founded in 1928, the Druid Theatre,
founded in 1975, and the Galway Arts Festival, begun in 1977; the archives of the
Lyric Players, Belfast; the Arthur Shields Archive; the Siobhan McKenna collection
covering the theatre, television and film career of the actress; and the Photographic
Archive, with special focus on Galway and UCG (University College Galway).
Literary papers are also held, most notably those of John McGahern and Thomas
Kilroy. Of special historical interest are two sets of papers relating to the Earls of
Lucan. This County Mayo family goes back to the sixteenth century and this archive
holds special importance for nineteenth and twentieth century Irish history,
particularly in relations to land issues.

Though the library does not offer a family history enquiry service, the
Department of Special Collections does house a collection of local history books and
journals which would be helpful to the family historian. In addition, microfilm
copies of both Irish national newspapers such as the *Irish Independent, Irish Times*
and *Irish Press* and local Galway newspapers are held by the Library.

LOCATION
Take N6 into Galway, follow signs for West Galway and Salthill. At junction of N6
and Newcastle Road, turn left. Take next left turn into campus. The Department of
Special Collections is located on the ground floor of the library.

DIOCESE OF CLONFERT ARCHIVE

St Brendan's, Coorheen
LOUGHREA, COUNTY GALWAY
Ireland

TELEPHONE: (091) 841 560
E-mail: clonfert@iol.ie
Website: www.clonfertdiocese.ie

HOURS
By appointment

ACCESS AND SERVICES
Visitors welcome but by appointment only. Advance notice and references required.
Pencils only. Photography not permitted. No disabled access facilities. No
photocopying or microfilm facilities available.

CONTACT
Bishop John Kirby

DESCRIPTION
Small diocesan archive, with few documents dating before 1900. There was no permanent residence until 1907. Some bishops, on transfer, took their papers with them to their new assignments. Clonfert is one of the smallest dioceses in Ireland, with just 24 parishes.

HOLDINGS
Records and documents relating to the administration of the Roman Catholic Diocese of Clonfert.

LOCATION
Bishop's House Coorheen Loughrea Co Galway.

EAST GALWAY FAMILY HISTORY SOCIETY CO. LTD.

Woodford Heritage Centre
WOODFORD, LOUGHREA, COUNTY GALWAY
Ireland

TELEPHONE: (090) 974 9309; FAX: (090) 974 9546
E-mail: galwayroots@eircom.net or galwayroots@gmail.com
Website: www.rootsireland.ie or www.galwayroots.com

HOURS
M–Th, 09:30–16:30; F, 09:30–13:00

ACCESS AND SERVICES
The East Galway Family History Society offers a full range of genealogical services to people interested in researching their East Galway ancestors at the Woodford Heritage Centre or online at www.rootsireland.ie. All the civil records are available online at rootsireland but not all Roman Catholic records are available, please contact the Centre for further details. Initial enquiries are answered promptly; family history reports usually takes approximately four to six weeks. The East Galway Family History Society offers a range of publications relating to the area for sale. These include: *Lough Derg: the Westside Story* (map); and *Woodford: a Guide to its Sights*.

CONTACT
Monica Hynes

DESCRIPTION
One the Irish Family History Foundation's two designated family research centres for County Galway, the other being Galway Family History Society West, Galway City. Chief towns and villages of East Galway include: Ballinasloe, Loughrea, Gort, Portumna, Glenamaddy and Mountbellew.

HOLDINGS
The earliest Roman Catholic baptismal parish records computerised at this centre start in 1800 approximately. The earliest Church of Ireland records date from 1747 for Loughrea. Other major sources include: civil records of births, deaths and marriages 1864–1900, Griffith's Valuation, tithe applotment books, 1821 Census

(partial), 1889 Woodford Parish Census, 1901 and 1911 Censuses, 1908 Pension
Returns, Trade Directories, Lewis Topographical Dictionary, Burkes Peerage and
Baronetage, School Rollbooks, Emigrant Lists and many other sources pertaining to
individual parishes.

LOCATION
14.5 miles south of Loughrea on the R351. Loughrea is 26.28 miles southeast of
Galway City on the M6.

COUNTY KERRY

KERRY GENEALOGICAL RESEARCH CENTRE

Note: Formerly the Killarney Genealogical Centre, the Kerry Genealogical Research Centre is no longer in operation. Catholic and Church of Ireland parish record transcripts for the nineteenth century, however, are readily available online at: www.irishgenealogy.ie/index.html. These records include all available pre-1900 baptism and marriage records (and Church of Ireland burials, where available).

KERRY ARCHAEOLOGICAL AND HISTORICAL SOCIETY
See KERRY LOCAL HISTORY AND ARCHIVES COLLECTION, Tralee

KILLARNEY GENEALOGICAL CENTRE
See KERRY GENEALOGICAL RESEARCH CENTRE

KERRY LOCAL HISTORY AND ARCHIVES COLLECTION

Kerry County Library, Moyderwell
TRALEE, COUNTY KERRY
Ireland

TELEPHONE: (066) 712 1200 (County Library), (066) 712 1200 (Local History and Archives Department); FAX: (066) 712 9202 (County Library), (066) 712 9202 (Local History and Archives Department)
E-mail: info@kerrylibrary.ie, localhistory@kerrylibrary.ie
Website: www.kerrylibrary.ie

HOURS
County Library: M, W, F–Sa, 10:00–17:00; Tu, Th, 10:00–20:00
Local History and Archives Department: M–F, 10:00–17:00

ACCESS AND SERVICES
Visitors welcome. Membership available on application at no charge. ID required. Charges levied, however, on borrowing of books (30c per item borrowed; children up to and including second level students exempt from these charges). Online catalogue. The library is a focal point for cultural and educational activities in the

community. Services include internet workstations, with free access for public use. Kerry Archaeological and Historical Society, established in 1967 for the collection, recording, study and preservation of material relating to the history and antiquities of County Kerry, also operates from the library.

CONTACT
Michael Lynch, Archivist and Local History Manager.
E-mail: archivist@kerrylibrary.ie

DESCRIPTION
The Kerry County Library is the flagship library in the nine library county system that also includes the following branch libraries: Killarney (tel. (064) 32655, fax (064) 36065); Ballybunion (tel. (068) 27615) Cahirciveen (tel. (066) 947 2287); Castleisland (tel. (066) 714 1485); Dingle (tel. (066) 915 1499); Kenmare (tel. (064) 41416); Killorglin (tel. (066) 976 1272); and Listowel (tel. (068) 23044). The Local History and Archives Department at Kerry County Library Headquarters, Tralee, was officially opened on 25 March 2002.

HOLDINGS
The library houses approximately 38,000 volumes of general educational and recreational interest. It is also home to the Kerry Local History Collection. This section aims to collect and make available as comprehensively as possible a collection of material relating to the history of the county, including published books, manuscripts, photographs, newspapers, video and sound recordings. The collection includes: a comprehensive collection of local newspapers dating back to the 1820s; a collection of books in Kerry and by Kerry authors; local maps (Ordnance Survey 6 inch); Board of Guardian minute books, 1840s–1922; Rural District Council minute books and financial records, 1899–1925; county and urban rates and valuation records, 1900–86); county Grand Jury presentments, 1875–99; County Board of Health minute books and administration files, 1923–42; County Committee of Agriculture minute books, 1920–88; periodicals, e.g. *Journal of the Royal Society of Antiquaries of Ireland, Journal of the Cork Historical and Archaeological Society*; Irish Folklore Commission Schools Collection, 1937–8 (on microfilm); tithe applotment books, 1820–35; Griffith's Valuation (*c.* 1850); 1901 and 1911 censuses (on microfilm); Tralee Gaol register, 1882–8; and specialised collections of papers and family histories, including the Reidy family (literary papers), Fr Ferris (topographical notes), papers relating to the Denny Estate, papers relating to Antarctic explorer Tom Crean, Thomas Ashe papers and material on Roger Casement. There are also two significant collections of solicitors' papers (M.J. Byrne and Co., Listowel and Dr J.D. O'Connell, Tralee), which include substantial estate and land material for the Listowel/North Kerry area and for the Kenmare/Dromore/South Kerry area. Business archives include collections relating to O'Brien Corkery General Merchants, Kenmare (1860s–1960s), William Lynn and Sons, Tailors, Tralee (1916–70) and Dingle Harbour Commissioners (*c.* 1900–*c.* 1970).

Local newspaper holdings include: *Chute's Western Herald*, 1812–35; *Kerry Advocate*, 1914–15; *Kerry Champion*, 1928–58; *Kerry Evening Post*, 1829–1917; *Kerry Evening Star*, 1902–14; *Kerry Examiner*, 1840–56; *Kerry Independent*, 1880–84; *Kerry News*, 1924–41; *Kerry People*, 1902–22; *Kerry Press*, 1914–16; *Kerry Reporter*, 1924–35; *Kerry Sentinel*, 1878–1917; *Kerry Star*, 1861–3; *Kerry Weekly Reporter and Commercial Advertiser*, 1883–1920; *Killarney Echo and South Kerry*

Chronicle, 1889–1920; *An Lóchrann,* 1913–20; *Munster Life,* 1897; *Raymond's Kerry Herald,* 1856; *Tralee Chronicle and Killarney Echo,* 1843–75; *Tralee Chronicle and Killarney Chronicle,* 1860–67; *Tralee Liberator,* 1914–39; *Tralee Mercury,* 1829–39; *Weekly Chronicle,* 1873; *Kerry's Eye,* 1974–present; *Kerryman,* 1904–present; *The Kingdom,* 1984–present; *Killarney Advertiser,* 1974–present. The collection also includes a good representation of national newspapers, including *Freeman's Journal,* 1763–1860, *The Nation,* 1842–85; *Irish Press,* 1931–95, and *Irish Times,* 1859–present.

LOCATION

Tralee town centre, at the corner of Dean's Lane and Moyderwell.

COUNTY KILDARE

NATIONAL UNIVERSITY OF IRELAND, MAYNOOTH JOHN PAUL II LIBRARY

MAYNOOTH, COUNTY KILDARE
Ireland

TELEPHONE: (01) 708 3884; FAX: (01) 628 6008
E-mail: reader.services@nuim.ie
Website: www.nuim.ie/library

HOURS
Term time: M–Th, 08:30–22:00 (service hours, 09:15–21:00); F, 08:30–19:00
(service hours, 09:15–18:00); Sa, 10:00–17:00 (service hours, 10:15–16:30); Su,
closed except for specific dates in January and May

Vacation period: M–F, 08:30–17:00 (service hours, 10:15–16:30)

ACCESS AND SERVICES
Visitors admitted at Librarian's discretion. External readers welcome when material
not available elsewhere. Annual membership fee for borrowing privileges.
Wheelchair access. Photocopying and microform prints available for a fee. Leaflets
and booklets describing services available. For access to early printed books and
archives, both housed in the Russell Library, see ST PATRICK'S COLLEGE
MAYNOOTH ARCHIVES and ST PATRICK'S COLLEGE MAYNOOTH – RUSSELL
LIBRARY. NUI Maynooth provides the library service in the John Paul II Library
and the Russell Library. There is a branch library of the university at the Kilkenny
Campus (telephone (056) 75919). A major extension to the John Paul II Library
was recently completed.

CONTACT
Cathal McCauley, Librarian. Telephone: (01) 708 3879; Mobile: 0870562830;
e-mail: Cathal.mccauley@nuim.ie
Helen Fallon, Deputy Librarian Telephone: (01) 708 3880; Mobile: 0876110656;
e-mail: Helen.b.fallon@nuim.ie

DESCRIPTION
Following two centuries of internationally renowned scholarly activity on the
Maynooth campus the National University of Ireland, Maynooth was established

under the 1997 Universities Act as an autonomous member of the federal structure known as the National University of Ireland. With more than 7,000 fulltime students and another 3,500 registered as part-time, NUI Maynooth has 26 Academic Departments which are organized into three Faculties: Arts, Celtic Studies and Philosophy; Science and Engineering, and Social Sciences. Building on a tradition of scholarship and excellence in all aspects of its teaching and learning, and research activities, within the liberal arts and sciences tradition, NUI Maynooth is committed to being a first class research-led centre of learning and academic discovery. It is located on a pleasant university campus in Ireland's only university town 20km west of Dublin, and has recently undergone a major phase of expansion in research, teaching and service facilities. The spacious campus is laid out in its own extensive grounds in rural surroundings, and is divided between an older complex of fine nineteenth century buildings and a modern complex of teaching, research, accommodation, and support facilities.

HOLDINGS
The library houses a collection of more than 250,000 volumes, with significant collections built up by scholar professors from the mid-nineteenth century onwards. Particular strengths are in theology, religion and history. Early printed books, manuscripts and archives are housed in the Russell Library. The Library is part of the Irish Research electronic Library (IReL) consortium and provides access to over 46,000 electronic journals. A large range of eBooks and databases are available.

LOCATION
15 miles west of Dublin, off the M4. Served by buses 66, 66X and 67A from Dublin city centre and by trains from Dublin's Connolly station. The campus is located in the village centre. The John Paul II Library is located in the south (old) campus, across the footbridge *en route* to the north (new) campus.

ST PATRICK'S COLLEGE MAYNOOTH ARCHIVES

Russell Library
MAYNOOTH, COUNTY KILDARE
Ireland

TELEPHONE: (01) 628 5222; FAX: (01) 628 9063
E-mail: library.russell@nuim.ie
Website: www.spcm.ie

HOURS
By appointment.

ACCESS AND SERVICES
Visitors welcome, but advance notice and ID required. Wheelchair access. Laptops permitted; pencils only. Leaflets and pamphlets available. For access to College Archives permission must first be sought from the College Archivist. Archival materials, including Salamanca Archives, may then be consulted in the Russell Library. Publications of interest include: Patrick J. Corish, *Maynooth College, 1795–1995* (Dublin, 1995); Patrick J. Hamell, *Maynooth Students and Ordinations, 1795–1984* (Maynooth, 1982–4); Patrick J. Corish, 'Maynooth College Archives', in *Catholic Archives* 13 (1993), 46–8; Regina Whelan Richardson (ed.) *The Salamanca letters: a catalogue of correspondence (1619–1871)* (Maynooth, 1995).

CONTACT
Librarian, Russell Library

DESCRIPTION
St Patrick's College, Maynooth was founded in 1795 to educate and train Catholic clergy. In 1896 it was established as a pontifical university and in 1910 it also became a recognised college of the National University of Ireland. St Patrick's College is the National Seminary of Ireland and is administered separately from the National University of Ireland Maynooth.

HOLDINGS
The archive houses the original records of the college plus the historical archive of the Irish College of Salamanca in Spain. Though more than 11,000 priests have been ordained at Maynooth, a fire in 1940 destroyed the matriculation register for the period 1795–1940, removing an important family history record. This is a small domestic archive, of limited importance to genealogists. The Salamanca Archive of some 50,000 documents contains administration records not only of the Irish College in Salamanca (1592–1950s), but also other Irish Colleges in Spain, including Alcala, Santiago and Seville. The archive is currently being catalogued. See also *The Salamanca Letters: a Catalogue of Correspondence (1619–1871)* (Maynooth, 1995).

LOCATION
In St Patrick's House, the Gothic quadrangle beyond St Joseph's Square, in the south cloister.

For the early-printed books and manuscripts of St Patrick's College Maynooth, *see* NATIONAL UNIVERSITY OF IRELAND MAYNOOTH – RUSSELL LIBRARY

NATIONAL UNIVERSITY OF IRELAND MAYNOOTH – RUSSELL LIBRARY

MAYNOOTH, COUNTY KILDARE
Ireland

TELEPHONE: (01) 708 3890; FAX: (01) 628 6008
E-mail: library.russell@nuim.ie
Website: http://library.nuim.ie/russell

HOURS
M–Th, 10:00–13:00, 14:00–17:00

ACCESS AND SERVICES
Researchers welcome, but advance notice and ID requested. Visitors admitted at Librarian's discretion. Wheelchair access. Laptops permitted; pencils only. Leaflets and pamphlets available. Publications of interest include: Agnes Neligan (ed.), *Maynooth Library Treasures* (Dublin, 1995). Printed holdings are being added to the main NUIM online catalogue, 40% incorporated to date. Meanwhile, there are three card catalogues for books in Russell Library. These are also incorporated in John Paul II Library card catalogue. There is a published catalogue for Irish manuscripts: Paul Walsh, *Catalogue of Irish MSS in Maynooth College Library, Part 1* (Má Nuad, 1943); Pádraig Ó Fiannachta, *Clár Lámhscríbhinní Gaeilge Mhá Nuad*, fascicles 2–8 (Má Nuad, 1965–73); Pádraig Ó Fiannachta, *Clár Lámhscríbhinní Gaeilge: Leabhlarlanna*

na Cléire agus Mionchnuasaigh, fascicles 1–2 (Baile Átha Cliath, 1978–80). Further additions to the Manuscript Collection are detailed in *Seanchas Ard Mhacha* VII, 2 (1974), *Léachtai Cholm Cille* XI (1980), XVI (1986). There is a separate catalogue of the HBS Bible collection. Incunabula are listed in the *Incunabula Short Title Catalogue* and relevanteighteenth century holdings in the *English Short Title Catalogue* (under St Patrick's Library)

CONTACT
Librarian, Russell Library

DESCRIPTION
The first foundation, St Patrick's College, Maynooth was set up as the National Seminary in 1795 to educate and train Catholic clergy. In 1896 it was established as a pontifical university and in 1910 it also became a recognised college of the National University of Ireland. In 1997 St Patrick's College and the newly formed National University of Ireland Maynooth became two separate institutions. Lay students were first admitted to Maynooth in 1966 and today the National University of Ireland, Maynooth has an enrolment of some 9,000 students. The library is administered by NUI Maynooth and serves both institutions. The first library building, designed by A.W. Pugin (1812–52), was completed in 1861. In 1984 it was renamed for Charles Russell, President of Maynooth, 1857–80; it served as the main college library until the opening of the John Paul II Library in 1984.

HOLDINGS
The Russell Library houses the university's collection of rare and early printed books and manuscripts. The collection totals more than 32,000 books, plus maps, architectural records, illuminated manuscripts and some 300 volumes of Irish manuscripts. The pre-1851 books collection focuses on theological works, many of which were printed on the continent, but also includes significant holdings in history, travel, classics, antiquities and science. Important holdings include: 59 incunabula, Maynoothiana, rare and interesting printings and bindings; over 1,200 bound volumes of eighteenth and nineteenth century pamphlets, variously acquired, on diverse subjects; a Bible collection, including over 2,000 Bibles in almost 600 languages, from the sixteenth century to the 1960s, on permanent loan since 1986 from the National Bible Society of Ireland (formerly the Hibernian Bible Society, founded in 1806). The Map Collection includes a complete bound set of 6 inch Ordnance Survey maps, 1833–45, and a set of 1 inch Ordnance Survey maps (1903) with parish boundaries marked.

The Manuscript Collection is especially strong in Irish language materials. The Irish language manuscripts represent in particular the collections of three men: John Murphy (1772–1847), Bishop of Cork; Eugene O'Curry (1796–1862), Professor of Irish History and Archaeology at the Catholic University of Ireland; and Laurence Renehan (1797–1857), President of Maynooth College and of the Celtic Society. The Murphy Collection contains 114 bound volumes bequeathed to the college in 1848. The O'Curry Collection contains 115 volumes of material, all collected or transcribed by Eugene O'Curry. The Renehan Collection contains material collected for an ecclesiastical history of Ireland and, in addition to the Irish language material, includes 79 bound volumes of manuscripts in English, French and Latin. The Irish language manuscript collections are described and listed in a printed catalogue begun by Rev Paul Walsh in 1943 and completed by an tAthair Pádraig Ó Fiannachta.

These have been microfilmed and may be consulted in the John Paul II Library. The earliest have also been digitised and are accessible on the website of Irish Script on Screen, www.isos.dias.ie hosted by the Dublin Institute of Advanced Studies. Private papers include the papers of Revd John Francis Shearman, antiquary; John Canon O'Hanlon, author of the monumental *Lives of the Irish saints*; and Revd Desmond Forristal, broadcaster and playwright.

LOCATION
In St Patrick's House, the Gothic quadrangle beyond St Joseph's Square, in the south cloister.

KILDARE COLLECTIONS AND RESEARCH SERVICES

Riverbank, Main Street
NEWBRIDGE, COUNTY KILDARE
Ireland

TELEPHONE: (087) 987 1046, (045) 448 351/352;
E-mail localhistory@kildarecoco.ie; mailto:localhistory@kildarecoco.ie
Website: www.kildare.ie/library

Note: Kildare Collections and Research Services incorporates the three related departments, Archives, Local Studies and Genealogy, under one roof. *See* separate entries below. While visitors are welcome, re-scheduled opening times of the branch library and demands on resources make it necessary to recommend that planned research would be by appointment.

KILDARE COLLECTIONS AND RESEARCH SERVICES – ARCHIVES

Riverbank, Main Street
NEWBRIDGE, COUNTY KILDARE
Ireland

TELEPHONE: (087) 987 1046, (045) 448 351/352;
E-mail localhistory@kildarecoco.ie
Website: www.kildare.ie/library

Some archival material on www.kildare.ie/ehistory www.kildare.ie/ehistory

HOURS
By appointment only

ACCESS AND SERVICES
Limited access provided by the Local Studies Department, strictly by appointment.

DESCRIPTION
Kildare County Council developed a specially adapted storage facility which was assigned for the archives at Newbridge. In preparing for this, it was first necessary to identify and preserve the public archive collections held in various locations throughout the county.

HOLDINGS
Quality archive collections have survived for County Kildare, but these are currently uncatalogued and are, therefore, not readily accessible:

Grand Jury collection (1809–93 – incomplete); Naas and Athy Poor Law Union records; Celbridge Poor Law Union records almost non-existent; Athy, Naas, Celbridge, Edenderry Rural District Council records; Athy Urban District Council; Some Interment records are also now available on microfilm; some Private Papers.

LOCATION
Beside the public library as part of Kildare Collections and Research Services, Newbridge, County Kildare. First turn on the left after the bridge from Dublin.

KILDARE COLLECTIONS AND RESEARCH SERVICES – LOCAL STUDIES DEPARTMENT

Riverbank, Main Street
NEWBRIDGE, COUNTY KILDARE
Ireland

TELEPHONE: (087) 987 1046, (045) 448 351/352;
E-mail localhistory@kildarecoco.ie
Website: www.kildare.ie/library

HOURS
Tu–F, 10:00–13:00, 14:00–16:30; Sa, 10:00–13:00, 14:00–16:30

ACCESS AND SERVICES
By appointment recommended. Physical access is through the branch library next door which is now closed most mornings (Thursday excepted).

CONTACT
Librarian

DESCRIPTION
The Local Studies Department forms an integral part of the Kildare County Library Arts Service and ultimately, in partnership with Archives and Genealogy, has become an integral part of the Riverbank Cultural Campus. The Local Studies Collection is located in Kildare Collections and Research Services. It is the focal point for local history research in County Kildare for historians and enthusiasts alike. The Reading Room and research facilities have greatly enhanced the services on offer. The collection will be added to the computerised catalogue on the county library's Horizon system, further enhancing the service and making it more accessible. Many important primary resources have also been added to the website to allow researchers even greater accessibility to the collection.

HOLDINGS
As well as containing an extensive collection of secondary source material the Local Studies Department includes many original sources. Among the most important items in the collection are the Ballitore Manuscripts, consisting of files of late nineteenth century correspondence, school notebooks, drawings etc of the

Shackletons and other Quaker families from Ballitore, County Kildare. The Teresa
Brayton Collection of books, newspaper cuttings and personal items forms another
important part of the Local Studies Department's collection. Perhaps the most
valuable source for the study of local history is the Journal of the County Kildare
Archaeological Society, first published in 1891 and now available on DVD. In
addition, the Local Studies Department holds Griffith's Valuation; tithe applotment
books; 6 inch Ordnance Survey Maps, 1837, and other maps of the county from the
eighteenth century; rentals from the Marquis of Drogheda and Verschoyle Estates;
Mansfield Estate Papers; photographs from the Lawrence Collection etc. Microfilm
holdings include the 1901 and 1911 censuses, Irish statutes, 1310–1761 and index;
Journal of the House of Lords, 1634–98, 1703–25, 1727–52; *Journal of the House of
Commons*, 1613–1800; *Memorials of the Dead*; *Ordnance Survey Field Name Books*.
Newspaper holdings on microfilm below.

The Local Studies Department currently provides restricted access to the archives
of Kildare County Council.

The Local Studies Department has an extensive and impressive collection of
local and national newspapers and periodicals.

Newspapers on Microfilm
Leinster Leader, 1881/2–present; *Kildare Observer*, 1880–1935; *Freeman's Journal*,
1763–1831; *Leinster Express*, 24 Sept 1831–84; *Irish Times*, March 1859–December
1895, 1904, 1905, 1914–23, January 1997–2003; *Dublin Penny Journal*, 1832–6;
Carlow Nationalist (later Kildare edition)1889–present
Newspapers in Hard Copy
Leinster Leader, 1983–present; *Kildare Nationalist*, 1983–present; *Weekly Nation*,
1898 (bound 1 vol.); *Weekly Nation*, 1899–present (bound 1 vol.); *The Nation*,
December 1843–September 1844 (bound 1 vol.); *Dublin Penny Journal*, 1832–3,
1834–5; *Dublin Journal*, 1862; *Duffy's Hibernian Magazine* II (July–December
1862), III (January–June 1863); *Curragh News* (bound photocopy),
February–September 1891; *Ballitore Magazine* (bound photocopy) 2nd series 1821;
Leixlip Life (bound 4 vols), April 1973–March 1982; *Newbridge: New Link
Magazine*, 1973–6; *Maynooth Newsletter*, 1975–present; *Lucan Times*,
November–December 1989, 1990, January, March–May 1991.

Periodicals
Journal of the County Kildare Archaeological Society I–XX (ii) (1891–present); *Journal
of the Royal Society of Antiquaries* 1–132 (1849–present); *Irish Sword* 1–23
(1949–present); *Quarterly Bulletin of the Irish Georgian Society* I–X (1958–67);
Collectanea Hibernica 1–45 (1958–2003); *Analecta Hibernica* 1–29 (1930–80)
32–36 (1985–95); *Irish Historical Studies* 1–6, 9, 13, 18–22, 24, 27, 29, 31, 36–44,
81, 82 (incomplete); *Archivum Hibernicum* I–XXII (1910–74), XXXIV–XXXV
(1977–81, 1988, 1990, 1993, 1995); *Studia Hibernica* 1–8, 10, 12–13, 15, 19
(incomplete); *Béaloideas*, 1927–2001 (incomplete); *Royal Geological Society of
Ireland* III–IV (1844–50); X–XVIII (1862–89) (incomplete), index to vols I–XVIII;
Irish Ecclesiastical Record, 1906–60 (incomplete); *Wolfe Tone Annual*, 1935, 1937–40,
1942–3, 1945–52, 1954–8, 1961–2 (incomplete); *Capuchin Annual*, 1930–71,
1973–7 (incomplete); *Irish Texts* I–XXV, XXVII–LV; *Catholic Bulletin*, 1914,
1917–18, 1920, 1925; *Studies* 1912–72 (incomplete); *Record of the Maynooth Union*,
1909–39 (incomplete); *Clongownian*, 1895–1974 plus index, 1975–80; *Association*

for the Preservation of the Memorials of the Dead, 1895–1916 (incomplete), *Irish Family History* 2–20 (1986–2004); *Museum Ireland* 2–7, 9–13 (1992–2003) (incomplete).

Major addition to the holdings is in the form of an online site called EHistory; www.kildare.ie/ehistory which is regularly updated and averages 1,000 hits per week. The *Kildare Observer Newspaper* 1880–1935 is now online and searchable. Access is free courtesy of Kildare Library and Arts Services and the British Library and the link is on Ehistory.

Other databases and resources are available for free via the Kildare Library and Arts Website and there is free access to the Odnance Survey Historic Maps and the Archives of *The Irish Times* via the branch library network.

LOCATION
Beside the public library in the Kildare Collections and Research Services. First turn on the left after the bridge from Dublin.

KILDARE COLLECTIONS AND RESEARCH SERVICES – KILDARE GENEALOGY

Riverbank, Main Street
NEWBRIDGE, COUNTY KILDARE
Ireland

TELEPHONE: (045) 448350
E-mail:
Websites: www.kildare.ie/Library/KildareCollectionsandResearchServices/Genealogy/

HOURS
By appointment.
Tu–Th, 09:00–17:00, Lunch 13:00–14:00

ACCESS AND SERVICES
Visitors welcome. Approved family history research centre for those interested in tracing their family roots in County Kildare. Member of all Ireland network of genealogy centres affiliated to the Irish Family History Foundation. Consult website for fee schedule and application form.

CONTACT
Karel Kiely MA

DESCRIPTION
Kildare Genealogy has computerized many of the genealogical records of County Kildare including Roman Catholic and Church of Ireland registers; Griffith's Valuation, tithe applotment books, the 1901 census, gravestone inscriptions, the *Leinster Leader* newspaper. It has the largest database of County Kildare records in the world and is unique in its holdings of computerized indexes of parish records. The majority of its data is now accessible online at as part of an All Ireland database of genealogical records. This website allows users to search Co. Kildare records by surname, first name, year, and parish. Users can search adjoining counties where records may overlap between parishes. For those that do not know a county of origin in Ireland this website gives them a chance to pinpoint possible records.

HOLDINGS
The company has indexed church records for both Roman Catholic and Church of
Ireland parishes in County Kildare. Roman Catholic parish registers generally consist
of baptism and marriage registers, although a small number of burial registers also
exist. Owing to the fact that the Roman Catholic Church was suppressed (by the
Penal Laws) from the 1690s until 1829, the parish registers of different parishes have
varying start dates. The earliest registers which still survive start from about 1740.
Church of Ireland parish registers generally consist of baptism, marriage and burial
registers. These start much earlier than the Roman Catholic ones, with some Kildare
registers going back as far as the late 1600s. Lists of Catholic and Church of Ireland
records can be found on the company's website.

Note: the holdings are not available to the public onsite. They form the basis for a
commissioned research service or are available online.

LOCATION
Beside the public library. First turn on the left after the bridge.

COUNTY KILKENNY

KILKENNY FAMILY HISTORY

Rothe House and Garden
Rothe House, Parliament Street
KILKENNY, COUNTY KILKENNY
Ireland

TELEPHONE: (056) 772 2893
E-mail: info@rothehouse.com; kilkennyfamilyhistory@rothehouse.com
Website: www.rothehouse.com

HOURS
M–Sa, 10:30–17:00

ACCESS AND SERVICES
A fee based, not for profit organisation that offers genealogical research services to persons interested in tracing their roots in County Kilkenny. It is a member of the Irish Family History Foundation, the coordinating body for a network of government approved genealogical research centres in the Republic of Ireland and in Northern Ireland, which have computerised almost 20 million Irish ancestral records of different types (see www.rootsireland.ie homepage for lists these vital records). Initial enquiries usually replied to within one week. Record searches and partial searches usually take about one month and enquirers who commission full reports can anticipate a delay of about three months To make enquiry please email initially, or to request assessment please complete application form on our website: www.rothehouse/genealogy and send to: kilkennyfamilyhistory@rothehouse.com

Our assessment costs €90, single record searches cost €30. Payment facilities available via pay pal in www.rothehouse.com. Alternatively enquirers can log onto www.rootsireland.ie search and view themselves where records can be purchased for a small fee.

Among the numerous surnames in Kilkenny City and County are Murphy, Walsh, Brennan, Maher, Butler, Phelan (and O'Phelan), Grace, Fitzpatrick, Comerford and Ryan. The main towns and villages in this county in addition to Kilkenny City are: Castlecomer, Callan, Freshford, Johnstown and Thomastown. Relevant publications include: *Old Kilkenny Review*, 1978, 1980, 1986, 1988, 1990–94; *Kilkenny Graveyard Inscriptions*, (Knocktoper No. 1 and St Patrick's No. 2); W. Nolan and K. Whelan (eds) *Kilkenny: History and Society*; and *Kilkenny City and County: a Photographic Record.* See website for a more comprehensive listing and prices.

CONTACT
Researcher

DESCRIPTION
Kilkenny Family History is the primary genealogical research service for County Kilkenny, with some 2,000,000 genealogical records computerised.

HOLDINGS
Church records from 1754 to 1900 have been computerised. Kilkenny Archaeological Society library at Rothe House also holds copies of: Indexed *Pigot's* and *Slater's Directories*; various periodicals, including *Old Kilkenny Review*, various estate rentals; a listing of some of the records of Kilkenny Corporation; and files of the *Kilkenny Journal* newspaper and some of the *Moderator*, neither of which is currently indexed, though indexing of the eighteenth century items has begun.

LOCATION
City centre, opposite the courthouse, a ten minute walk from Kilkenny Castle. The nearest car park is on Parliament Street at the Market Cross Shopping Centre.

KILKENNY COUNTY ARCHIVES
See KILKENNY COUNTY LIBRARY, Kilkenny

KILKENNY COUNTY LIBRARY

Kilkenny County Library HQ,
John's Green House,
John's Green,
KILKENNY, COUNTY KILKENNY
Ireland

TELEPHONE: (056) 779 4160; FAX: (056) 779 4168
E-mail: lstudies@kilkennylibrary.ie
Website: www.kilkennylibrary.ie

HOURS
M–F, 09:00–13:00, 14:00–16:45; closed bank and public holidays

ACCESS AND SERVICES
Visitors welcome, but advance notice preferred. Advance booking of microform reader/printers required. Internet access available. Disabled access facilities. Fees for photocopying, microform prints and e-mail usage. Entire collection catalogued online. There is a printed catalogue for the Local History Collection. Free brochures available, and an in-house guide and directory of services available for consultation in the Local Studies Department. The library's website has a section devoted to local studies and provides a guide for researchers of genealogy in Kilkenny.

CONTACT
Declan Macauley, Executive Librarian
Damien Brett, Senior Library Assistant

DESCRIPTION
Headquarters library of the County Kilkenny library system. The library houses the county's main local history collection.

HOLDINGS
The library system houses a collection of some 300,000 books, plus journals, manuscripts, maps, microforms, newspapers, pamphlets, photographs and recordings. The Local History Collection will be of special interest to visitors. It consists of important holdings of local history items, a collection of material by Kilkenny authors or pertaining to Kilkenny, local newspapers, genealogical historical sources and Kilkenny files collected from assorted publications.

The library also oversees the Kilkenny County Archives, but most of these records are held offsite so advance booking is essential. The archives include Board of Guardian minute books for the Poor Law Unions of Castlecomer, Thomastown and Urlingford, c. 1850–c. 1900, and also Callan and Kilkenny, 1842–1922 (some gaps in all series). The minutes detail the management of the workhouses where the destitute poor were accommodated.

Grand Jury records include printed presentments for the Kilkenny City and County, 1839–56. Poll books for North Kilkenny 1897 and 1900 and registers of voters 1924–47 and 1964–present also survive. Local authority records include those of the Kilkenny County Council and Rural District Councils from 1899 and there are also deposits of records of local business firms including indentures of apprentices.
Genealogical resources are especially strong. These include virtually all the standard sources for Kilkenny, such as Griffith's Valuation (microfilm and hard copy); Ordnance Survey maps; 1901 and 1911 censuses; tithe applotment books; lists, directories and various surveys; and a very strong local newspaper collection going back to 1767. See website for details.

LOCATION
Kilkenny city centre. The Local Studies Department is located at John's Green House, John's Green, Kilkenny.

THE LIBRARY, KILKENNY ARCHAEOLOGICAL SOCIETY

Rothe House
16 Parliament Street
KILKENNY, COUNTY KILKENNY
Ireland

TELEPHONE: (056) 772 2893
E-mail: librarian@kilkennyarchaeologicalsociety.ie; info@rothehouse.com
Website: www.kilkennyarchaeologicalsociety.ie

HOURS
Tu, 14:30–16:30; W, 10:30–12:30; Sa, 14:30–16:30; at other times by appointment.

ACCESS AND SERVICES
The library is located in recently renovated premises on the second floor of Rothe House with pleasant views of the recreated 17th century garden and courtyards. Wheelchair accessible. A lift is available; if you wish to avoid the stairs, please ask reception staff for directions and guidance on use. There are internet and

powerpoints in the library, a photocopier and microfilm reader/printer. Non-flash photography is encouraged. Use of the Library is available to members without charge, but any visitor is welcome to use the library on payment of a small sessional charge. Staffing is provided by volunteers and while every effort is made to adhere to opening times there may be occasions when this is not possible. If your visit involves a journey you may wish to check in advance that the library will be open. The volunteers have differing levels of knowledge and skills and advance notice of the purpose of your visit may enable the Library to provide a more focussed service.

CONTACT
Honorary Librarian
Note: The Honorary Librarian is elected at the Annual general Meeting of the society and may change from year to year.

DESCRIPTION
Kilkenny Archaeological Society, a county-wide society based in the city of Kilkenny in the south east of the Republic of Ireland, owns and occupies a sixteenth-century house built by John Rothe, a Kilkenny merchant, in 1594. The house, and its garden, is open to the public and is a major tourist attraction in a city which styles itself 'the medieval capital of Ireland'. The name of the society is taken from a Victorian predecessor and it is nowadays a historical society pursuing and encouraging much more than just archaeology. One important aspect of its activities is the conduct of a members' library and archive on the premises.

HOLDINGS
The Library has an extensive collection of books, maps and journals relating to many aspects of county Kilkenny, and of Irish history in general. There is a computer catalogue, and a printed version is made periodically. The Society has published an annual journal, the *Old Kilkenny Review*, since 1946 for which the library holds author and title indexes. A complete run is held of the *Journal of the Royal Society of Antiquaries of Ireland*, which was Kilkenny based in the mid-nineteenth century.
  Society members have undertaken the listing of many graveyard inscriptions which are available together with several published works. These are noted on our web site.
  Printed copies of Griffith's Valuation for County Kilkenny are available.
Also in paper format are extensive runs of local newspapers, including *Finns Leinster Journal*, *Moderator* and *Kilkenny People*, commencing in 1780. They cannot be photocopied, but may be photographed.
  The Library holds the original, unpublished, Grand Jury maps of *c.* 1810–20 for the county except for the baronies of Gowran and Kilkenny, and the Ordnance Survey maps of *c.* 1840 and *c.* 1900.
  Other collections include photographs, slides and 1901 census on microfilm. Files of cuttings, research notes etc. have been created over many years for family names and for subject headings; listings are available on computer and hard copy.
  Some 60 boxes of family and legal archives are held with a variety of finding aids ranging from general (box headings) to specific (box contents).

LOCATION
Rothe House is situated close to the city centre, just two minutes walk from large car parks at the Market Yard and Market Cross.

COUNTY LAOIS

LAOIS AND OFFALY FAMILY HISTORY RESEARCH CENTRE
See IRISH MIDLANDS ANCESTRY, Tullamore, COUNTY OFFALY

LAOIS COUNTY LIBRARY – LOCAL STUDIES COLLECTION
Laois County Library Headquarters
Aras an Chontae, J.F.L. Avenue
PORTLAOISE, COUNTY LAOIS
Ireland

TELEPHONE: (057) 867 4315 (HQ); Local Studies: (057) 867 4315 (HQ)
E-mail: library@laoiscoco.ie
Website: www.laoislibraries.ie

HOURS
Headquarters: M–Th, 09:00–13:00, 14:00–17:00

ACCESS AND SERVICES
Visitors are welcome; however, appointments are necessary for microfilm.
Modest membership fee required for borrowing privileges. Photocopying and
scanning services available.

CONTACT
Bernie Foran, Acting County Librarian. E-mail: bforan@laoiscoco.ie
Local Studies; Jackie Mc Intyre/Mary White. E-mail: library@laoiscoco.ie

DESCRIPTION
Headquarters library for County Laois, with branch libraries in:

> Portlaoise Branch Library: Contact Suzanne Carroll. Tel. (057) 862 2333;
> e-mail: scarroll@laoiscoco.ie;
>
> Abbeyleix Library: Contact Aideen McDonald. Tel. (057) 873 0020;
> e-mail: amcdonald@laoiscoco.ie;
>
> Mountmellick Library: Contact Assistant Librarian. Tel. (057) 864 4572;
> e-mail: bconnell@laoiscoco.ie;

Mountrath Library: Contact Walter Lawlor. Tel. (057) 875 6378;
e-mail: wlawler@laoiscoco.ie;

Durrow: Contact Catherine Hutchinson. Tel. (057) 873 6090;
e-mail: chutchinson@laoiscoco.ie;

Rathdowney: Contact Catherine Fitzpatrick. Tel. (0505) 46852;
e-mail: cafitzpatrick@laoiscoco.ie;

Timahoe: Contact Mairín Scully. Tel. (057) 862 7231;
e-mail: mscully@laoiscoco.ie;

Ballylinan: Contact: Niamh Boyce. Tel. (059) 862 5007;
e-mail: nboyce@laoiscoco.ie;

Portarlington: Contact Adrian Dunne. Tel. (057) 864 3751;
e-mail: adunne@laoiscoco.ie;

Stradbally: Contact Julie Shead. Tel. (057) 864 1673;
e-mail: jshead@laoiscoco.ie.

HOLDINGS
The Local Studies Collection, which is located at the headquarters library, consists of manuscripts, local newspapers, books, pamphlets, photographs, maps, estate papers and author materials relating to County Laois and Ireland. Estate papers include rentals for the Tipperary estate of the Countess of Milltown (1862–1969). The Poor Law Archive comprises minute books for the Poor Law Unions of Abbeyleix, Donamore and Mountmellick, c. 1844–c. 1920. The School Scheme Collection of folklore of 1937/8 is available on microfilm.
     Newspaper holdings include the *Leinster Express*, 1831, and the *Nationalist* and *Leinster Times*, 1883. Other Archive material includes: Helen Roe Collection, 1923–32; Archives of Perry's Brewery Rathdowney, 1835–1923; Lough Letters, 1877–1931; Joe O Neill Diaries, 1960–82; and the Bannon Collection, 1930–50.
     The library is building a collection of all published material on County Laois, including a complete set of journals of the Royal Society of Antiquities of Ireland. Survey works include tithe applotment books (1830s) and Griffith's Valuation (1850s). The Library also holds copies of 'The Cosby Papers 1558–1955, a descriptive listing of archives realting to the Cosby Family held at Cosby Hall, Stradbally'.
     The collection also has a complete set of the *Kildare Archaeological Journal*. There is a good collection of photographs of the area, including the Eason Collection, the Lawrence Collection, the Scully Collection and the Redmond Collection. Map holdings are highlighted by Sir William Petty's maps, 1685, Taylor and Skinner road maps, 1778, and the six inch Ordnance Survey maps of Queen's County (now County Laois), 1841.

The Laois County Council Archive includes rate books, 1934–57, microfilm copies of the tithe surveys for the county, 1823–38, the tenement valuation, c. 1853 and the 1901 census, microfilmed records of county council maintained cemeteries in County Laois (1904–present).

LOCATION
Town centre.

COUNTY LEITRIM

LEITRIM COUNTY LIBRARY (LEABHARLANN CHONTAE LIATROMA)

Main Street
BALLINAMORE, COUNTY LEITRIM
Ireland

TELEPHONE: (071) 964 5582 (Library), (071) 964 5567 (Local Studies); FAX:
(071) 964 5572 (Library)
E-mail: ballinamorelibrary@leitrimcoco.ie, localstudies@leitrimcoco.ie
Website: www.leitrimlibrary.ie

HOURS
M, W, F, 10:00–17:30; Tu, Th, 10:00–20:00; Sa, 10:00–17:00

ACCESS AND SERVICES
Visitors welcome. Disabled access; free internet access; photocopying and microform
prints available for a modest fee. The entire collection is catalogued and can be
consulted at the above website.

CONTACT
Reference staff

DESCRIPTION
The library is the central public library for County Leitrim.

HOLDINGS
The library houses the usual range of public library material. Of principal interest to
visitors would be the Local History Collection, which includes Board of Guardian
minutes and oral interviews with local people. Of special genealogical interest are
holdings of Griffith's Valuation, tithe applotment books, the 1901 and 1911
censuses, Ordnance Survey maps, estate papers and a newspaper collection, all
focusing on County Leitrim. There is also a collection of some 3,000 photographs,
mostly dating from after 1970.

LOCATION
Main Street, Ballinamore.

LEITRIM GENEALOGY CENTRE (SINSEARLANN LIATROMA)

Main Street
BALLINAMORE, COUNTY LEITRIM
Ireland

TELEPHONE: (071) 964 4012
E-mail: info@leitrimroots.com
Website: www.leitrimroots.com

HOURS
M–F, 09:00–13:00, 14:00–17:00; closed bank holidays

ACCESS AND SERVICES
Visitors welcome. Disabled access. Service fees apply. Genealogical research service
for the County of Leitrim, based on fees set by the Irish Family History Foundation.
Local publications on sale.

DESCRIPTION
Leitrim Genealogy Centre, established in 1986, is the Irish Family History
Foundation's designated genealogical research centre for County Leitrim. The centre
is one of the longest established IFHF centres. It provides full time professional
genealogy services for County Leitrim. Chief surnames found in County Leitrim
include: Reynolds, McGowan, Rooney, Flynn, Kelly, Gallagher, Moran, Dolan,
McLoughlin and McMorrow.

HOLDINGS
Main records include: Roman Catholic records (the earliest of which date from
1823); Church of Ireland records dating from 1783; Methodist records dating from
1840; Presbyterian records dating from 1829. Church records up to 1900 have been
computerised. Civil records of birth, marriage and death from 1864 (we hold civil
records pre and post 1900). The centre also holds copies of: Griffith's Valuation,
tithe applotment books, the 1901 and 1911 Censuses, Ordnance Survey maps,
gravestone inscriptions, estate papers and newspapers all focusing on County
Leitrim. Online research site available at http://leitrim.rootsireland.ie/ Full details of
the service we provide and the sources available are detailed on our website.

LOCATION
At rear of courthouse.

COUNTY LIMERICK

LIMERICK ANCESTRY

The Granary
Michael St
LIMERICK CITY, COUNTY LIMERICK
Ireland

Note: Limerick Ancestry closed in February 2004, and as of July 2013 had not resumed operation.

LIMERICK CITY ARCHIVES

Archives for Limerick City
City Hall
Merchant's Quay
LIMERICK CITY, COUNTY LIMERICK
Ireland

TELEPHONE: (061) 407 293; Fax: (061) 415 266
E-mail: archives@limierickcity.ie; jhayes@limerickcity.ie
Website: www.limerickcoco.ie

HOURS
By appointment

ACCESS AND SERVICES
Visitors welcome, but by appointment only. Advance notice, ID and registration required. Readers must agree to observe the regulations of the archives. In 2007 the Archives moved to a purpose built building on the outskirts of Limerick City.

CONTACT
Jacqui Hayes, Limerick City Archivist; E-mail: jhayes@limerickcity.ie

DESCRIPTION
Limerick City Archives provides for the collection and preservation of archives relating to Limerick City and makes archives available to the public. Archives are the raw material of history and the archives service is committed to preserving and documenting the past to ensure that the history of the city is accessible to its citizens.

HOLDINGS
Limerick City Archives has a large collection of material relating to its parent body –
Limerick City Council and it has also collected archive material relating to older
administrations, including Limerick Union, Limerick Rural District Council, private
papers and collections relating to the commercial and cultural aspects of life in
Limerick City.

Holdings include administrative records for Limerick City (from 1841, with
some older material related to St Michael's parish dating back to 1809) and County
Limerick (from 1899, plus older Board of Guardian material and Grand Jury
presentments).

There are almost complete collections of minute books for the Boards of
Guardians of the Poor Law Unions of Kilmallock, Limerick and Newcastle West
c. 1840–1922. There are minutes covering the period 1850–1922 for Croom Poor
Law Union and the period 1870–91 for Glin. For Rathkeale only a single volume
survived a fire at the workhouse; this covers the period January–November 1921.
Kilmallock Poor Law Union also has rate books for the period 1842–73.
For St Michael's parish in the city of Limerick there is another series of rate books
for the years 1810–46 (with gaps; microfilm copies available in PRONI). These are
part of the archive of the Commissioners for the improvement of the parish.

There are also the following records with specific information about individuals:
a register for St John's Fever and Lock Hospital, 1816; a microfilm copy of a census
of Shanagolden and Foynes area of County Limerick 1846 giving names,
occupations and numbers in each household, which carries several thousand names.
This census was organised by Lord Monteagle and other local landlords. The original
manuscript is held in the National Library of Ireland (MS 582). The manuscript
runs to about 50 A3 size pages; estate papers: rent book for Lord Monteagle's estate,
1831–50; the archive of the old Limerick Corporation includes records of the
Mayor's Tholsel or Small Debtors' Court, 1773–95 and 1811–13, a Court of Claims
register, 1823–41, a register of admissions, 1832–41, and a register of paying orders,
1777–1801.

The archives also hold the private records of: solicitors (some 4,000 property deeds);
the Encumbered Estates Court; the Monteagle Estate, 1800–1949; Limerick
Chamber of Commerce; Limerick Harbour Commissioners; various companies; as
well as microfilm collections of Limerick material held elsewhere. Property deeds
have been fed to a local database, as have microfilm holdings. Handlists (short) of
the various private collections also exist. Limerick Archives collects anything to do
with the administrative, social, economic and cultural history of Limerick, and
administrative collections for the city and county, e.g.: P14/Monteagle Estate Papers;
PO1/Limerick Chamber of Commerce; PO2/Limerick Harbour Commissioners;
PO9/Limerick Water Works Company; P10/Limerick County Militia Financial
Records, 1803–29; P11/Geary's Biscuit Factory Papers; P12/Cannock and
Company; P16/Limerick Custom House Papers; P21/Coote Family Papers; and
P22/De Vere Papers.

Limerick City has made many of its collection available online via a digital archive.
The digitised collections are freely available to the public to promote research into
the history of Limerick City via a virtual archive: www.limerick.ie.

LOCATION
Merchant's Quay, on outskirts of Limerick City.

LIMERICK CITY LIBRARY

The Granary
Michael Street,
LIMERICK CITY, COUNTY LIMERICK
Ireland

TELEPHONE: (061) 407 510; FAX: (061) 411 506
E-mail: citylib@limerickcity.ie
E-mail, Local Studies: mmaguire@limerickcity.ie
Website: www.limerickcity.ie/library
Website: Local Studies: www.limerickcity.ie/library/localstudies

HOURS
M–Tu, 10:00–17:30; W–F, 10:00–20:00; Sa, 10:00–13:00; closed Saturdays of bank
holiday weekends.

ACCESS AND SERVICES
Visitors welcome. Modest fees for photocopying and microfilm prints. Printing to
file from microfilm available – no charges but pre-booking essential. Borrowing
limited to general collection – Reference and Local Studies materials only available
for in-house usage. Fulltime librarian available to assist with queries/research in
Reference/Local Studies department. Disabled access facilities.

CONTACT
Damien Dullaghan, Senior Executive Librarian.
E-mail: damien.dullaghan@limerickcity.ie
Mike Maguire, Reference and Local Studies Librarian.
E-mail: mmaguire@limerickcity.ie

DESCRIPTION
The Central Library at the Granary, along with three branch libraries at Roxboro,
Caherdavin and Moyross, are funded by Limerick City Council. Limerick City
Library provides a host of library services to the community, including the Local
Studies Collection.

HOLDINGS
The Local Studies Collection contains books, journals, newspapers, a limited
photograph collection, files, maps, reports and ephemera relating to Limerick City
and County past and present. Of special interest is the extensive collection of books
relating to the history, antiquities and society of Limerick, including the Kemmy
Collection of books relating to Irish history, religion and politics. Other collections
include the Séamus Ó Ceallaigh GAA Collection containing the research files,
journals and books of the deceased *Limerick Leader* GAA columnist and renowned
GAA historian. The collection includes material dating to the early years of the GAA
in the Limerick area. The newspaper collection includes microfilm of: the *Limerick
Chronicle*, 1782–1975, 1982–present; *Limerick Leader*, 1893–present; *General
Advertiser or Limerick Gazette*, 1806–20; *Munster Journal*, 1749–84 and *Limerick
Evening Post*, 1811–19. Other material includes: the Journal of the Association for
the Preservation of the Memorials of the Dead in Ireland, 1888–1931; memorial
records of Irish soldiers who died in World War I; business directories from 1769;
Griffith's Valuation for Counties Limerick and Clare; list of landowners of one acre

and more for the whole of Ireland, 1876; Seamus Pender's 1659 census of Ireland; tithe applotment books for County Limerick; and registers of electors in Limerick City, 1923, 1931–present.

ONLINE RESOURCES
Limerick City Library has made an extensive portion of its collections available online through the Limerick City Council website at: www.limerickcity.ie/library/localstudies

The main online resources include the following:

BOOKS and JOURNALS – includes full, scanned copies of histories of Limerick by Ferrar (1787) and Lenihan (1866); full scanned copies of the *Old Limerick Journal* (all volumes to vol. 43, 2010); full, scanned copies of all volumes of the *Journal of the Limerick Field Club*; links to other Limerick-related books available online.

LOCAL STUDIES FILES – Limerick City Library maintains a collection of files on subjects of local interest, ranging alphabetically from the Abbey Fishermen to The Workhouse. The files mainly consist of newspaper cuttings and journal articles. It is not intended that these files would be regarded as definitive in their coverage and should generally be regarded as giving a 'taster' of the given subject. The files can be a very useful tool for anyone researching aspects of the history of Limerick and also should prove of interest to the casual reader of Limerick history (over 100 of these files are now online, but it is a work in progress).

OBITUARIES, DEATH NOTICES, ETC. from the *Limerick Chronicle* newspaper – full, scanned images of these materials from 1850 to 1907 (is a work in progress).

TRADES DIRECTORIES DATABASE – Fully searchable by surname, trade, address, etc., a database of all Limerick City-related content of directories held at Limerick City Library, from Ferrar's 1769 directory to the 1920 Cork & Munster Directory (over 60,000 entries).

REGISTERS OF ELECTORS – A number of registers for Limerick City are available in full. 1885, 1923, 1931, 1940, 1945, 1950

FAMILY HISTORIES – A collection of materials relating to various families of Limerick

FIELD NAME BOOKS for Limerick CITY and COUNTY – Presented on a parish by parish basis, alphabetically and with inter-active maps. *The Field Name Books of the County and City of Limerick* is a collection of more than 1,700 pages of notes taken by surveyors during the first ordnance survey of County Limerick, *c.* 1840. They comprise a vast quantity of data on the geography, placenames, antiquities and other miscellaneous information relating to Limerick. Supplementary to the Field Name Books are the Ordnance Survey Letters, correspondence between the surveyors in the field and the central office in Dublin – these letters contain useful additional materials.

WHO'S WHO OF LIMERICK – a listing of notable Limerick people compiled from the local studies and reference collections at Limerick City Library. Fairly comprehensive, almost 100 standard reference and local studies works were consulted in its compilation.

SÉAMUS Ó CEALLAIGH'S GREAT LIMERICK SPORTSMEN – A collection of more than 200 biographical profiles of noteworthy Limerick sportsmen. This collection constitutes an invaluable record of the great individuals in the history of Gaelic Games and Athletics in Limerick.

THE 1907 'SALE OF LIMERICK' CATALOGUE and MAPS – This catalogue and maps were drawn up for the sale of the ground rents of the Earl of Limerick in 1907. They constitute an invaluable record of property and mapping of large parts of Limerick City from early in the 20th century.

OTHER RESOURCES – There are many other materials available.

LOCATION
Limerick city centre, in a landmark eighteenth century granary and bonded warehouse which also houses Limerick Archives, close to the Hunt Museum.

LIMERICK COUNTY LIBRARY

Limerick County Library Headquarters
Lissanalta House
Dooradoyle Road
LIMERICK CITY, COUNTY LIMERICK
Ireland

TELEPHONE: (061) 496 526; FAX: (061) 583 135
E-mail: libinfo@limerickcoco.ie, limerickstudies@limerickcoco.ie
Website: www.lcc.ie/library

HOURS
M–F, 09:30–16:30

DESCRIPTION
Limerick County Council Library Service provides for the culture, education, information, learning, recreation and study needs of people of all ages in the county. The aim of the Library Service is to act as a focal point for social and cultural life by extending the joys of reading, lifelong learning and discovery to all. The service is delivered through a network of branches with main branches located at:

> Abbeyfeale – contact: Mike Sweeney, Senior Library Assistant.
> Tel. (068) 32488; e-mail: abbeyfealelibrary@eircom.net

> Adare – contact: Sarah Prendeville, Assistant Librarian
> Tel. (061) 396 822; e-mail: adarelibrary@excite.com

> Dooradoyle – Margaret O'Reilly, Executive Librarian
> Tel. (061) 496 860; e-mail: dooradoylelibrary@gmail.com

> Foynes – contact: Catherine Griffin, Branch Librarian
> Tel. (069) 65365; e-mail: foyneslib@eircom.net

> Kilmallock – contact: Noreen O'Neill, Executive Librarian
> Tel. (063) 20306; e-mail: kilmallocklib@limerickcoco.ie

> Newcastle West – Aileen Dillane, Executive Librarian
> Tel. (069) 62273; e-mail: newcastlewest@excite.com

Local Studies Collection and Archives – *see* separate entry below.

There are also branches at Askeaton, Ballingarry, Caherconlish, Cappamore, Dromcollogher, Galbally, Glin, Hospital, Kilfinane and Rathkeale and a fulltime mobile library service.

ACCESS AND SERVICES
Visitors welcome. No membership fee. Photocopying and microfiche print services available at cost of 20c per sheet. You can search the online catalogue to see what books are held in the library and to submit loan requests: Library online Catalogue. Library Services include:

Book Lending – Adult, Children, Teenage, Large Print, Gaeilge Audio-Visual Collection - (books on tape, CD and MP3 and language learning packs); Collection of films on DVD in main branches; Reference and Information Service (including study facilities); Information Technology – (automated library catalogue); Local Studies Service/Limerick Studies; Community Information; Local Authority Information; Internet Facilities – (free of charge); Exhibition Areas – (in main branches available to community); School Service; Adult Literacy Collection; Newspapers and Magazines; Children's Activities.

CONTACT
Damien Brady, County Librarian
Anne Bennett. Senior Executive Librarian

HOLDINGS
In addition to the standard educational and recreational material the Library holds a large collection of local studies material listed under Limerick Studies below.

LOCATION
Lissanalta House is located on the Dooradoyle Road next door to the Limerick County Motor Tax Office. There is free parking available in front of the Motor Tax Office.

LIMERICK STUDIES

LIMERICK COUNTY LIBRARY – LOCAL STUDIES COLLECTION AND ARCHIVES

Lissanalta House
Dooradoyle Road
LIMERICK CITY, COUNTY LIMERICK
Ireland

TELEPHONE: (061) 496 540/496 526; FAX: (061) 583 135
E-mail: limerickstudies@limerickcoco.ie
Website: www.lcc.ie/library

HOURS
M–F, 09:30–16:30

ACCESS AND SERVCES
Visitors welcome, free membership and disability access. Services which are available for historical research include PCs, internet access, photocopiers and printers. The Limerick Studies collection of books and journals is available for consultation only.

CONTACT

Tony Storan, Limerick Studies. E-mail: tstoran@limerickcoco.ie

Liam Dunne, Limerick Studies. E-mail: ldunne@limerickcoco.ie

DESCRIPTION

Limerick Studies is the Local Studies Department of Limerick County Library. It collects preserves and makes available material on the history, culture and heritage of Limerick. It also provides a home to Limerick County Archives, whose holdings may be accessed in the reading room by appointment.

HOLDINGS

LIMERICK STUDIES: Limerick Studies has over 3,500 books and 70 Journals of Limerick interest for consultation. There are also newspapers (including a full set of the *Limerick Leader* and *Irish Times* and the *Limerick Chronicle* back to 1825), over 300 hard copy maps, photographs, prints and postcards. The 1901 and 1911 Irish census records are available on disk while local census detail like Adare 1865 is available on PC. Census substitutes held include the tithe applotment books (1820s and 1830s) and hard copies of Griffith's Valuation and maps. A full set of the Field Name Books (1839/40) of John O'Donovan and the Irish Folklore Commission Schools Collection 1937/38 may also be accessed.

Limerick Studies has recently launched its media archive. The collection comprises over 300 items and documents life and lifestyles in Limerick during the twentieth century. This material previously stored in many different formats including cassette, video, DVD, CDR and PDF files can now be accessed in online formats including PDF and windows media files on Limerick Studies PCs. Book launches and exhibitions of local studies material regularly take place in the foyer of the building.

LIMERICK STUDIES ARCHIVES: Limerick Studies Archives is the repository in County Limerick for archival records of public and private nature. The public record holdings include Board of Guardian, Grand Jury, Rural District Council, Limerick County Council Minute Books and Limerick County Committee of Agriculture and Technical Instruction. The Private paper collections range from archives of private origin like the Monteagle and Coote Papers to business collections such as the William B. Fitt Auctioneer records.

Based at Limerick Studies, Lissanalta House, Dooradoyle Road, Limerick, the archives are open to the public from 09:30 to 16:30 Monday to Friday. Access is by appointment and contact for details of collections or to arrange an appointment can be made at limerickstudies@limerickcoco.ie or by phone at (061) 496 526. Readers are obliged to conform to the Regulations for Archives Readers. Photocopying is not permitted. Records of births, death or marriage are not available here. Limerick Genealogy provides a professional family history research service for Limerick City and County.

LOCATION

Limerick Studies is located at Lissanalta House on the Dooradoyle Road next door to the Limerick County Motor Tax Office. There is free parking available in front of the Motor Tax Office.

MARY IMMACULATE COLLEGE LIBRARY

Mary Immaculate College
South Circular Road
LIMERICK CITY, COUNTY LIMERICK
Ireland

TELEPHONE: (061) 204 370
E-mail: Senior staff can be contacted from the list here:
http://www.mic.ul.ie/library/Pages/contactus.aspx
Website: http://www.mic.ul.ie/library/Pages/default.aspx

HOURS
Semester time: M–F, 9:30–22:00; Sa, 14:00–18:00
Vacation period: M–F, 09:30–17:00

ACCESS AND SERVICES
Visitors welcome during vacation periods. Advance notice preferred during semester
time.
Library catalogue available via library web pages above.

CONTACT
Gerardine Moloney, Librarian. Tel. (061) 204 367

DESCRIPTION
Mary Immaculate College (MIC) is an autonomous third-level college offering
undergraduate and postgraduate degrees in education and the arts. It is situated close
to the river Shannon on the southern side of Limerick city and was established in
1898 by Bishop O'Dwyer and the Sisters of Mercy for the professional education of
Catholic primary school teachers. In 1991, the college was academically linked with
the University of Limerick (UL), which accredits the college's degree programmes.
There are over 3,000 students currently registered.

HOLDINGS
The library houses c. 200,000 volumes in subject areas including education,
theology and religious studies, Irish history, philosophy and the arts. Journal
holdings are listed in the library catalogue. Special collections include education
textbooks and a realia collection to support teaching practice.

LOCATION
The college is located within Limerick city and is accessible on foot or by taxi.

UNIVERSITY OF LIMERICK LIBRARY AND INFORMATION SERVICES

University of Limerick
LIMERICK CITY, COUNTY LIMERICK
Ireland

TELEPHONE: (061) 202 166; FAX: (061) 213 090
E-mail: libinfo@ul.ie
Website: http://www2.ul.ie/web/WWW/Services/Library

HOURS
University Library
Term time: M–F, 08:30–23:00; Sa, 09:00–19:00; Su, 11:00–18:00
Vacation period: M–F, 09:00–17:00
Special Collections
M–F, 09:00–17:00

ACCESS AND SERVICES
Visitors welcome, but advance notice preferred and ID required. For access to Special Collections Department advance notice especially appreciated. Disabled access. Photocopying and microform prints available for a fee. Leaflets and booklets describing services (both print and electronic) and special collections are available.

CONTACT
Mary Dundon, Head, Reader Services. E-mail: mary.dundon@ul.ie
Aoife Geraghty, Head, Information Services. E-mail: Aoife.Geraghty@ul.ie
Ken Bergin, Special Collections Librarian. E-mail: specoll@ul.ie

DESCRIPTION
The University of Limerick was established by the state in 1972 as The National Institute for Higher Education, Limerick. Full university status was granted by legislation enacted by the Irish parliament in 1989. It is the first new university established since the foundation of the state. The library supports the teaching and research interests of students and faculty, with special interests in the areas of engineering, science, business, computing, information sciences, education and the humanities.

HOLDINGS
The library houses some 300,000 volumes, plus significant holdings of journals, manuscripts, maps, newspapers, pamphlets, photographs and recordings. These represent general academic subjects, with special concentration on engineering, business and computing/information services. Special collections include: the Fr. Leonard Limerick Collection; the Dunraven Estate Papers; the Glin Estate Papers; the Conlan Coin Collection; the Kate O'Brien Papers; the Moyaliffe Castle Papers; the Jim Kemmy Papers; the Eoin O'Kelly Collection of early nineteenth century Irish banknotes; and the Norton Collection. The last of these consists of more than 12,000 volumes mostly of an Irish interest, with a special focus on the Shannon River Valley. Highlights of the Norton Collection include collections on Charles Stewart Parnell, Daniel O'Connell, Oliver Goldsmith and Eamon de Valera; early Irish grammars and catechisms; nineteenth century reports, commissions and inquiries; Ordnance Survey letters and maps; photograph albums; and travel literature.

LOCATION
Two miles east of the ancient city of Limerick; easily accessible by taxi or bus. Ample parking available in designated areas.

GLENSTAL ABBEY LIBRARY

MURROE, COUNTY LIMERICK
Ireland

TELEPHONE: (061) 386 103; FAX: (061) 386 328
E-mail: librarian@glenstal.org
Website: www.glenstal.org/library

HOURS
By appointment: contact Librarian

ACCESS AND SERVICES
The new library facility at Glenstal Abbey was opened in 2001 by the Benedictine
community to house its collection of books, manuscripts and archives, thereby
making these resources more readily available to the public. The new library is fully
equipped with conference facilities and details of courses and events are available on
the monastery website. Visitors welcome by prior appointment.

CONTACT
Fr Mark Patrick Hederman, OSB, Librarian

DESCRIPTION
Glenstal Abbey is a Benedictine monastery in County Limerick on the south-west
coast of Ireland. A 500-acre estate with streams, lakes and woodland paths surrounds
a castle built in the romantic Norman style. Originally the seat of the Anglo-Irish
Barrington family, the Abbey, which is dedicated to Saints Joseph and Columba, has
been home to a community of Benedictine monks since 1927. Libraries have always
been an important part of the Benedictine tradition since the order's founding in the
sixth century.

HOLDINGS
The collection has grown steadily from its humble origins in 1927 and is now one of
the most important private libraries in Ireland, holding approximately 58,000
volumes and nearly 100 journal runs. The focus of the library is primarily
theological but it contains substantial holdings in the areas of Irish history, Irish
literature, biography and art. It also has a collection of antiquarian books ranging in
date from the fifteenth to the nineteenth centuries and a programme to restore some
of the more important of these is proposed.

LOCATION
12 miles outside Limerick City, accessible by car (off the R506 from either the N7
from Dublin or the N24 from Tipperary) or by bus (from the Limerick Rail Station
once a day). The nearest airport is Shannon, about an hour's drive away.

COUNTY LONDONDERRY

LIBRARIES NI HERITAGE COLLECTION, COLERAINE LIBRARY

Coleraine Library
Queen Street
COLERAINE, COUNTY LONDONDERRY BT52 1BE
Northern Ireland

TELEPHONE: (028) 7034 2561
E-mail: colerainelibrary@librariesni.org.uk

HOURS
M–Th, 09:30–20:00, F–Sa, 09:30–17:00; Su, 13:00–17:00

ACCESS AND SERVICES
Visitors are welcome. Disabled access but no lift. The collection is on the first floor of the library and is non borrowable and reference only. There is also a lending collection of Irish stock adjacent to the reference collection. Microfilm reader/printers are available. Due to heavy demand for microfilm readers booking is advisable for this service.

Public Access Terminals with internet access are freely available for all Libraries NI members. Fees apply to photocopies, microfilm reader and IT printouts. Membership of library is open to anyone living, working or studying in the area. ID is required on registering. Heritage staff will assist and advise users seeking genealogical information.

CONTACT
Mary Bradley, Heritage Services Manager. E-mail: mary.bradley@librariesni.org.uk

DESCRIPTION
One of eleven Heritage Collections throughout Northern Ireland. The other Heritage Collections are: County Antrim (BALLYMENA LIBRARY, BELFAST CENTRAL LIBRARY); County Armagh (ARMAGH IRISH & LOCAL STUDIES LIBRARY, Armagh City); County Down (DOWNPATRICK LIBRARY, NEWRY CITY LIBRARY); County Fermanagh (ENNISKILLEN LIBRARY); County Londonderry (DERRY CITY CENTRAL LIBRARY); and County Tyrone (OMAGH LIBRARY, Omagh; MELLON CENTRE FOR MIGRATION STUDIES, Omagh).

HOLDINGS
Coleraine library's Irish Collection covers all aspects of life in Co. Londonderry and includes specialised and antiquarian books for family history research including the manuscripts and notebooks of Dr Hugh Mullin. There are volumes of the Ordnance Survey Memoirs 1830 and the accompanying maps. Also volumes of Griffith's Valuation with accompanying valuation maps and O.S. maps 1857, sheets 1–50.

Newspapers on microfilm include:

> *Coleraine Chronicle*, 1844–present;
> *Northern Constitution*, 1877–present;
> *Ballymoney Free Press*, 1970–present.

Church records (Births, Marriages, and Deaths) on microfilm:

> Ballycastle, Ballymena, Derry City, Coleraine, Limavady and Magherafelt, and many other areas—check with Coleraine library.

Other sources:

> Tithe Applotment Books 1826–38;
> Index to 1831 Census

Libraries NI Online Resources
Libraries NI customers have access to 'Online Resources' on the library website.

Ancestry Library Edition is an online genealogical collection accessible on the Libraries NI website to library members at any library in Northern Ireland. This resource is available only from the Libraries NI network and is not accessible to members from their home computers. The Ancestry Library Edition collection has approximately thousands of databases and billions of indexed names from key collections spanning the 14th century to present day enabling customers to search for vital information about their ancestors.

The 'JSTOR Ireland Collection' is fully searchable, consists of the digital content of journals and other material relating to Ireland, and will be of great interest to anyone researching Irish history, genealogy, archaeology, literature etc. Most of the material included was published in the 18th, 19th and 20th centuries.

The DIPPAM web resource is a virtual library of sources relating to the history of modern Ireland and its global diaspora. Documenting Ireland: Parliament, People & Migration (DIPPAM) is a collaboration project between Queen's University Belfast, The University of Ulster, The Centre for Migration Studies, Omagh, and Libraries NI, and has been funded by the Arts and Humanities Research Council. DIPPAM may be of particular interest to people involved in research the history of their locality or family, and for use in school history projects. It includes three searchable databases: Enhanced British Parliamentary Papers on Ireland (EPPI) – which comprises scans of over 15,000 official publications relating to all aspects of Irish affairs during the period of the Act of Union, 1800–1922, including bills, reports, royal commissions of inquiry and the published census returns. It is a rich source for the social history of Ireland, as well as for statistics and evidence relating to population, emigration, famine, crime and political movements: The Irish Emigration Database (IED) is made up of documents relating to Irish emigration since the eighteenth century, mainly to North America, and mostly drawn from archives in Northern Ireland and from private collections. The documents include emigrant letters, newspaper extracts, shipping advertisements, family papers and extracts from relevant publications and Voices of Migration and Return (VMR) is an oral history archive of over 90 life-narrative interviews conducted with emigrants and return-emigrants from the province of Ulster, collected between 2004 and 2008. The study participants represent a range of geographical origins within Ulster, class backgrounds and religious identities.

LOCATION
Town centre-adjacent car parking.

IRISH ROOM

County Hall, Castlerock Road
COLERAINE, COUNTY LONDONDERRY, BT1 3HP
Northern Ireland

Note: Closed; collection transferred to LIBRARIES NI HERITAGE COLLECTION, COLERAINE LIBRARY. *See* above entry.

UNIVERSITY OF ULSTER LIBRARY, COLERAINE CAMPUS

Cromore Road
COLERAINE, COUNTY LONDONDERRY, BT52 1SA
Northern Ireland

TELEPHONE: (028) 7012 4345; FAX: (028) 7012 4928
E-mail: sa.mclaughlin@ulster.ac.uk
Website: http://library.ulster.ac.uk/

HOURS
Term time: M–Th, 08:45–22:00; F, 08:45–20:00; Sa and Su, 13:00–17:00
Vacation period: M–Th, 09:00–17:00; F, 09:00–16:00
Hours can be checked at http://library.ulster.ac.uk/info/hour.php

ACCESS AND SERVICES
Visitors welcome but advance notice preferred. Borrowing privileges not usually extended to visitors unless via an access scheme. Access schemes which apply are:

SCONUL Access (http://library.ulster.ac.uk/info/sconul.php)
LISC Inspire (http://library.ulster.ac.uk/inspire/)
Alumni Association (http://library.ulster.ac.uk/alumni/)
Associate Students (http://library.ulster.ac.uk/associatestudents/)

Application in advance for access to Special Collections preferred.
Disabled access is available; full details at
http://library.ulster.ac.uk/info/disabilities/http://library.ulster.ac.uk/info/disabilities/;

Access to electronic resources is only available to staff and students of the University.
Access to the Library catalogue is available at http://zl1.ulster.ac.uk/TalisPrism/.
Purchase of photocopying card required for self-service photocopying.

CONTACT
Stephanie McLaughlin, Campus Library Manager

DESCRIPTION
The Coleraine campus is part of the four campus University of Ulster, which also
includes Belfast, County Antrim; Jordanstown, in Newtownabbey, County Antrim;
and Magee, in Derry, County Londonderry.

HOLDINGS
The library houses a collection of some 228,000 books, plus significant holdings of
print journals (535 titles), manuscripts, microforms, videos and pamphlets. It
contains major collections in the areas of social sciences, health sciences,
environmental sciences, business and management, informatics, arts and education.
    Electronic resources (only available to staff and students of the University)
comprise 192,000 eBooks and 17,000 eJournals.

The Special Collections section contains a number of important research collections,
including the Henry Davis Gift of early printed books and fine bindings, featuring
80 incunabula; the Irish Collection, including folklorist Henry Morris's collection of
Irish material, the library of Belfast poet John Hewitt, the library and archive of
writer Francis Stuart, the papers of playwright George Shiels and the Headlam-
Morley Collection on World War I. The library also contains the natural history
collections of A.W. Stelfox and E.N. Carrothers. Details on the main Special
Collections are available at http://library.ulster.ac.uk/specialcollections/. Further
details are also available on the RASCAL database (http://www.rascal.ac.uk/).

LOCATION
North coast of Northern Ireland, less than a mile from the Centre of Coleraine.
Directions and maps available at http://www.ulster.ac.uk/campus/coleraine/

BRIAN MITCHELL GENEALOGY SERVICE
See HERITAGE AND MUSEUM SERVICE DERRY CITY COUNCIL, Derry

CENTRAL LIBRARY
See LIBRARIES NI HERITAGE COLLECTION, DERRY CENTRAL LIBRARY,
below.

DERRY-LONDONDERRY GENEALOGY SERVICE
See HERITAGE AND MUSEUM SERVICE, Derry

DERRY CITY COUNCIL ARCHIVES
See HERITAGE AND MUSEUM SERVICE, Derry

HARBOUR MUSEUM
See HERITAGE AND MUSEUM SERVICE, Derry

HERITAGE AND MUSEUM SERVICE DERRY CITY COUNCIL

Foyle Valley Railway Museum Derry

Tower Museum
Union Hall Place
DERRY CITY, COUNTY LONDONDERRY
BT48 6LU

TELEPHONE: (028) 7137 2411; 7137 7331; FAX: (028) 7137 7633
E-mail: museums@derrycity.gov.uk
Website: www.derrycity.gov.uk/museums

ACCESS AND SERVICES
The Harbour Museum is currently undergoing a refurbishment, consequently, the
Derry Archive and Genealogy Service will now be delivered across other council
museum sites. This is a consolidation of services in anticipation of the opening of a
new Maritime Museum and Archive Centre at Ebrington Barracks in 2014.
    Appointments are recommended to access the collections. Photocopying and
digital imaging services are available on guidance from the Archivist.

CONTACT
Bernadette Walsh, City Archivist. E-mail: bernadette.walsh@derrycity.gov.uk

HOURS
Please consult the website for seasonal opening hours for all council museum sites.

DESCRIPTION
The Tower Museum includes two permanent exhibitions, *The Story of Derry*, a
chronological look at the development of the city from early times, and *An Armada
Shipwreck: La Trinidad Valencera*, containing a wide selection of artefacts excavated
from Kinnagoe Bay during the 1970s from the wreck of *La Trinidad Valencera*.
Visitors are welcome. An admission charge will apply for the Tower Museum.
Temporary exhibitions are free admission see website for current details.
    The Foyle Valley Railway Museum is a traditional transport museum with
original carriages and railway items on display. Admission is free.

HOLDINGS
Of special interest is the Derry City Council Archive Collection detailing the growth
and development of the city from the late seventeenth century onwards. Private
collections include the archives of various local businesses, including transportation
companies; community organisations, such as the Northern Ireland Civil Rights
Association (NICRA), and the papers of prominent Derry citizens. The collection
also includes corporation records dating back to 1673, legal deeds, court records,
architectural drawings, maps and a photographic collection. Private collections
include items relating to the railway industry, the textile industry of the North West
and material relating to local businesses. Donations have also included a large
collection of photographs and paper documents from members of the City of Derry
Sub Aqua Club relating to the excavation of *La Trinidad Valencera* in Kinnagoe Bay.
    The minute volumes from 1673–1901 are available on line, following a
partnership project with the Public Record Office of Northern Ireland
www.proni.gov.uk/index/search_the_archives/derrycorporationarchive-3.htm

The service also includes the Brian Mitchell Genealogy Service.

A database of over one million records, dating from 1642 to 1922, was created, between 1982 and 2007 as a project of the Inner City Trust, from the major civil and church registers of the city and county of Derry-Londonderry and Inishowen, County Donegal. This database contains:

> Pre-1922 civil birth and marriage registers
> The early baptismal and marriage registers of 97 churches (38 Roman Catholic Church, 24 Church of Ireland and 35 Presbyterian)
> Headstone inscriptions from 118 graveyards
> Census returns and census substitutes from 1663 through to 1901

The ancestors of the vast majority of Derry's citizens are recorded in the database. You can now access this database by searching, for free, the indexes to the Derry Genealogy Database online at www.derry.rootsireland.ie and then purchasing, on a pay-per-view basis, any selected record. You can also book a free 15 minutes consultation with the genealogist at genealogy@derrycity.gov.uk.

The Archive Collections are available for consultation by appointment only. Unlisted collections will not be made available to the public.

LOCATION
City centre, opposite the Guildhall, close to the city walls (Tower Museum), and riverside alongside Craigavon Bridge (Foyle Valley Railway Museum).

LIBRARIES NI HERITAGE COLLECTION, DERRY CENTRAL LIBRARY

Local Studies
Derry Central Library
35 Foyle Street
DERRY CITY, COUNTY LONDONDERRY BT48 6AL
Northern Ireland

TELEPHONE: (028) 7127 2300; FAX: (028) 7126 1374
E-mail: derrycentrallibrary@librariesni.org.uk; jane.nicholas@librariesni.org.uk; ann.duffy@librariesni.org.uk
Website: www.librariesni.org.uk

HOURS
M, 08:30–21:00; Tu–Th, 08:30–20:00; F, 08:30–17:30; Sa, 09:15–17:00

ACCESS AND SERVICES
Visitors are welcome. The library is wheelchair accessible. Some of the collection is reference only; however, there are borrowable copies of many of the popular titles. Microfilm reader /printers are available. Due to heavy demand for microfilm readers, booking is advisable for this service. Public Access Terminals with internet access are freely available for all Libraries NI members. Fees apply to photocopies, microfilm reader and IT printouts. Membership of library is open to anyone living, working or studying in the area. ID is required on registering. Heritage staff will assist and advise users seeking genealogical information.

CONTACT
Deirdre Nugent, Heritage Services Manager.
E-mail: deirdre.nugent@librariesni.org.uk

DESCRIPTION
Opened in 1990, this handsome facility is the main branch library for Derry City, located just outside the city walls.

HOLDINGS
Derry Central Library houses an important Heritage collection with strong holdings of genealogical interest, and collects and archives materials covering all aspects of life in the county: postcards and photographs; journals; newspaper cuttings; local and regional newspapers on microfilm; maps; books by local authors and those locally produced, including street directories and volumes of Griffith's Valuation. The Heritage Collection includes more than 15,000 volumes, 2,500 photographs, which includes the Bigger McDonald Collection, and 2,000 maps, with special emphasis on the west of County Londonderry, including Limavady and Dungiven. Of special genealogical interest are: holdings of local newspapers on microfilm dating back to 1829; Ordnance Survey maps, 1834, 1854, 1907 and c. 1948 series; 1901 and 1911 census data; local history files; and an index to hearth money rolls for County Antrim (1669), County Londonderry (1663) and County Tyrone (1666). A collection of materials relating to 'The Troubles' and events in and around the city during this period are also available, including The Saville Report, also known as The Bloody Sunday Inquiry.

Libraries NI Online Resources
Libraries NI customers have access to 'Online Resources' on the library website.

Ancestry Library Edition is an online genealogical collection accessible on the Libraries NI website to library members at any library in Northern Ireland. This resource is available only from the Libraries NI network and is not accessible to members from their home computers. The Ancestry Library Edition collection has approximately thousands of databases and billions of indexed names from key collections spanning the fourteenth century to present day enabling customers to search for vital information about their ancestors.

The 'JSTOR Ireland Collection' is fully searchable, consists of the digital content of journals and other material relating to Ireland, and will be of great interest to anyone researching Irish history, genealogy, archaeology, literature etc. Most of the material included was published in the eighteenth, nineteenth and twentieth centuries.

The DIPPAM web resource is a virtual library of sources relating to the history of modern Ireland and its global diaspora. Documenting Ireland: Parliament, People and Migration (DIPPAM) is a collaboration project between Queen's University Belfast, The University of Ulster, The Mellon Centre for Migration Studies, Omagh, and Libraries NI, and has been funded by the Arts and Humanities Research Council. DIPPAM may be of particular interest to people involved in research the history of their locality or family, and for use in school history projects. It includes three searchable databases: Enhanced British Parliamentary Papers on Ireland (EPPI) – which comprises scans of over 15,000 official publications relating to all aspects of Irish affairs during the period of the Act of Union, 1800–1922, including bills, reports, royal commissions of inquiry and the published census returns. It is a rich source for the social history of Ireland, as well as for statistics and evidence relating to population, emigration, famine, crime and political movements: The Irish Emigration Database (IED) is made up of documents relating to Irish emigration since the eighteenth century, mainly to North America, and mostly drawn from

archives in Northern Ireland and from private collections. The documents include
emigrant letters, newspaper extracts, shipping advertisements, family papers and
extracts from relevant publications and Voices of Migration and Return (VMR) is an
oral history archive of over 90 life-narrative interviews conducted with emigrants
and return-emigrants from the province of Ulster, collected between 2004 and 2008.
The study participants represent a range of geographical origins within Ulster, class
backgrounds and religious identities.

LOCATION
On the west bank of the River Foyle, just south of the entrance to the city walls and
opposite the bus station. City car park nearby.

TOWER MUSEUM
See HERITAGE AND MUSEUM SERVICE, Derry

WORKHOUSE MUSEUM
See HERITAGE AND MUSEUM SERVICE, Derry

UNIVERSITY OF ULSTER LIBRARY, MAGEE CAMPUS

Northland Road
DERRY CITY, COUNTY LONDONDERRY, BT48 7JL
Northern Ireland

TELEPHONE: (028) 7167 5264; FAX: (028) 7167 5626
E-mail: cr.cregan@ulster.ac.uk
Website: www.ulster.ac.uk/library

HOURS
Term time: M–Th, 08:45–22:00; F, 08:45–20:00; Sa–Su, 13:00–17:00
Vacation period: M–Th, 09:00–17:00; F, 09:00–16:00

ACCESS AND SERVICES
Visitors welcome. Borrowing privileges and database searching not usually extended
to visitors. Application for access to Special Collections Department preferred.
Disabled access. The entire University of Ulster shares a common catalogue database.
About 90 per cent of Magee holdings are catalogued online. Fees apply for
photocopying and microform print services.

CONTACT
Ciaran Cregan, Campus Library Manager.

DESCRIPTION
The Magee campus is part of the four-campus University of Ulster system, which
also includes Belfast (County Antrim), Coleraine (County Londonderry) and
Jordanstown (in Newtownabbey, County Antrim). Magee was founded in 1865 to
prepare entrants for the Presbyterian ministry, and in 1984 Magee University
College became part of the University of Ulster. The existing library was opened in
September 2002.

HOLDINGS
The library houses a collection of some 80,000 bound volumes, plus significant holdings of journals (600 titles), microforms, newspapers, pamphlets and photographs. It specialises in the areas of informatics, art and design, business and management, social sciences, life sciences and engineering. It houses the important Irish Collection, consisting of some 6,000 volumes and 900 pamphlets, including a rare collection on the Siege of Derry in 1689. The Rare Book Collection has a particular strength in eighteenth century Irish printing. Other collections of interest include the Spalding Collection on eastern civilisations, a small collection of manuscripts on Irish Presbyterianism and a collection of some 3,000 photographic negatives of local interest. Journals in the collection include: *Derry Almanac*; *Journal of the Royal Society of Antiquaries of Ireland*, 1890–1992; and *Ulster Journal of Archaeology*, 1853–present.

LOCATION
From the south of the city approach by the Foyle Bridge and follow directions to the Magee Campus.

COUNTY LONGFORD

LONGFORD COUNTY LIBRARY – ARCHIVES AND LOCAL STUDIES

Longford County Library Headquarters
Town Centre
LONGFORD
Ireland

TELEPHONE: (043) 334 1124; FAX: (043) 334 8576
E-mail: archivist@longfordcoco.ie; library@longfordcoco.ie
Website: www.longfordlibrary.ie

HOURS
M–Th, 09:30–13:00, 14:00–17:30; F, 09:30–13:00, 14:00–17:00; closed weekends.

ACCESS AND SERVICES
Visitors welcome. Free internet access. Modest fees for photocopying and microfilm
print services. Photocopying of archives is not permitted, unless where a collection
has been microfilmed. Visitors may use digital cameras. Membership required for
borrowing privileges. Disabled access facilities.

CONTACT
County Librarian or Local Authority Archivist

DESCRIPTION
Archives and Local Studies are based in County Library HQ. There are six branch
libraries operated by Longford County Library Headquarters: Ballymahon,
Edgeworthstown, Granard, Drumlish Lanesboro and Longford. Each branch library
has a small quantity of publications and resources on that particular area, but no
archival collections. The Longford Branch Library offers a business information
service. The library system is funded by Longford County Council.

HOLDINGS
Local studies
A large collection of books, pamphlets and other works on County Longford.
Collections of the works of the county's three great writers, Oliver Goldsmith, Maria
Edgeworth and Padraic Colum, and scholarly studies of them. Longford newspapers
on microfilm and in hardcopy including *The Longford Messenger* (1837), *The
Longford Journal* (1839–88; 1899–1914; 1935–7), *Longford Leader* (since 1897),

Longford News (since 1961, with gaps) and *The Longford Telegraph* (1948–54). Major genealogical sources include the tithe applotment books (1823–35) on microfilm and 'Griffith's Valuation' (1854) in bound volumes.

Archival collections

Grand Jury: manuscript books including presentments, 1759–1899; abstracts of presentments, 1817–99.

Longford Poor Law Union: Board of Guardians minute books, 1839–1922; minutes of Board of Guardians under Labourers' Acts, 1886–96.

Granard Poor Law Union: Board of Guardians minute books, 1855–1920.

Ballymahon Poor Law Union: Board of Guardians minute books, 1881–1921; return of Guardians and Officers, 1850–1919; return of admissions and births and deaths, 1858–1909 (some gaps); return of dispensaries, 1900–20.

Rural District Council minute books: Longford, 1899–1924; Granard No. 1, 1899–1925; Ballymahon, 1900–25; assorted material relating to labourers' cottages and other works.

County council: minutes, 1899–1999; county register of separate charges, 1899–1925; financial records, 1940–77; motor tax records, 1933–68; registers of driving licences, 1938–44, 1962–70; county manager's orders, 1942–80; registers of electors, 1948–54, 1981–2; burial registers of council-owned cemeteries, mainly twentieth century.

Longford Town Commissioners/Urban District Council: minutes, 1897–1989; some rate books, 1904–27; some material on housing.

Granard Urban District Council/Town Commissioners: minute books, 1920–41, 1957–2002; some material on housing.

Board of health and public assistance: minute books, 1926–41.

Drumlish Dispensary Committee: minute book, 1871–99.

County Committee of Agriculture: various records 1933–68.

Longford Militia regulations and record book, 1793–1855; Maria Edgeworth letters and notes, 1815–49; estate papers of the King Harman family, Newcastle House, mainly 1849–1951; rent books, account books and some other records of various estates including: Newcomen/ Kingston, 1816–1909; Fetherston, 1820–46; West, 1839–86; Shuldham, 1850–81; Ledwith, 1853–82; and Howison, 1856; account books of land agents: William Ferguson 1818–56; the Bole family, 1849–1904; and Charles Webb, 1895–1908; papers of local historian, S.F. Ó Cianáin, *c.* 1902–43; papers of the Farrell family, 1919–35, including material on the I.R.A. and Dáil court in Rathcline parish; papers of the guilds and federation of the Longford Irish Countrywomen's Association, 1948–2007; papers of local historian, Paddy Whelan, mainly concerning Ballymahon; letters of the Brooke family and relatives, 1771–1835, particularly concerning the early years of Methodism; records of Gaigue N.S., Lanesborough Mixed N.S., Lanesborough Boys' N.S., Fardromin N.S., Ardagh Demesne N.S., Colehill N.S., Clonfide N.S., Legga N.S., Edenmore N.S., Moyne N.S., Drumlish N.S. and Ballymahon Church of Ireland N.S.; maps of the manors of Granard and Ballymacormack, early 1790s; the O'Neill manuscripts (five volumes of stories and poetry in Irish), early nineteenth century (microfilm).

LOCATION

Town centre.

LONGFORD RESEARCH CENTRE

Longford Roots
17 Dublin Street
LONGFORD TOWN
Ireland

TELEPHONE: (043) 41235; FAX: (043) 41279
E-mail: longroot@iol.ie

HOURS
M–F, 10:30–12:30

ACCESS AND SERVICES
Longford Research Centre offers a fee based genealogical research service for persons
interested in tracing their roots in County Longford. Application form can be
obtained from the centre's website, by e-mail or by contacting the centre directly. An
initial search fee of €75 (or equivalent) required. The centre tries to keep fees to a
minimum and the initial search fee charge is also the maximum amount charged.
Success cannot be guaranteed in any search, however, and an unsuccessful search is
usually more time consuming than a successful one. Please allow six to eight weeks
for reply.

CONTACT
Jude Flynn, Historian
Pauline Flood, Genealogist, Tel.: (043) 334 1235

DESCRIPTION
Longford Research Centre is the Irish Family History Foundation's designated
research centre for County Longford. The IFHF is the coordinating body for a
network of government approved genealogical research centres in the island of
Ireland that have computerised tens of millions of Irish ancestral records of different
types. Common County Longford surnames include: Farrell (or O'Farrell), Quinn,
Kenny, Kiernan, Mulvey, Smith, Leavy, Kelly, Glennon, Keenan, Casey and Murphy.

HOLDINGS
The centre has computerised church records of baptisms, marriages and burials for
the majority of Catholic parishes as early as 1779 and some Church of Ireland,
Methodist and Presbyterian parishes. Also available to the centre are Griffith's
Valuation, tithe applotment books, the 1901 census and civil records.

LOCATION
Town centre.

COUNTY LOUTH

LOUTH COUNTY ARCHIVES SERVICE

Old Gaol, Ardee Road
DUNDALK, COUNTY LOUTH
Ireland

TELEPHONE: (042) 932 4358
E-mail: archive@louthcoco.ie
Website: www.louthcoco.ie

HOURS
By appointment, M–F, 09:00–12:00, 14:00–16.00

ACCESS AND SERVICES
Appointment should be made beforehand, preferably one week in advance. Readers required to complete application form on first visit. Free internet access available to users. Only catalogued collections available. Material cannot be borrowed. Reproduction fees apply. Partial wheelchair access. Service has an online archive catalogue available via its website. Digitisation of the Grand Jury query books for the years 1815, 1823–1899 is currently being explored. The Service has commenced making its collections available on the Irish Archives Resource portal: www.iar.ie.

CONTACT
Lorraine McCann, County Archivist. E-mail: lorraine.mccann@louthcoco.ie

DESCRIPTION
Louth County Archives Service was founded in 2000 as a result of the passing of the 1994 Local Government Act. It is a repository for the public and private archives of County Louth. This means that it holds and seeks the acquisition of archives of Louth Local Authorities and their predecessor bodies in addition to private archives that document the history and development of the county such as those of individuals, organisations, clubs, societies, businesses, landed estates, and national schools. The Service makes available to users collections that have been catalogued. The mission statement of Louth County Archives is: 'the identification, preservation and availability of the valuable public and private archives of County Louth'.

HOLDINGS
Holdings include almost complete series of minute books for the Boards of
Guardians of the Poor Law Unions of Ardee and Dundalk, *c.* 1841–1924, and also
Drogheda (with gaps). There are a few admission registers for Ardee workhouse,
c. 1880–*c.* 1910.

Rate books survive for the Dundalk area, *c.* 1840–*c.* 1960, with a
complementary set of manuscript valuation records, *c.* 1900–*c.* 1940. There is
coverage for all of County Louth in the valuation series.

Fortunately for Louth, a county in the Pale region, exceptionally early records of
town corporations survive, including Drogheda (1503–1970), Dunleer (1683,
1709–1773), Carlingford (1694–1835), Dundalk (1594, 1655–1674, 1822–42),
followed by Dundalk Town Commissioners (1840–99) and Dundalk Urban District
Council (1899–1971). There are records for Ardee Corporation and Ardee Town
Commissioners (*c.* 1650–*c.* 1970) and Louth County Council (1899–1970s) and
Rural District Council Records (1899–1925).

Grand Jury query books are available for the years 1786–1810, 1815, 1823–99;
statutes (1310–1612), 1634–1847, and a Grand Jury minute book of the Board of
Superintendence of Louth County Gaol 1837–53.

Minute books for the Louth County Committee of Agriculture (1901–85) are
held as are papers of the Dundalk Harbour Commissioners (1840–1983) and
Presbyterian Church Records for Dundalk and Carlingford ((1655–), 1831–1959,
1991).

National school archive collections are held for Dun Dealgan national school
(1867–1985), Ardee national school (1862–87), St Nicholas national school,
Dundalk (1855–1954), Plaster national school in the parish of Ballymascanlon
(1888–1936), St Laurence's national school, Omeath (*c.* 1876–1928), St Peter's
Church of Ireland national school, Drogheda (1893–1987), and St Peter's National
School, Dromiskin (1862–2007, predominant 1900–48).

Private papers include the Filgate of Lisrenny Papers, 1757–1964; Caraher of
Cardistown Family Papers, 1738–1954; The Roden Collection, 1611–1986; Joseph
Dolan papers, 1901–33; The Paddy Mallon – Great Northern Railway (Ireland)
Collection, 1838–1984; Bellingham family of Castlebellingham, 1813–1905, 1967;
Moore (of Carlingford) Rentals, 1878–1963; Macardle Moore and Company
collection, eighteenth century – twentieth century; Emmet Band, Dundalk, 1942–7;
Hatch family papers, 1731–1882, 1959–71; Anglesey estate rentals, 1810, 1856;
Collon estate rental account, 1779–81; County Louth Recruiting Committee, 1916;
Patrick Reilly, Millockstown, Ardee, 1873–1900; Rahanna House papers, 1855–7;
Major O'Reilly, Knockabbey Papers, 1719–40, 1854–69, 1911–28; General
Accounts of the Catholic rent and Louth Confraternity, 1822–5; Brigid Cassidy,
Mullacrew, 1871–1931; Samuel Lockington and company, 1905–38; Kirwan of
Castletown Papers, 1909–18; Premises at Castle St, Ardee, 1784–1901; Hinds'
Dundalk Estate, 1832–82; Dickie Estate, 1840–98; Fitzpatrick/Kirkland Papers,
1793–1865, 1984; Eastwood papers, 1902–45; Phillips of Belcotton papers, 1789,
1817; MacIvor estate, Dunmahon, 1893–7; Percy Fitzgerald Estate, Fane Valley,
1824–1912; Donaldson of Philipstown Papers, 1737–1876; Johnston of Lisdoo
papers, 1799–1935; Ardee Papers, 1760–1925; Saint Nicholas Mens Institute,
Church Street, Dundalk, 1908–10, 1913–58; Ravensdale Park auction catalogue,
1920; Louth Papers, 1722–77, 1832–3, 1900; Edward O'Callaghan's estate, 1822–5;
Earl of Carlingford estate indentures, 1696, 1725; Dundalk & Newry Steam Packet

Company engineer's report book, 1917–18; Henry Backhouse and Company, 1926–79; Charles MacMahon Papers, 1827–1921; Tempests Annuals 1915–76; Louth Farming Collection, 1801–1912; Louth Hall estate papers, 1851–1922; Craven of Drumcashel papers, 1658–86, 1798, 1819–51; Papers of Stannus estate, 1709–1848; MacNeill Estate, 1900–33; Documents relating to Haggardstown Parochial House, 1883–1907; Canon MacIomhair papers, 1835–1913; Dun Dealgan Museum Papers, 1906–65; Papers of historian John D'Alton, 1844–64; Fortescue family of Stephenstown House photograph album, 1861–72; Papers of several Co. Louth priests, 1867–1944; Dundalk Grammar School, 1856–96; Mr Joseph Fitzsimons, Dunbin, Dundalk, 1847–1936; Canice O'Mahony, 1974–2010; Old Dundalk Society's Photographic Collection, nineteenth – twenty-first centuries; Bernard (Bennie) Rice family of Mullaghatina and Chapel Street, Dundalk, c. 1900–74; Folklore and traditions in the Rathcor area, 1938–60; Peadar MacCuarta (Peter McCourt) papers, 1863, 1885, 1897, 1903–95, 2006 (predominantly 1930–70); Papers of Mrs Breige McCourt (nee Murphy), c. 1940s–50s; Tillage & Fertiliser Schemes, 1945–70; Ancient Order of Hibernians, Dundalk Branch, 1907–2004; Ancient Order of Hibernians, Haggardstown Branch, 1912–83; Election Archive Collection, nineteenth–twentieth centuries.

An Oral History Archive collection contains approximately 174 interviews taken between 1980 and 2005.

LOCATION
Entrance on Ardee Road, near entrance to Dundalk Garda Station. Limited car parking available on Ardee Road adjacent to the building. Three minutes' walk from Dundalk train station.

LOUTH COUNTY LIBRARY – REFERENCE AND LOCAL HISTORY LIBRARY

Dundalk Branch Library
Roden Place
DUNDALK, COUNTY LOUTH
Ireland

TELEPHONE: (042) 935 3190
E-mail: library@louthcoco.ie
Website: www.louthcoco.ie

HOURS:
Dundalk Branch Library: Tu–Th, 10:00–20:00; W, F, Sa, 10:00–17:00; Closed Saturdays of bank holiday weekends.
Dundalk Reference and Local History Library: Tu–Sa, 10:00–13:00, 14:00–17:00

ACCESS AND SERVICES
Visitors welcome. Disabled access facilities; free internet access for members. Dundalk-Europe Direct Centre; The County provides an Archive's Service (see separate entry).

CONTACT
Alan Hand, Reference Librarian. E-mail: referencelibrary@louthcoco.ie

DESCRIPTION
The library is the flagship library in a five library county system. Louth County
Council also operates branch libraries in: Drogheda (041) 983 6649; Ardee (041)
685 6080; Dunleer (041) 686 1270; and Carlingford (042) 938 3020. A Mobile
library and School's Service are also provided.

HOLDINGS
The holdings reflect the general educational and recreational reading interests of a
public library, but there are several collections of interest to visitors, especially
genealogists. Collections include: Lawrence Collection of photographs of County
Louth; General photographic collections; Local newspapers in hardcopy and
microfilm; and School's Folklore collection 1937/8.

Journals of local interest include: *County Louth Archaeological and Historical
Journal*; *Tempest's Annual*; *Clogher Record*; *Breifne*; *Riocht na Midhe*; *Seanchas Ard
Mhacha*; *Termonfeckin Historical Society Journal*; and the *Journal of the Old Drogheda
Society*.
Holdings of genealogical interest include: Database of Catholic Church records for
County Louth – mid 1700s to 1900; tithe applotment books – 1820s on microfilm;
List of Freeholders – 1820s; Griffith's Valuation – 1854; Local History books and
directories; Collection of maps relative to County Louth. Genealogical Research
Service available.

LOCATION
Town centre. Car parking facilities (fees apply); Entrance to car park is from
Ramparts Road.

COUNTY MAYO

BALLINA LIBRARY
See THE JACKIE CLARKE RESPOSITORY, Ballina

THE JACKIE CLARKE REPOSITORY
Ballina Library, Pearse Street
BALLINA, COUNTY MAYO
Ireland

TELEPHONE: (096) 904 73508

HOURS
To be confirmed.

ACCESS AND SERVICES
Non-lending collection: access restricted to academic scholars and *bona fide* researchers working on bibliographies or other studies of Irish material.

DESCRIPTION
The new library, which opened in Ballina in 2006, includes the library of the late Jackie Clarke, a local businessman and noted collector of books and antiquarian material. The collection represents the fruits of over 40 years of collecting and is regarded as one of the finest private libraries in the country.

CONTACT
Librarian

HOLDINGS
The Jackie Clarke Library includes extensive coverage of Irish history and politics with many rare and unique items and is particularly strong regarding the 1798 Rebellion, the 1916 Rising and the IRA campaigns from the 1940s to the 1960s. It comprises books, photographs, posters, legal papers, badges, newspapers, circulars, reports, letters, periodicals, memorial cards, minute books and articles from newspapers. The Irish revolutionary period from the Siege of Limerick to Wolfe Tone, the Young Irelanders, the Fenians, the Famine, the Land Wars, the War of Independence, the Civil War and the IRA campaigns from the 1940s to the 1990s

are all represented in this collection. Mayo's involvement in all events is highlighted and many rare documents of local interest are included in the collection.

LOCATION
Town centre.

MAYO NORTH FAMILY HERITAGE CENTRE

Enniscoe, Castlehill
BALLINA, COUNTY MAYO
Ireland

TELEPHONE: (096) 31809; FAX: (096) 31885
E-mail: northmayo@gmail.com
Website: www.mayo.irishroots.net; www.heritageatenniscoe.com/research.html

HOURS
M–F, 09:00–16:00

ACCESS AND SERVICES
Mayo North Family Heritage Centre offers a fee based genealogical research service for persons interested in tracing their roots in North Mayo. Application form available on the centre's website; initial search fee of €95 (or equivalent) required. See website for sample report and explanation of terms and sources used in the reports. General enquiries answered immediately; otherwise response depends on type of research commissioned. Average cost of full report is €300. This centre and South Mayo Family Research Centre, Ballinrobe have worked closely together for nearly 15 years and share resources, including a website. There is a museum, gardens and shop at the centre. Seasonal operating hours: telephone for details. Disabled access.

CONTACT
Bridie Greavy, Supervisor

DESCRIPTION
Mayo North Family Heritage Centre is one of the Irish Family History Foundation's two designated research centres for County Mayo. The IFHF is the coordinating body for a network of government approved genealogical research centres in the Republic of Ireland and Northern Ireland that have computerised tens of millions of Irish ancestral records of different types. Common North Mayo surnames include: Gallagher, Durkan, McHale, Barrett, Kelly, Loftus, Gaughan and Lavelle.

HOLDINGS
The two Mayo centres have jointly compiled and input almost 2,000,000 genealogical records to a computer database, relying chiefly on church and civil records. These sources include: Griffith's Valuation (1856); parochial registers of baptism and marriage for Roman Catholic parishes including Kilconduff from 1808 and Church of Ireland parishes including Killala from 1704. For Methodist churches in the Castlebar circuit there are registers from 1829 and for the Presbyterian Church at Turlough the registers date from 1819. The earliest burial register is for Kilfian parish (probably Church of Ireland) from 1826. Other sources indexed include the civil registers of births, marriages and deaths beginning in 1864; the 1901 and 1911

censuses; all pre-1990 gravestone inscriptions; tithe applotment books (1825–42); some school roll books; some rent books; ads placed in the *Boston Pilot*, 1831–1900; and lists of Famine immigrants to the port of New York, 1847–51.

LOCATION
On the grounds of the Enniscoe Estate, 3.5 miles south of Crossmolina on the R315 route to Castlebar.

SOUTH MAYO FAMILY RESEARCH CENTRE

Main Street
BALLINROBE, COUNTY MAYO
Ireland

TELEPHONE: (094) 954 1214; FAX: (094) 954 1103
E-mail: soumayo@iol.ie
Website: www.mayo.rootsireland.ie

HOURS
M–Th, 09:30–12:00, 13:30–16:00; F, 09:30–12:00

ACCESS AND SERVICES
South Mayo Family Research Centre offers (1) online access fee based to recordes of baptisms, marriage and deaths , genealogical research service for persons interested in tracing their roots in South Mayo. Application form available on the centre's website; initial search fee of €95 (or equivalent) required, but discountable from cost of a comprehensive family history report. See website for sample report and explanation of terms and sources used in the reports. General enquiries answered immediately; otherwise response depends on type of research commissioned. Average cost of full report is €300. Several other searches, e.g. gravestone search, birth search, marriage search, location search, are available for €15–€40 per search. These results are usually provided to visitors to the centre within two hours.

This centre and Mayo North Family Heritage Centre (Ballina) have worked closely together for nearly 15 years and share resources, including a common website.

CONTACT
Gerard M. Delaney, Manager

DESCRIPTION
South Mayo Family Research Centre is one of the Irish Family History Foundation's two designated research centres for County Mayo. The IFHF is the coordinating body for a network of government approved genealogical research centres in the Republic of Ireland and in Northern Ireland that have computerised tens of millions of Irish ancestral records of different types. Common South Mayo surnames include: Walsh, Burke, Gibbons, Prendergast, Joyce, Murray, Gallagher, Lydon, Heneghan, Murphy, O'Malley, Kelly, Moran, Duffy, O'Connor, Waldron and Farragher.

HOLDINGS
The two Mayo centres have jointly compiled and input over 2,500,000 genealogical records onto an electronic database, relying chiefly on church and civil records. These sources include: Griffith's Valuation (1855–7); all the parochial registers of baptism and marriage for Roman Catholic parishes, the earliest of which is Crossboyne and Tagheen with registers from 1791. For Church of Ireland parishes

the earliest registers are for Kilmaine and date from 1744. The earliest Presbyterian registers surviving are for Aughavale and date from 1853.

Other sources indexed include the civil registers of births, marriages and deaths beginning in 1864; the 1901 and 1911 censuses of population; all pre-1950 gravestone inscriptions; and tithe applotment books (1825–42).

LOCATION
Town centre, Main Street, Ballinrobe.

MAYO COUNTY LIBRARY – LOCAL STUDIES DEPARTMENT

Pavilion Road
CASTLEBAR, COUNTY MAYO
Ireland

TELEPHONE: (094) 9047 5557; FAX: (094) 902 4774
E-mail: ihamrock@mayococo.ie
Website: www.mayolibrary.ie

HOURS
Tu, W, 10:00–20:00; Th, F, 10:00–13:00, 14:00–17:00; Sa, 10:00–16:00

ACCESS AND SERVICES
Visitors welcome. Free internet access. Photocopying available for a modest fee. Membership required for borrowing privileges. Disabled access facilities.

CONTACT
Ivor Hamrock, Librarian
Austin Vaughan, County Librarian. E-mail: avaughan@mayococo.ie

DESCRIPTION
The Local Studies Department is located in Castlebar Library and is the central repository for a wealth of material on the history and heritage of County Mayo from earliest times to the present. Mayo County Library collects comprehensively material of local interest, including books, manuscripts, journals, newspapers, photographs, maps, CD-ROMs, microfilm and ephemera. It is part of the county library system, headquartered at Mountain View, Castlebar, County Mayo (telephone (094) 904 7573). Mayo County Library Service operates 17 branch libraries. The Castlebar Library also offers a business information centre.

HOLDINGS
All the County Mayo branch libraries hold collections relating to the local history of their surrounding area. The Local Studies Department offers one of the strongest collections of its kind in all of Ireland. Special collections include: Michael Davitt (1846–1906) – complete works and related biographical and historical material; George Moore (1852–1933) – literary works, related biographical and critical material and the 1798 Rebellion – events in Mayo. The department also maintains a collection of books, articles, maps and illustrations on County Mayo. The library website features three online exhibitions: In *Humbert's Footsteps Mayo 1798, The Famine in Mayo and Michael Davitt Father of the Land League.*

Archival materials include: Ballinrobe Poor Law Union records (1844–1926), including minute books, financial records, outdoor relief records and outgoing letter books. The department also maintains a collection of all journals published locally, including: *Cathair na Mart* (journal of the Westport Historical Society), annually, 1982–present; *North Mayo Historical and Archaeological Society Journal*, annually, 1982–95. Official publications of special local interest include: *Report of Her Majesty's Commissioners of Inquiry into the Working of the Landlord and Tenant (Ireland) Act* (Bessborough Commission, 1870); *British Parliamentary Papers, Famine Series*, vols 1–8 (1968–70); *Digest of Evidence Taken before Her Majesty's Commissioners of Inquiry into the State of the Law and Practice in Respect to the Occupation of Land in Ireland* (Devon Commission, HMSO 1847); Congested Districts Board for Ireland papers; and socio-economic reports on 21 districts in County Mayo (1892/9).

The Photographic Archive includes: the Wynne Collection, containing approximately 2,000 photographs taken by Thomas Wynne of Castlebar and his descendants, dating from 1870, featuring scenes of the west of Ireland, landscapes, architecture, streetscapes, studio portraits, historical events etc; selected views of Mayo subjects from the Lawrence Collection of the National Library; postcards of County Mayo scenes from *c.* 1900. Also worth mentioning is a large collection of illustrations from nineteenth century newspapers depicting social and political events in the west of Ireland.

The Newspaper Collection includes extensive holdings of local and national papers dating from pre-Famine times to the present. Some of these newspapers are now available in digital format. See website for listings.

The Map Collection is also noteworthy and includes: a map of the Maritime County of Mayo in 25 sheets that was begun in 1809 and ended in 1817, by William Bald FRSE, printed in 1830 (scale two inches); Ordnance Survey 6 inch maps of County Mayo, 1839 and 1900; recorded monuments protected under Section 12 of the 1994 National Monuments (amendment) Act; and the County Mayo archaeological constraint maps, Office of Public Works, 1999.

Of special genealogical interest are the department's holdings of: tithe applotment books, *c.* 1830 (on microfilm); rental records for a number of estates including that of Lord Lucan's; records for R.C. parishes of Burrishoole, Achill and Ballycroy; Methodist baptismal records for Castlebar, Westport and Ballinrobe and gravestone inscriptions for Castlebar Old Cemetery, Meelick and Bushfield, Ballinrobe;. Finally, the department houses the impressive Folklore Collection, including microfilm copies of most of the material collected by schools in County Mayo for the Schools Scheme of 1937–8 project, an 18 month effort by schoolchildren to document a wide range of Irish folk tradition, including folk tales and folk legends, riddles and proverbs, songs, customs and beliefs, games and pastimes and traditional work practices and crafts. *See also* JACKIE CLARKE REPOSITORY, Ballina.

LOCATION
Town centre.

NATIONAL MUSEUM OF COUNTRY LIFE
See NATIONAL MUSEUM OF IRELAND, Dublin

MICHAEL DAVITT MUSEUM

Straide
FOXFORD, COUNTY MAYO
Ireland

TELEPHONE: (094) 903 1942/(094) 903 1022
E-mail: davittmuseum@eircom.net; info@michaeldavittmuseum.com
Website: www.michaeldavittmuseum.com

HOURS
Open seven days a week, 10:00–18:00; closed annually for Christmas from 23
December through 2 January inclusive, and also for Good Friday. Special
arrangements can be made by contacting the museum beforehand if earlier opening
is required.

ACCESS AND SERVICES
Visitors welcome. Disabled access. Admission fees apply. Pencils only in archives.
Limited Internet access and photocopying services available Monday through Friday
only for a modest fee. Pencils, books, postcards and small souvenirs for sale.
Museum also offers guided tours, a permanent exhibition and an audiovisual
presentation. Group and coach tour rates available, with special emphasis on School
Tours, ranging from Primary to Third Level Institutions. Adequate parking facilities
for all vehicles – free of charge. The Michael Davitt Museum grounds are
meticulously manicured and offer ideal photographic settings/opportunities, coupled
with excellent picnic area facilities. Other attractions in the area include Foxford
Woollen Mills, Museum of Country Life, Jackie Clarke Museum, Céide Fields, and
Hennigan's Heritage Centre.

CONTACT
Curator

DESCRIPTION
The museum celebrates the life and work of the nineteenth century Irish nationalist
and radical land reformer Michael Davitt (1846–1906). It is housed in the restored
pre-Penal church in the village of Straide, County Mayo, where Michael Davitt was
baptised in 1846. Davitt is buried nearby in the grounds of the thirteenth century
Straide Abbey.

HOLDINGS
The museum offers vast research facilities and contains an extensive collection of
documents, photographs, Land Acts, correspondence, postcards and other material
connected with the life of Michael Davitt.
      These include: police reports, prison reports relating to Davitt and the Land
League; correspondence to and from Davitt; photographs of evictions, family
photos, Land League posters, personal items (i.e. rosary beads, walking stick, a dried
flower collected in the Holy Land and postcards from all parts of the world he sent
to his children); Land Acts from 1881; drums and flutes connected with the Land
League; cartoons and tributes and salutations paid to Davitt.

LOCATION
On the N58, between the towns of Castlebar and Ballina, north-west of Knock.

COUNTY MEATH

MEATH COUNTY LIBRARY HEADQUARTERS

Railway Street
NAVAN, COUNTY MEATH
Ireland

TELEPHONE: (046) 902 1134; FAX: (046) 909 7001
E-mail: localstudies@meathcoco.ie

Website: www.meath.ie/library, see also www.askaboutireland.ie (click on 'Places',
then 'County Meath')

HOURS
M, W, F–Sa, 10:00–17:00; Tu, Th, 10:00–20:30

ACCESS AND SERVICES
Visitors welcome. Wheelchair access. Photocopying at 20c per sheet and microfilm
printing at 60c for A4 and 80c for A3. Free membership and free internet access.

CONTACT
Tom French, Local Studies Librarian. E-mail: tfrench@meathcoco.ie
or telephone (046) 909 7374 (direct line).

DESCRIPTION
The library is the headquarters library for the county system, which includes 13
branch libraries.

HOLDINGS
In addition to the normal educational and recreational materials found in a county
library, Meath maintains a special collection on local history and genealogy.
Of special interest to family history researchers are Dr Beryl Moore's recordings of
gravestone inscriptions. Dr Moore was an indefatigable worker and she recorded all
the inscriptions in more than 35 graveyards in County Meath. She ranged all over
the county, except perhaps in the north-east part near the border with County
Monaghan. Her recordings are available in typescript. Some examples of her work
have been published in the *Journal of the Meath Archaeological and Historical Society*
and in *The Irish Ancestor*. The inscriptions of several other graveyards have been
recorded subsequently and many others are currently being recorded.
Meath is exceptionally fortunate to have available some 50 volumes of records of

the Meath County Infirmary including a (damaged) register of patients *c.* 1780–*c.*
1800 and also diet books listing the names of patients. Minute books for the Boards
of Guardians of the Poor Law Unions of Dunshaughlin, Kells, Navan and Trim
survive for the period *c.* 1840–*c.* 1920 and there is also an incomplete series for
Oldcastle. The Poor Law Archive includes some rate books for the period *c.* 1925–*c.*
1940.

The records of Meath County Council between the years 1899–1970 are
arranged and listed. For the towns of Kells and Navan there are records of Town
Commissioners from *c.* 1830 and Urban District Council records from 1899. For
Trim some Corporation records for the seventeenth and eighteenth centuries survive.

There are Town Commission records from *c.* 1880 to *c.* 1929 and Urban
District Council records from *c.* 1920. A quantity of Trim records was destroyed
during an occupation of the Town Hall in September 1920.

Other items of interest include newspapers, including the *Meath Herald*,
1845–1936; *Meath Chronicle*, 1904–present (microfilm and hard copy); *Meath
People*, August 1857–63 (on microfilm); the *Irish Peasant*, February 1904 (one issue),
1903–06 (on microfilm); *The Meath Reporter* 1888–1901 (incomplete) on microfilm
and the *Drogheda Independent*, 1924–48 (on microfilm).

The 1901 census for County Meath is available on microfilm, as are the 1911
census returns; there are also the surviving fragments of the 1821 census for 19
parishes in the baronies of Upper and Lower Navan and a register of persons
planting trees in the county, 1814.

The Schools Folklore collection (1937–8) is available on microfilm for some 135
Meath national schools.

The business archive of Gogarty printers, Kilmainhamwood, has been donated.
Of particular interest to social historians are several hundred posters advertising
social, leisure, political and fund-raising events in North Meath mainly from the
1950s onwards.

The Meath Oral History Project is ongoing and to date has recorded over 100
hours of interviews on life and work in Meath. Interviews are listed on the library
catalogue.

County Meath Committee of Agriculture records are available, including
Minute Books from 1905 to 1982; Financial Statement Receipt Book, 1928 to
1986; Attendance and Address Registers from 1909 to 1988 as well as records on
various farm schemes.

Landed Estate records include Lord de Ros rentals, volume 1, 1870s comprising
Ongenstown, Canon Row, Brews Hill, Trimgate street (in poor condition). Volume
2, opened by Baroness de Ros in May 1903, includes estates of Coddington, Lindsay
and Ponsonby Lindsay. Volumes 3 to 6, de Ros *et al*, are dated 1900–02, 1914–15,
1917–21, and 1921–4.

Naper Estate rentals date from 1846 to 1932, in 9 folio volumes, with *lacunae* at
1895–1903 and 1915–23. Cash books date from 1935 to 1944 and 1942 to 1947.
Rentals of the estates of Thomas [Cherburgh] Bligh in the counties of Meath,
Wicklow and Dublin are in six large volumes dated 1822 to 1932. The rental covers
the Brittas estate of Thomas Bligh in the townlands of Raffin, Ballynaticknuff,
Kinahan, Ballinaclose, Lisnagroagh, Eivy, Cornecarrow, Boynagh, Ahafarnan,
Corrickienan, Tyvocher, Newtowncarnecliff, Castletown-Kilberry, Kilgriffin,
Rahood, Butterstown, Butlerstown, Thomastown, Newtwon, Painstown, Yellow
Leas, Castletownkilpatrick, Fyagh, Carriga, Scribogue, Largy, Rathlagan, Hermitage

and Brittas; also Altadore in county Wicklow and Dawson Street in Dublin. The Blighs, Cromwellian Adventurers, acquired *c.* 25,000 acres of land in Meath in 1654.

Rent Roll and Account book of the Earl of Darnley, 1874–6, for his estates in the greater Athboy area of Meath.

Digitisation of some 3,000 Meath images and *c.* 600 files of Meath ephemera is underway with an upgrade of the library's Local Studies website due shortly.

LOCATION
Town centre, opposite the bus stop. Public car parks on Circular Road, Fair Green and at the adjacent County Hall.

MEATH HERITAGE AND GENEALOGY CENTRE

Town Hall, Castle Street
TRIM, COUNTY MEATH
Ireland

TELEPHONE: (046) 943 6633; FAX: (046) 943 7502
E-mail: meathhc@iol.ie
Website: www.meathroots.com

HOURS
M–Th, 09:00–17:00; F, 09:00–14:00

ACCESS AND SERVICES
The Meath Heritage and Genealogy Centre offers a fee based record search service for those interested in tracing their family roots in County Meath. Enquirers to this centre can expect a reply within about two weeks. A copy of the centre's application form can be found on website. €30 euro (or equivalent) fee required for initial search. Common surnames in Meath include: Reilly, Smith, Lynch, Brady, Farrell, Farrelly, Kelly, O'Brien, Daly and Maguire. Chief towns include: Navan, Trim, Kells, Slane and Dunshaughlin. The centre offers a range of publications, including: *Trace your Meath Ancestors*; *The Boyne*; *The Battle of the Boyne*; *Trim*; and *Wellington*.

CONTACT
Noel E. French

DESCRIPTION
Meath Heritage and Genealogy Centre is the IFHF's designated research centre for the County of Meath. The IFHF is the coordinating body for a network of government approved genealogical research centres in the Republic of Ireland and in Northern Ireland that have computerised tens of millions of Irish ancestral records of different types.

HOLDINGS
The centre has computerised over 400,000 records to date. Church records computerised include: Roman Catholic records from 1742, Church of Ireland records from 1698 and Presbyterian records for Kells from 1873. Census returns have also been computerised.

LOCATION
Town centre, beside Trim Castle.

COUNTY MONAGHAN

MONAGHAN COUNTY LIBRARY

98 Avenue
CLONES, COUNTY MONAGHAN
Ireland

TELEPHONE: (047) 74712
E-mail: moncolib@monaghancoco.ic
Website: www.monaghan.ie/library or www.clennon@monaghancoco.ie

HOURS
M, 11:00–20:00, Tu–Fri, 11:00–17:00

ACCESS AND SERVICES
Visitors welcome, but ID required. Borrowing privileges for visitors available.
Consult Librarian. The library provides a genealogical reference service. Free internet
access for all members, 45 minutes per day. Annual membership fee, €3.

CONTACT
Catherine Elliott Acting County Librarian. E-mail: celliott@monaghancoco.ie
Local History Queries: Catriona Lennon. E-mail: clennon@monaghancoco.ie

DESCRIPTION
Headquarters Library in Clones, opened in 2008. There are five branch libraries in
the county, the others are Monaghan Town, Carrickmacross, Castleblayney, and
Ballybay.

HOLDINGS
Good local history collection, supported by a general collection of Irish interest, with
strong genealogical resources. Sources include: 1901 and 1911 censuses for County
Monaghan (on microfilm); Griffith's Valuation; tithe applotment books; gravestone
inscriptions recorded in printed sources for Catholic, Church of Ireland and
Presbyterian cemeteries throughout much of the county; street directories for
County Monaghan, including *Pigot's Directory* (1824), *Ulster Counties Directory*
(1895), *Gillespies County Monaghan Directory* (1897), *Monaghan County Alphabetical
List* (1900), *Monaghan County Yearbook* (1913), *Northern Standard Centenary
Supplement Directory* (1939), *MacDonalds Irish Directory* (1952) and *Members of the
Established Church in Clones* (1823); rentals, including Anketell Estate, 1784–1876

and Newbliss Estate, 1840–43 and 1852–3; parish histories; GAA club histories; and family histories.

Newspaper holdings include: *Northern Standard*, 1839–present; *People's Advocate*, 1876–1906; *Farney Leader*, 1908–09; *Clones Weekly Chronicle*, July 1883–November 1883; *Monaghan People*, 1906–08; *Anglo Celt*, 1885–1928; and *Dundalk Democrat*, 1849–1950.

Roman Catholic records for the Diocese of Clogher up to 1880 on microfilm.

Death Notices and Obituaries extracted from the Northern Standard 1839–1914, also from *The Peoples Advocate*, 1876–1906 Carrickmacross Workhouse Minute Books.

LOCATION
Town centre, in new purpose-built library. Parking is available directly in front of the building, with wheelchair access car parking available immediately in front of the main entrance. Clones is the most ancient of the towns in County Monaghan, built around the site of a sixth century monastery founded by St Tiarnach.

THE HERITAGE CENTRE

St Louis Convent
MONAGHAN
Ireland

Note: The Heritage Centre colsed in 2010.

MONAGHAN ANCESTRY

6 Tully
MONAGHAN
Ireland

TELEPHONE: (087) 631 0360 (for appointment only)
E-mail: theomcmahon@eircom.net
Website: www.monaghan.rootsireland.ie

HOURS
By appointment

ACCESS AND SERVICES
Note: Visitors welcome by appointment, but postal enquiries preferred. Monaghan Ancestry offers a fee based genealogical research service for those interested in tracing their Monaghan roots. Estimates of costs made based on availability of records, estimated time involved in preparing a report and format in which information is required. The centre is currently working on preparing Church records (bmds) for inclusion on the rootsireland.ie website, and will be uploading material to this site on an ongoing basis.

CONTACT
Theo McMahon. Telephone: (087) 631 0360 (for appointment only);
E-mail: theomcmahon@eircom.net

DESCRIPTION
Monaghan Ancestry is the designated Irish Family History Foundation research
centre for County Monaghan. The IFHF is the coordinating body for a network of
government approved genealogical research centres in the Republic of Ireland and in
Northern Ireland that have computerised nearly 20 million Irish ancestral records of
different types.

HOLDINGS
Monaghan Ancestry has computerised all Roman Catholic baptism and marriage
records, from their commencement up to and including 1880. Other sources include
tithe applotment books for 22 of the 23 civil parishes. Only one parish, Tydavnet,
does not have a detailed return in this series. Other records include: Griffith's
Valuation, 1858–61; the 1901 census for Counties Monaghan, Fermanagh and
Tyrone; gravestone inscriptions; international genealogical index, 1988 and 1992;
Royal Irish Constabulary records, 1816–1921; civil records (non-Roman Catholic)
of marriages for most parishes, 1845–1900; old age pension claims, some with
abstracts from the 1841 and 1851 censuses; rentals of the Rose Estate, Tydavnet,
1839–47 (these compensate to some extent for the loss of the tithe applotment book
for certain townlands in this parish); Templeton Estate rentals (mostly in Muckno
parish) for 1805; Forster Estate rentals for certain townlands, 1802–08; Murray Ker
Estate rentals (Kileevan/Newbliss), 1881–1911 and 1937; Kane Estate rentals, 1764;
Famine Relief Books for Donagh and Errigal Truagh parishes by townland,
January–May 1847; Donaghmoyne vaccination register, 1869–84; index to Clogher
wills, 1659–1857; Lennard Barrett Estate records and rentals for Clones,
1682–1845. In addition, the centre maintains a reference library, which includes all
publications of the Clogher Historical Society, 1953–present.

LOCATION
Near town centre, in a private residence.

MONAGHAN COUNTY MUSEUM

1–2 Hill Street
MONAGHAN
Ireland

TELEPHONE: (047) 82928; FAX: (047) 71189
E-mail: comuseum@monaghancoco.ie
Website: www.monaghan.ie

HOURS
M–F, 11:00–17:00; Sa, 12:00–17:00

ACCESS AND SERVICES
Visitors welcome. Free admission. There is a virtual tour of the first floor available
on the ground floor for visitors with limited mobility as well as large print
information panels, automatic doors and a hearing loop system available in the
reception area and temporary display gallery. Access to archives by appointment
only. The museum offers an award winning exhibitions and education programme,
featuring material dating from c. 5000 BC to the present. Of special interest is Cross
of Clogher, a fourteenth century oak cross decorated with bronze and semi-precious

metals. Museum also houses a fine collection of early medieval crannog (lake dwelling) artefacts as well as a large collection of Carrickmacross and Clones Lace.

CONTACT
Liam Bradley, Curator

DESCRIPTION
Monaghan County Museum was established in 1974 by Monaghan County Council. It moved into its present quarters in 1986. It was the first full time staffed local authority county museum in the Irish Republic and gained distinction in 1980 and 1993 by winning two European and Irish museum awards. The Monaghan County Museum received the Irish Museum of the Year Award for Best Collections Care, 2004. It became the first local authority museum in the Republic of Ireland to achieve full accreditation under the Heritage Council's Museum Standards Programme for Ireland (MSPI) in 2008.

The museum's mission is to protect and preserve the cultural diversity and historical richness of the region and to bring that diversity and richness to as wide an audience as possible.

HOLDINGS
In addition to artefacts and paintings, the museum has a small archive focusing on County Monaghan records. These include estate papers, some of which extend beyond the boundaries of Monaghan; Monaghan County Council minutes, rate books and ledgers, 1899–1959; Monaghan Urban District Council records; and personal papers, including those of Charles Gavan Duffy (1816–1903). *See also* FRANCISCAN LIBRARY KILLINEY for more information about Duffy records (specifically those of George Gavan Duffy, son of Charles), in the care of University College Dublin – Archives Department. The museum recently acquired a book of maps dating to 1791 of the Clermont Estate, which later became the Rossmore Estate covering the extended area around Monaghan Town. The book contains 90 maps of the estate's holdings, with detailed records of each tenant.

LOCATION
Town centre. Located on a hillside, across from Market House. Public car parks nearby.

COUNTY OFFALY

IRISH MIDLANDS ANCESTRY (LAOIS AND OFFALY FAMILY HISTORY RESEARCH CENTRE)

Bury Quay
TULLAMORE, COUNTY OFFALY
Ireland

TELEPHONE: (0506) 21421
E-mail: info@offalyhistory.com; info@irishmidlandsancestry.com
Website: www.irishmidlandsancestry

HOURS
M–F, 09:00–16:00

ACCESS AND SERVICES
The centre offers a fee based, full range genealogical research service. Appointments preferred for consultations at €25 per hour (deductible from further fees). Reports range from €149 to €300 plus postage. Initial enquiries are answered promptly; research usually takes from four to six weeks. The centre has indexed some 750,000 records in its database. Application form is available on the centre's website. Main surnames associated with Counties Laois and Offaly include: Kelly, Dunne, Molloy, Carroll, Egan, Dempsey, O'Connor, Daly, Fitzpatrick and Lalor. Principal towns include: (Offaly) Tullamore, Birr, Clara, Edenderry; (Laois) Portarlington, Portlaoise, Mountmellick and Mountrath. Publications offered by the centre include: *The Long Ridge* (Killeigh); *Quakers of Mount Mellick*; *Falling into Wretchedness: Ferbane, County Offaly in the Famine Times*; *Clara Parish: Burials from the Earliest Times*; and *Durrow in History*. Prices are exclusive of shipping and handling. See publications list at: www.offalyhistory.com/content/reading_resources/sale_publications/esker_press.

CONTACT
John Kearney, Coordinator

DESCRIPTION
Irish Midlands Ancestry, under the aegis of Offaly Historical and Archaeological Society, is the Irish Family History Foundation's designated research centre for the counties of Laois (formerly Queen's County) and Offaly (formerly King's County). The IFHF is the coordinating body for a network of government approved

genealogical research centres in the Republic of Ireland and in Northern Ireland that have computerised tens of millions of Irish ancestral records of different types.

HOLDINGS
The centre has indexed all available church records in the Laois and Offaly area. The earliest Roman Catholic parish records date from 1763. The earliest Church of Ireland records date from 1699 and the latest from 1876. Methodist records begin in 1830. Other material indexed includes: civil records for Laois and Offaly, 1864–1900; the Birr Workhouse register; births, marriages and deaths recorded in the *King's County Chronicle* newspaper (1845–65) and the *Leinster Express* (1831–51); entries in trade directories for the period 1788–1908; and the Geashill Estate rental for 1883.

LOCATION
Town centre, next to Tullamore Dew Heritage Centre.

OFFALY COUNTY LIBRARY – LOCAL STUDIES AND ARCHIVES SERVICE

O'Connor Square
TULLAMORE, COUNTY OFFALY
Ireland

TELEPHONE: (057) 934 6832
E-mail: libraryhq@offalycoco.ie
Website: www.offaly.ie

HOURS
Tu, 09:30–20:00; W–F, 09:30–17:30; Sa, 09:30–13:00; appointments may be made for Local Studies and Archives during Library opening hours.

ACCESS AND SERVICES
Appointment is necessary to consult any item from the Local Studies and Archives collection. Photocopying service available subject to copyright law. Restrictions may also apply in cases where material is sensitive or fragile. Microfilm reader/printer service provided.

CONTACT
Local Studies Librarian

DESCRIPTION
The Local Studies and Archives Department holds a rich collection of material relating to Offaly.

HOLDINGS
The collection includes extant local government archives, private papers, local newspapers from the mid-nineteenth century to the present day, photographs and other images, maps and plans, local folk songs, printed books, journals and other media relating to the history and heritage of the county.

Staff will take telephone enquiries, although more complex enquiries should be made by letter or e-mail. It is the library's policy to assist and facilitate visitors in their research but not to undertake research.

Researchers can consult the online library database for printed and other local sources.

LOCATION
Town centre.

OFFALY HISTORICAL AND ARCHAEOLOGICAL SOCIETY
See IRISH MIDLANDS ANCESTRY, Tullamore

COUNTY ROSCOMMON

GENERAL REGISTER OFFICE

Government Offices, Convent Road
ROSCOMMON
Ireland

Note: While the GRO has moved to Roscommon Town, the Research Room continues to be located in Dublin, relocated from Joyce House, 8–11 Lombard Street East, to Block 7 Floor 3, Irish Life Centre, Lower Abbey Street, Dublin 1. See note at GENERAL REGISTER OFFICE, Dublin.

TELEPHONE: (090) 663 2900; FAX: (090) 663 2999
E-mail: use responder form on website
Website: www.groireland.ie

HOURS
M–F, 09:30–16:30; closed bank holidays

ACCESS AND SERVICES
Visitors welcome in Research Room on first come, first served basis. For €2, researchers can do a five year search of a given type of index book (births, marriages or deaths); for €20 they can gain access to all index volumes for the entire day. Index books contain references to microfilm records of actual register entries, copies of which are then available from staff at a cost of €4 each. Copies may not always be available on the day ordered; limit of five copies per person per day. Additional copies posted out within two weeks. Details of type and extent of records held by the GRO can be found on its website. Birth certificate contains the date and place of birth, forename, father's name, place of residence and occupation, mother's name and maiden surname, and the name and address of the person who registered the birth. Death certificate contains name and address of the deceased person, date and place of death, marital status, occupation, age at last birthday, cause of death, and the name and address of the person who registered the death. A pre-1957 marriage certificate contains the date and place of marriage, the age, name and marital status, occupation and pre-marriage address, father's name and occupation of both spouses. A post-1957 marriage certificate contains the date and place of marriage, the age, name, marital status, occupation, pre-marriage address, parents' names of both spouses and the couple's future intended place of residence.

Requests for certificates should be made in writing, including as many details as possible of the event(s) in question. Mastercard and Visa credit cards accepted in person, by post or by fax. See website for details. GRO accepts personal cheques/bank drafts, international money orders and Irish postal orders denominated in euro. Note: euro denominated personal cheques, bank drafts or international money orders must be drawn on a branch of a bank located in the Republic of Ireland and be acceptable for clearance through the Irish cheque clearing system. Cash should be sent by registered post. There is ordinarily a five to six week backlog, though requests may be processed more expeditiously for good cause.

The GRO does not provide research assistance.

CONTACT
Research staff

DESCRIPTION
The GRO is solely concerned with the administration of the civil registration system in Ireland. It provides photocopies or certified copies of entries in its birth, death or marriage registers on receipt of a postal application accompanied by the appropriate fee. The records and index are in a manual format, arranged chronologically, so specific details, especially dates, are needed for a search. Other details, such as the location of the event, the parents' names and the mother's maiden name of the ancestor in question, are helpful.

Fee Schedule
Please check website, as fees are subject to change.
Certificates (including particular search fees): birth, death, marriage, short birth, €10; additional copies, €8.
Authentication of an existing certificate, €10; additional copies, €10.
Search and photocopy of an entry in the register, €6; additional copies, €4.

HOLDINGS
The GRO holds index books for birth, death and marriage records after 1864 and microfilm records of the actual register entries. Note: for baptisms, marriages and burials prior to 1864, the only source for registration (except for non-Roman Catholic marriages, which have been civilly registered since 1845) is parish registers. To use these resources effectively, it is necessary to know the religious affiliation and often even the place of baptism, marriage or burial of the ancestor. Roman Catholic parish registers are still held by the parish priest, but most dating up until 1880 are available on microfilm in the National Library of Ireland. Access may require the written permission of the parish priest. Church of Ireland parish registers dating up until 1870 are public records. Most are still held in the local parishes, while some are held at the National Library of Ireland, Dublin, the Representative Church Body Library, Dublin, or the Public Record Office of Northern Ireland, Belfast. Presbyterian records are arranged by congregation and enquiries should be directed to the Presbyterian Historical Society, Belfast.

LOCATION
Town centre, close to the N63 and N61, near Abbey Street and the Roscommon County Library.

ROSCOMMON COUNTY LIBRARY

Abbey Street
ROSCOMMON
Ireland

TELEPHONE: (090) 663 7271; FAX: (090) 663 7101
E-mail: roslib@roscommoncoco.ie
Website: www.roscommoncoco.ie/en/services/library/

HOURS
Tu, Th, 13:00–20:00; W, 13:00–17:00; F–Sa, 10:00–13:00, 14:00–17:00; closed
Mondays

ACCESS AND SERVICES
Visitors welcome. Photocopying, internet and wifi services available.

CONTACT
Richard Farrell, County Librarian. E-mail: rfarrell@roscommoncoco.ie

DESCRIPTION
Headquarters library for the county system, which also includes branches in
Castlerea, Boyle, Elphin, Strokestown and Ballaghaderreen.

HOLDINGS
In addition to the usual collection of educational and recreational material, the
library houses a very fine local history and genealogy collection and archive. Archival
material includes: Board of Guardian minutes for Boyle, Castlerea, Roscommon and
Strokestown; Rural District Council minutes for Athlone No. 2, Boyle, Carrick-on-
Shannon, Castlerea, Roscommon and Strokestown; minutes of the Boyle Dispensary
District, Roscommon County Council, Roscommon Pension Committee and
Roscommon Town Commissioners; Strokestown Rural District Council Labourers'
Acts (acting as Rural Sanitary Authority); and Roscommon Grand Jury records.
Newspapers on microfilm include: *Boyle Gazette and Roscommon Reporter*, 1891;
Dublin Penny Journal, 1832–6; *Irishman*, 1819–25; *The Nation*, 1842–52;
Roscommon Constitutionalist, 1889–91; *Roscommon Herald*, 1882–present;
Roscommon Journal and Western Impartial Reporter, 1828–1927; *Roscommon Weekly
Messenger and Roscommon Messenger*, 1848–1935; *Western Nationalist* (later
continued as the *Roscommon Champion*), 1907–20; and *Strokestown Democrat*,
1913–48. The library also houses microfilm copies of other material of local interest,
including *History of Roscommon* (one reel); *Irish Topographical Prints and Original
Drawings* (three reels); *Monasteries of Roscommon* (one reel); Moran Manuscripts,
1548–50 (two reels); Rev John Keogh's *Statistical Account of Co. Roscommon*
(originally drawn up for Sir William Petty's Down Survey, 1683); and the Irish
Folklore Commission Schools Collection (1937/8) for Roscommon (14 reels).
Digitised editions of the Roscommon Herald (1882–2008) and Roscommon
Champion (1944–2009) are also available at all libraries.
　　Requests for access to archive material should be made in advance to the Co.
Librarian, Richard Farrell. E-mail: rfarrell@roscommoncoco.ie

LOCATION
Town centre.

COUNTY ROSCOMMON HERITAGE AND GENEALOGY COMPANY

Church Street
STROKESTOWN, COUNTY ROSCOMMON
Ireland

TELEPHONE: (071) 9633 380; FAX: (071) 9634 935
E-mail: info@roscommonroots.com
Website: www.roscommonroots.com

HOURS
M–F, 14:30–16:30

ACCESS AND SERVICES
The County Roscommon Heritage and Genealogy Company offers fee based, full
range genealogical research service to persons interested in tracing their family roots
in County Roscommon. Enquiries usually answered in about four to six weeks, but
during the summer season it may take slightly longer. Application form available
through website, where details of service provided and charges also listed. Common
surnames in County Roscommon are: Hanley, Beirne, Kelly, Brennan, Connor,
Flynn, Cox, McDermott, Brady and Farrell. Chief towns and villages in County
Roscommon include: Roscommon, Strokestown, Boyle, Elphin, Loughlynn,
Ballaghadereen, Castlerea and Knockcroghery.

CONTACT
Mary Skelly

DESCRIPTION
The County Roscommon Heritage and Genealogy Company is the designated Irish
Family History Foundation centre serving County Roscommon. The IFHF is the
coordinating body for a network of government approved genealogical research
centres in the Republic of Ireland and in Northern Ireland that have computerised
tens of millions of Irish ancestral records of different types.

HOLDINGS
The company has access to over 1,000,000 genealogical records relating to the
county. Main records include: Roman Catholic records starting between 1789 and
1865 depending on the parish; Church of Ireland records starting between 1796 and
1877 depending on the parish; Presbyterian records starting between 1857 and
1861; and Methodist records starting in the early 1840s. The company has also
computerised Griffith's Valuation; tithe applotment books; a list of '40 shilling
freeholders' for 1876; Pakenham-Mahon eviction lists from 1847; and Royal Irish
Constabulary records. The earliest census available that covers a large part of County
Roscommon dates from 1749. The company also holds civil records of birth,
marriage and deaths for the county from 1864 to 1900.

LOCATION
Town centre.

COUNTY SLIGO

COUNTY SLIGO HERITAGE AND GENEALOGY SOCIETY

Aras Reddan,
Temple Street
SLIGO TOWN, COUNTY SLIGO
Ireland

TELEPHONE: (071) 914 3728
E-mail: heritagesligo@eircom.net or info@sligoroots.com
Website: www.sligoroots.com

HOURS:
M–F, 09:00–17:00

ACCESS AND SERVICES
Genealogical Research Services:
County Sligo Heritage and Genealogy Centre offers a comprehensive range of genealogical research services to people tracing their County Sligo roots from all over the world. The centre has over 25 years experience in carrying out ancestral research and has enabled countless people to discover their family lineage. The Centre is based in the Failte Ireland North West Tourism Centre in Temple Street in Sligo town. If you would like us to undertake research on your behalf there are a number of services that we offer:

Single Search. For a fixed fee, we can search our database for a single baptism, marriage or death record. If a record is located it will be sent to you by email or post for no extra charge.

Family Search. For a fixed fee, we can carry out a 'Family Search'. This search covers research in church and civil records for the marriage of a couple and for all children recorded baptized and born to this couple.

Initial Research Assessment. This is the first stage of commissioning the compilation of a comprehensive Family History Report. Our assessment option involves carry out detailed research of all our genealogical sources for records pertaining to your ancestors.

Research Processing Time
Please note that genealogical research is a time consuming process. From when we receive your completed Research Questionnaire and fee, to the completion of a Family History Report normally takes about eight to twelve weeks. Initial enquiries answered as soon as possible. Seasonal demand can increase this waiting period, so we always recommend initiating your research in good time, well in advance of a planned visit to County Sligo. This is also of importance if the research is being carried out for a special family occasion.

Payment options
Credit Card. The Society accepts payment by Credit Card (Mastercard or Visa). If you intend to pay by credit card, we recommend you contact us with details of your card by telephone using the following telephone number: 00353 71 9143728.

Cheque/Money Order. The Society also accepts payment by Cheque or Money Order. If you wish to pay by this method, you can forward a cheque/money order (drawn to the equivalent amount) and made payable to Co. Sligo Heritage and Genealogy Society. This can be remitted to the Society at the following address: Co. Sligo Heritage and Genealogy Centre, Aras Reddan, Temple St., Sligo, Ireland.

Paypal. The Society also accepts payment by Paypal.

Visitor Services
Visitors are welcome. The following services are available to those visiting the Heritage and Genealogy Centre in person in Temple Street, Sligo.

Research Consultation Service. If you are visiting the centre and need some assistance with your own research, then a personal consultation with an experienced researcher can be arranged in advance. The researcher will assist you with all the professional advice they can, from their experience dealing with family history research. This service is by appointment only and is subject to availability.

Location Search. A location search endeavours to identify the parish or townland, where your ancestors came from, thereby enabling you to visit the area they once resided. As part of the location search, you are provided with various maps of the area outlining the area relevant to your search.

Same Day Research Facility. For persons visiting the area with a limited time available, and who wish to have research carried out, we offer a 'Same Day Search Facility'. Persons wishing to avail of this service must bring all their family information with them on visiting the centre. This service is subject to availability.

Online Shop. Co. Sligo Heritage and Genealogy Society operate an online shop through the website www.sligoroots.com selling a range of Sligo goods including the following:

> An interesting variety of books either with a genealogical or local Sligo History theme.
> A collection of Greeting Cards, each with a beautiful image of County Sligo.
> A software package specially designed to enable you to create your own family tree or chart.

CONTACT
Adrian Regan, Manager. E-mail: manager@sligoroots.com

DESCRIPTION
The society is the designated Irish Family History Foundation centre for County
Sligo. IFHF centres aim to create a comprehensive database of genealogical sources
that are known to exist, including church records of all denominations, civil records,
land valuations, census records, gravestone inscriptions and various other local
sources. The Sligo centre offers a genealogical research service for County Sligo.
Common surnames in County Sligo include: Gallagher, Brennan, MacGowan, Kelly,
Gilmartin, Healy, Walsh, Hart, Feeney and MacDonagh. Towns in County Sligo
include Sligo Town, Ballymote, Tobercurry and Collooney.

HOLDINGS
The society has collected more than 500,000 records relating to County Sligo. These
have been computerised and are available on the database at the centre. These
records include church records (Roman Catholic dating back to 1796, Church of
Ireland dating back to 1762, Presbyterian dating back to 1806 and Methodist dating
back to 1819); the 1901 census; Griffith's Valuation, 1858; tithe applotment books,
1823–37; the Elphin diocesan census of 1749; gravestone inscriptions; and various
other genealogical sources.

LOCATION
In the North-West Tourism Complex, Sligo town centre.

SLIGO COUNTY LIBRARY

Sligo Central Library,
Stephen St.
SLIGO TOWN, COUNTY SLIGO
Ireland

TELEPHONE: (071) 911 1850, (071) 911 1675; FAX: (071) 914 6798
E-mail: sligolib@sligococo.ie
Website: www.sligolibrary.ie

HOURS
M–F, 09:30–12:45, 14:00–16:45

ACCESS AND SERVICES
Visitors welcome. No admission fees. Collection catalogued online in 2002. Printed
catalogue and finding aids available. Publications include: John C. McTernan (ed.),
*Sligo: Sources of Local History: a Catalogue of the Local History Collection, with an
Introduction and Guide to Sources*, new edition (Sligo, 1994)

CONTACT
See e-mail

DESCRIPTION
The main library for Sligo Town and County Sligo, with three additional service
points.

HOLDINGS
In addition to the standard general collection, the library offers a good local history
collection focusing on Sligo, the Yeats family, Countess Markievicz and the Gore-
Booth family and the archaeology of Sligo. There is also a collection of newspapers

published in Sligo from 1822 to the present. Special collections include those on:
W.B. Yeats, Jack B. Yeats, Countess Markievicz, autographs and local authors.
Genealogical holdings for County Sligo include recordings of all gravestone
inscriptions in some 150 graveyards in the county.

For landed estates there are some 90 volumes in the archive of an estate agent
named Robinson who managed many estates in the county. This includes rentals for
various estates from *c.* 1850.

There are also parish records (not complete), directories and details of World
War I dead. There are microfilm copies of the 1901 census for County Sligo, tithe
survey 1823–38, and also a set of the printed Griffith's Valuation for the county,
c. 1855.

LOCATION
Ground floor of Sligo Central Library.

COUNTY TIPPERARY

BRÚ BORÚ CULTURAL CENTRE

Rock of Cashel
CASHEL, COUNTY TIPPERARY
Ireland

TELEPHONE: (062) 61122; FAX: (062) 62700
E-mail: info@bruboru.ie; bruboru@comhaltas.com
Website: www.bruboru.ie; http://tipperarysouth.rootsireland.ie/

HOURS
May–September: M–F, 09:00–17:00
October–April: M–W, 09:30–16:30

ACCESS AND SERVICES
The Brú Ború Cultural Centre offers a fee based full genealogical service to enquirers, with access to church, civil, land and census records for South Tipperary. Initial enquiries usually receive a reply within one month. Application form is available on the centre's website. The initial search fee, to accompany the form, is €75. Fees vary. The Centre's databases of births, marriages and deaths for South Tipperary are available to search online at: www.rootsireland.ie

CONTACT
Deirdre Walsh

DESCRIPTION
Brú Ború Heritage Centre is the designated Irish Family History Foundation centre serving South Tipperary. The IFHF is the coordinating body for a network of government approved genealogical research centres in the Republic of Ireland and in Northern Ireland that have computerised tens of millions of Irish ancestral records of different types. Brú Ború, which means the palace of Ború, is a cultural and interpretative village designed around a village green dedicated to the study and celebration of Irish music, song, dance, storytelling, theatre and Celtic studies. Common surnames in South Tipperary include: Ryan, Dwyer, Maher, O'Brien, Hayes, Quirke, Treacy, O'Meara, Macken, Maloney, Lonergan and Kearney. Main towns in South Tipperary include: Cashel, Cahir, Tipperary, Clonmel and Carrick-on-Suir.

HOLDINGS

The centre holds some Roman Catholic records, the earliest of which date from 1778. These records, dating up until 1880, have been computerised. The centre has also computerised civil birth, death and marriage records for the period 1864–1921 and non-Roman Catholic civil marriage records for the period 1845–64. The centre also holds copies of the 1901 and 1911 census returns; tithe applotment books; Griffith's Valuation; RIC indexes, Lewis's Topographical Dictionary of Ireland; Civil Survey; Gravestone Inscriptions; Hearth Money Rolls; and Landowners in Ireland, 1871. The centre has access to approximately 500,000 records.

LOCATION

At the foot of the Rock of Cashel, historic castle ruins just outside the town of Cashel.

GPA BOLTON LIBRARY

GPA Building, John Street
CASHEL, COUNTY TIPPERARY
Ireland

TELEPHONE: (062) 61944; FAX: (062) 61944
E-mail: boltonlibrary@oceanfree.net

HOURS

M–F, 10:00–17:00; closed weekends except by special arrangement. **Note:** Because of staffing shortages and pastoral obligations, it is best to confirm visits to the Library in advance. While every effort is made to keep to the opening hours, circumstances may not always make this possible.

ACCESS AND SERVICES

Visitors welcome. Admission fees apply. Tours available, 10:30–16:30 Advance notice required. No disabled access facilities.

CONTACT

The Very Rev Dr Philip Knowles, Dean of Cashel and Curator. Telephone: (062) 61232; e-mail: knowlesph@iolfree.ie; Hannah Murphy, Library Assistant.

DESCRIPTION

The library is housed in a small but handsome eighteenth century building near the Church of Ireland's Cathedral Church of St John the Baptist and St Patrick's Rock. The library was restored with a large grant from GPA. More recently the library has entered into a management arrangement with the University of Limerick. The library has been in its current quarters since 1836. Some of its greatest treasures are on exhibit.

HOLDINGS

The library primarily houses the eighteenth century private libraries of Archbishop Bolton of Cashel (d. 1744) and Archbishop William King of Dublin (1650–1729). It also houses portions of the collections of Archbishop Narcissus Marsh of Dublin (1638–1713), of Bishops Jephson and Foley and of the Abbé Bignon. The collection totals some 12,000 volumes, plus a small but significant collection of manuscripts, bound pamphlets and artefacts. It also includes maps and newspapers. Though the focus of the collection is on religion and theology, it covers a wide range of interests, including literature, the physical sciences, law, medicine, philosophy, astronomy, Irish history and Irish politics. The Rare Book Collection contains some real gems. These include the 'smallest book in the world', a collection of some 20 incunabula, including a copy of the *Nuremburg Chronicle* (1493) and the 1473 Strasbourg edition of Vincent of Beauvais's *Speculem Historical*; a good representation of early presses, including Estienne, Koberger, Froben, Caxton and Aldus Manutius; and a collection of more than 200 bound volumes of pamphlets and broadsides dealing primarily with politics and controversies. The manuscript holdings include several medieval codices, the oldest dating from the twelfth century; three Irish manuscripts, including a *c*. 1716 copy of Geoffrey Keating's *Foras Feasa ar Eirin* in the hand of Dermot O'Connor; and a 1717 Hebrew manuscript of the translation of the *Irish Book of Common Prayer*, one of only four copies extant. The collection also houses about 900 early Irish imprints. Of special genealogical interest are the diocesan records of births, marriages and deaths going back to 1668. Also there are minute books of the Diocesan Council and account books; a printed copy of Griffith's Valuation and printed books of Cashel Diocese dating from 1855 to 1891.

LOCATION
Town centre, just to the right of the Church of Ireland Cathedral Church of St John the Baptist and St Patrick's Rock.

TIPPERARY NORTH GENEALOGY CENTRE

The Governor's House, Kickham Street
NENAGH, COUNTY TIPPERARY
Ireland

TELEPHONE: (067) 33850; FAX: (067) 33586
E-mail: tipperarynorthgenealogy@eircom.net
Website: www.rootsireland.ie or www.tipperarynorth.ie/genealogy
Facebook: www.facebook.com/GenealogyinNorthTipperary

HOURS
M–F, 09:30–17:00

ACCESS AND SERVICES
Tipperary North Genealogy and Heritage Services provide a family history research service for people whose ancestors originated in North Tipperary. Research done on a small fee basis. No waiting list; visitors given priority. We also have an Online Research Service where you can undertake research yourself see www.rootsireland.ie

CONTACT
Nora O'Meara, MA, Genealogist, North Tipperary.

DESCRIPTION
North Tipperary Genealogy Centre is the designated Genealogy Centre for North Tipperary which is run under the auspices of the North Tipperary County Council and is affiliated to the Irish Family History Foundation.
There is a similar Genealogy Centre in most counties in Ireland. It is a company limited by guarantee with charitable status and managed by a Board of Directors who give their time voluntarily. The IFHF is the coordinating body for a network of government approved genealogical research centres in the Republic of Ireland and in

Northern Ireland that have computerised tens of millions of Irish ancestral records of different types. Most of these counties now have their records online at www.rootsireland.ie.

Common surnames in North Tipperary include: Ryan, O'Brien, Kennedy, O'Meara, Maher/Meagher, Burke, Gleeson, Carroll, Hogan and Kelly. Towns and villages in North Tipperary include: Nenagh, Templemore, Thurles, Roscrea, Borrisokane, Borrisoleigh, Cloughjordan and Newport.

HOLDINGS
The centre currently has computerised about 600,000 genealogical records. Main records include: Roman Catholic records, the earliest of which date from 1792; Church of Ireland records, some of which date from 1755; Methodist records dating from 1834; tithe applotment and Griffith's Valuation lists; civil birth, death and marriage records, 1864–1911; gravestone inscriptions for all of North Tipperary; and the 1901 census. Note: church and civil records terminate in 1900 or 1911. In addition to the main sources, the centre has also computerised Civil Survey and hearth money rolls (seventeenth century); street directories (nineteenth and twentieth century); encumbered estates records for Nenagh, 1854; Vestry Book for Borrisokane (nineteenth century); Poor Law rate books for Nenagh and Thurles Poor Law Unions, 1840s; and births, deaths and marriages in the *Nenagh Guardian*, 1838–66.

LOCATION
In the former residence of the County Gaol Governor (1842–86), which has been a convent, a secondary school and, since 1984, a heritage centre.

CASHEL AND EMLY ARCHDIOCESAN ARCHIVES (ROMAN CATHOLIC)

Archbishop's House
THURLES, COUNTY TIPPERARY
Ireland

TELEPHONE: (0504) 21512; FAX: (0504) 22680
E-mail: office@cashel-emly.ie
Website: homepage.eircom.net/~cashelemly/genealogy

HOURS
Closed to visitors

ACCESS AND SERVICES
Parish records available through Tipperary Family History Research Centre (*see* separate entry). Originals made available only in exceptional circumstances.

CONTACT
Tipperary Family History Research Centre, Excel Centre, Mitchell Street, Tipperary. Telephone: (062) 80555; fax: (062) 80552; e-mail: research@tfhr.org; website: www.tfhr.org

HOLDINGS
Archives house archdiocesan records for the Roman Catholic Archdiocese of Cashel and Emly. These include the historical papers of the archbishops of Cashel and Emly from the early eighteenth century as well as parish records of marriages and baptisms for the forty-six parishes of the archdiocese, some of which date back to the

mid eighteenth century. The forty-six parishes of the archdiocese embrace part of North and South Tipperary as well as East and South-East Limerick.

LOCATION
Archbishop's House, Thurles.

TIPPERARY LIBRARIES – TIPPERARY STUDIES

Tipperary Studies
The Source
Cathedral Street
THURLES, COUNTY TIPPERARY
Ireland

TELEPHONE: (0504) 29278; FAX: (0504) 21344
E-mail: studies@tipperarylibraries.ie
Website: www.tipperarylibraries.ie

HOURS
M, 10:00–13:00, 14:00–17:30; Tu–Th, 10:00–17:30; F–Sa, 10:00–13:00, 14:00–17:00. Closed on Saturday of Bank Holiday Weekend. Staff shortages may sometimes result in unscheduled lunch time closures (13:00 to 14:00). Prior booking is advised when microfilm resources are required.

ACCESS AND SERVICES
Visitors welcome. Disabled access facilities. Laptops permitted. Small fee charged for photocopies and microfilm copies. It is advisable to book microfilm equipment in advance. Certain archival material may not be copied. Internet and Wi Fi services available. As Tipperary Studies is a research library, there is no membership charge, fees being confined to the price of any copies made. Digital cameras may be used to copy some of the archival resources.

CONTACT
Mary Guinan-Darmody
John O'Gorman

DESCRIPTION
Tipperary Studies is the main research library for Tipperary Libraries. The department houses the most comprehensive collections of sources for all aspects of Co. Tipperary, its history, heritage and culture. *Finding Tipperary: a guide to the resources of the Tipperary Studies Department, Tipperary County Library, Thurles, County Tipperary* (Marnane & Guinan Darmody), while not a bibliography of Tipperary sources, is a detailed guide to the range of sources available in Tipperary Studies. Copies may be purchased directly from Tipperary Studies. Tipperary Libraries also serves as the headquarters for the County Tipperary Historical Society. Information regarding the society is available through the Tipperary Libraries website.

HOLDINGS
Tipperary Studies houses a large collection of published titles on all aspects of Co. Tipperary, historical, archaeological, sociological and pictorial. Books by Tipperary authors are also included in the collection. The large journal collection is augmented

by the online resource, JSTOR, as is the comprehensive local newspaper collection
(hardcopy and microfilm) by the Irish Newspaper Archive website
www.irishnewsarchive.com . Maps of the county including the first edition
Ordnance Survey maps are available for consultation. Online access is available to
both Griffith's Valuation maps and Ordnance Survey maps. Genealogical resources
include the 1901 and 1911 census returns, Griffith's Valuation, tithe applotment
books, Ordnance Survey House Books, Gravestone inscriptions, Hearth Money
Records 1665/6–7. A large amount of Poor Law material is available for the unions
of the county. However, it is necessary to note that as most of the Poor Law Union
of Carrick was located in Co. Kilkenny, it is Kilkenny County Library that holds all
surviving records for this union. Grand Jury presentments c. 1840–1910, nineteenth
century statutes, some landed estate records, local photos all add to the value of the
Tipperary Studies collection.

LOCATION
Town centre.

TIPPERARY FAMILY HISTORY RESEARCH CENTRE

Excel Heritage Centre, Mitchell Street
TIPPERARY
Ireland

TELEPHONE: (062) 80555; FAX: (062) 80552
E-mail: research@tfhr.org
Website: www.tfhr.org

HOURS
M–F, 09:30–16:30; closed bank holidays

ACCESS AND SERVICES
Visitors welcome. Free consultation provided. Fees for research services carried out
by TFHR personnel. Internet access available for a small fee.

CONTACT
Charlotte Crowe

DESCRIPTION
Tipperary Family History Research Centre, established in April 2001 as successor to
Tipperary Heritage Unit, conducts research within the records of the Cashel and
Emly Archdiocesan Archives (Roman Catholic), Thurles, County Tipperary.

HOLDINGS
Over 600,000 marriage and baptismal records, representing all 46 parishes that make
up the Archdiocese of Cashel and Emly, have been indexed to date. The archdiocese
includes parishes in parts of North and South Tipperary and South-East Limerick.
Some records date back to the late 1700s, but the vast majority date from the 1800s
up to 1900.

LOCATION
Excel Heritage Centre, town centre. From Main Street turn onto St Michael's Street
and take first left onto Mitchell Street. Car Park adjacent to Excel Centre.

COUNTY TYRONE

IRISH WORLD FAMILY HISTORY CENTRE

Family History Suite, 51 Dungannon Road
COALISLAND, COUNTY TYRONE, BT71 4HP
Northern Ireland

TELEPHONE: (028) 8774 6065
E-mail: info@irish-world.com
Website: www.irish-world.com

HOURS
M–F, 10:00–16:00; appointment preferred

ACCESS AND SERVICES
Visitors welcome. In addition to providing full fee based genealogy research service,
Irish World offers a range of heritage related products such as full colour coats of
arms and publications on local history. The centre also has an online index to nearly
half a million gravestone inscriptions from some 700 graveyards across historic
Ulster.

CONTACT
Willie O'Kane, Research Consultant

DESCRIPTION
Irish World is the designated Irish Family History Foundation centre for Counties
Tyrone and Fermanagh. It is now part of www.rootsireland.ie, the leading online
database for Irish family research.

HOLDINGS
Irish World holds computerised baptism, marriage and death records for 22 Roman
Catholic parishes, most dating up until the year 1900. Starting dates vary
significantly, the earliest being 1783. Computerised records for five pre-1901
Church of Ireland parishes also vary, the oldest dating to 1801. The computerised
records for Presbyterian parishes reflect only baptisms and marriages, with the
earliest dating to 1821. See website for specific parishes and inclusive dates.
Other sources include: civil records of births and deaths, 1864–1921, for Counties
Fermanagh and Tyrone; civil records of marriages, 1845–1921, for Counties
Fermanagh and Tyrone; 1901 census for Counties Fermanagh and Tyrone; Griffith's

Valuation for all of Ireland; tithe applotment books for Counties Antrim, Armagh, Londonderry, Down, Fermanagh, Tyrone, Monaghan, Cavan and Donegal; gravestone inscriptions for over 900 cemeteries in Counties Antrim, Armagh, Derry, Down, Fermanagh and Tyrone; list of flax growers for all of Ireland, 1796; crime and punishment records for all of Ireland, 1799–1800; transportation registers for all Ireland, 1839–57; and index to RIC records for all of Ireland, 1816–1921.

LOCATION
Easily accessible in spacious enterprise Centre on the outskirts of Coalisland village

CENTRE FOR MIGRATION STUDIES
See (immediately below) LIBRARIES NI HERITAGE COLLECTION, MELLON CENTRE FOR MIGRATION STUDIES, Omagh.

LIBRARIES NI HERITAGE COLLECTION, MELLON CENTRE FOR MIGRATION STUDIES

The Mellon Centre for Migration Studies
Ulster American Folk Park
Mellon Road, Castletown,
OMAGH, COUNTY TYRONE, BT78 5QY
Northern Ireland,

TELEPHONE: (028) 8225 6315; Fax: (028) 8224 2241
E-mail: mcms@librariesni.org.uk
Website: www.qub.ac.uk/cms; www.nmni.com/uafp

HOURS
M–F, 10:30–17:00; closed weekends and Public Holidays

ACCESS AND SERVICES
Visitors are welcome at no charge. Disabled access. Browsable, reference only collection. Collection accessible via online catalogue at www.librariesni.org.uk. Microform reader/printer available. Public Access Terminals with internet access available free to all Libraries NI members, otherwise charge applies. Fees apply to photocopies, microform reader and IT printouts. The Centre offers courses for visiting groups tailored to individual needs. It also hosts conferences, seminars and programmes on migration related topics. Staff respond to enquiries and offer advice on family history research involving migration records. Publications include: the autobiography of Thomas Mellon, whose family home is the nucleus of the Ulster American Folk Park, entitled *Thomas Mellon and His Times* (1994); E. Margaret Crawford (ed.) *The Hungry Stream: Essays on Emigration and Famine* (1997); Patrick Fitzgerald and Steve Ickringill (eds), *Atlantic Crossroads: Historical Connections between Scotland, Ulster and North America* (2001); Patrick Fitzgerald and Brian Lambkin, *Migration in Irish History, 1607–2007 [2008]*. Booklets about The Ulster American Folk Park, Omagh, and the Mellon house are also available. The Park offers a café.

CONTACT
Christine Johnston, Senior Library Asst.
E-mail: Christine.Johnston@librariesni.org.uk

DESCRIPTION

The Mellon Centre for Migration Studies aims to serve the community as a leading international institution for the study of human migration, focusing on the peoples of Ireland worldwide. Migration studies is about advancing the understanding of the movement and settlement of people (including immigration, internal migration, seasonal migration and emigration) through multidisciplinary approaches (including history, politics, economics, language, literature, art and religion). The centre is a project of the Scotch-Irish Trust of Ulster, which supports the work of the Ulster American Folk Park through partnership with the Department of Culture, Arts and Leisure, Libraries NI, PRONI, Queen's University Belfast and the University of Ulster. MCMS is a member of the Association of European Migration Institutions (www.aemi.dk) and has close links with the Ulster Historical Foundation (www.ancestryireland.com).

HOLDINGS

The MCMS library contains some 16,800 volumes, 1,340 maps, plus significant holdings of journals, microforms and recordings. The focus of the collection is on Ireland and North America in the eighteenth and nineteenth centuries, and the links between the two. The collection was organised originally to support the activities of the Ulster American Folk Park and to this end the library developed strengths in the fields of agriculture, architecture, crafts and industry, social customs, biography, politics and religion. More recently the collection has expanded to cover the seventeenth and twentieth centuries and all aspects of Irish migration worldwide. Special collections of note include the MCMS Irish Emigration Database, which contains some 33,000 primary source documents on all aspects of Irish emigration to North America, including Canada, from the early 1700s to the 1900s. Begun in 1988, new documents are being added to this database on a regular basis. Types of documents include ship passenger lists, emigrant letters, family papers and diaries of emigrants, shipping advertisements, newspaper reports, death and marriage notices of former emigrants, birth notices of children of Irish parentage, government reports and statistics of Irish emigration to North America.

The full Irish Emigration Database is accessible in all Libraries NI public libraries through the public access terminals and in the Search Room of PRONI. Remote online access to the Irish Emigration Database (excluding Irish Ship Passenger Lists) is available at www.dippam.ac.uk. Remote online access to the Irish Ship Passenger Lists on the IED is available at www.rootsireland.ie

LOCATION

Ulster American Folk Park, five miles north of Omagh, on the main A5 road between Omagh and Strabane.

By Bus from Belfast: Goldliner Express Bus No. 273 from Belfast to Derry passes the main gates of the Ulster American Folk Park. The Express stops on request outside the main gates of the Folk Park.

The nearest local bus station is in Omagh, which also has a local service passing the Museum. In addition, taxis are usually available at Omagh Bus Station. More information on bus services is available from Translink, www.translink.co.uk

LIBRARIES NI HERITAGE COLLECTION, OMAGH

Local Studies
Omagh Library
1, Spillars Place
OMAGH, COUNTY TYRONE, BT78 1HL
Northern Ireland

TELEPHONE: (028) 8224 4821; Fax: (028) 8224 6716
E-mail: omaghlibrary@librariesni.org.uk
Website: www.librariesni.org.uk

HOURS
M–Th, 09:00–20:00, F, 09:00–17:30; Sa, 09:00–17:00

ACCESS AND SERVICES
Visitors are welcome. The library is wheelchair accessible. The collection is mainly
non-circulating, reference only; however, there are borrowable copies of many of the
popular titles. Microfilm reader/printers are available. Due to heavy demand for
microfilm readers, booking is advisable for this service. Public Access Terminals with
internet access are freely available for all Libraries NI members. Fees apply to
photocopies, microfilm reader and IT printouts. Membership of library is open to
anyone living, working or studying in the area. ID is required on registering.
Heritage staff will assist and advise users seeking genealogical information.

CONTACT
Deirdre Nugent, Heritages Services Manager. E-mail:
deirdre.nugent@librariesni.org.uk

DESCRIPTION
Omagh Library is the branch library for the largest town in County Tyrone.

HOLDINGS
Local Studies collects and archives materials covering all aspects of life in the county:
postcards and photographs; journals; newspaper cuttings; local and regional
newspapers on microfilm; maps; books by local authors and those locally produced
and a selection of specialised and antiquarian books for family history research,
including street directories, volumes of Griffith's Valuation and gravestone
inscriptions.

It has the Board of Guardian minutes for Castlederg, Clogher, Omagh and
Strabane, c. 1840–1900 on microfilm, and duplicates of valuation records that have
been returned from PRONI. The local valuation records now held in the Omagh
Library cover the Rural District Council areas of Omagh, Castlederg, Clogher and
Strabane. These volumes cover the years 1920–30, 1934–5 and 1957.

Omagh Library also houses the 'Omagh Bomb Archive' which includes over
10,500 newspaper articles, 15,000 emails, 818 books of condolence, 52 videos,
nearly 3,000 floral tribute cards, 1,000 sympathy cards and 20 patchwork quilts and
cushions presented by the NI Patchwork Guild following the tragic Omagh
Bombing of August 15, 1998, which claimed the lives of 29 people, including a
woman pregnant with twins. Some 220 others were injured. The bombing was the
work of the Real IRA, a dissident Republican paramilitary group, dissatisfied with
the Good Friday Agreement of April 10, 1998. Public access is welcome, however,
appointment may be necessary.

Libraries NI Online Resources
Libraries NI customers have access to 'Online Resources' on the library website.

Ancestry Library Edition is an online genealogical collection accessible on the Libraries NI website to library members at any library in Northern Ireland. This resource is available only from the Libraries NI network and is not accessible to members from their home computers. The Ancestry Library Edition collection has approximately thousands of databases and billions of indexed names from key collections spanning the fourteenth century to present day enabling customers to search for vital information about their ancestors.

The 'JSTOR Ireland Collection' is fully searchable, consists of the digital content of journals and other material relating to Ireland, and will be of great interest to anyone researching Irish history, genealogy, archaeology, literature etc. Most of the material included was published in the eighteenth, nineteenth and twentieth centuries.

The DIPPAM web resource is a virtual library of sources relating to the history of modern Ireland and its global diaspora. Documenting Ireland: Parliament, People and Migration (DIPPAM) is a collaboration project between Queen's University Belfast, The University of Ulster, The Mellon Centre for Migration Studies, Omagh, and Libraries NI, and has been funded by the Arts and Humanities Research Council. DIPPAM may be of particular interest to people involved in research the history of their locality or family, and for use in school history projects. It includes three searchable databases: Enhanced British Parliamentary Papers on Ireland (EPPI) – which comprises scans of over 15,000 official publications relating to all aspects of Irish affairs during the period of the Act of Union, 1800–1922, including bills, reports, royal commissions of inquiry and the published census returns. It is a rich source for the social history of Ireland, as well as for statistics and evidence relating to population, emigration, famine, crime and political movements: The Irish Emigration Database (IED) is made up of documents relating to Irish emigration since the eighteenth century, mainly to North America, and mostly drawn from archives in Northern Ireland and from private collections. The documents include emigrant letters, newspaper extracts, shipping advertisements, family papers and extracts from relevant publications and Voices of Migration and Return (VMR) is an oral history archive of over 90 life-narrative interviews conducted with emigrants and return-emigrants from the province of Ulster, collected between 2004 and 2008. The study participants represent a range of geographical origins within Ulster, class backgrounds and religious identities.

LOCATION
The Library is located in the Town centre, between Dublin Road and the Drumragh River.

ULSTER AMERICAN FOLK PARK

2 Mellon Road, Castletown
OMAGH, COUNTY TYRONE, BT78 5QU
Northern Ireland

TELEPHONE: (028) 8224 3292; Fax: (028) 8224 2241
E-mail: info@nmni.com
Website: www.nmni.com/uafp

HOURS
October to February: Tu–F, 10:00–16:00; Sa and Su, 11:00–16:00
March to September: Tu–Su, 10:00–17:00; closed Mondays with exception of N.I.
bank holidays.

ACCESS AND SERVICES
Visitors welcome. Admission fees apply: adults, £6.50; children (5–16 years), seniors
and persons with disabilities, £4.00; families, £18.50; reduced rates available for
groups. Children four and under free of charge. Educational visits must be booked
in advance. Disabled access facilities. Free parking. Craft and gift shop, restaurant.

CONTACT
Catherine McCullough, Head of Learning and Partnership, National Museums
Northern Ireland
Dr Phil Mowat, Head of Emigration, National Museums Northern Ireland.

DESCRIPTION
Large and sophisticated outdoor museum and indoor galleries devoted to Ireland
and the New World in the eighteenth and nineteenth centuries. Restored and
replicated structures, including a full scale emigrant ship, offer the visitor an
opportunity to visit Ireland in the eighteenth and nineteenth centuries, board an
emigrant ship and emerge in the New World. Exhibitions trace the history of the
times, with special attention to agriculture, crafts, transportation and society. The
original homesteads of the Mellon, Campbell, Devine, Hupp, Hughes and Fulton
families are on display. The park is a wonderful place to entertain and educate
children and adults. It is part of National Museums Northern Ireland, which also
includes the Ulster Folk and Transport Museum, Holywood; the Ulster Museum,
Belfast; and the Armagh County Museum, Armagh.

HOLDINGS
See LIBRARIES NI HERITAGE COLLECTION, MELLON CENTRE FOR
MIGRATION STUDIES, Omagh (above). The museum itself features exhibitions
focusing on emigration, folklife of Ireland and America, agriculture, crafts,
education, religion, shops and shipping, all with relevance to the eighteenth and
nineteenth centuries.

LOCATION
Five miles north of Omagh, on the main A5 road between Omagh and Strabane.
By Bus from Belfast: Goldliner Express Bus No. 273 from Belfast to Derry passes
the main gates of the Ulster American Folk Park. The Express stops on request
outside the main gates of the Folk Park.
    The nearest local bus station is in Omagh, which also has a local service passing
the Museum. In addition, taxis are usually available at Omagh Bus Station. More
information on bus services is available from Translink, www.translink.co.uk

COUNTY WATERFORD

WATERFORD COUNTY ARCHIVES SERVICE

Dungarvan Library, Davitt's Quay
DUNGARVAN, COUNTY WATERFORD
Ireland

TELEPHONE: (058) 23673; (058) 41231; FAX: (058) 42911
E-mail: archivist@waterfordcoco.ie
Website: www.waterfordcoco.ie

HOURS
Tu, 10:00–14:00; F, 13:00–17:00; or by appointment

ACCESS AND SERVICES
Visitors welcome. For detailed description of services visit website. Archives Service located in library building; while no parking is available immediately outside the library, parking is available nearby.

CONTACT
Archivist

DESCRIPTION
The Archives Service is housed in Dungarvan Library and holds records of local authorities in County Waterford, past and present, plus private collections relating to Waterford.

HOLDINGS
The County Archives hold: Grand Jury records; Board of Guardian records; Rural District Council records (from 1899); Waterford County Council records; Dungarvan Town Council records; and private papers.

There are virtually complete sets of minute books of the Boards of Guardians for the Poor Law Unions of Dungarvan, Kilmacthomas, Lismore and Waterford, c. 1843–1923. There are also valuation books recording payments of Grand Jury cess from 1869. Those dating up to 1875 are in annual volumes but a single large volume covers the period c. 1876–c. 1900. Since these volumes record the names of taxpayers annually, a search can show the probable year of death of a person when the name disappears. These records are arranged by barony, townland and parish. On some estates payment of county cess was the responsibility of the landlord, in which case the names of occupiers of holdings are not given. These books thus contain fewer names of occupiers than surviving Poor Law rate books or the valuation revision books held in the Valuation Office, Middle Abbey Street, Dublin. There is also a collection of Grand Jury records dating up until 1899 including presentments from 1865 and contract books for the period 1829–67.

The Waterford County Council records includes, Minutes of the Council from 1899, planning records under the first Town and Regional Planning Act, 1934 and records of infrastructure projects such as, water supply schemes, bridges, roads and housing schemes.

Private papers include the Chearnley Papers (1671–1915), relating to lands predominantly in West Waterford; and the Hugh Ryan Papers, containing an important collection of political pamphlets relating to Irish nationalism and records relating to a survey carried out by Ryan of the gravestones of Mothel and Rathgormack. The County Archives holds the Lismore Castle Papers (*c.* 1750–1969), mainly the nineteenth century records, including rentals, tenants' application books and agents' correspondence. The earlier records for the Lismore Estate are held by the National Library in Dublin and the County Archive holds part of this collection on microfilm. The Villiers-Stuart Papers are available on microfilm; also on microfilm are the tithe applotment books for County Waterford and the Roman Catholic parish records for County Waterford. The Archive also holds the de la Poer estate collection, relating to lands in Gurteen Le Poer, Kilsheelan and East Waterford but this collection will not be accessible until a Descriptive List has been completed.

LOCATION
Dungarvan Library building, town centre. Dungarvan lies between Cork City and Waterford City on the N25. There is a frequent bus service between Cork City and Dungarvan and between Waterford City and Dungarvan.

WATERFORD COUNTY LIBRARY HEADQUARTERS

Ballyanchor Road
LISMORE, COUNTY WATERFORD
Ireland

TELEPHONE: (058) 21370
E-mail: libraryhq@waterfordcoco.ie
Website: www.watefordcountylibrary.ie

HOURS
Library HQ Hours, M–F, 09:00–17:00
Library Branch Hours: See website www.waterfordcountylibrary.ie

ACCESS AND SERVICES
Visitors welcome. Disabled access facilities. Laptops permitted. WiFi for Library members as part of membership fee; €2.00 per session to non members. Fee charged for photocopies and printing.

CONTACT
Eddie Byrne, Acting County Librarian

DESCRIPTION
Library headquarters mainly deals with administrative issues pertaining to the seven libraries in the county system: Cappoquin, Dungarvan, Dunmore, Kilmacthomas, Lismore, Portlaw, and Tramore. The Waterford Municipal Library, Waterford City, is administered separately. Each library in the system offers the usual educational and recreational collections, plus access to the library system's online database and free internet access.

HOLDINGS
The library holds an impressive local studies and family history collection, of which core resources are all accessible online. Of special genealogical interest are: civil records for County Waterford, including all deaths registered from 1 January 1864 to 31 December 1901; Griffith's Valuation, 1848–64; gravestone inscriptions; historical trade directories, 1824–1910; war memorials; and Ordnance Survey maps and photographs. In addition, major texts, including the *Waterford and South East of Ireland Archaeological Journal* and *Decies* are now available on the website as .pdfs. The local newspaper *The Dungarvan Leader* from 1943–83 is now available online and we are working our way through the second local newspaper *The Dungarvan Observer.*

A photographic collection of over two thousand images has been added to the site. This is also an ongoing project and we see it growing year on year.

The Waterford Places database contains pages for every barony, parish and townland in County Waterford. Each page organises resources to help you conveniently locate the most relevant information about your area. Included for each Parish, for example, are extracts from *Place-names of Decies, The Parliamentary Gazetteer of Ireland 1843–1844* [Waterford extracts], *Ordnance Survey Letters*, and the *Irish Tourist Authority Survey* [1941–5] as well as finding and links to electronic resources such as images, maps, eBooks and eJournals.

The Co. Library works very closely with Waterford Co. Archives who have built up an impressive collection of online material
www.waterfordcoco.ie/en/services/archives/

LOCATION
At the western end of Lismore, on main Killarney road.

WATERFORD CITY ARCHIVES

Waterford City Council, City Hall, The Mall
WATERFORD CITY, COUNTY WATERFORD
Ireland

TELEPHONE: (051) 843 123; FAX: (051) 879 124
E-mail: archives@waterfordcity.ie
Website: www.waterfordcity.ie/archives

HOURS
By appointment, M–F, 09:00–17:00

ACCESS AND SERVICES
Visitors welcome, but by appointment only. Readers required to complete an application form on their first visit and issued with a reader's ticket valid until the end of the calendar year. Photocopying facilities available at Archivist's discretion

and depending on copyright restrictions as well as nature and condition of material in question. Much of the material has been listed and searchable databases for some categories of records are being prepared on an ongoing basis.

In general Waterford City Archives cannot undertake detailed genealogical and historical searches, although it does contain material of genealogical interest. Each query will be dealt with on an individual basis, however, and where the City Archivist can help, he will do so.

CONTACT
Donal Moore, City Archivist

DESCRIPTION
Waterford City Council was the first local authority to appoint an archivist under the terms of Section 65 of the 1994 Local Government Act encouraging the establishment of local archives. A building in the centre of the medieval city was provided as a home for the City Archives and has been converted on a phased basis to provide work areas, secure storage spaces and a reading room.

HOLDINGS
The core of the archives' collections comprises material originating within Waterford City Council (formerly Waterford Corporation) dating back to the late sixteenth century. Nevertheless, a conscious decision was made that the new facility would be a city archives and not just a repository for Waterford City Council's own records. The archives have acquired a substantial number of items and collections by groups, individuals, companies and institutions in the city and there is an active acquisitions policy. At present the transfer or purchase of several significant collections of archival material created in the city is being negotiated. The objective exists also to 'repatriate' at least some of the material that left the city over the years and is now housed in repositories outside the city.

Principal holdings include:
Waterford Corporation minute books, 1654–1990s (59 volumes); Waterford Corporation committee records, 1778–1940s (19 committees); Town Clerk's Office records, 1700–1990s; Finance Office records, 1796–1980s; City Engineer's Office records, 1700–1990s, including over 2,500 maps and plans (drawings) for the city and its environs from the eighteenth century to the present, plus many reports and photographs of completed and proposed works; estate records, 1670s–1970s, including searchable database of expired leases of Waterford Corporation property, 1670s–1970s (over 1,100 entries); motor registration files from 1923; over 2,500 photographic prints of buildings, streets, events and people in the city, 1870s–present; primary school records (Mount Sion, St Patrick's, Manor St John's and Presentation Primary Schools, 1880–1990s and others); over 1000 small, private and institutional collections.

Waterford City Archives also hold the records of Waterford Chamber of Commerce (1797–1998) and Waterford Harbour Board (1816–1970s). In 2005 the archives purchased the Annie Brophy Photographic Collection, a significant collection of over 60,000 photographic negatives spanning the period from the 1920s to the 1970s.

LOCATION
Occupies a prominent position on High Street in the centre of the medieval city.
Part of the building dates back at least as far as the seventeenth century.

WATERFORD CITY COUNCIL CENTRAL LIBRARY

Lady Lane
WATERFORD
Ireland

TELEPHONE: (051) 849 975; FAX: (051) 850 031
E-mail: citylibrary@waterfordcity.ie
Website: www.waterfordcity.ie/library

HOURS
M–Tu, Th, F, 10:00–17:30; Sa, 10:00–13:00, 14:00–17:30; W, 10:00–20:00

ACCESS AND SERVICES
This is the main library in a three branch library system operated by the Waterford
City Council. The other branches are: Ardkeen (tel. (051) 849 755; fax (051) 874
100; hours: M, Th, F, 10:00–17:30; Sa, 10:00–13:00, 14:00–7:30; Tu,
10:00–20:00); Brown's Road (tel. (051) 849 845; hours: Tu, W, F, 10:00–13:00,
14:00–17:30).

All three branches have full disabled access with lifts, platform lifts, braille signs and
a hearing loop in the Central Library. Catalogue available online with access to
holdings and renewals for members. Service provides 50 personal computers with
free internet access to members. Total number of Internet sessions provided in 2011
= 36,932. Other services available include audio listening, television facilities, plasma
information screen, optical scanning facilities and photocopying. Meeting,
exhibition and lecture spaces are also available.

CONTACT
Jane Cantwell, City Librarian. E-mail: jcantwell@waterfordcity.ie

DESCRIPTION
Waterford City Council Central Library reopened in January 2004 after extensive
renovation and expansion to over 2,000 square metres. It extends to three public
floors and an administrative floor at the upper level. The library has received an
OPUS Building Award, an RIAI Award and the 2005 CILIP Award as winner of the
Library as Heart of the Community category. It houses the Index Gallery, a free
space for art and other exhibitions. The Ardkeen branch, based in a busy shopping
centre, was a winner of the 2003 CILIP Award and is a vibrant community library.

HOLDINGS
The library houses 159,728 volumes. In addition to its educational and recreational
holdings, the library has a solid local history and genealogical collection that
includes most of the standard reference sources, such as Waterford newspapers
including online access to the *Munster Express*, online and microfilm access to
Griffith's Valuation, Ordnance Survey maps for Kilkenny and Waterford City and
County, the 1901 and 1911 censuses, city maps and infirmary records. Free access

for members to online genealogical resources including *Find My Past* and *Ancestry*.
Central Library contains a Familysearch centre. Further information about our Local
Studies Department can be found at
www.waterfordcity.ie/library/localstudies/index.htm

LOCATION
Central Library: city centre.
Ardkeen Library, Ardkeen Shopping Centre, Dunmore Road.
Brown's Road Library, Paddy Brown's Road.

WATERFORD HERITAGE SERVICES

St Patrick's Church, Jenkin's Lane
WATERFORD
Ireland

TELEPHONE: (051) 876 123; FAX: (051) 582 595
E-mail: mnoc@iol.ie
Website: www.waterford-heritage.ie; www.irishroots.net/waterford

HOURS
M–Th, 09:00–17:00; F, 09:00–14:00

ACCESS AND SERVICES
The Waterford Heritage and Genealogy Centre offers a fee based, full range
genealogical research service for enquirers interested in tracing their roots in
Waterford City and County. Application form can be found on the centre's website.
The centre does commissioned work and does not have Public Reading Rooms
where people can do their own research. Chief surnames of County Waterford
include: Power, Walsh, O'Brien, Murphy, Ryan, McGrath, Foley, Flynn, Morrissey,
Kelly, Phelan and Sullivan. Main towns include: Waterford, Dungarvan, Lismore,
Cappoquin, Clonmel and Carrick-on-Suir (Clonmel and Carrick-on-Suir straddle
the Tipperary–Waterford border). Publications include (prices quoted are in US$,
inclusive of postage and handling): *The Connerys: Making of a Waterford Legend* ,
$16; J. Walsh (ed.), *Sliabh Rua: a History of its People and Places*, $40; and Frank
O'Brien, *The O'Briens of Déise*, $25.

CONTACT
Carmel Meehan

DESCRIPTION
The Waterford Heritage and Genealogy Centre is the designated Irish Family
History Foundation centre serving Waterford City and County. The IFHF is the
coordinating body for a network of government approved genealogical research
centres in the Republic of Ireland and in Northern Ireland that have computerised
tens of millions of Irish ancestral records of different types.

HOLDINGS
Church records form the major source of electronic data. Roman Catholic records in
County Waterford start in the year 1706; the latest parish to begin keeping records
did so in 1852. Church of Ireland records in Waterford have various starting dates,
depending on the parish, between 1655 and 1870. The earliest surviving and

complete census for Waterford is that of 1901. Some census extracts for the period 1766 to 1851 also survive. Other genealogical sources available include: polling lists from 1755 and 1775; the Civil Survey of Ireland, compiled in the years 1654–6; subsidy rolls for County Waterford, 1662; householders of Waterford City, 1663; freemen of Waterford list, 1542; street and trade directories from 1788; gravestone inscriptions; local newspapers, 1771–present; biographical entries in local newspapers, 1770s–1820s; and a local history collection.

LOCATION
Town centre, in the former eighteenth century priest's residence next to St Patrick's Church.

COUNTY WESTMEATH

AIDAN HEAVEY PUBLIC LIBRARY ATHLONE

Athlone Civic Centre, Church Street,
ATHLONE, COUNTY WESTMEATH
Ireland

TELEPHONE: (090) 644 2157/58/59.
E-mail: gobrien@westmeathcoco.ie
Website: see www.athlone.ie/genealogy, www.westmeathcoco.ie/library

HOURS
M, 10:00–17:30; Tu, Th, 10:00–20:00; W, 11:00–17:30; F, 10:00–17:00; Sa,
10:00–13:30

ACCESS AND SERVICES
Visitors welcome. Membership required for borrowing privileges. Disabled access.
Fifteen public access computer terminals with internet access. **Note:** Special
restrictions apply with regard to the use of the Aidan Heavey Collection for which a
prior appointment must be made to view items.

CONTACT
Gearoid O'Brien, Senior Executive Librarian

DESCRIPTION
Large municipal library, the flagship branch of Westmeath County Library Service,
with strong Irish, local studies and genealogy holdings. Staff will help with advice
and information where possible. For best results write or e-mail with details of needs
before visit. Specialises in material relating to South Westmeath. For North
Westmeath research purposes, *see* WESTMEATH COUNTY LIBRARY AND
ARCHIVES SERVICE – LOCAL STUDIES AND ARCHIVES COLLECTION, below.

HOLDINGS
In addition to its main lending collection, Athlone Library holds a reference
collection with a number of relevant genealogical sources.

The library recently acquired an outstanding collection of rare books and special
materials, the Aidan Heavey Collection, that qualifies it as a major research library.
The collection has been described by Dr Pat Wallace, Director of the National

Museum of Ireland, as 'an unparalleled gift with attaching obligations and responsibilities. Personally I feel it's reason enough to permanently move to Athlone!'

THE AIDAN HEAVEY COLLECTION

In 2006, the Athlone Library opened The Aidan Heavey Collection to the public. Aidan Heavey assembled one of the finest private libraries in Ireland, known especially for the very fine condition of its materials. Aidan Heavey and his wife Maureen donated the collection to his home town of Athlone. The collection includes several thousand volumes focusing on Irish history, topography and literature. In addition, the collection includes periodicals, journals, papers, manuscripts, photographs, documents, prints, drawings and a large collection of related ephemera. The collection totals more than 20,000 items. Highlights of the collection include an extensive Oliver Goldsmith collection featuring several first editions; an important collection of Douglas Hyde material, including photographs and manuscripts; rare Bibles and prayer books in Irish, including a copy of Bishop Bedell's *Irish Bible* of 1685; and an extensive collection of sixteenth and seventeenth century rarities, including books, pamphlets and atlases – all in very fine condition. The Aidan Heavey Collection also includes a fine collection of tours of Ireland in the eighteenth and nineteenth centuries; a comprehensive collection of Cuala Press, Dun Emer and Dolmen Press publications; a substantial collection of 1916 material, including original letters from Pearse, MacDonagh and Casement; and a very fine collection of twentieth century Irish literature, including many signed and limited editions by Yeats, Gogarty, Beckett, Kinsella, Heaney, Kennelly, Montague, O'Connor, O'Faoláin and O'Flaherty.

The Aidan Heavey Collection is a closed access collection. An appointment must be made to view items from the collection. Apply to Gearoid O'Brien at gobrien@westmeathcoco.ie or using contact details above.

Special Collections

The Kirby Collection contains approximately 250 different editions of *The Vicar of Wakefield* by Oliver Goldsmith (1728–74), a native of Westmeath. Many of the editions are illustrated and represent the work of the main Irish, British and continental illustrators of the day. The collection contains a number of fine bindings.

The Burgess Collection was assembled by Dr John B. Burgess (1885–1960) of Athlone. It contains: Athlone directories; wills and deeds; registers of Kiltoom Parish Church, St Mary's Parish Church and several other churches in the Athlone area; Athlone newspapers; a dictionary of Athlone biography; and vestry minutes of the Franciscan Abbey, Athlone. The John Broderick Collection contains an extensive collection of books, reviews, typescripts, etc by John Broderick (1927–89), the Athlone born novelist and critic.

LOCATION

Town centre, in Athlone Civic Centre.

DÚN NA SÍ HERITAGE CENTRE

Knockdomney
MOATE, COUNTY WESTMEATH
Ireland

TELEPHONE: (090) 648 1183; FAX: (090) 648 1661
E-mail: dunnasimoate@eircom.net
Website: www.rootsireland.ie; www.dunnasi.ie

HOURS
M–Th, 10:00–16:00; F, 10:00–15:00; weekends by appointment only.

ACCESS AND SERVICES
Dún na Sí Heritage Centre offers a fee based genealogical service to enquirers and
has access to church, civil, land and census records for County Westmeath.
Application form available on website.

CONTACT
Caroline Ganley

DESCRIPTION
Dún na Sí Heritage Centre is the Irish Family History Foundation's designated
research centre for County Westmeath. The IFHF is the coordinating body for a
network of government approved genealogical research centres in the Republic of
Ireland and in Northern Ireland that have computerised tens of millions of Irish
ancestral records of different types. Chief surnames in County Westmeath include:
(Mc)Geoghegan, O'Growney, Brennan, O'Coffey, O'Mulleady, O'Malone, O'Daly,
McAuley and McCormack. Main towns and villages include: Mullingar, Athlone,
Moate and Kilbeggan.

HOLDINGS
The centre has access to approximately 750,000 records. Main records include the
following: Roman Catholic records for County Westmeath, starting in 1737;
Church of Ireland records dating from 1710 (some available); Presbyterian records
dating from 1800 (some available). Other sources include: Griffith's Valuation; *Pigot's
Directory*; *Slater's Directory*; estate lists; voter lists; and the 1901 and 1911 census.

LOCATION
Mount Temple Road, 0.6 miles from the Gap House pub.

WESTMEATH COUNTY LIBRARY AND ARCHIVES SERVICE – LOCAL STUDIES AND ARCHIVES COLLECTION

Library Headquarters
County Buildings
MULLINGAR, COUNTY WESTMEATH
Ireland

TELEPHONE: (044) 933 2162
E-mail: library@westmeathcoco.ie
Website: www.westmeathcoco.ie/library

HOURS
By appointment only

ACCESS AND SERVICES
By appointment. Reference only. Fees for photocopying.

CONTACT
Paula O'Dornan, Acting County Librarian

HOLDINGS
Archival Material
Local government records include the following: Grand Jury presentments outlining the construction of roads in the county, 1802–87; Board of Guardian minute books, which detail the operation of the Poor Law system in the nineteenth and early twentieth centuries for Athlone (1849–1920) and Mullingar (1857–1921); Rural District Council minute books for Athlone (1899–1925), Ballymore (1900–25), Delvin (1919–23), Kilbeggan (1914–17) and Mullingar (1899–1925); valuation lists (1904–72); Board of Health and Public Assistance minute books (1922–42); Westmeath County Council minute books (1899–1986); and Mullingar Commissioners' Books (1923–57). Many of these have been microfilmed and are available in the Local Studies Collections in Athlone and Mullingar.

Private papers include the following: the Fr Paul Walsh Papers, containing notes and unpublished material relating to this distinguished historian and scholar, born at Ballinea, Mullingar; and the Laurence Ginnell Papers, containing a selection of papers relating to this North Westmeath MP who was born in Delvin, County Westmeath.

The Howard Bury Collection, on permanent loan to the library, includes personal diaries and accounts of travel from the early nineteenth century to details of local politics and electioneering in the mid-nineteenth century. It also includes prisoner of war diaries and accounts of the geographical and mountaineering expeditions of Colonel Howard Bury, and papers relating to the Belvedere Estate. The collection is named after Colonel Howard Bury, the former owner of Belvedere House.

The Irish Collection is also housed at Westmeath County Library Headquarters and comprises a wide range of material on all aspects of Irish society.

Local Studies Collections
AIDAN HEAVEY LIBRARY, Athlone
See separate entry above.

MULLINGAR PUBLIC LIBRARY
County Buildings
Mount Street
MULLINGAR, COUNTY WESTMEATH
Ireland

TELEPHONE: (044) 9332161
E-mail: mgarlib@westmeathcoco.ie
Website: www.westmeathcoco.ie/library

CONTACT
Ms Cailin Gallagher, Executive Librarian

ACCESS AND SERVICES
By appointment. Reference only. Fees for photocopying.

DESCRIPTION
The Local Studies Collection is part of the County Westmeath library system. In recent years, resources relating to North Westmeath have been made available in Mullingar Library and resources relating to South Westmeath have been made available in the Aidan Heavey Library, Athlone. *See* separate entry above for Aidan Heavey Library. For further information visit the Library's website at www.westmeathcoco.ie/library/

HOLDINGS
The Local Studies Collections contain a wealth of books, maps, journals, newspapers, photographs and ephemera relating to every aspect of life in County Westmeath, past and present. All books in the collection have a connection to Westmeath, in terms of authorship or subject matter. Authors represented in the library collections include: John Broderick, Leo Daly, Alice Dease, J.P. Donleavy, Desmond Egan, Lawrence Ginnell, Josephine Hart, Marian Keaney, Thomas Pakenham, Brinsley MacNamara, T.P. O'Connor, Padraic O'Farrell, A.J. Stanley, Michael Walsh, Fr Paul Walsh, Oliver Goldsmith and Christopher Nolan. The collection also includes directories, almanacs, topographical dictionaries, parish histories, GAA histories and unpublished works such as theses and project material. There are some 3,500 items in this collection.

Newspaper holdings on microfilm include:

> *Westmeath Journal*, 1813, 1823–34, *Midland Chronicle* and *Westmeath Independent*, 1827, *Athlone Independent*,1833–6, *Athlone Sentinel*, 1834–61, *Westmeath Guardian*, 1835–96, *Athlone Conservative Advocate*, 1837, *Athlone Mirror*, 1841–2, *Westmeath Herald*, 1859–61, *Westmeath Independent*, 1860–1920, 1923–2011, *Westmeath Examiner*, 1882–2011, *Athlone Times*, 1887, 1889–1900, *Midland Reporter* and *Westmeath Nationalist*, 1891–1939, *Athlone News* 1961–2, *Athlone Observer*, 1985–1995, and *Midland Herald*, 1949–58.

Holdings are split between the Local Studies Departments in Athlone and Mullingar so please check website for details or e-mail library@westmeathcoco.ie in advance of any visit.

Special Collections
The Photographic Collection contains some 2,500 prints of Westmeath and housed primarily in the Local Studies Dept in Mullingar Library. Maps include: Petty maps for County Westmeath; revised Ordnance Survey maps (1837) and their accompanying letters and name books, compiled under the direction of John O'Donovan; Geological Survey of Ireland, Westmeath (1860, 1 inch; 1913, 6 inch); Mullingar (1911, revised 1953, scale 1:2,500); *Irish Historical Towns Atlas No. 5, Mullingar* (Royal Irish Academy); and *Irish Historical Town Atlas No. 6, Athlone* (Royal Irish Academy).

Other records of special genealogical interest include: census records for the nineteenth century in addition to Pender's Census, 1659; and 1901 and 1911 census manuscript forms, providing detailed information on each resident of the county are available on microfilm. Gravestone inscriptions are available for several parishes including: Athlone Abbey Graveyard; Mount Temple Churchyard; Templecross Cemetery, Tristernagh Ballynacargy; All Saints, Mullingar; Lynn Church, Mullingar; Kilbixy Graveyard, Ballinacargy; Quaker Graveyard, Moate; St Mary's Church of Ireland, Moate, Kilcleigh and Killomenaghan. Additional graveyards may be available courtesy of local historians – please double check with the library.

See separate entry above for Aidan Heavey Library, Athlone, for special collection holdings in the Athlone Library.

LOCATION
Town centre.

COUNTY WEXFORD

WEXFORD COUNTY ARCHIVE & RECORDS CENTRE

6A Ardcavan Business Park,
ARDCAVAN, COUNTY WEXFORD
Ireland

TELEPHONE: (053) 919 6572
Email: archivist@wexfordcoco.ie
Website: www.wexford.ie/wex/Departments/Archive

HOURS
By appointment only

ACCESS AND SERVICES
Access to collections in the county archive is by advance appointment only. While every effort is made to facilitate researchers, access to certain materials may be restricted if documents are deemed too fragile or are closed for a period due to sensitive content. Where collections have been microfilmed and/or digitised, only access to this alternative format is given. Collections are only generally made available once they have been processed, i.e. cleaned, arranged and listed. Photocopying is not permitted but digital photography is available.
New web pages for the county archive are currently under construction – once completed, recently digitised county council minutes from 1899 to 1997 will be made available online

CONTACT
Gráinne Doran, Archivist

DESCRIPTION
The Archive is responsible for identifying, collecting and making available the archives, both public and private of County Wexford, and for managing the records of Wexford County Council. The premises at 6A Ardcavan Business Park houses the county archive which is located in a large windowless air-conditioned strongroom on the first floor, and the records centre for storage and management of Wexford County Council's non-current records.

HOLDINGS
Manuscript materials include grand jury presentments, workhouse records, rural

district council material, county council minutes and managers' orders. Private collections include solicitors' records, estate paper collections, maps and drawings, literary papers, harbour records, school records and records of local businesses, clubs and societies. Some of the more significant private collections include the Lord Templemore papers (deeds, estate rentals, hunting journals relating to Dunbrody Park, Arthurstown, Co. Wexford, early-nineteenth to mid-twentieth century), the Lorna Rosbottom family archive (relating to many generations of the Hughes family from Ballytrent, Co. Wexford, 1573–1980s) and the Wexford Harbour Commissioners' collection (1831–1961). The Wexford Festival Opera archive (1951–present) is among the holdings and is managed by the Archive on behalf of Wexford Opera House.

LOCATION
Wexford County Archive Service is located at 6A Ardcavan Business Park, Ardcavan, approx. 1.5 miles outside Wexford town on the R741 coast road.

WEXFORD COUNTY LIBRARY – LIBRARY MANAGEMENT SERVICES

Wexford County Council,
Block D, Floor 2
CARRICKLAWN, COUNTY WEXFORD
Ireland

TELEPHONE: (053) 919 6560
E-mail: libraryhq@wexfordcoco.ie
Website: www.wexford.ie/library

HOURS
See website

ACCESS AND SERVICES
Visitors welcome by appointment, but advance notice essential.

CONTACT
See e-mail

DESCRIPTION
This is the management headquarters for County Wexford, which operates branch libraries in Bunclody, Enniscorthy, Gorey, New Ross, the County Library in Wexford Town and the Archives and Documentation Centre in Ardcavan. *See* separate entries for ARCHIVES SERVICE and WEXFORD TOWN LIBRARY— LOCAL STUDIES COLLECTION.

HOLDINGS
In addition to its general educational and recreational collection of more than 200,000 volumes, the library system maintains collections in local and Irish history, genealogy, local authors, local prints and photographs, archives, local newspapers (nineteenth century) and maps, as well as the 1798 Collection. For the bicentenary of the 1798 Rebellion, the service compiled a brochure entitled *Mightier than the Sword* (1998), which lists various introductory sources held by the libraries documenting the history and culture of Wexford. These resources include all the standard genealogical reference sources. The Photographic Collection, the oral

history audio collection and full text articles from three of County Wexford's local history journals are accessible via the library catalogue: this resource is in development.

LOCATION
Carricklawn, approximately 2 miles from Wexford town centre, beside Wexford General Hospital, on the N11.

WEXFORD TOWN LIBRARY—LOCAL STUDIES COLLECTION

Mallin Street
WEXFORD TOWN, COUNTY WEXFORD
Ireland

TELEPHONE: (053) 912 1637
E-mail: wexfordlib@wexfordcoco.ie
Website: www.wexford.ie/library

HOURS
M–Tu, 10:30–17:30; W, 10:30–20:30; Th–Sa, 10:30–17:30

ACCESS AND SERVICES
Visitors welcome. Beautiful new library offers a variety of programs, lectures, readings and exhibits. Wheelchair accessible. Houses a Local Studies collection. See HOLDINGS. The Local Studies Collection is searchable by author, title and subject on the Library's Online Catalogue. View an item's full catalogue record for details of its contents and location.

CONTACT
Fionnuala Hanrahan, County Librarian. E-mail: fionnuala.hanrahan@wexfordcoco.ie
Local Studies Librarian. E-mail: localstudies@wexfordcoco.ie

DESCRIPTION
Westford Town Library is part of the Wexford County Library system, headquartered in Carricklawn. In addition to its general collection, the Library houses a Local Studies collection.

HOLDINGS
The public access Local Studies Collection is in Wexford town. Local Studies in the Wexford Town Library includes resources that relate to the history, archaeology, economy, religion, landscape and cultural heritage of the county as well as to its natural and built environment. It also contains works by Wexford-born authors, regardless of subject matter. Local Studies contains material in a wide range of formats, including books, journals and periodicals, local newspapers, genealogical sources (censuses, parish registers, gravestone inscriptions, directories, Griffith's Valuation, tithe applotment books, etc.), maps and plans, photographs and postcards, oral histories and folklore, theses, reports and studies, audio and video cassettes and CDs, ephemera, and Wexford County Library publications. The Wexford branch also houses a microform collection which includes:

> local newspapers
> censuses of 1901 and 1911
> Tithe Applotment books

Schools Folklore collection, 1938
Roman Catholic parish registers of Ferns diocese to 1880
6 inch Ordnance Survey maps c. 1840

LOCATION
Town centre.

COUNTY WEXFORD HERITAGE AND GENEALOGY SOCIETY

Yola Farmstead Folk Park, Tagoat
ROSSLARE, COUNTY WEXFORD
Ireland

Note: Closed, with no indication of reopening in the near future, at least not at its previous location. For genealogy enquiries for County Wexford, please contact:

Secretary, Irish Family History Foundation,
c/o Kildare History and Family Research Centre,
Riverbank, Main Street, Newbridge, Co,
Kildare, Ireland.
E-mail: info@ifhf.ie

WEXFORD TOWN LIBRARY

See WEXFORD COUNTY LIBRARY – LIBRARY MANAGEMENT SERVICES, Ardcavan

COUNTY WICKLOW

WICKLOW COUNTY ARCHIVES

County Council Buildings
Station Road
WICKLOW TOWN
Ireland

Note: Service is unavailable until January 2014.

TELEPHONE: (0404) 20126
E-mail: cwright@wicklowcoco.ie
Website: www.wicklow.ie/archives/wicklow_archive.htm

HOURS
M–F, 10:00–17:00 (appointment necessary)

CONTACT
Catherine Wright, Archivist

DESCRIPTION
The function of the Wicklow County Archives is to identify, collect, preserve and make available the archives, both public and private, of County Wicklow and to manage the records of Wicklow County Council.

HOLDINGS
Major holdings include:

> Grand Jury (Spring 1819–Spring 1899)
> Poor Law Unions – Board of Guardians Minute Books
> * Rathdrum (1839–1921)
> * Shillelagh (1852–1914)
> Workhouse registers (available on microfilm in Wicklow Family History Centre and Bray library)
> * Rathdrum workhouse (1849–1914)
> * Shillelagh workhouse (1842–1921)
> Rural District Councils – Minute Books
> * Rathdrum (1899–1925)
> * Shillelagh (1899–1920)

Wicklow County Council Minute Books (1899–2003)
Urban District Councils (Bray, Wicklow)
Board of Health and Public Assistance (Minute Books only; subject to restrictions)

LOCATION
At the northern end of Wicklow Town, beside the fire station and train station.

WICKLOW COUNTY LIBRARY – LOCAL STUDIES COLLECTION
See also WICKLOW FAMILY HISTORY CENTRE and WICKLOW COUNTY COUNCIL ARCHIVES

Wicklow County Council Library Service Headquarters
Boghall Road,
BRAY, COUNTY WICKLOW
Ireland

TELEPHONE: (01) 286 6566; FAX: (01) 286 5811
E-mail: library@wicklowcoco.ie
Website: www.wicklow.ie

HOURS
By appointment within the opening hours of Ballywaltrim Branch library: Tu, Th, Sa, 10:00–13:00, 14:00–17:00; W, 14:00–17:00, 18:00– 20:00

ACCESS AND SERVICES
Visitors welcome. Items may not be borrowed from the Local Studies Collection. Photocopying facilities are available as well as microfilm printing.

CONTACT
Brendan Martin, County Librarian

DESCRIPTION
The Local Studies Collection is housed in Ballywaltrim Library at the Wicklow County Library Headquarters in Bray. The County Library operates branch libraries in: Arklow (0402-39977); Ballywaltrim (01-2723205); Baltinglass (059-6482300); Blessington (045-891740); Bray (01-2862600); Carnew (053-9426088); Dunlavin (045-401100); Enniskerry (01-2864339); Greystones (01-2873548); Rathdrum (0404-43232); Tinahely (0402-38080); and Wicklow (0404-67025).

HOLDINGS
The Local Studies Collection includes books, journals, files and local historical society publications on topics relating to County Wicklow, its people and places. There are several special collections, most notably the J.M. Synge Collection, the Charles Stewart Parnell Collection and the 1798 Collection. Also available are Cantwell's *Memorials of the Dead*, the Coughlan Papers, the Irish Folklore Commission's School's Folklore Scheme (1937–8), Griffith's Valuation (Wicklow extracts), workhouse records from Rathdrum and Shillelagh, and the tithe applotment books (Wicklow extracts). Newspapers on micrfofilm include:

> *Wicklow Newsletter* (1858–1926)
> *Bray Gazette* (1861–73)
> *Wicklow People* (1889–)

Wicklow Star (1895–1900)
Arklow Reporter (1890–93)
Wicklow Standard (1900–01)
Bray Herald (1905–27)
Wicklow Post (1935)
East Coast Express (1936–8)
Bray Tribune (1939–43)
Bray People (1988–)

LOCATION
Ballywaltrim Library, Boghall Road, Bray, Co. Wicklow.
Bray is easily reached from Dublin city centre using the DART and Dublin Bus services.

WICKLOW FAMILY HISTORY CENTRE

Wicklow County Council
County Council Buildings
Station Road
WICKLOW TOWN
Ireland

Note: Service is unavailable until January 2014.

TELEPHONE: (0404) 20126
E-mail: wfh@eircom.net
Website: www.wicklow.ie/familyhistorycentre

HOURS
M–F, 10:00–17:00 (appointment necessary)

ACCESS AND SERVICES
The centre offers a fee based genealogical research service to persons interested in tracing their roots in County Wicklow. Research reports range in fee from €36.30, €114.95, and €250.00 depending on information available and service required; please allow four to eight weeks for initial report. Application forms can be found on website.

CONTACT
Contact administrative staff Wicklow County Council

DESCRIPTION
The Wicklow Family History Centre is a genealogy research service established in 1987 by Wicklow County Council.

HOLDINGS
Records computerised include Roman Catholic and Church of Ireland parish records, baptisms and marriages in Presbyterian churches and baptisms within the circuit of Methodist churches in the county. In all, the centre holds over 275,000 baptism, 50,600 marriage and 40,000 burial records. Roman Catholic records do not normally include burial records. The earliest parish records for County Wicklow are Church of Ireland records, dating from the seventeenth century. The records for Roman Catholic parishes as a rule do not start until the early nineteenth century,

although Wicklow Town records commence in 1747 – a distinction shared by only a few parishes in the whole of Ireland. Other sources held include: tithe applotment books; Griffith's Valuation printed reports and the accompanying maps; graveyard inscriptions; census returns of 1901 and 1911; Ordnance Survey townland maps; parish maps, place name histories; hearth money rolls of 1669; the Religious Census, 1766; poll book, 1745–59; corn growers, carriers and traders list, 1788–90; material relating to the 1798 Rebellion; Wicklow Gaol records; convict records; commercial directories; lists of landowners.

LOCATION
At the northern end of Wicklow Town, beside the fire station and train station.

THE COUNTIES OF IRELAND

Donegal

Derry/
Londonderry

Antrim

Tyrone

Leitrim

Fermanagh

Armagh

Down

Sligo

Monaghan

Mayo

Cavan

Louth

Roscommon

Longford

Meath

Galway

Westmeath

Offaly

Dublin

Kildare

Laois

Wicklow

Clare

Carlow

Tipperary

Kilkenny

Wexford

Limerick

Kerry

Waterford

Cork

A BRIEF GUIDE TO THE IRISH FAMILY HISTORY FOUNDATION AND THE MAIN SOURCES FOR TRACING IRISH ANCESTORS

Karel Kiely

The Irish Family History Foundation (IFHF) is a network of 33 local county genealogy centres covering the island of Ireland that offer professional family history research services and an online research service at www.rootsireland.ie

These centres, many of which have been in operation for over 25 years, were formed in the 1970s and early 1980s when there was an upsurge in interest in roots and ancestor tracing. Following a model created at the centres in Corofin, County Clare and in County Limerick, local groups around Ireland began to index their county's records. In 1984 many of these groups, in association with individuals interested in genealogy, came together to form the Irish Family History Society whose role was to develop standard procedures for indexing records and facilitate the development of links between the various groups. Gradually the indexing centres came to recognise that they shared a range of concerns and interests that could best be furthered by an umbrella organisation dedicated to catering for the needs of local genealogy centres which became the Irish Family History Foundation.

The demand for genealogical research services from the Irish Diaspora required an all-island network of centres that led to the involvement of the centres from Northern Ireland. The initial work done on the indexation of the sources was manual: records were transcribed on to index cards, sorted and filed alphabetically. In the early 1990s a standard computer system and bespoke software were introduced in the majority of centres. The IFHF identified the various church records of baptisms, marriages and deaths as a priority for computerisation. Other primary sources such as Griffith's Valuation, Tithe Applotment Books, the 1901 and 1911 census returns and gravestone inscriptions were also included in the databases. Many centres also computerised civil records of births, deaths and marriages.

Substantial progress has been made in providing visitor facilities throughout the country with many centres operating full heritage/visitor centres and tourist offices. Some centres are based in the finest visitor facilities on the island, including Brú Ború in Cashel, Rothe House, Kilkenny and the

Harbour Museum, Derry. These county genealogy centres have become a valuable part of the heritage and tourism infrastructure in their communities throughout the island of Ireland.

WWW.ROOTSIRELAND.IE

The Irish Family History Foundation began the roll out of an online research service in mid-2007, providing access to its county database to the public for the first time. The delivery and continued development of the online service is funded solely by the IFHF and its member centres. The service was developed in two phases: in the initial phase access was provided to search the databases of twelve individual county genealogy centres. The second phase saw the development of an all-Ireland Online Research Service in March 2008. This phase included the addition of over 17 million records from twenty-two counties.

The advent of the website offered those who wished to trace their Irish family history access to the largest database of vital Irish records for the first time. It is especially valuable for those who do not know the county of origin of their ancestor. The creation of www.rootsireland.ie is the most significant development in Irish genealogy since the 1980s. The advantage of using the data on rootsireland.ie is that it was compiled from original sources, not copies or microfilms, by local people that were familiar with local names and places. The databases of individual centres were independently audited by Eneclann Ltd. in 1999 and the error rating was found to be well within accepted norms for historical records.

The IFHF continues to support and assist its centres in computerising the remaining church records and other sources. The county genealogy centres also continue to offer a commissioned research service for those who do not want to carry out their own research. Contact details for all the member centres are available on the website. The IFHF is working to establish centres where there is currently no local genealogy service in operation. It will continue to improve the databases, support centres and promote the services it offers to a local and worldwide audience.

RESEARCHING IRISH FAMILY HISTORY

Sources used for Irish family history research were originally recorded for other reasons such as taxation or as sacramental records. Family history research is a secondary use of this material. However, it is the original reason for this data being recorded that determines the structures, access and guardianship of these historical records. As many of those with Irish ancestry do not know where their ancestor may have originated in Ireland it makes sense to bring together all the available databases for the individual counties on one site to assist research. The all-Ireland database at **www.rootsireland.ie** offers the most efficient means of locating ancestors where no place of origin is known and of working out the complex relationships that family history research entails.

Parish Registers
Parish Registers of all denominations are the primary source for searching Irish ancestry. They are the best starting point as they include baptisms, marriages and sometimes deaths for all classes of the population. They also pre-date civil registration which did not begin in Ireland until 1864 (non-Catholic marriages were recorded from 1845).

Roman Catholic registers are kept in individual parishes and, in most cases, were not deposited in national repositories. This ensured their survival from the Public Record Office fire in 1922 and makes them one of the most comprehensive records available. The IFHF centres have compiled computerised indexes from the original registers of all the major churches in Ireland. Please consult the information under Online Sources on the **www.rootsireland.ie** website for the individual county centres to find out which parishes are computerised. As work in the centres is ongoing, records for further parishes will be available on an ongoing basis.

A number of counties, including County Kerry and Dublin City records are at **www.irishgenealogy.ie** and copies of Catholic registers are available to search up to c. 1880–82 at the National Library of Ireland (**www.nli.ie** for details).

The Church of Ireland or Anglican church, as the Established Church, had a more regular system of recording entries, using formatted books long before its Catholic counterpart, thus often making its registers easier to research. Many of these can be searched at www.rootsireland.ie. The original registers may be held locally by the rector or, more usually, will be in the RCB (Representative Church Body) Library. Please see **http://ireland.anglican.org** for further information.

Civil Registration
Civil registration of births, marriages and deaths began in Ireland in 1864; the registration of non-Catholic marriages began in 1845. Many county genealogy centres have computerised these records (check

www.rootsireland.ie for details for individual counties); indexes of these records are also available on a number of websites including www.findmypast.ie Researchers can visit the General Register Office Research Room at the Irish Life Centre, Lower Abbey St., Dublin, or order certificates; further details can be found at www.groireland.ie.

Census Returns

For the purpose of genealogical research in Ireland the first two complete census returns are those of 1901 and 1911. Some county genealogy centres hold partial surviving census returns for other years. Please check the Online Sources list at www.rootsireland.ie for each county to see what is available. From 1821 a census was carried out every ten years. Unfortunately, a large amount of this material was either destroyed in the Civil War in 1922 or by British government order, being pulped for paper during the First World War. The returns give detailed information relating to all persons, including householders and their dependents, residents of army and R.I.C. barracks, convents, hospitals, and other institutions, similar to present day censuses. The barony, civil parish and townland were the territorial divisions used. Researchers can search the 1901 and 1911 Census returns online at the National Archives website www.nationalarchives.ie (Please bear in mind that some areas have been omitted and a standard surnames facility does not exist on this site).

Gravestone Inscriptions

These can be very useful, particularly the Church of Ireland ones. However, many people did not erect gravestones. The recording of inscriptions varies from county to county and is also work that is ongoing in many places. Again, please check the Online Sources on www.rootsireland.ie and also with county library services in the particular county that you interested in for up to date information on available records.

Griffith's Valuation

The Primary Valuation of Tenements, also known as Griffith's Valuation, was undertaken in order to establish the value of land and buildings in Ireland as a basis for levying a local system of fair taxation under the Irish Poor Law Act of 1838 and was carried out between 1848 and 1864. It listed every property holder in the country, with details of their houses, outbuildings, fields and gardens. The purpose of the vast survey was financial: to estimate the net annual value of every property in Ireland and determine the local taxation rate payable by each householder. It can be a useful indicator of the possible location of a particular family in an area, especially if the surname is an uncommon one. It is accessible on a number of websites: www.rootsireland.ie has an index only, compiled in the 1980s; the full Valuation can be accessed at www.askaboutireland.ie – a resource developed by the county libraries in the Republic of Ireland.

The Public Record Office of Northern Ireland has digitised the Valuation Revision Books (VAL/12B) for Northern Ireland, which cover the period from the original Griffith's Valuation up to the 1930s, marking changes in occupancy. These can be viewed at PRONI's website: www.proni.gov.uk.

Tithe Applotment books
The Tithe Applotment books provide a record of the tithable land in each parish and were compiled in accordance with the Irish Tithe Composition Acts passed between 1823 and 1838. The purpose was to make an assessment of land values for the payment of tithes which was a tax levied on land for the support of the church. Tithe was a tax paid to Established Church (Church of Ireland), calculated as one-tenth of the rateable value of one's agricultural produce. Although an excellent genealogical source, it was only concerned with persons occupying upwards of 5 acres of land, thus excluding other classes such as cottiers, landless people and those living in urban settlements. The Ulster tithe records, as well as some other census substitutes can be accessed at www.rootsireland.ie; tithes for the whole country can be found at www.nationalarchives.ie (please note there are some areas missing).

GENERAL ADVICE BEFORE ENGAGING WITH ANY WEBSITE RESEARCH

How should one start researching Irish Ancestry?
Trying to locate a particular person in the millions of Irish records can be daunting. A name or surname is not enough. You need to compile as much information as possible before you can start searching records in order to have the best possible chance of locating your ancestors. It is easier to focus on one or two individuals initially as you gain experience in your research. You should start your research where you know the ancestor spent the last years of their lives. Where did they live and where did they die? Do they appear in census records in their adopted country? Where were they married? Where were their children baptised? Are there other Irish families in the same area? Was there an obituary in a local paper? If you start in your ancestor's home county or country and go back from location to location retracing the ancestor's footsteps you may be able to pinpoint locations where you need to search for records. If your ancestor emigrated from Ireland you do not start your research in Ireland. It is also important not to skip generations.

What makes up a picture of your ancestors?

> Name and name variations
> Age
> Occupation
> Religion
> Spouse's name
> Parents' names
> Possible age of parents
> Other family members

It is important to try to establish when a person left Ireland as this may help to establish their age when they emigrated. If they were very young they may have been with their parents or other siblings. If older they may have already been married and travelling with a spouse and perhaps even children born in Ireland. The year of emigration can be checked with particular events in Irish history as different groups migrated at different times from particular locations. If you can learn when your ancestor left Ireland it may point to a particular location in Ireland. If you can establish the ship, date and port of arrival you can look for the passenger list for a particular voyage. This can provide information about whether they travelled with family members, neighbours or friends.

If your ancestors did not emigrate from Ireland you will still need to follow the same steps by working back from the present, generation by generation. Use gravestones, memorial cards, and family memories to assist you. You will need to know a first name, surname and approximate year of birth, marriage or death. Remember there may be many variations of the surname. It is also important to know the religious denomination.

There are many people who do not have a county or parish of origin for their Irish ancestor. This means that a search can be practically impossible in some cases where the surname is very common (though perseverance can pay off for a few); however, it can still be possible for some people to locate their Irish ancestor because of an unusual first name or because the combination of a husband's name and a wife's name reduces the likely possibilities. The Online Research System at **www.rootsireland.ie** offers you the ability to search across all the records of the participating counties or to select one or more counties to limit/extend your searches.

Problems you may encounter conducting Irish research
If your ancestor was born or married before 1820 it can be difficult to locate records of baptism and marriage. Many Catholic parishes (and Presbyterian congregations) did not keep records until around this date. The start dates of

parishes vary from county to county. Church of Ireland (Anglican) parishes can be available from a much earlier date; however, a lot of these records were lost during the Irish Civil War. A county genealogy centre's database may assist in such cases by pinpointing the occurrence of a surname in a particular parish or location within a parish. The original parish registers can vary in content; there are omissions, gaps, mixing up of names, incorrect dates, torn or damaged pages and so on.

Some Basic Searching Tips for www.rootsireland.ie

The recording of first names (or Christian names) varies from record to record, e.g. Elizabeth or Lizzie, Patrick or Pat. Please consult the First Names listing for guidance. Remember the wild card search facility can be used, e.g. PAT% or %LIZ%. On some records one or more of the parents' first names may not have been recorded in the original source, may have been illegible or been recorded incorrectly by the priest/minister.

Because of the variant spelling of Irish surnames it is useful for a genealogist to be able to search for a range of spellings of a surname by the input of one surname only. Thus a search for the surname *Smith* can find all the records for *Smith, Smyth, Smythe,* and possibly another half a dozen variants.

When performing a Standard Surname search on **www.rootsireland.ie**, the search results includes the 'surname (plus variants)'. Clicking on this link will allow you to view all surname variations that are being matched for your search. You should first try the Standard Surname match to find what you are looking for and, if that returns too many records, select the Exact Match to reduce the number of results. Note that there are no standard first names used in the searches. First names searches are always done as a wild card search, e.g. the first name of Mar% will return matches for Mary, Maria, etc. but if you enter Mary, variants such as Maria will not be returned. A list of first name variations is provided on the site. Often the mother's surname was not recorded on baptismal records or it may be recorded on one child's baptism but not on that of a subsequent child.

You can search by year and increase or decrease the span of years according to your knowledge of possible dates of events. If a lot of records are returned for your search criteria (> 10) and no year was entered you will need to enter a year +/- 10 or 5 years to narrow your search results. You can choose to search all counties or one county or any combination of counties. You can search by parish on a county's own page on the site.

Please check the current Sources list for the county's whose records you wish to search to see what is available online. You may be searching for records too early or too late for the available sources. Computerisation is still ongoing and computerised indexes to the parish records you wish to search may not yet be available. There are few records in the database pre-1700 or after *c*. 1920. Some parish registers have gaps in their records. Some civil births, deaths and marriages were not registered.

If you are unable to find the records that you are looking for please bear in mind the following:

Have you checked all the alternative or variant spellings of surnames and first names? As the parish registers were usually completed by the officiating minister, priest or registrar, it is not uncommon to find variations in the spellings used. Parish registers can be difficult to decipher; names and addresses were not standardised, and it may not be possible to find a complete family in one parish as families did move between neighbouring parishes and bordering counties.

The relevant set of church/civil records which contain your ancestors' records may not yet be computerised and available online. If you cannot find what you are looking for please note that not all records are online yet but may be held in the local genealogy centre and can be searched by the centre's staff on request. Please contact the relevant centre directly for more information. Alternatively a manual search of the originals or copies of original records may need to be made in a local archive, eg the Public Record Office of Northern Ireland, or the RCB Library, Dublin to try locate the record of an ancestor.

For further information on tracing your Irish roots and using the website please see **www.rootsireland.ie** or email enquiries@rootsireland.ie

TITHE AND VALUATION RECORDS *c.*1823

Brian Trainor

Farmers of most agricultural land in Ireland were liable to pay to the rector of the established Church of Ireland a tithe or tax of one tenth of the yearly produce of the land and stock. This tax was especially unpopular with Presbyterians and Roman Catholics. Agitation against the tax forced the Government to change the law and make the tithe charge a financial one (instead of crops etc.) and levied on the landlord rather than on the tenant. In order to determine the amount of money to be charged in lieu of tithe all agricultural land liable to tithe had to be surveyed and valued. This work was done by local surveyors and the detail given is variable; unfortunately there are no maps accompanying the survey showing the locations of farms. The surveys provide the names of lease-holding tenants in each townland and thus serve as a sort of a farm census for the whole country.

The tithe surveys for parishes in Northern Ireland for the years 1823–38 are deposited in the Public Record Office of Northern Ireland (FIN/5A) and those for the Republic of Ireland are available in the National Archives, Dublin (OL4). In order to conserve the original documents only microfilm copies of these surveys are produced to the public. The tithe applotment books for the Republic of Ireland have been digitised and are available online for free through the website of the National Archives of Ireland **www.titheapplotmentbooks.nationalarchives.ie.**

The earliest full valuation of property in Ireland was carried out in the 1830s. This valuation was carried out in each townland and parish and the surveyor's manuscript field books of this 'townland valuation' for parishes in Northern Ireland are deposited in the Public Record Office of Northern Ireland (VAL/1B) and those for the Republic are in the National Archives (OL4). No detail is given of buildings unless these were valued at £3.00 or more and this lower limit was raised to £5.00 in 1838 thus excluding most rural houses. Most of Ulster was valued before the threshold was raised to £5.00. With the result that many buildings in the North around £2.00 valuation are included. In towns many houses were substantial enough to reach the valuation of £3.00 or £5.00 and in these cases detailed measurements of rooms and outbuildings are sometimes given as well as names of occupiers. For the town of Downpatrick the names of 330 occupiers are given in the field book for the parish of Down *c.* 1838 (VAL/1B/378 and OL4.0459). The National Archives, Dublin has another set of these valuation field books 1830s for most parishes in Northern Ireland except for Co. Tyrone.

The first detailed valuation of all properties in Ireland began in the province of Leinster during the Great Famine in 1846, and the valuation was completed in Northern Ireland 1858–64. The manuscript field books of this valuation for Northern Ireland with annotated maps showing the precise location of holdings are held in PRONI (VAL/2B) and also the annual revisions recording changes in occupancy, consolidation of farms and the upheavals resulting from the Land Acts from the 1850s up to *c.* 1930s (VAL/12B). Similar records exist for all parishes in the Republic of Ireland but these are held in the Valuation Office, Middle Abbey Street, Dublin.

Sir Richard Griffith, the great Commissioner of Valuation who was responsible for these massive surveys by central government arranged that a summary version of the valuation of 1846–64 for the whole country be made available in print. Some 200 volumes were published as official papers, one for each Poor Law Union or part. This printed valuation popularly known as 'Griffith's Valuation' appeared in the period 1847–1865. It is doubtful if any country in the world has such ready access in printed form to records detailing the value and acreage of farms and buildings, usually with the names of landlords and the exact locations marked on official maps held in the Public Record Office of Northern Ireland and in the Valuation Office, Dublin. A microfiche copy of the printed version of the valuation is available in the National Archives, Dublin.

Griffith's Valuation is now available online through a number of websites. The best website, which is free, and includes scans of the valuation maps, showing the individual farm holdings is available at: **www.askaboutireland.ie**.

In addition, the Public Record Office of Northern Ireland has now digitised the Valuation Revision Books (VAL/12B) for Northern Ireland, which cover the period from the original Griffith's Valuation up to the 1930s, marking changes in occupancy. These can be viewed at PRONI's website: **www.proni.gov.uk**.

In the National Archives the staff cataloguing their valuation records of the 1830s inherited difficulties in dealing with large counties such as Cork and Tipperary, since these had been subdivided into two or three sections for the cataloguing of their holdings of Tithe Applotment books 1823–1838. For County Cork over twenty parishes are divided between N[orth], S[outh] and E[east], and since parishes can still be further divided between two or three baronies it will be appreciated that no exact positioning of particular records (census searches, house books, etc.) can be readily achieved.

Tom Quinlan, Senior Archivist in the National Archives, has been my indispensable support as I toiled with catalogues. He saved me from many errors. I take responsibility for those that remain in this present text.

The following tables provide the exact references for each parish for the tithe and valuation records that are held in PRONI and the National Archives, Dublin. This will be of particular use to family and local historians researching in these institutions.

PARISH/TOWN/VILLAGE	TITHES 1823–38 FIN 5A/	VALUATION 1830S VAL 1B/ FIELD BOOK (NA) OL4.	TENEMENT VALUATION c.1861–2 VAL 2B/1/	VALUATION REVISIONS c.1860–c.1930 VAL 12B/
Aghagallon	3	165A-B, 0069	54	9/1A-E
Aghalee	4	166, 0070	58B	9/2 A-E
Ahoghill	10	15D, 176, 179, 0001, 0059, 0080, 0082	64 A-C	3/1 A-E, 3A-D, 4A, 5A-J, 9A-D, 14A-F, 18A-E, 19A-D
Antrim	13	16, 0083, 180	5A-C, 51, 69	1/1A- F, 2A-C, 3A-C, 11A, 12A 22A-E, 28A-E
Ardclinis	15	147A-B, 0050	38	7/1A-E
Armoy	21	130, 0032 141, 0044	23A-B 37	2/1A-E 4/1A-D
Ballinderry	26	167, 0071	55A-B, 58B	9/3A-C
Ballintoy	27	131, 0033	24A-B	2/2A-E, 6A-D, 8/1A-E, 8A-E, 9/3A-E, 9A-E, 10A-F, 17A-E
Ballycastle (Ramoan)		280	2B, 1/28C	2/4A, 5A-C
Ballyclare (B'linny & B'nure)			7B	5A-B, 6A-B
Ballyclug	30	11, 0002	1	3/2A-E, 4A, 5A-V
Ballycor	24	0007/8	6, 11	4A-E, 7/2A-D
Ballyeaston (B'cor & Rashee)	24			
Ballylinny	38 & 67	112, 0014	7A	1/4A-E, 7A-F
Ballymartin	39 & 67	113, 0015, 124, 0025	11	1/14A-F, 29A-F
Ballymoney	40	142A-D 154 0045	35A-F 50A	4/3A-G, 5A-E, 12A-E, 14A-F, 23A-F, 24A-D
Ballymena (Kirkinriola)			66A-F	3/5K-V
Ballynure	44	114, 0016	11, 12	1/4A-E, 7/3A-E
Ballyrashane	46	137, 0039 30/14A-D	30A 6/1A-C	4/4 A, 5A-E,
Ballyscullion	47	181, 0084	72B	3/4A, 6A-E
Ballyscullion Grange of	Nil	182, 0089		3/4A, 6A-E
Ballywillin	51	137, 0040	30A	4/4A; 6/1A-C, 2A-E
Belfast	36	see Shankill	18, 21A-D	43/
Billy	56	132, 0034 138, 0041	24B 25A-B 31	2/6A-D, 9A-E, 10A-F, 4/5A-E, 6A-C, 7A-E, 30/8A-D
Blaris	57	168, 0072	56A-B 3	8/9A-T, 10A-C, 11A, 12A-E, 20/6A-G, 16A-E
Broughshane (Racavan)			3C	3/7A-E
Bushmills (Billy)			26	4/6A-C; 30/8A-D
Camlin	63	169, 0073	52	1/16A-F

PARISH/TOWN/VILLAGE	TITHES 1823–38 FIN 5A/	VALUATION 1830S VAL 1B/ FIELD BOOK (NA) OL4.	TENEMENT VALUATION c.1861–2 VAL 2B/1/	VALUATION REVISIONS c.1860–c.1930 VAL 12B/
Carncastle	66	150, 0055	42	7/4A-E
Carnmoney	67	115A-B, 0017	13A-B	5/7A-G, 12A-K
Carrickfergus	70	187, 0031	22A-E,	7/5A-F, 6A-D, 7A-C
Connor	83	12, 0003	2A-B, 8A	1/13A-E, 3/4A, 18A-E
Craigs (Ahoghill)	10	155 176 178 A-B	45, 65A-B	3/3A-D, 4A, 13A-E, 14A-F, 19A-D 20A-D
Cranfield	85	183, 0085	70	1/15A-F
Crumlin (Camlin)			51	1/16A-F
Culfeightrin	87	133, 0035	27A-B	2/8A-D, 11A-F, 15A-D, 16A-D
Derryaghy	91B	125, 0026 170, 0074	19A-B 57	8/2A-G, 5A-E
Derrykeighan	93	134, 0042, 139A-B	32	4/5A-E, 10A-E
Dervock (Derrykeighan)			33	4/10A-E
Doagh, Grange of	102	17A-B, 0009	7A	1/4A-E
Doagh, Village		7B		
Donegore		18, 0010	8A-B	1/17A-E
Drumbeg	117	126	20	8/15A-J, 20/3A-E
Drummaul (Randalstown)	124	184, 0086	71A-D	1/10B-E, 3/9A-D, 11A-D, 22A-F; 23A, 24A, 27A-E, 28A-E
Drumtullagh, Grange of	Nil	25B	2/9A-C	2/9A-E
Dunaghy	128	156, 0060	46A-B	3/4A, 8A-D, 22A-D
Dundermot, Grange of	130	157, 0062	46B	3/4A, 12A-D
Duneane	132	185, 0087	71D 72A-B	3/4A, 25A-E 10A-E, 15A-F
Dunluce	134	140	34A-B	4/4A, 5A-E, 21A-C, 6/1A-C, 2A-E
Finvoy	142	158A-C 0061	47A-B	4/11A-E, 12A-E, 25A-E
Glenavy	147*	171, 0075	58A-B	8/4A-D; 9/3A-E
Glenarm (Tickmacrevan)			41B	7/9A-H, 10A-E
Glenwhirry	Nil	13, 0004	3A	3/4A, 17A-D
Glynn	149	116	14	7/11A-D
Gracehill (Ahoghill)			64D	
Inispollan, Grange of	Nil	0051	39	2/14A-E
Inver	158	117, 0019	14	7/14A-G, 15B-M
Island Magee	159	118, 0020	15	7/12A-G
Kilbride	162	19, 0011	8B	1/4A-E, 20A-F
Killagan	172	144, 159, 0047	48	4/15A-F
Killdollagh	169	0063, 0046		30/14A-D

PARISH/TOWN/VILLAGE	TITHES 1823–38 FIN 5A/	VALUATION 1830s VAL 1B/ FIELD BOOK (NA) OL4.	TENEMENT VALUATION c.1861–2 VAL 2B/1/	VALUATION REVISIONS c.1860–c.1930 VAL 12B/
Killead	174	164A-C 0068	53A-C	1/8A-F, 9A-F, 19A-E, 26A-E
Killyglen, Grange of	181	151, 0056	44A	7/4A-E
Kilraghts	188	145, 0048	36	4/18A-E
Kilroot	190	119, 0021	16	7/18A-E
Kilwaughter	192	152A-B, 0057	43	7/13A-F
Kirkinriola	194	177, 66B-F, 0081	66A*	3/4A, 5A-V, 14A-F, 19A-D
Lambeg	196	127, 0028 172, 0076	59	8/7A-D, 9L 20/10A-F
Larne	197	153, 0058	44A-C	7/14A-G, 15A-M, 16A
Layd	198	148A-D, 0053	40A-B, 19A-F	2/7A-E, 14A-F,
Layd, Grange of	Nil	0052	39	2/14A-D
Lisburn	(See Blaris)		61A-D	
Loughguile	208	146A-D, 0049 160, 0064	37 & 48	4/1A-D, 2A-D, 8A-E, 9A-D, 15A-F
Magheragall	217	174, 0077	55B 62A-B	8/6A-F, 13A-E
Magheramesk	221	175, 0078	62B	8/14A-D
Mallusk, Grange of	259	0067		
Muckamore, Grange of	Nil	163	52	1/1A-F, 2A-C, 3A-C
Newtown Crommelin	228	161, 0065	49, 21A	3/22A-D
Nilteen, Grange of	110	9, 0012	17A-E	
Portglenone	232	178A-B	67A-C	3/1A-E, 4A, 20A-D, 23A-E
Portrush (Ballywillin)			30B	4/22A-D
Racavan	250	14A-B, 0005	3A-B	3/4A, 7A-E, 24A-D
Raloo	234	120, 0022	17A-B	7/17A-E
Ramoan (Ballycastle)	235	135, 0037	28A-B	2/3A-G, 16A-D, 17A-E
Randalstown (Drummaul)			71E	23A, 24A
Rasharkin	236	162, 0066	50A-B	3/4A, 13A-E, 15A-D, 4/16A-F, 17A-E
Rashee	24	111, 0013	10	1/25A-F
Rathlin Is	238	136, 0038	29	17A-E, 18A-D
Shankill	36	121A-B, 0023	18	5/3A-F, 4A-D,
	247	128 A-B, 0028	21A-D	5A-E, 6A-E, 8A-F
Shilvodan, Grange of	83	186, 0088	73	28A-E
Skerry	250	15A-C, 0006	4A-C	3/7A-E, 16A-D, 21A-D

PARISH/TOWN/VILLAGE	TITHES 1823–38 FIN 5A/	VALUATION 1830S VAL 1B/ FIELD BOOK (NA) OL4.	TENEMENT VALUATION c.1861–2 VAL 2B/1/	VALUATION REVISIONS c.1860–c.1930 VAL 12B/
Stranocum (Ballymoney)			33	
Templecorran	257	122	16	7/18A-F
Templepatrick	259	123A-B, 0024 129A-B, 0030	7B, 10, 11, 18, 21C	1/14A-F, 29A-F
Tickmacrevan (Glenarm)	263	149, 0054	41A,	7/9A-H, 10A-E
Tullyrusk	269 & 147		173A-B	63 8/16A-D
Whitehead				7/19A

* Includes mill book

PARISH/TOWN/VILLAGE	TITHES 1823–38 FIN 5A/	VALUATION 1830S VAL 1B/ FIELD BOOK (NA) OL4.	TENEMENT VALUATION c.1864 VAL 2B/1/	VALUATION REVISIONS c.1860–c.1930 VAL 12B/
Acton			32D	
Armagh	20	21A & B, 224 234, 0090 0110	1A-G, 22	10/4A-H, 5A-C, 6A-C, 7A-C, 8A-C, 9A-E, 25A-E
Ballymore	41	214, 248 0120	32A-C, 32E	11/1A-C, 11/5A-G, 15/23A-D, 15/24A-D
Ballymyre	42	239, 0102	13	15/2A-D
Blackwatertown (Clonfeacle)		249	2B	
Camlough (Killevy)		178		
Charlemont (Loughgall)		249	2B	
Clonfeacle	79	22, 225A & B 234, 0111	2A, 23	10/12A-F, 23A-E, 30A-E, 38A-D,
Creggan	86	240A & B 0103	14A-G	12/2A-E, 3A-4E, 5A-E, 6A-E,
			7A-D, 13/1A-F	
Crossmaglen (Creggan)			14G	
Derrynoose	95	23, 235, 248 0091, 0131	3A-C, 40	10/11A-E, 17A-E, 19A-D, 26A-C, 28A, 39A-E
Drumcree	119	226A & B, 234, 0112	24A-H	14/2A-C, 6A-C, 12A-13B, 14A
Eglish	136	24, 236, 248 0092, 0132	4, 41	10/10A-D, 22A-E
Forkill	143	215, 247, 248 0121, 0126	32E, 35A-C	12/5A-C,15/13A-B, 18A-D, 24A-C
Grange	150	25, 227, 234 0093, 0113	5, 25	10/23A-E, 25A-E, 31A-E, 33A-E
Jonesborough	160	243, 248, 0127	36	15/15A-C
Keady	161	26A-D, 237 248-9, 0094 0133	6A-D, 3B-C, 42	10/3A-B, 17A-E, 19A-D, 26A-C, 27A-C, 28A-B
Kilclooney	225	210A & B 216, 248, 249 0098, 0122	9A-C	10/13A-D, 29A-D, 34A-E
Kildarton	20 etc			10/24A-D, 25A-E, 29A-C
Killevy	178	217, 244A & B 248, 0123 0128	32E, 34C, 37A-J	12B, 15/1A-D, 1F, 1H, 3A-E, 6A-J, 15A-C, 17A-C, 18A-D, 22A-24C
Killylea (Tynan)		249		
Killyman	183	228, 234, 0114	27	10/30A-C
Kilmore	186	218, 248 229A & B 0115, 0124	26A-D, 33	10/25A-E, 11/4A-F, 31A-E, 33A-E, 37A-F
Lisnadill	202	27, 211, 241 0095, 0099 0104	8A, 10A-B 12B, 15	10/3A-D, 9A-E, 11A-E, 29A-D, 32A-E

PARISH/TOWN/VILLAGE	TITHES 1823–38 FIN 5A/	VALUATION 1830s VAL 1B/ FIELD BOOK (NA) OL4.	TENEMENT VALUATION c.1864 VAL 2B/1/	VALUATION REVISIONS c.1860–c.1930 VAL 12B/
Loughgall	206	28, 230, 234 249, 0096	7, 28A-C	10/2A-E, 10/25A-E, 31A-E, 33A-E, 38A-D
Loughgilly	207	212, 219 245A & B, 248 0100, 0125	11, 29, 34A-C, 38A-B	10/34A-C, 11/3A-D, 15/3A-E,19A D, 23A-D, 24A-D
Lurgan (Shankill)			20C-G	14/9A-H
Magheralin	219	220, 234, 0106	17	14/5A-C
Markethill (Mullaghbrack)			12C	
Middletown (Tynan)				43D
Montiaghs	223	221, 234, 0107	18	14/11A-C
Mountnorris (Loughgilly)				32D
Mullaghbrack	225	213, 231, 234 0101, 0117	12A-B, 29	10/24A-D, 34A-E, 11/3A-E
Newry	226 246A-E, 248	232, 234, 0118, 0130	39A-C H, 22/16A-C	10/33A-D, 15/1A-17A-C, 18A-D
Newtownhamilton	229	242A & B 0105	16A-D	12/1A-D, 5A-E, 6A-E, 8A-E
Poyntzpass (Ballymore)				32D
Portadown (Drumcree etc)			24E-H	14/13A-N
Richhill (Kilmore)			26E	
Seagoe	245	222, 234, 0108	19A-D	14/3A-C, 4A-C, 7A-C
Shankill	248	223A & B 234, 0109	20A-G	14/5A-C, 9H
Tandragee (Ballymore)			11	11/5A-G
Tartaraghan	255	233A & B 234, 0119	21A-C	10/2A-C, 30A-C, 14/15A-D
Tynan	270	29A & B 238, 248 0097, 0134	8A, B 43A-D	10/11A-E, 17A-E, 22A-E, 35A-E, 39A-E

PARISH/TOWN/ VILLAGE	TITHES 1823–38 FIN 5A/	VALUATION 1830S VAL 1B/ FIELD BOOKS OL4. (NATIONAL ARCHIVES)	TENEMENT VALUATION c.1861–4 VAL 2B/3/	VALUATION REVISIONS c.1861–c.1930 VAL 12B/
Aghaderg	1	337, 351, 0419	42, 55B-D	16/14A-D, 18A-E, 22A-D
Annaclone	11	352, 0438, 0439	56	16/1A-F
Annahilt	12	338A & B, 383, 0445	35	20/1A-E
Ardglass	16	368, 311B, 0451	70A-B	18/1A-F, 27A
Ardkeen	17	35, 0388	7A-B, 23, 27	28/2A-F, 23/19A-F
Ardquin	18	36, 0389	8	18/2A-F
Ballee	23	369, 311B, 0452	71	18/1A-F, 22A-E
Ballyculter	32	370, 311B, 0453	72	18/11A-E, 22A-E, 25A-F
Ballyhalbert (St Andrew's)	33	0312, 0395	7B, 9	23/1A-4F, 19A-F
Ballykinler	35	376A & B, 311B	76	18/5A-F
Ballynahinch			28B	
Ballyphilip Slanes & Witter (Portaferry)	45 & 49	37, 0390	10	18/20A-F, 23/27A-D
Ballytrustan	45 & 49	38, 0391	11	18/20A-D, 23/27A-D
Ballywalter	50	39, 0392	9	23/6A-F
Banbridge (Seapatrick)			64B, C	16/7A-C, 8B-D
Bangor	54	31, 315, 0384, 0398	1A-C, 7B	23/7A-K, 8A
Blaris	57	324, 339 0406, 0420,	24A, 43	9A-S, 20/6A-D, 16A-G
Bright	62	377, 311B, 0458	77	18/15A-E
Castleboy	exempt	310, 0393	12	18/2A-F
Castlewellan (Kilmegan)			63B	18/4G
Clonallan	75	353, 0440	57A-C, 60A	22/5A-D, 23A-G, 25A-C
Clonduff	77	354, 0432	49A-C	22/6A-D, 10A-D, 12A-D, 20A-B, 20D, 20F-H
Clough (Loughinisland)			66D	18/5A-E
Comber	82	316A-C, 0407	2, 16A & B 25A	18/5A-E, 11A-F, 20A-E, 20/11A E, 23/3A-F
Crossgar (Kilmore)			28B	16/9A-E, 18/6A-F, 27A
Donaghadee	104	32, 0385	3A-C	23/10A-C, 13A-E 15A-B
Donaghcloney	105	340, 0423	44A-B 46C	21/4A-F, 9A-F
Donaghmore	108	355, 0441	58A-B	22/9A-E, 11A-E
Down	111	378, 0459	78A-D	18/7A-K, 12A-E, 26A-E
Dromara & Magherahamlet	112	341, 356, 384, 0421, 0433, 0446	36, 37, 50A-B	16/2A-E, 9A-E, 20/9A-D
Dromore	113	342, 0422	38A-F	16/10A-F, 21A-E, 23A-E, 20/2A-D

PARISH/TOWN/ VILLAGE	TITHES 1823–38 FIN 5A/	VALUATION 1830S VAL 1B/ FIELD BOOKS OL4. (NATIONAL ARCHIVES)	TENEMENT VALUATION c.1861–2 VAL 2B/3/	VALUATION REVISIONS c.1861–c.1930 VAL 12B/
Drumballyroney	116	357A & B	59A-C	16/4A-E, 24A-E, 22/20A-B, 20D, 20F-H
Drumbeg	117	326, 0408	25B-C	20/3A-E, 10B-E
Drumbo	118	327, 0409	25A-C	20/3A-E, 7A-F, 11A-E
Drumgath	120	358 & A B	59C 20C,	22/10A-D, 20A, 20E-H
Drumgooland	122	359, 0434	51A-D 20A-E	16/5A-F, 15A-D,
Dundonald	131	317, 0399	17	17/8A-G, 23/5A-F
Dundrum (Kilmegan)			79	18/9A-E, 27A
Dunsfort	135	371, 311B, 0454, 2360	73	18/11A-11E
Garvaghy	146	343, 360	39, 52	16/3A-E, 12A-E
Gilford (Tullylish)		0424, 0435	48E-F	16/13A-B
Greyabbey	151	33, 0386	4	23/16A-F, 21A-E
Groomsport			5	
Hillsborough	152	344A & B	45A-C	20/5A-D, 14A-E
Holywood	exempt	318	18A-D	10A-G, 11A-E, 17/2A-J, 10A-D, 43L/1-2, 43N/1-2
Inch	154	372, 0456	74	18/13A-D
Inishargy	155	311A & B, 0394	13	23/4A-F, 19A-F
Kilbroney	163	361, 0442	61A-B, 65A	19/15A-E, 21A-F
Kilclief	164	373, 379, 311B,0460	70A	18/25A-F
Kilcoo	166	362, 0436	53A-B, 62	19/7A-F, 11A-E
Kilkeel	171	390A & B 0464	81A-H	19/4A-E, 13A-E, 14A-J, 18A-E, 19A-F
Killaney	Nil	328, 0410	26	20/15A-D
Killinchy	179	319, 329, 335 0400, 0411, 0417	19, 23, 27, 33	18/14A-E, 19A-E 23/3A-F, 18A-E, 28A-E
Killyleagh	182	331, 336	34A-C	18/6A-F, 16A-F
Killough		0412, 0418	80B	18/15A-E, 27A
Kilmegan	184	363A & B 380, 311B 385,0447, 0461	63A, 66B-C 79	18/4A-G, 9A-E, 24A-E
Kilmood	185	320, 0401	20	23/18A-E
Kilmore	187	330, 386 0413, 0448	28A, 66A 68	18/6A-F, 18A-E, 19A-E, 23A-D
Kircubbin (Inishargy)			5	
Knockbreda	195	321, 332 0402, 0414	18D, 21, 29	17/3A-B, 6A-H 20/7A-D
Knockbreda (Belfast Co. Borough)			43A/5-10, 15-23, 43K/1	43A/28-34, 38-39
Knockbreda (Ballymacarrett ED)			43A/28-34, 38-39	43A/28-34, 38-39
Lambeg	196	333, 0415	30	20/10A-F

PARISH/TOWN/ VILLAGE	TITHES 1823–38 FIN 5A/	VALUATION 1830S VAL 1B/ FIELD BOOKS OL4. (NATIONAL ARCHIVES)	TENEMENT VALUATION c.1861–4 VAL 2B/3/	VALUATION REVISIONS c.1861–c.1930 VAL 12B/
Lisburn (Blaris)			24B	
Loughbrickland (Aghaderg)			55A	
Loughinisland	209	387, 0449	66A-C	18/5A-F, 23A-D, 24A-E
Maghera	211	364, 0437	54	19/17A-F
Magheradrool	215	388A & B 0450	67A-B 68	18/3A-G, 10A-E 20/13A-E
Magherahamlet	112		68	18/10A-E, 20/9A-D
Magheralin	219	346, 0425	46A-C, 47C	21/1A-E, 6A-F, 7A-E
Magherally	220	345, 0426	40	16/19A-E
Moira	222	347, 0427	47A-C	21/7A-E
Newcastle (Kilmegan)			53A	19/20A-D
Newry	Nil	365, 389 0465	69A-K	16/3A-E, 22/7A-F, 14A-L, 16A-C, 17A-C, 19A-F
Newtownards	227	34, 322 0387, 0403	6A-D, 22A-B	23/21A-E, 22A-E, 23A-C, 24A-F, 25A-N
Newtownbreda (Knockbreda)			31	
Portaferry (See Ballyphilip)			14 23/26A	18/20A-F, 27A,
Rathfriland (Drumballyroney)			60B-C	22/21A-B, 22A-B
Rosstrevor (Kilbroney)			61C	
Rathmullan	239	374, 381, 311B, 0395	72, 80A	18/11A-E, 15A-E, 26A-E
St Andrew's (Ballyhalbert)	241	312, 0462		
Saintfield	242	334	32A-C	18/19A-E, 20/18A-E
Saul	244	375, 311B, 0416, 0457	75	18/7A-K, 22A-E
Seaforde			66D	
Seapatrick	246	348A & B, 366, 0428/9	41, 64A 44A	16/6A-H, 8A-D, 19A-E
Shankill		349, 0430	46A, 47B	21/5A-D
Slanes	45	313, 0396	15	23/27A-D
Strangford			14	
Tullylish	266	350, 0431	44B, 48A-D	16/25A-H, 21/4A-F, 8A-F
Tullynakill	267	323, 0404/5	23	23/28A-E
Tyrella	271	382, 311B, 0463	80A	18/26A-E, 27A
Waringstown (Donaghcloney)			44C	
Warrenpoint	75	367, 0443/4	65A-B	23A-G, 25A-C
Witter (Ballyphilip)	45	314, 0397		

PARISH/TOWN/ VILLAGE	TITHES 1823–38 FIN 5A/	VALUATION 1830S VAL 1B/ FIELD BOOKS OL4. (NATIONAL ARCHIVES)	TENEMENT VALUATION c.1861–2 VAL 2B/4/	VALUATION REVISIONS c.1861–c.1930 VAL 12B/
Aghalurcher	6 also D998/22/1	428A-B, 0502-4	19A-E	28/5A-D, 6A-D, 7A-E, 10A-E, 11 A-E, 19A-E, 20A-E, 21A-E, 22A-F, 23A-F, 24A-E
Aghavea	8	429, 0505-7	20A-C	28/6A-E, 11A-E, 13A-E, 19A-E, 22A-F
Belleek	55	415A-B, 0490	10	24/1A-E, 2A-E, 7A-E
Boho	60	41, 422, 0466 0496	1 & 15	24/6A-E, 26/1A-E, 22A-E, 37A-D
Cleenish	72	42, 432, 430A & B, 432, 0467-9 0497, 0508-9 0511 430A-B	1, 2A-D 7E 21	24/6A-E; 26/7A-E, 10A-E, 19A-D, 20A-E, 23A-E, 24A-F, 30A-F, 31A-E, 32A-E, 37A-E
Clones*	MIC 442/10	46, 0474	5A-D 6	25/1A-D, 2A-E 3A-E, 5A-E, 7A-E, 8A-D, 10A-E
Currin*	MIC 442/10	47A-D, 49 0475	6	
Derrybrusk	92	431, 433 0510, 0512	22	26/4A-E, 26A-E, 28/5A-E
Derryvullen	96	419 0491 0498 434 0513	11A-B 21, 22, 23A-C	26/2A-E, 3A-F, 5A-F, , 10A-E, 17A-K, 31A-E 27/9A-E, 11A-E, 13A-E, 15A-E,
Devenish	101	424 A-D 0498	16A-D	24/4A-E, 8A-E, 26/12A-F, 16A-E, 17A-K, 33A-E, 35A-E, 36A-E, 37A-E
Drumkeeran	123	416 A-B 0492, 3819	12A-C	27/3A-E, 4A-E, 5A-E, 6A-E, 7A-F, 8A-E, 16A-E
Drummully Ederny (M'culmoney)	125	410A-C 0476-9	6, 7B 13D	25/2A-E, 4A-E
Enniskillen	137	425A-B 435A-B 0499, 0514 3820/1	20C, 23A & B 24A-H	26/3A-F, 4A-E, 5A-F, 6A-F, 17A-K, 18A-H, 25A-E, 28/11A-E, 31A-E, 38A-F
Galloon	145	48, 411, 412 0478-81	5B, 7A-E	25/3A-E, 4A-E, 6A-E, 7A-E, 8A-E, 9A-E, 28/3A-E, 7A-E, 8A, 14A-E
Inishmacsaint	156	426A-C 0500	17A-D	24/3A-E, 5A-E, 26/12A-F, 36A-E

PARISH/TOWN/ VILLAGE	TITHES 1823–38 FIN 5A/	VALUATION 1830s VAL 1B/ FIELD BOOKS OL4. (NATIONAL ARCHIVES)	TENEMENT VALUATION c.1861–2 VAL 2B/4/	VALUATION REVISIONS c.1861–c.1930 VAL 12B/
Kesh (M'culmoney)			13D	
Killesher	177	43 0472, 0482-6	3A-C	26/9A-E, 11A-E, 13A-F, 19A-F, 27A-E
Kinawley	Nil	44, 413	4A-B 8A-E	26/9A-E, 11A-E, 28A-F, 29A-E, 28/1A-E, 2A-E, 12A-E, 15A-E, 16A-E, 17A, 25A-E
Lack (M'culmoney)			13D	
Lisnaskea (Aghalurcher)			27	
Magheracross	213	417, 436 0515	25A-B	26/2A-E, 3A-F, 34A-F, 27/2A-E, 9A-F
Magheraculmoney	214	418 0493	13A-D	27/7A-F, 10A-E, 12A-E, 14A-E, 15A-E
Newtownbutler (Galloon)			7F	
Pettigoe (T'carn)			12D	
Rosslea (Clones)			5E	
Rossory	240	45, 427A-B 0473, 0501	18 & 24B	26/7A-E, 16A-E, 17A-K, 30A-F, 32A-E
Templecarn	MIC 442/9	421 A-B 0494	14	27/3A-E
Tempo (Enniskillen)			28	
Tomregan	MIC 442/2	414, 0487-9	9	28/2A-E
Trory	265	420 437A-B, 0495, 0516	23C, 26	26/2A-E, 27/11A-E

* For border parishes, original records, were retained in Dublin and are now in the National Archives; microfilm copies MIC 442 in PRONI. Parishes include Clones, Currin, Templecarn and Tomregan.

PARISH/TOWN/ VILLAGE	TITHES 1823–38 FIN 5A/	VALUATION 1830S VAL 1B/ FIELD BOOKS OL4. (NATIONAL ARCHIVES)	TENEMENT VALUATION c.1858–9 VAL 2B/5/	VALUATION REVISIONS c.1860–c.1930 VAL 12B/
Aghadowey	2	51	1A-C, 2	30/1A-E, 2A-E, 6A-F, 11A-E, 13A-F, 15A-E, 18A-E
Aghanloo	7	511, 520, 1071	17A-B	31/1A-E
Agivey	nil	52	2	30/2A-F, 34/2A-E
Arboe	14	522, 1079, 1079A	25, 43A	34/26A-F
Artrea	22	523	26A-C, 43A	34/4A-E, 9A-G, 16A-E, 20A-F, 24A-F, 26A-F
Ballinderry	25	525, 1081	27, 43A	9/3A-C
Ballyaghran (Agherton)	28	539A & B 546A	10, 15A-B	30/4A-F, 17A-H
Ballymoney	40	540, 546A	11, 15B	4/3A-G
Ballynascreen	43	524, 1082	28A-C,	34/5A-E, 8A-E, 43A & C, 12A-F, 25A-F
Ballyrashane	46	53, 546A & B, 1068	12, 15B	30/14A-F
Ballyscullion	47	526, 1083	29A-B, 43B	34/6A-G, 9A-G
Ballywillin	51	541A-C, 546A	13, 15B	13A-G, 19A-E, 30/4A-F
Balteagh	52	513A & B 516, 1072	18	31/13A-G, 19A-E, 21A-E
Banagher	53	512A-E 548A & B 1073, 1095	19, 44	31/11A-E, 12A-F, 21A-F
Bellaghy (B'scullion)			29C	
Bovevagh	61	514A-C, 516 1074	17B, 20A-B, 21C	31/6A-E, 14A-E, 23A-D
Camus (Macosquin)	64A			
Carrick*		515	17B, 24A	31/13A-G, 14A-E, 23A-E, 24A-E
Castledawson (Magherafelt)			37H	
Clondermot (Glendermot)	76	549A-D	45A-D, 50	32/1A-G, 12A-F, 14A-F, 33/4A-C
Coleraine	81	53, 542A-D, 546A & C, 1069	3B-F, 14, 15B	30/4A-G, 9A-D, 14A-D, 17A-H
Cumber Lower	88	552, 1096	46, 50	32/1A-G, 4A-F, 13A-F
Cumber Upper	89	554, 1097	47A-B 50	31/12A-F, 32/2A-F, 5A-F
Derry, Deanery of	91A			
Derryloran	94	527, 1084	30, 43A	34/19A-F
Desertlyn	98	528, 1085	31A-B,	34/2A-E, 7A-E, 43A & C, 20A-F
Desertmartin	99	529, 1086	32A-B, 42	34/2A-F, 7A-E, 43A, 11A-F, 14A-E
Desertoghill	100	54A-C	4A-B	29/1A-D, 30/6A-F, 12A-F, 19A-F

PARISH/TOWN/ VILLAGE	TITHES 1823–38 FIN 5A/	VALUATION 1830s VAL 1B/ FIELD BOOKS OL4. (NATIONAL ARCHIVES)	TENEMENT VALUATION c.1858–9 VAL 2B/5/	VALUATION REVISIONS c.1860–c.1930 VAL 12B/
Drumachose	115	517A-F	17B, 22A-C	31/13A-G, 16A-E, 18A-G
Draperstown (Ballynascreen)			42	
Dunboe	129	55A & B	5A-C	30/3A-G, 5A-F, 10A-F
Dungiven	133	518A-C, 1075	21A-D	31/9A-F, 14A-E, 15A-F
Errigal	140	56	5C, 6A	30/12A-F, 13A-F, 31/12A-F, 13A-F, 18A-E, 19A-F
Faughanvale	141	550A & B 1098	48A-B, 50	31/3A-G, 10A-E, 32/6A-F, 12A-F
Fermoyle**	129		7	30/3A-E, 10A-E, 15A-E
Garvagh (Errigal)			6B	
Kilcronaghan	167	530, 1087	33A, 43A	34/8A-E, 14A-E, 28A-E
Kildollagh	169	543, 546A	15A-B	30/14A-F
Killelagh	196	532A & B 1070	34, 37A & D 43B	34/27A-E, 29A-E
Killowen	180	57	8	30/5A-F, 9A-D
Kilrea	189	58, 544, 1088	35, 43B	29/3A-F; 30/21A-21D
Learmont***	53	551	49A-B, 50	32/2A-F, 3A-F
Limavady (Drumachose)			22B-C	
Lissan	203	533A & B 1089	36A-B 43A & C 16C-H	34/15A-F, 19A-F,
Londonderry (Templemore)				
Macosquin	64A	59	5C, 9A-B	30/5A-F, 11A-F, 15A-E, 20A-F
Maghera	212	534A & B 1090	37A-G, 43B & C	34/8A-E, 11A-F, 13A-E, 17A-G, 23A-F, 27A-E, 29A-E
Magherafelt	216	535 1091	38A-C, 43A	34/2A-E, 9A-G, 18A-F
Magilligan	252	519A-C, 520 1076	17B, 23	31/1A-E, 3A-G, 4A-D, 5A-E
Moneymore			31B	
Swatragh (Maghera)			37G	
Tamlaght	251	536, 1092	39, 43A	34/26A-F
Tamlaghtard (Magilligan)	252			31/1A-E, 3A-G, 4A-F, 5A-E
Tamlaght Finlagan	253	521A-C 1077	24A-C	31/3A-G, 18A-G, 20A-G, 24A-E
Tamlaght O'Crilly	254	510, 537 545, 1093	40A-C, 43B	29/1A-D, 2A-D, 30/21A-D, 34/10A-F

PARISH/TOWN/ VILLAGE	TITHES 1823–38 FIN 5A/	VALUATION 1830S VAL 1B/ FIELD BOOKS OL4. (NATIONAL ARCHIVES)	TENEMENT VALUATION c.1858–9 VAL 2B/5/	VALUATION REVISIONS c.1860–c.1930 VAL 12B/
Templemore	91A	547A-F, 553A-D 1078	16A-J	32/8A-G, 10A-G, 11A-ZD, 33/1A-B, 2A-F, 3A-C, 5A-C
Termoneeny	261	538A & B 1094	41, 43B-C	34/17A-G, 23A-F, 28A-E
Upperlands (Maghera)				34/30A

* This parish was created in 1846 from parts of Balteagh, Bovevagh and Tamlaght Finlagan.
** This parish was created in 1043 out of Dunboe.
*** This parish was created in 1831 from parts of Banagher and Cumber Upper and Lower.

PARISH/TOWN/ VILLAGE	TITHES 1823–38 FIN 5A/	VALUATION 1830S VAL 1B/	TENEMENT VALUATION c.1860 VAL 2B/6/	VALUATION REVISIONS c.1860–c.1930 VAL 12B/
Aghaloo	5	66B	6A-C	36/3A-D, 4A-B 38/3A-F, 8A-F, 21A-F
Aghalurcher	6	61A & B	1	36/11A-F, 14A-F
Arboe	14	618	18A-E 27	37/1A-F, 4A-G, 10A- F, 13A-G
Ardstraw	19	633A-F	35	35/5A-F, 8A-F, 17A-F
		637A-F	40A 47C	19A-F, 39/10A-E 41/27A-F, 42/ 1A-F, 2A, 7A-F, 12A-F, 17A-F, 27A-H
Artrea	22	619	19	37/4A-G, 21A-F
Ballinderry	25	620A & B	20	37/13A-G
Ballyclog	29	621A & B	21	37/1A-F
Beragh (Clogherny)		626A		
Bodoney Lower	58	643	45A-B	39/1A-E, 2A-E, 4A-D, 6A-E, 13A-D
Bodoney Upper	59	644 A & B	46 A-C	30/3A-E, 5A-F, 7A-G, 9A-G, 11A-G
Camus	64B & C	638 A-C	41	42/10A-G, 31A-M
Cappagh	65	626B	28 645A & B	41/6A-F, 17A-F, 47A-C 19A-F, 24A-F, 26A-F, 31A-F, 32A-G
Carrickmore (T'maguirk)		626A		
Carnteel	68	68	6C, 7A-B	36/3A-D, 4A-B, 5A-B, 7A-F, 18A-F, 38/1A-F, 3A-F, 10A-F
Castlederg (Urney)		626A		35/1A, 6A-F
Coagh (Tamlaght)		66A		
Coalisland (D'henry)		66A		
Clogher	73	62A-K 647	2A-F	36/1A-F, 2A-F, 6A-F, 8A-F, 9A-F, 10A-F, 11A-F, 14A-F, 16A-G
Clogherney	74	627	29	41/4A-G, 6A-F, 14A-F, 35A-F, 39A-F
Clonfeacle	79	610	9A-D	38/4A-F, 5A-F, 6A-F, 14A-F, 22A-F
Clonoe	80	69	10A-B	38/20A-F, 23A-F

PARISH/TOWN/ VILLAGE	TITHES 1823–38 FIN 5A/	VALUATION 1830S VAL 1B/	TENEMENT VALUATION c.1860 VAL 2B/6/	VALUATION REVISIONS c.1860–c.1930 VAL 12B/
Cookstown (Derryloran)		66A		
Cumber Upper		641		37/7A-C
Derryloran	84	622A & B	22A -B	37/5A-K, 7A-C, 11A-F, 15A-F, 21A-F
Desertcreat	97	623	24A-D	37/16A-F, 17A-F, 18A-F, 21A-F
Donacavey	103	63A & B, 628	2B, 3A-B 30	41/8A-F, 13A-E, 15A-F, 22A-F, 23A-F, 39A-F, 42A-E
Donaghedy	Nil	639A & B	42A-D	39/8A-E, 12A-E, 42/6A-G, 18A-G, 19A-G, 22A-F, 26A-G
Donaghenry	107	611	11A-B 18E	37/20A-G, 21A-F, 38/25A-F
Donaghmore	109A	612	12A-C	38/2A-F, 9A-F, 11A-F, 13A-F, 14A-F, 15A-F, 17A-N
Dromore	114	626A, 629	31A-B 33B	40/4A-F, 5A-F, 41/5-F, 16A-F, 25A-F, 43A-F
Drumglass	121	613	13 17A-N	38/5A-F, 15A-F,
Drumquin (Longfield E &W)		626A		
Drumragh	126	630A & B	32A -B	41/6A-F, 10A-F, 29A-F, 34A-M, 36A-M, 39A-F
Dungannon Middle	617		38/17A-N	
Errigal Keerogue	139	64A & B	4A-B	36/7A-F, 12A-F, 13A-F, 15A-F, 38/1A-F
Errigal Trough	MIC 442/10	65A-C	5	
Gortalowry (Derryloran)		66A		
Irishtown		626A		
Kildress	170	624	24A 25A-C	37/2A-F, 9A-F, 14A-F, 15A-F
Killeeshil	175	67	6C, 8	38/1A-F, 10A-F
Killyman	183	614	15A-C	38/5A-F, 16A-F
Kilskeery	191	631A & B	33A-B	40/1A-E, 2A-F, 4A-E, 5A-F
Learmount*			42D	
Leckpatrick	201	640	43A-B	42/5A-G, 22A-F, 31A-M
Lissan	203	625	26	37/3A-F, 11A-F
Longfield East	204	633A-F	36	41/18A-F, 34A-F

PARISH/TOWN/ VILLAGE	TITHES 1823–38 FIN 5A/	VALUATION 1830S VAL 1B/	TENEMENT VALUATION c.1860 VAL 2B/6/	VALUATION REVISIONS c.1860–c.1930 VAL 12B/
Longfield West	205	633A-F	37A-B	35/4A-F, 9A-F, 11A-F, 21A-F
Loy (Derryloran)		66A		
Omagh (Drumragh)				41/37A-G
Magheracross	213		33B	40/1A-E, 42/27A-H
Newtownstewart (Ardstraw)			40B	
Pomeroy	231	66A, 615	16A-D	37/16A-F, 38/2A-F, 13A-F
Stewartstown (Donaghenry)		66A		
Strabane (Camus & Urney)				42/31E-M
Tamlaght	251		27	37/4A-G
Termon Rock (Carrickmore)		626A		
Termonamongan	260	633A-F	38A-C	35/10A-F, 13A-F, 14A-F, 16A-F, 20A-F
Termonmaguirk	262	632, 646	34A-C	41/2A-F, 7A-F, 12A-F, 28A-F, 35A-F, 40A-F
Trillick (Kilskeery)		626A		
Tullyniskan	268	616	17	38/25A-F
Urney	MIC 442/8B	633A-F 642	39, 44	35/6A-F, 13A-F, 16A-F, 42/1A-F, 20A-G, 31A-M

* One townland only in Co Tyrone parish created 1831 from parts of Banagher and Cumber Upper and Lower.

There are two volumes containing valuations of properties in towns and villages in Co. Tyrone. Val 1B|66A includes Coagh, Coalisland, Cookstown (including the townlands of Gortalowry and Loy which are both partly within Cookstown), Pomeroy and Stewartstown. Val 1B|626A includes Beragh, Castlederg, Dromore, Drumquin, Fivemiletown, Termon Rock (Carrickmore), Irishtown (an unofficial name probably for an area on the outskirts of Omagh), and Trillick.

PARISH	TITHES 1823–38 TAB 3/	FILM	VALUATION FIELD BOOK 1830s OL4./ HOUSE BOOK [OL5.]	TENEMENT VALUATION FICHE C.1852–3	1841/1851 CENSUS SEARCH Cen /s/3
Agha	32	1	0163, 2016	2.G.12.	23-26
Aghade	43	2	0147	3.F.10.	12
Ardoyne	23	1	0148/53, 0179, 2036	2.B.4., 3.F.13	13-15
Ardristan	25	1	0180, 2037	2.B.4.	48
Ballinacarrig	6	1	0135, 1994,	1.B.4.	
Ballon	42	2	0154	3.G.2.	
Ballycrogue	7	1	0136, 1995	1.B.7.	
Ballyellin	36	1	0155, 0164, 0194, 2017	3.A.6., 3. G.9., 4.C.8.	16-17, 72-73
Baltinglass	13	1	0181, 2038	2.B.6.	49
Barragh	45	2	2005, 0197, 2010, 2059	3.G.10.	82
Carlow	4	1	0137, 1996	1.B.8.	1-5
Clonmelsh	5	1	0138, 1997	1.D.13.	
Clonmore	22	1	0182, 2039	2.B.7.	50-51
Clonygoose	37	2	0165, 2018	3.A.10.	27-28
Cloydagh	26	1	0174, 0139, 1998, 2028	1.E.1., 1.F.8.	42-43
Crecrin	21	1	2040, 0183	2.C.1.	
Dunleckny	33	1	0166, 2019	3.B.6.	29-30
Fennagh	24	1	0184, 0167, 2020, 2041, 0156	2.C.2., 3.C.9., 4.A.12.	18, 31
Gilbertstown	40	2	0157	4.A.13.	
Grangeford	9	1	0140, 1999	1.E.1.	
Hacketstown	19	1	0185, 2042	2.C.8.	52-54
Haroldstown	18	1	0186, 2043	2.D.5.	55
Kellistown	8	1	0141, 00158, 2000	1.E.6., 4.B.2.	6
Killerrig	3	1	0142, 2001	1.E.8.	7-9
Killinane	30	1	2029, 0168, 0175, 2021	1.F.12., 3.D.5.	44
Kiltegan	15	1	0187, 2045	2.D.8.	
Kiltennell	38	2	0169, 2022	3.D.5.	32-34
Kineagh	12	1	0188, 2044	2.D.9.	
Lorum	35	1	2023	3.E.4.	35-39
Moyacomb	46	2	0198	2.G.3.	83-84
Myshall	44	?	0159, 0170, 2011	3.E.10., 4.B.4.	19-22
Nurney	31	1	0143, 0160, 0171, 2002, 2024	1.E.11., 3.E.11., 4.C.4.	10
Oldleighlin	28	1	0176, 2030	1.G.1.	45-47
Painestown	1	1	0144	1.E.12.	
Rahill	11	1	0189, 2046	2.D.12.	57
Rathmore	17	1	0190, 2047	2.D.14.	58
Rathvilly	14	1	0191, 2048	2.E.1.	59-63
Sliguff	34	1	0172	3.E.13.	40-41
St.Mullin's	47	2	0195, 2056	4.C.10.	74-77
Straboe	16	1	0192, 2049	2.E.12.	64
Templepeter	41	2	0161	4.C.4.	
Tullowcreen	27	1	0177, 2031	2.A.4.	
Tullowmagimma	10	1	0145, 0162, 2003	1.E.4., 4.C.6.	11
Tullowphelim	20	1	0193, 2050	2.E.13.	65-71
Ullard	39	2	0196, 0173, 2025	3.E.10.	78-81
Urglin	2	1	0146, 2004	1.F.3.	
Wells	29	1	0178, 2032	2.A.11.	

PARISH	TITHES 1823–38 TAB 4/	FILM	VALUATION FIELD BOOKS 1830s OL4./ HOUSE BOOKS [OL5.]	TENEMENT VALUATION FICHE C.1857	1841/1851 CENSUS SEARCH Cen /s/4
Annagelliff	13	5	0224, [0061], [3787]	5 G 6	516-540
Annagh	16	5	0219, 0220, 0233, [0060 0069/70]	5.A.6., 5.F.2. 7.C.8.	470-482, 782-803
Bailieborough	23	5A	0199, 0206, [3772/5, 3798/9]	1.D.6., 1.A.14.	162-195
Ballintemple	26	5B	0212, [0047]	4.B.8.	284-341, 469
Ballyconnell (Tomregan)			[3800/01]		
Ballyjamesduff (Castlerahan)			[3802]		
Ballymachugh	28	5B	0213, [0048/9]	4.C.14.	342-3
Belturbet (Annagh & Drumlane)			[2387]		
Castlekeeran (Loughan)			[3764]		
Castlerahan	32	5B	2028A, [3764], [0037]	10.B.2.	2-40
Castleterra	11	4	0225, [0062/3]	6.A.6.	541-581
Cavan (Urney)			[3803]		
Crosserlough	30	5B	0200, [0038], 0214, [0050/1], 0226, [0064], 2029A, [3764], [3788],	6.C.3., 4.D.10. 4.F.10., 10.C.11.	41-86, 344-359, 582-584
Denn	14	5	0201, [0039], 0215, [0052/3], 0227, [3770], 2030A, 2033A, [3789/90]	6.C.4. 10.G.12. 4.E.5., 5.A.4. 10.C.13.	87-91, 360-365, 412, 585-631
Drumgoon	19	5A	0207, [0071], 0234	7.D.4., 8.D.8.	196-214, 632, 804-824
Drumlane	6	4	0221	2.D.12., 5.C.4.	483-513
Drumlumman	27	5B	0216, [0054/5]	4.E.9., 9.D.4.	366-440
Drumreilly			0238, [0079], 0239	2.E.4.	932-935
Drung	17	5	0235, [0072/3]	7.F.3.	825-857
Enniskeen	24	5A	0208, [3776/8]	1.E.13.	215-229
Kilbride	29	5B	0217, [0056], [3786]	4.E.9., 10.F.14.	441-449
Kildallan	7	4	0245	3.C.8., 3.E.12.	119-1134
Kildrumsherdan	18	5	0236, [0074/6]	7.G.12.	858-885
Killashandra	8	4	0246, [3804]	3.D.10., 3.F.2.	1135-1210, 1212
Killinagh	1	3	0240, [0080]	8.G.12.	936-1007
Killinkere	31	5B	0202, [0040], 0228, [3766], 2034A, [3791/2]	6.D.6., 1.B.9. 10.D.2.	92-120, 635-645
Kilmore	12	4	0218,[0057/8], 0229, [0065], [3793]	6.D.8., 4.E.11.	450-468, 646-675
Kinawley	3	4	0241, [0081/2], 0242	2.E.6., 9.B.6.	1008-1032
Knockbride	21	5A	0209, [3779/81], [3813]	2.B.8., 8.E.11.	231-257
Larah	20	5A	0230, [0066], 0237, [0077/8], [3794/6]	6.E.12., 5.G.3., 8.C.4.	676-704 887-931
Lavey	15	5	0231, [0067], [3795/6] [0041], [3767], [3764]	6.F.7. 9.G.10. 10.D.3.	705-757, 886 121-123
Loughan or Castlekeeran					
Lurgan	33	5B	0203, [0042], [3768]	10.D.8.	124-136
Moybolgue	25	5A	0210, [3782/3]	1.G.13.	258-262
Mullagh			0204, [0043], 2031A, [3771], [3806]	1.A.14., 9.G.10., 10.F.2.	137-154

PARISH	TITHES 1823–38 TAB 4/	FILM	VALUATION FIELD BOOKS 1830s OL4./ HOUSE BOOKS [OL5.]	TENEMENT VALUATION FICHE C.1857	1841/1851 CENSUS SEARCH Cen /s/4
Munterconnaught			0205, [0044], 2032A, [3769]	10.F.4.	155-161
Scrabby	9	4	0247, 2037A	4.B.5., 9.F.2.	1211, 1213-1227
Shercock	22	5A	0211, [0045], [3784/5], [3897]	2.A.4.	263-283
Swanlinbar (Kinawley)			[3808]		
Templeport	2	3	0243, [0083/4]	2.F.8., 9.B.7.	1033-1105
Tomregan	5	4	0222, [0059] 0244, [0085/6]	3.B.10., 2.D.13., 5.E.13.	514-515, 1106, 118
Urney	10	4	0223, [0068] 0232, [3797]	5.E.14., 6.G.10.	758-781
Virginia (Lurgan)			[3806]		

TOWNS	VALUATION HOUSE BOOK 1830s [OL5.]
Belturbet	[2387]
Kingscourt	[3799] [3805]

The 1821 census is available in the National Archives for 16 parishes: Annagelliff, Ballymachugh, Castlerahan, Castleterra, Crosserlough, Denn, Drumlumman, Drung, Kilbride, Kilmore, Kinawley, Larah, Lavey, Lurgan, Mullagh, Munterconnaught.

PARISH	TITHES 1823–38 TAB 5/	FILM	VALUATION FIELD BOOK 1830s OL4./ HOUSE BOOK [OL5.]	TENEMENT VALUATION FICHE 1855	1841/1851 CENSUS SEARCH Cen /s/5
Abbey	3	6	0268, 3818	1.A.12.	96-100
Bunratty	76	11	0248	2.D.10.	1
Carran	10	6	0269	1.B.5., 1.F.6.	101-106
Clareabbey	45	9	0304	3.D.8., 6.E.2.	638-640
Clondagad	46	9	0305	6.C.14.	641-664, 689
Clonlea	49	10	0314, 3840	9.D.4., 11.C.14.	874-878
Clonloghan	71	11	0249	2.D.14.	2
Clooney	18	7	0286	1.F.8., 4.G.4.	30-38, 303-311
Clooney	30	8	0262 08, 3807/08, 3809	2.G.10., 11.A.12.	30-38, 303-311
Doora	31	8	0263 8, 3809/10	2.G.12.	39-40
Drumcliff	43	9	0306	3.F.13.	665-677
Drumcreehy	2	6	0270, 3819	1.B.11.	107-110
Drumline	72	11	0250	2.E.3.	3
Dysert	25	8	0297, 3834	1.F.14., 3.C.6.	554-560
Feakle	33	8	0322	10.D.11., 11.E.2.	994-1042
Feenagh	73	11	0251	2.E.6., 11.C.8.	
Gleninagh	1	6	3820, 0271	1.C.7.	111-113
Inagh	24	7	0298	4.F.2.	561-594
Inchicronan	27	8	0264, 3811/2	3.A.6., 11.B.5.	41-71
Inishcaltra			0323	10.E.10.	
Kilballyowen	57	10	0309	7.D.6.	694-724
Kilchreest	63	11	0279, 3828	5.F.10.	146-155
Kilconry	75	11	0252	2.E.9.	4-5
Kilcorney	9	6	0272	1.C.9.	114
Kilfarboy	39	9	0294	4.C.12.	407-435
Kilfearagh	56	10	0310	8.F.5.	725-758
Kilfenora	16	6	0287, [2412]	1.F.9., 4.G.13.	312-318
Kilfintinan	77	11	0254	9.B.5.	6-12
Kilfiddane	62	10	0280, 3829	5.G.6., 6.F.4.	173-191
Kilfinaghta	74	11	0253	2.E.11., 9.A.12., 11.C.8.	
Kilkeedy	20	7	0299	1.F.14.	595-606
Killadysert	64	11	0281, 3831	6.A.6.	156-172
Killaloe	53	10	0315, [0087], [2420/22]	9.D.8., 10.B.12.	879-880
Killard	41	9	0295	7.A.6.	436-496
Killaspuglonane	14	6	0288	5.A.9.	319-324
Killeany	8	6	0273, 3821/22	1.C.12.	115-116
Killeely	78	11	0255	9.C.1.	13-15
Killilagh	12	6	0289	5.A.13.	325-354
Killimer	65	11	0282, 3832	6.F.4.	192-216
Killinaboy	21	7	0300, 3836	2.A.1.	607-613
Killofin	66	11	0283, 3830	6.B.9.	291-302
Killokennedy	51	10	0316, 3841/42	9.D.10.	881-888
Killonaghan	5	6	0274, 3823	1.C.14.	117-129
Killone	44	9	0307	3.E.4.	692-693
Killuran	48	10	3845, 3846, 0317	9.E.8., 11.D.7.	
Kilmacduane	55	10	0311, 3833	7.B.9., 8.A.12.	759-800
Kilmacrehy	13	6	0290	5.B.12.	355-369
Kilmaleery	70	11	0256	2.F.2.	16-17
Kilmaley	42	9	0308	3.E.11., 6.E.2.	678-688
Kilmanaheen	17	7	0291	5.C.12.	370-389

PARISH	TITHES 1823–38 TAB 5/	FILM	VALUATION FIELD BOOK 1830s OL4./ HOUSE BOOK [OL5.]	TENEMENT VALUATION FICHE 1855	1841/1851 CENSUS SEARCH Cen /s/5
Kilmihil	60	10	0284	3.C.4., 6.F.12.	217-274
Kilmoon	6	6	0275, 3824	1.D.5., 5.E.10.	130-131
Kilmurry	61	10	0285	6.C.5., 6.G.12.	18-23, 275-290, 497-553, 690
Kilmurry	40	9	0296	4.E.10., 7.B.9.	18-23, 275-290, 497-553, 690
Kilmurry	69	11	0257	11.C.10.	
Kilnamona	26	8	0301, 3837	3.C.14.	
Kilnasoolagh	67	11	0258	2.F.5.	24-25
Kilnoe	37	9	0324	10.E.10., 11.E.10.	691-693, 1043-1044
Kilraghtis	29	8	0265, 3813/14	3.B.2.	72-74
Kilrush	59	10	0312	8.D.3.	801-815
Kilseily	50	10	0318, 3847, 3848	9.E.9.	889-898
Kilshanny	15	6	0292	5.E.2.	390-406
Kiltenanlea	54	10	0319, 3849	9.F.9.	899-926
Kiltoraght	19	7	0293	1.F.10., 5.E.8.	406
Moyarta	58	10	0313	8.C.2.	817-873
Moynoe	35	8	0325	10.F.6.	1045-1053
Noughaval	11	6	0276, 3825	1.D.7., 1.F.6.	132-134
O'Briensbridge	52	10	0320, 3850	9.G.8., 10.C.14.	927-938
Ogonnelloe	47	10	0321, 3851	10.C.14.	939-943
Oughtmama	4	6	0277, 3826	1.D.9.	135-144
Quin	32	8	0266, 3815	3.B.9., 11.B.11.	75-89
Rath	22	7	0302, 3838	2.B.4., 4.G.2.	
Rathborney	7	6	0278, 3827	1.E.1.	145
Ruan	23	7	0303	2.B.10.	629-637
St Munchin	79	11	0259	9.C.7.	
St Patrick's	80	11	0260	9.C.10.	
Templemaley	28	8	0267, 3816/17	1.F.4., 3.B.11.	90-95
Tomfinlough	68	11	0261	2.F.9.	26-29
Tomgraney	34	8	0326, [2439]	10.F.11.	1054-1064
Tulla	36	9	0327, [0088, 2440/42]	11.E.2.	1080-1084

TOWNS	VALUATION HOUSE BOOK 1830s [OL5.]	TOWNS	VALUATION HOUSE BOOK 1830s [OL5.]
Ballyvaghan (Corranroo)	[2388/89]	Kilkishen	[2416]
		Killadysert	[2417]
Broadford	[2391]	Kilrush	[2423/26]
Carrigaholt	[2392]	Labasheeda	[2427/29]
Clare	[2393/94]	Lahinch	[2411, 2412, 2430]
Cooraclare	[2395]	Liscannon	[2412]
Corofin	[2396/98]	Milltown Malbay	[2431/33]
Crusheen	[2399/400]	Newmarket-	
Ennis	[2401/09]	on-Fergus	[2434/35]
Ennistymon	[2410, 2411, 2412]	Scariff	[2436]
Kilkee	[2413/15]	Sixmilebridge	[2437/38]

PARISH	TITHES 1823–38 TAB/	FILM	VALUATION FIELD BOOK 1830s OL4./ HOUSE BOOK [OL5.]	TENEMENT VALUATION FICHE 1851/3	1841/1851 CENSUS SEARCH Cen /s/6
Abbeymahon	6S/66	25	2203, [0470/71]		
Abbeymahon	6S/66	25	2203, [0470/71]	21.C.10.	932-938
Abbeystrowry	6S/52	24	[0260/63]	10.A.6.	267-270
Aghabulloge	6N/48	19	[0682/83]	32.E.8.	1082-1096
Aghacross	6E/32a	13	2160, [0314/5]	13.C.2.	
Aghada	6E/105	16	[0506/8]	23.C.9.	956-958
Aghadown	6S/55	24	[0264/67]	10.B.12.	271-277
Aghern	6E/69	14	[0658/60]	27.D.2.	1058a-1059
Aghinagh	6N/50	19	[0684/87]	32.F.13.	1097-1102
Aglish	6N/56	20	[0688/89]	31.F.12., 32.G.9.	
Aglishdrinagh	6N/24	18	2254, [0757/58]	23.E.2.	
Ardagh	6E/87	15	[0509/10]	22.D.10.	959
Ardfield	6S/61	24	2204, [0472/73]	21.D.8.	939
Ardnageehy	6E/42	13	[0009/11]	2.D.4., 3.C.1.	32-39
Ardskeagh	6E/2	12	[0452/53]	19.C.10.	
Athnowen	6N/57	20	[0699]	31.F.13., 32.A.10.	1103
Ballinaboy	6S/25	23	2220, [0370/72, 0597/98, 0599, 0570/72, 0690/91]	14.G.8., 32.B.2., 25.F.4., 24.F.4., 24.F.10.	973-974, 1104-1105
Ballinadee	6N/46	19	[0181/3], [0720/21]	33.F.10., 8.C.2., 8.C.4.	
Ballinadee	6S/74	25	2104, 2244, [0181/3]	33.F.10., 8.C.2., 8.C.4.	
Ballintemple	6E/108	16	[0511]	23.D.6.	960
Ballyclogh	6N/34	18	2255, [0410], [0759/61] [2445]	18.C.2., 35.D.12., 35.E.6.	1271
Ballycurrany	6E/53	14	2045a/46a, [0112/13]	3.B.6.	40
Ballydeloher	6E/59	14	[0114/17]	2.D.6.	
Ballydeloughy	6E/12	12	[0435A], 0446]	19.C.12.	891
Ballyfeard	6S/29	23	2221, [0600/02]	25.E.14., 25.F.8.	1021
Ballyfoyle	6S/35	23	2222, [0603/05]	25.E.14., 25.F.12.	1022
Ballyhay	6E/1	12	[0452/53]	19.D.2.	892
Ballyhay	6N.20	18	2256, [0762/63]	35.E.14.	
Ballyhooly	6E/27	13	[0436/37], [2448/49]	19.C.2., 19.D.4.	893
Ballymartle	6S/26	23	[0599, 0606, 0672, 0673]	25.F.1., 25.G.2., 27.G.2.	1023-1025
Ballymodan	6S/20	22	2105, 2233 [0184/5, 0638/40]	26.E.14., 8.C.2., 8.C.14.	234-236, 1037-1050
Ballymoney	6S/70	25	2106, [0186/7]	8.C.2., 8.D.12.	237
Ballynoe	6E/70	15	[0661/63]	27.D.6.	1060-1062
Ballyoughtera	6E/94	15	[0512/13]	23.D.10.	
Ballyspillane	6E/62	14	2047a/48a, [0118/19]	3.G.11.	
Ballyvourney	6N/38	19	2245, [0722/23]	33.F.10.	1135-1170
Barnahely	6S/41	23	[0573/75]	24.F.4, 24.G.2.	975-981
Bohillane	6E/99	16	[0514]	23.E.2.	
Bregoge	6N/31	18	2257, [0764/66]	35.F.4.	
Bridgetown	6E/25	18	[0440]	19.D.10.	894
Brigown	6E/33	13	2161/62, [0316/23],	13.C.4.	465-470
Brinny	6S/17	22	2107, 2223, 2234 [0188, 0644/45, 0607/08]	26.G.4., 25.F.1., 25.G.8., 8.E.12.	1051-1052

PARISH	TITHES 1823–38 TAB	FILM	VALUATION FIELD BOOK 1830s OL4./ HOUSE BOOK [OL5.]	TENEMENT VALUATION FICHE 1851/3	1841/1851 CENSUS SEARCH Cen /S/6
Britway	6E/50	14	2049a/51a, [0664/66, 0120/21]	3.C.13., 3.G.13., 27.D.13.	41-42
Buttevant	6N/32	18	2258, [0767/69], [2461]	35.D.12.	1272-1280
Caheragh	6S/46	24	[0268/73], 2139/43, 2157		278-288
Caherduggan	6E/87	12	[0438/39],	19.E.2.	
Caherlag	6E/60	14	2051a/52a, [0122/23]	2.D.10., 4.A.1.	43-44
Cannaway	6N/55	19	[0695/96]		1110
Carrigaline	6E/84	15	2189, [0373/74, 0609/12, 0576/78]	14.C.9., 25.G.10., 24.F.4., 24.G.10.	493-509, 982-998
Carrigaline	6S/38	23	[0373/74, 0609/12, 0576/78]	14.C.9., 25.G.10., 24.F.4., 24.G.10.	
Carrigdownane	6E/13	12	[0446/47]	19.E.8.	
Carrigleamleary	6E/15	12	[0441/42]	19.E.10.	
Carrigrohane	6E/77	15	[0375/76, 0697/98]	15.A.7., 32.B.4.	1106-1109
Carrigrohane	6N/64	20	[0375/76, 0697/98]	15.A.7., 32.B.4.	
Carrigrohanebeg	6N/58	20	[0699], [0700]	32.B.10.	
Carrigtohill	6E/61	14	2053a, [0124/26]	2.E.3., 4.A.2.	45-50
Castlehaven	6S/53	24	2144, [0274/77]	10.D.7.	289-330
Castlelyons	6E/44	14	2054a/55a, 2163/64 [0324/25, 0127/30] [2460]	13.E.4., 3.C.14.	51-54
Castlemagner	6N/10	18	[0411], [2462]	16.D.12.	
Castletownroche	6E/17	12	[0443], [2466/68],	19.C.2., 19.E.4.	895
Castleventry	6S/13	22	2205, [0189/91, 0474/75]	6.D.4., 21.E.4.	331, 940
Churchtown	6N/27	18	2259, [0412/13], [0770/71] [2472]	16.E.9., 35.D.13., 35.G.8.	1281
Clear Island	6S/58	24	[0278/80]	10.E.11.	332
Clenor			[0444/45]	19.F.10.	
Clondrohid	6N39	19	2246, [0724/27]	33.G.14.	1171-1190
Clondulane	6E/38a	13	[0326]	13.E.8.	471
Clonfert	6N/1	17	[0414, 0420, 0431]	16.E.10.	710-733
Clonmeen	6N/13	18	[0415]	17.B.10.	734-740
Clonmel	6E/66	14	2056a, 2058a, [0131/33]	2.E.3.	55-62
Clonmelsh	6E/66	14		2.E.3.	
Clonmult	6E/58	14	2059a, 2060a, [0515/16, 0664/66, 0134/35]	4.B.3., 27.D.13., 23.E.4.	
Clonpriest			[0517/18]	22.E.4.	
Clontead	6S/83, 84	26	[0672/73, 0679]	27.G.3.	1074
Cloyne	6E/98	16	[0519, 0530/31]	23.E.4.	961
Coole	6E/45	14	[0136/38]	3.D.13.	
Cooliney	6N/23	18	2260, [0772/73]	36.A.2.	
Corbally	6N/66	20	[0699], [0700]	32.B.12.	
Corcomohide	6N/18	18	2261, [0774/75]	36.A.4.	
Cork City Parishes	6E/80	15		30.F.4., 30.D.8., 29.A.12., 29.G.14., 28.F.4., 28.G.3.	
Corkbeg	6E/107	16	[0528/29]	23.F.12.	
Courtmasherry			[0476]		
Creagh	6S/56	24	[0281/84]	10.F.2.	333-336

PARISH	TITHES 1823–38 TAB	FILM	VALUATION FIELD BOOK 1830s OL4./ HOUSE BOOK [OL5.]	TENEMENT VALUATION FICHE 1851/3	1841/1851 CENSUS SEARCH Cen /s/6
Cullen	6N/11	18	[0416, 0599, 0613]	18.F.10., 25.G.12.	741-780, 1026
Cullen	6S/27	23	2224, [0416, 0599, 0613]	18.F.10., 25.G.12.	
Currykippane	6E/75	15	2190, [0377/78]	15.A.10.	
Dangandonovan	6E/88	15	[0526/27]	22.F.1., 23.G.3.	
Derryvillane			2165/66 [0327/29], [0446/47]	19.G.2., 13.F.2.	472, 896
Desert	6S/79	26	2108, 2206 [0192/3, 0477/78]	21.E.6., 8.E.14.	
Desertmore	6N/61	20	[0701/02]	31.F.14.	1111-1112
Desertserges	6S/71	25	2109, 2131, 2235 [0194/6, 0646/47]	26.G.8., 8.F.4.	238-241, 1053-1054
Donaghmore	6S/68	25	2207, [0479/80, 0092/94], [3807]	33.A.7., 1.G.8., 21.E.8.	
Donaghmore	6N/49	19	[0479/78, 0092/94] [0703/04], [3807]	33.A.7., 1.G.8., 21.E.8.	1113-1114
Doneraile	6E/5	12	[2595/97]	19.C.3., 19.G.4.	897-900
Drinagh	6S/51	24	[0197/8, 0285/87]	6.D.12., 7.F.8., 10.G.13.	337-339
Drishane	6N/36	19	2247, [0417/18], [0728/29] [2599]	18.G.12., 34.G.12	781, 1192-1236 ?
Dromdowney	6N/35	19	2262, [0776/77]	36.A.6.	
Dromdaleague	6S/50	24	[0288/91]	11.A.8.	340-341
Dromtarriff	6N/12	18	[0419]	17.D.3.	782-784
Dunbulloge	6E/41	13	2061a, 2191 [0139/40, 0379]	2.E.10., 15.A.14.	62-65
Dunderrow	6N/68	20	[0614/15, 0672, 0674] [0705/06]	25.F.1., 26.A.4., 27.G.11.	
Dunderrow	6S/24	23	2225, [0614/15, 0672, 0674]	25.F.1., 26.A.4., 27.G.11.	1075, 1115-1117
Dungourney	6E/57	14	2062/63a [0525, 0141/42]	4.B.6., 23.G.6.	
Dunisky	6N/44	19	2248, [0730/31]	34.B.10.	1236-1237
Dunmahon	6E/20	12	2167, [0449]	20.A.12., 13.F.4.	901
Durrus	6S/45	24	2038a, 2039a, 2145/46, [0292, 0089/90]	1.A.14., 12.F.14.	342-350
Fanlobbus	6S/9	22	2110, 2132, [0199/201]	7.A.4.	351-356
Farahy	6E/7	12	2168, [0330/32, 0450]	20.B.2., 13.F.6.	902
Fermoy	6E/38	13	2169, 2201/2, [0333/37]	13.F.8.	473-474
Garranekinnefeake	6E/97	16	[0524]	23.G.8.	972
Garrycloyne	6N/54	19	[0095/97, 0697/98]	32.C.2., 2.A.2.	1118-1123
Garryvoe	6E/100	16	[0523]	23.G.12.	
Glanworth	6E/18	12	2170/71, [0338/40, 0451]	19.C.3., 20.B.8., 14.A.6.	903-905
Glenor	6E/16	12			
Grenagh	6N/72	20	[0098/100, 0697/98] [3808]	32.C.9., 2.A.4.	22-27
Gortroe	6E/49	14	2064/65, [0143/44]	3.D.14.	66
Hackmys	6N/22	18	2263, [0778/79]	36.A.8.	
Ightermurragh	6E/95	15	[0520/22]		963

PARISH	TITHES 1823–38 TAB	FILM	VALUATION FIELD BOOK 1830s OL4./ HOUSE BOOK [OL5.]	TENEMENT VALUATION FICHE 1851/3	1841/1851 CENSUS SEARCH Cen /s/6
Inch	6E/103	16	[0539/40]	24.A.11.	
Inchigeelagh	6N/42	19	2249, [0732/37]	33.D.12., 34.B.11.	
Inchigeelagh	6S/6	21	[0202/4]	33.D.12., 34.B.11., 7.D.8.	1238-1246
Inchinabacky	6E/65	14	2065a, [0145]	4.B.13.	
Inishcarra	6N/52	19	[0707/08]	32.C.9.	1124
Inishkenny	6N/69	20	[0380/83], [0699], [0700]	15.A.14.	510
Inishkenny	6E/83	15	2192, [0380/83]	32.D.6., 15.A.4.	
Inishannon	6S/22	23	2111, 2226 [0205/6, 0616/18]	25.F.1., 26.A.8., 8.G.8.	242-243, 1027-1029
Imphrick	6E/41	12			906
Imphrick	6N/29	18	2264, [0452/53], [0780/81]	36.A.10., 20.C.6.	
Island	6S/62	24	2112, 2208 [0207/8, 0481/82]	21.E.10., 8.G.14.	
Kilbolane	6N/17	18	2265, [0782/83]	35.D.13., 36.A.12., 31.G.3.	1282-1288
Kilbonane	6N/60	20	[0709/10]		1127
Kilbrin	6N/7	17	[0421/22]	17.D.12.	788-791
Kilbrittain	6S/73	25	2113, [0209/10]	9.A.4.	
Kilbrogan	6S/19	22	2236, [0641/45, 0648/51]	26.G.12.	1055
Kilbroney	6N/30	18	2266, [0784/85]	36.B.12.	1289
Kilcaskan	6S/2	21	2090/93, [0175]	4.E.4.	90-129
Kilcatherine	6S/1	21	2094/96, [0176/77]	5.A.4.	130-188
Kilcoe	6S/48	24	2147, 2158/59, [0293]	11.G.10.	358-366
Kilcorcoran	6N/6	17	[0423/24]	17.E. 10.	
Kilcorney	6N/37	19	[0738/40]	35.C.1.	1247-1251
Kilcredan	6E/101	16	[0537/38]	24.B.2.	
Kilcrohane	6S/44	23	2148, [0294/95]	12.A.10.	357, 367-374
Kilcrumper	6E/21	12	2172/73, [0341/42]	19.C.3., 20.C.10., 14.A.10.	
Kilcully	6E/74	15	[0384/85]	15.B.5.	
Kilcummer			[0454/56]	20.C.14.	
Kildorrery	6E/30	13	2174/75, [0343/45, 0457/58]	20.D.4., 14.A.12.	
Kilfaughnabeg	6S/14	22	2114, 2133 [0211/13]	6.D.10., 7.F.11.	375-378
Kilgarriff	6S/75	25	2115, 2209 [0214, 0483/84]	9.A.12., 21.E.14., 8.C.3.	244
Kilgrogan	6N/28	18	2267, [0786/87]	36.C.2.	
Kilgullane	6E/34	13	2176, [0346/47, 0449]	20.D.6., 14.B.6.	479
Kilkerranmore	6S/59	24	2210, 2216 [0215/17, 0485/87]	6.D.12., 21.F.2.	941-942
Killaconenagh	6S/4	21	2097/100, [0178/79]	5.C.8.	218-233
Killanully	6S/39	23	[0386], [0579/81]	25.A.14., 15.B.6.	999
Killanully	6E/86	15	2193, [0386]	25.A.14., 15.B.6.	
Killaspugmullane	6E/51	14	2066, [0146/47]	2.F.14.	68-69

PARISH	TITHES 1823–38 TAB	FILM	VALUATION FIELD BOOK 1830s OL4./ HOUSE BOOK [OL5.]	TENEMENT VALUATION FICHE 1851/3	1841/1851 CENSUS SEARCH Cen /s/6
Killathy	6E/28	13	[0458a]	20.D.8.	
Killeagh	6E/90 & 91	15	[0532/36], [2615]	22.F.1., 24.B.4.	964-966
Killeenemer	6E/19	12	[0449]	20.D.12.	
Killowen	6S/18	22	2237, [0652/53]	27.B.2.	
Killowillan	6E/110	16		27.B.2.	
Kilmacabea	6S/11	22	2117, 2134 [0218/20, 0296/97]	7.G.7., 11.B.14.	380-384
Kilmacdonogh	6E/96	16	[0544/45]	22.F.11., 24.B.4.	
Kilmaclenine	6N/33	18	2268, [0788/89]	36.C.4.	1290
Kilmahon	6E/104	16	[0541/43]	24.B.5.	
Kilmaloda	6S/72	25	2119, [0221/3]	8.C.3., 9.C.8.	245-246
Kilmeen	6S/10	22	2120, 2135, [0224/27, 0488/89, 0425/26]	17.E.12, 19.A.9., 6.D.12., 7.D.11., 21.F.12.	
Kilmeen	6N/5	17	2211, [0224/27, 0488/89, 0425/26]	17.E.12, 19.A.9., 6.D.12., 7.D.11., 21.F.12.	247-249, 785-787, 792-813, 943
Kilmichael	6N/45	19	2250, [0741/44]	33.E.9., 34.D.1., 7.E.4.	
Kilmichael	6S/7	21	2121, 2136, [0228/31]	33.E.9., 34.D.1., 7.E.4.	1252-1253
Kilmocomoge	6S/5	21	2042a, 2043a 2118, 2149, [0232/33, 0298/99, 0091]	1.B.3., 6.D.2., 12.A.6.	1-21, 379
Kilmoe	6S/49	24	2150/52, [0300/303]	12.G.10.	385-409
Kilmoney	6S/42	23	[0582/83]	25.B.2.	
Kilmonogue	6S/32	23	2227, [0091], [0619]	25.F.1., 26.B.2.	1030-1032
Kilmurry	6N/47	19	2251, [0718/19], [0745/47]	34.D.3., 31.G.9.	1254-1255
Kilnaglory	6N/63	20	[0387/88], [0699], [0700]	15.B.7., 32.D.10.	
Kilnaglory	6E/82	15	2194, [0387/88]	15.B.7., 32.D.10.	
Kilnagross	6S/77	26	2122, [0234]	9.D.6.	
Kilnamanagh	6S/3	21	2101/03, [0180]	5.F.5.	189-217
Kilnamartery	6N/40	19	2252 [0748/50]	34.D.13.	1256-1257
Kilpatrick	6S/31	23	[0620/22, 0584/85]	26.B.8., 25.B.6.	1000
Kilphelan	6E/35	12	2177/78, [0348/49]	14.B.10.	
Kilquane	6E/52	14	2067, 2069/70, [0452/3]		
Kilquane		12	2067, [0148]	2.G.6., 20.D.14.	
Kilroan	6S/82	26	[0404/05, 0672, 0674]	16.B.2., 27.G.14.	
Kilroe	6N/8	18	[0427]	17.G.10.	814
Kilsillagh	6S/69	25	2212, [0490/91]	21.F.14.	944
Kilshanahan	6E/48	14	2070/71, [0149/50]	3.E.9.	67
Kilshannig	6N/16	18	2200, [0428]	18.C.8.	815-843
Kilworth	6E/36	13	2179, [0350/51] [2616]	14.B.12.	475-478
Kinneigh	6S/8	22	2137, [0235/37]	6.C.6., 7.E.8.	250-253
Kinsale	6S/85	26	[0675/76, 0677]	28.A.1.	1077-1078, 1298
Kinure	6S/33	23	[0623/25]	25.F.1., 26.B.12.	1033
Knockavilly	6S21	23	[0626/27]	25.F.2., 26.C.2., 31.G.10.	

PARISH	TITHES 1823–38 TAB	FILM	VALUATION FIELD BOOK 1830s OL4./ HOUSE BOOK [OL5.]	TENEMENT VALUATION FICHE 1851/3	1841/1851 CENSUS SEARCH Cen /s/6
Knockavilly	6N/67	20	[0626/27], [0711/12]	25.F.2., 26.C.2., 31.G.10.	1126
Knockmourne	6E/68	14	2072, 2180 [0352, 0667/68, 0151]	14.C.10., 3.E.13., 27.D.14.	70, 480-482, 1063-1066
Knocktemple			[0429]	17.G.14, 18.E.13.	844-851
Lackeen	6N/26	18	2269, [0790/90a]	36.C.6.	
Leighmoney	6S/28	23	2228, [0628, 0629]	26.C.6.	1034
Leitrim	6E/39	13	2181/82, [0353/55]	14.C.12.	
Liscarroll	6N/25	18	2270, [0791/93], [2627]	35.D.13., 36.C.8.	1291-1293
Liscleary	6S/40	23	[0586/88]	25.B.8.	1001-1002
Lisgoold	6E/54	14	2073/75, 0152/53	4.C.1.	
Lislee	6S/67	25	2213, [0492/94]	21.G.2.	945-953
Lismore & Mocollop	6E/40	13	2185, [0356/57]	14.D.4.	483-485
Litter	6E/29	12	[0358/59, 0459/60]	20.E.2., 14.D.6.	907
Little Island	6E/60	14	2075/76, [0154/56]	2.G.9.	
Macloneigh	6N/43	19	[0751/52]	34.E.11.	1269-1270
Macroney	6E/37	13	2185, [0360/64]	14.D.10.	489-490
Macroom	6N/41	19	2253, [0753/56], [2628/30]	34.F.2.	1258-1268
Magourney	6N/59	19	[0713/15]	33.B.12.	1128-1129, 1134
Mallow	6N/15	18	[0461, 0430], [2631/37]	19.C.3., 20.E.6., 18.E.14.	908-923
Mallow	6E/14	12	[0461, 0430]	19.C.3., 20.E.6., 18.E.14.	
Marmullane	6S/36	23	[0589/91]	24.F.5., 25.B.15.	1003-1005
Marshalstown	6E/32	13	2186, [0365/67]	14.E.6.	486-488
Matehy	6N/53	19	[0716/17]	32.D.14.	1130-1133
Middleton	6E/93	15	[0546/50], [2638/39]	24.B.10.	
Mogeely	6E/71, 89	15	[0551/55, 0669/71]	27.E.7., 24.D.3.	967, 1067-1073
Mogeesha	6E/64	14	2077/78 [0556/57, 0157]	4.C.5., 24.D.13.	968
Monanimy	6E/24	12	[0462/63]	19.C.3., 20.G.6.	924-925
Monkstown	6S/37	23	[0592/94]	24.F.5., 25.C.8.	1006-1016
Mourneabbey	6E/22	12	[0464]	21.A.2., 2.B.2.	28-31
Mourneabbey	6N/71	20	[0464, 0101/04]	21.A.2., 2.B.2.	
Moviddy	6N/59	20	[0718/19]	31.G.13.	
Murragh	6S/15	22	2123, 2238/39, [0238/40, 0654/55]	6.C.13., 27.B.4.	1056-1057b
Myross	6S/54	24	[0304/8]	11.C.5.	410-441
Nohaval	6S/34	23	2229, [0630/32]	26.C.10.	
Nohavaldaly	6N/4	17	[0432]	18.A.5.	852-876
Rahan	6E/23	12	[0465/66]	19.C.4., 21.A.4.	926-929
Rathbarry	6S/60	24	2214, [0241/43 [0495/6]	6.E.4., 22.A.8.	954
Rathclarin	6S/78	26	2124, [0244/46]	8.C.3., 9.D.14.	254-256
Rathcooney	6E/73	15	2195, [0389/91]	15.B.8.	511-517

PARISH	TITHES 1823–38 TAB	FILM	VALUATION FIELD BOOK 1830s OL4./ HOUSE BOOK [OL5.]	TENEMENT VALUATION FICHE 1851/3	1841/1851 CENSUS SEARCH Cen /s/6
Rathcormack	6E/43	13	2079/80, [0158/60]	3.E.14.	71-79
Rathgoggan	6N/21	18	2271, [0794/97]	35.D.13., 36.D.2.	1294-1297
Ringcurran	6S/86	26	2230, [0629, 0633, 0672, 0674, 0677/80]	26.D.2.	1076, 1079-1081
Ringrone	6S/81	26	2125, [0247, 0406/07, 0672, 0674, 0680]	8.C.3., 9.E.12., 16.A.14., 16.B.6., 28.D.2.	257, 707
Ross	6S/12	22	2126, 2138, 2215 [0248, 0250/52, 0497/98]	6.E.5., 22.B.4.	258-264
Rosskeen	6N/14 6N/70	18 20	[04330]	18.A.8.	877
Rostellan	6E/102	16	[0556/59]	24.E.1.	969
Shandrum	6N/19	18	2272, [0798/99]	35.D.14.	
Skull	6S/47	24	2153/56, [0309]	12.B.14.	442-463
St Anne's (Shandon)	6E/77	15	[0392/94], [2497/515]	15.C.8.	518-520, 601-609, 610
St Finbar's	6E/79	15	[0395/96], [2516/27]	32.A.7., 15.D.3.	521-534,
St Finbar's	6N/62	20	[0395/96], [0699]	32.A.7., 15.D.3. 611-649	
St Mary's (Shandon)	6E/76	15	2196, [0397/98], [2428/47]	15.F.8.	535-539, 650-676
St Michael's	6E/46	14	2081, 2197, [0161/63, 0399]	2.G.12., 15.F.14.	
St Nathlash	6E/10	12	[0467]	21.B.12.	930
St Nicholas	6N/65	20	[0400/1], [0699], [0700]	32.E.7., 15.G.1.	
St Nicholas	6E/81	15	2198, [0400/01] [2548/64]	32.E.7., 15.G.1.	677
Subutler	6N/9	18	[0434], [3809]	18.A.10.	
Templebodan	6E/55	14	[0164], 2081	4.C.10.	80
Templebreedy	6S/43	23	[0595/96]	24.F.5., 25.D.8.	1017-1020
Templebryan	6S/76	26	2127, [0253/54	9.F.4.	
Templemartin	6S/16	22	2240, [0656/57]	27.B.12.	
Templemichael	6S/23	23	2231, [0634/35]	26.D.4.	
Templemolaga	6E/31	13	2187, [0368/69]	14.F.2.	491-492
Templenacarriga	6E/56	14	2083/84, [0165]	4.D.2.	
Templeomalus	6S/63	24	2216, [0499/500]	22.B.6.	
Templequinlan	6S/64	25	2128/2217, [0255/56, 0501/02]	22.B.12., 9.F.8.	
Templeroan	6E/6	12	[0468]	19.C.4., 21.B.6.	931
Templerobin	6E.67	14	2085/86, [0166/71]	3.G.14.	81-89
Templetrine	6S/80	26	2129, [0257/58, 0408/09]	8.C.3., 9.F.10., 16.A.14., 16.C.6.	708
Templeusque	6E/47	14	2087, [0172/73]		
Timoleague	6S/65	25	2130, 2218, [0259, 0503], [2657]	22.C.2., 9.G.2.	265-266, 955
Tisaxon			2241	28.D.7.	
Titeskin	6E/106	16	[0560/61]	24.E.4.	
Trabolgan	6E/109	16	[0562/63]	24.E.6.	
Tracton	6S/30	23	2232, [0636/37a]	25.F.2., 26.D.8.	1035-1036

PARISH	TITHES 1823–38 TAB	FILM	VALUATION FIELD BOOK 1830s OL4./ HOUSE BOOK [OL5.]	TENEMENT VALUATION FICHE 1851/3	1841/1851 CENSUS SEARCH Cen /s/6
Tullagh	6S/57	24	[0310/13]	11.D.1.	464
Tullylease	6N/2	17	2273 [0435] [0800/01]	18.A.11., 36.F.4.	878-890
Wallstown	6E/9	12	[0458a, 0469]	21.B.12.	
Whitechurch	6E/72	15	2199 [0105/08, 0174/74a, 0402/03]	2.B.14., 3.B.13., 15.G.10.	
Whitechurch	6N/73	20	[0105/08, 0174/74a, 0402/03]	2.B.14., 3.B.13., 15.G.10.	541
Youghal	6E/92	15	[0564/69], [2661/69]	22.G.9	970 972

TOWNS & VILLAGES	VALUATION HOUSE BOOK 1830s [OL5.]	TOWNS & VILLAGES	VALUATION HOUSE BOOK 1830s [OL5.]
Aghern Village	[2482]	Glanmire	[2607]
Bandon	[2454/58] [0641/43]	Glanworth	[2608/09]
Bantry	[2459]	Holy Trinity	[2483/96]
Ballincollig	[2443/44] [0693/94]	Inishannon	[2610]
Ballycottin	[2446, 2447]	Kanturk	[2611/13]
Ballyclogh	[2627]	Killawillin	[2614]
Ballymagooly	[2450]	Killeagh	[2615]
Ballynacorra	[2451/52]	Kilworth	[2616]
Ballyneen	[2453]	Kingwilliamstown	[2469]
Ballynoe Village	[2482]	Kinsale	[2617/21, 2623/24]
Berehaven	[2465]	Lady's bridge	[2625/26]
Boherboy	[2469]	Millstreet	[2640]
Bridebridge	[2460]	Miscellaneous	[2579/94]
Castlemartyr	[2463/64] [0520/22]	Mitchelstown	[2641/42] [0322?]
Castletown		New Glanmire	[2643]
(Berehaven)	[2465]	Newmarket	[2644]
Castletownsend	[2658] [0304/8]	Newmarket	[2469]
Cecilstown	[2469]	Passage West	[2645]
Charleville	[2470/71] [0794/92]	Queenstown	[2646/49] [0166/71]
Churchtown	[2627]	Riverstown	[2650]
Clonakilty	[2473/78]	Rockmills	[2651]
Cloyne	[2479/80]	Ross Carbery	[2652/53]
Coachford	[2481] [0713/15]	Scartlea	[2447]
Cobh		Shanagarry	[2447]
(See Queenstown)	[2481]	Shanagarry	[2654]
Conna Village	[2482]	Shanballymore	[2655]
Carraglass Village	[2482]	Skibbereen	[2656]
Douglas	[2598]	St Paul's	[2565/69]
Dunmanway	[2600/602]	St Peter's	[2570/78]
Farsid	[2660]	Union Hall	[2658] [0304/8]
Fermoy	[2603/06]	Watergrasshill	[2659]
Freemount	[2469]	Whitegate	[2660]

PARISH	TITHES 1823–38 TAB 7/	FILM	VALUATION FIELD BOOKS 1830s OL4./ HOUSE BOOKS [OL5.]	TENEMENT VALUATION c. 1857 FICHE	1841–1851 CENSUS SEARCHES Cen /s/7
Aghanunshin	18	29	0353, 2316, [0818]	9.A.12.	671-680
Allsaints	29	30	0365, [0832]	9.G.6., 11.A.2.	1345-1357
Aughnish	16	29	0354, 2317, [0819/20]	9.B.4. 12.D.11.	681-696
Ballintra (Drumhome)			[2671]		
Ballyshannon (Kilbarron)			[2671]		
Bundoran (Inishmacsaint)			[2671] [3810]		
Burt	25	30	0346, 2310/11, [0816]	10.C.10.	563-583
Carndonagh			2306		
Clonca	1	27	0340, 2307	7.B.4.	487-502
Clondahorky	10	28	0355, 2318, [0821]	3.F.10.	697-747
Clondavaddog	7	27	0356, 2319, [0822]	13.B.4.	748-808, 1667
Clonleigh	35	31	0368, 2329/30, [0833]	14.C.5.	1358-1384, 1387-8, 1930
Clonmany	2	27	0341, 2308	7.C.13.	503-517 [T550/37 in PRONI]
Convoy	36	31	0366, [0834]	14.F.2.	1528-1558
Conwal	17	29	0357, 0367, 2320/21, 2331	9.D.1. 11.C.12. 15.F.10.	809-882 1559-1580
Culdaff	4	27	0342, 2309, [0812/3]	7.E.10.	518-526
Derry (Templemore)					
Desertegny	20	29	0347	8.E.8.	584-595
Donagh	3	27	0343	7.G.6.	527-539
Donaghmore	39	31	0369, 2332, [0835]	13.E.8. 14.G.12.	1581-1621 1645
Donegal	49	32	0378-79, [2671]	2.G.6.	1668-1715
Drumhome	49	32	0380, [0842]	1.A.12.	1716-1799, 1847
Fahan Lower	21	30	0348	8.F.1.	596-629
Fahan Upper	22	30	0349, 2312	10.D.8.	630-644
Gartan	14	29	0358, 2322, [0823]	4.A.7. 9.B.6.	883-905
Glencolumbkille	42	32	0328, [0802] 2275, 2284	4.G.8.	1-51
Inch	24	30	0350, 2313/14	10.E.5.	645-653
Inishkeel	28	30	0329, 0336, 2276, 2285, 2289/90, 2300/02, 2305, [0803/04]	5.G.2. 5.B.3.	52-85 316-372
Inishmacsaint	52	32	0381	1.E.8.	1800-1808 1814-1819, 1824
Inver	46	32	0330, [0805/06], 2277	2.B.2.	86-187, 714

PARISH	TITHES 1823–38 TAB 7/	FILM	VALUATION FIELD BOOKS 1830s OL4./ HOUSE BOOKS [OL5.]	TENEMENT VALUATION c. 1857 FICHE	1841–1851 CENSUS SEARCHES CEN S|7|
Kilbarron	51	32	0379	1.B.14.	1803, 1807-1813
			0382	7.A.4.	1819-1885
Kilcar	42	32	0331, 2278	5.C.1.	188-222
Killaghtee	45	32	0332, 2279-80,	2.D.9.	223-245
			2287, [0807]	5.D.9.	
Killea	33	31	0370,	11.B.2.	1389-1393
			[0836]		
Killybegs Lower	41	32	0333, 0337,	6.C.4.	246-261, 351
			2281, 2285,	5.D.12.	373-377
			2292/3,		
			[0808/09]		
Killybegs Upper			0334, 2282,	5.E.9.	262-284
			2286-7, [0810]		
Killygarvan	13	29	0359, 2323,	12.G.13.	562, 906-930, 786
			[0824]		
Killymard	47	32	0335, 2283,	2.E.12.	278, 285-315, 714
			2288, [0811]		
Kilmacrenan	15	29	0360, 2324,	4.A.9., 9.C.7.	802, 931-993
			[0825]	12.F.3.	
Kilteevoge	37	31	0371	15.C.2.	1384-6,
					1622-1644
Laghy			[2671]		
(Drumhome)					
Leck	30	31	0372	9.G.6.	863, 1394-1409
Letterkenny			[3811]		
(Conwal)					
Lettermacaward	27	30	0338, 2294/95,	6.C.7.	378-397
			2303		
Malin (Clonca)			[3812]		
Mevagh	11	28	0361, 2325	11.C.14.	517, 994-1075
Mintiaghs	19	29	0351	8.G.10.	650-653
(Barr of Inch)					
Moville Lower	5	27	0344,	8.A.14.	540-550
			[0814]		
Moville Upper	6	27	0345,	8.C.11.	551-562
			[0815]		
Muff	13	30	0352, 2315, [0817]	10.E.8.	654-670
Raphoe	34	31	0373, 2333-5,	10.B.3.	1410-1445
			[0837/8]	13.G.6.	1532, 1547
Raymoghy	34	31	0374,	10.A.3.	1357-1667
			[0839/40]	11.B.6.	1446-1486
Raymunterdoney	9	28	0362, 2326,	14.A.13.	1076-1094
			[0826]	4.A.11.	
Stranorlar	38	31	0375, 2336	15.D.8.	1645-1660
Taughboyne	32	31	0376,	11.B.9.	506, 1487-1527
			[0841]	14.B.3.	1373, 1470
Templecarn	50	32	0383	3.D.4.	1886-1929
Templecrone	26	30	0339, 2304,	6.D.4.	398-486
			2296/9		
Templemore	20	29	0364,		
			[0827/9]		

PARISH	TITHES 1823–38 TAB 7/	FILM	VALUATION FIELD BOOKS 1830s OL4./ HOUSE BOOKS [OL5.]	TENEMENT VALUATION c. 1857 FICHE	1841–1851 CENSUS SEARCHES CEN S|7|
Tullaghobegley	8	28	0363, 2327, [0827/29]	4.B.8.	433, 1095-1319
Tullyfern	12	29	0364, 2328, [0830/31]	12.B.11.	768, 794, 1320-1344
Urney	40	32	0377, 2337	13.F.10.	1661-1667

TOWNS	VALUATION HOUSE BOOK 1830s [OL5.]
Ballyshannon	[2671]
Bundoran	[3810, 2671]
Letterkenny	[3811]
Lifford	[2670]
Malin	[3812]
Pettigoe	[2671]
Killybegs	X.056 valuation book 1857

PARISH	TITHES 1823–38 TAB 9/	FILM	VALUATION FIELD BOOKS 1830s OL4./ HOUSE BOOKS [OL5.]	TENEMENT VALUATION 1848–52 FICHE	1841–1851 CENSUS SEARCHES Cen /s/9
Aderrig	49	34		4.G.2., 5.B.13	
Artaine/Artane		34	[0864/65], [2711]	2.G.10	
Baldongan	5	33	[0843]	1.A.8., 1.G.7	
Baldoyle		34		2.G.12.	
Balgriffin	34	34	[0866/67], [2711]	3.A.3.	
Ballyboghil	14	33		2.A.3., 2.A.6.	
Ballyfermot & Palmerstown	59	34	[0931]	7.A.14., 8.A.7.	
Ballymadun	10	33	[0856]	2.A.8., 2.C.10.	
Balrothery	2	33	[0844/45], [2673]	1 A 9., 1.G.7.	1 5
Balscaddan	1	33	[0846/47]	1.C.3.	
Booterstown	71	35	[2675], [0895]	3.G.6., 4.C.7., 5.C.14.	300-301
Castleknock	26	34	[3814]	2.D.6., 2.G.1.	26
Chapelizod	27	34		2.E.6., 2.G.1.	27-28
Cloghran	31	34	[0868/69], [2711]	2.E.9., 2.G.1.	
Clondalkin	58	34	[0931a/34]	4.G.2., 5.B.1., 7.B.1, 8.A.7.	334-339
Clonmethan	12	33	[0857]	2.A.10., 2.C.10	20
Clonsilla	25	33	[0862]	2.E.10., 2.G.10	
Clontarf	46	34	[0870/71]	3.A.8.	30-31
Clonturk		34	[0872/74]	3.B.3.	32
Clorhran		33			
Coolock	35	34		3.B.12.	33-34
Cruagh	66	35		7.B.13., 8.A.7.	340
Crumlin	62	34	[0935], [2676]	7.C.1., 8.A.8.	341
Dalkey	78	35	[0896], [2677]	5.D.12.	302-305
Donabate	17	34		4.C.14., 4.F.6.	277-278
Donnybrook (St. Mary's)	68	35	[0897], [0936], [2679/87]	7.C.6., 8.A.8., 3.G.7., 5.E.7.	41-52
Drimnagh	61	34		7.C.7.	
Dublin city (No parish)					54-77, 79-87, 89, 92-135, 137-165, 167, 169-188, 190-209, 211, 213-215, 217-242, 244-251, 255-270, 272-275, 349, 362-3, 374
Esker		34		4.G.2., 5.B.13., 7.C.8., 8.A.8.	288-290
Finglas	24	33	[2690]	4.D.2., 4.F.6., 2.E.13., 2.G.1.	
Garristown	7	33	[0858]	2.A.13., 2.C.10.	21-23
Glasnevin	37	34	[2691], [0875/76]	3.C.2.	
Grallagh	8	33		2.B.13., 2.C.10.	
Grangegorman	43	34	[0877]	3.C.8.	35, 58, 212, 216
Hollywood	9	33	[0859]	2.B.14., 2.C.11.	
Holmpatrick		33	[0848]	1.C.9., 1.G.7	6-11
Howth	42	34	[0878], [3818]	3.C.11.	
Kilbarrack	41	34	[0879/80]	3.D.5.	36

PARISH	TITHES 1823–38 TAB 9/	FILM	VALUATION FIELD BOOKS 1830s OL4./ HOUSE BOOKS [OL5.]	TENEMENT VALUATION 1848–52 FICHE	1841–1851 CENSUS SEARCHES Cen /s/9
Kilbride	53	34		4.B.6.	291
Kilgobbin	79	35	[0898/99]	5.E.9.	306
Kill	77	35	[0900]	5.E.13.	307-308
Killeek	20	33		4.D.3., 4.F.6.	
Killiney	80	35	[0901/02]	5.F.6.	309-310
Killossery	15	33		4.D.4., 4.F.6.	
Killester	45	34	[0881]		
Kilmactalway	51	34		4.G.6., 5.B.13.	292
Kilmacud	73	35		5.F.10.	
Kilmahuddrick	52	34		4.G.9., 5.B.13.	
Kilsallaghan	19	33		4.D.6., 4.F.6.	279
Kiltiernan	81	35	[0903]	5.F.11.	311
Kinsaley	32	32	[0882]	3.D.8.	37
Leixlip	47	34		4.G.9., 5.B.13.	293-294
Lucan		34	[2705]	4.G.11., 5.B.14.	295-296
Lusk	4	33	[0849/53], [2706]	1.D.11., 1.G.8.	12-19
Malahide	28	34	[0883/84]	3.D.12.	38-39
Monkstown	75	35	[0904/21], [2707]	4.B.8., 4.C.7., 5.F.14.	312-318
Naul	6	33	[0860]	2.C.4., 2.C.11.	24-25
Newcastle	54	34	[2708]	5.A.1., 5.B .14.	297-298
Old Connaught	83	35	[0922]	6.D.4.	319
Palmerston	59	34	[0937], [2709]	7.C.9., 8.A.8.	
Palmerstown	11	33	[0861]	2.C.7., 2.C.11.	342-344
Portmarnock	33	34	[0885]	3.E.4.	
Portraine	18	33		4.D.9., 4.F.7.	
Raheny	40	34	[0886/88], [2710/11]	3.E.7.	
Rathcoole	55	34	[2715]	5.A.8., 5.B.14.	299
Rathfarnham	69	35	[0863], [0923], [3815]	7.C.14., 8.A.8., 6.D.12.	320-325
Rathmichael	82	35	[0924]	6.E.13.	
Saggart	56	34	[2720]	5.B.3., 5.C.1.	
Santry	30	34	[0894], [2711]	3.F.5.	
St Brides's					271
St Brigid's					78
St Catherine's	63	34	[0938]	7.C.14., 8.A.8.	345-346
St George's	44	34	[0889/91]	3.E.11.	252
St James'	60	34	[0939/42]	2.F.12., 2.G.1.	29, 166, 347-348, 350
St John's					168
St Jude's					351
St Kevin's					88
St Margaret's		34	[0894]	3.F.2.	40
St Mark's		35		4.B.9., 4.C.7.	
St Michan's					136, 243
St Mary's	85	36			
St Nicholas Within					210
St Nicholas Without			[0943/44]		
St Paul's					254

PARISH	TITHES 1823–38 TAB 9/	FILM	VALUATION FIELD BOOKS 1830s OL4./ HOUSE BOOKS [OL5.]	TENEMENT VALUATION 1848–52 FICHE	1841–1851 CENSUS SEARCHES Cen /s/9
St Peter's		35	[0945/47]	7.D.14., 8.A.9., 4.B.9., 4.C.7.	352-361
St Patrick's	84	36			
St Thomas'					90
St Werburgh's					276
Stillorgan	77	35	[0925/26]	6.F.4.	326
Swords	16	33	[2724/25]	4.D.14., 4.F.7., 3.F.10.	280-287
Tallaght	65	35	[0948/51], [2726]	7.G.3., 8.A.9.	364-373
Taney	70	35	[0927/28]	4.C.6., 6.F.10.	53, 327 328
Tully	76	35		6.G.9.	329-330
Ward		33		2.F.13.	
Westpalstown	13	33		2.C.9., 2.C.11.	
Whitechurch	72	35	[0929/30]	6.G.12.	331-333
Williamstown			[3816/17]		

TOWNS	VALUATION HOUSE BOOK 1830s [OL5.]	TOWNS	VALUATION HOUSE BOOK 1830s [OL5.]
Artaine	[2711]	Haroldscross	[2694, 2696, 2697]
Balbriggan	[2672/73]	Haroldcross E	[2695]
Balgriffin	[2711]	Islandbridge	[2698]
Ballybough	[2711]	Killester S.	[2711]
Balrothery	[2673]	Kilmainham	[2699]
Blackrock	[2674], [0904/21]	Kingstown	[2700/03] [0904/21]
Booterstown	[2675]	Little Bray	[2704]
Clontarf E	[2711]	Lusk	[2706]
Coolock	[2711]	Portobello	[2694]
Crumlin	[2676]	Raheny	[2710/11]
Dalkey	[2677]	Rathmines W	[2696]
Dolphin's Barn	[2678]	Richmond	[2711]
Donnybrook	[2679/87]	Ranelagh N	[2712]
Drumcondra	[2688]	Ranelagh S	[2713/14]
Dundrum	[2689]	Rathmines E	[2716/17]
Finglas	[2690]	Rathmines W	[2717]
Glasnevin	[2691]	Rush	[2718/19] [0854]
Glasthule	[2692]	Skerries	[2721/23] [0855]
Goldenbridge	[2693]		

PARISH	TITHES 1823–38 TAB 11/	FILM	VALUATION FIELD BOOKS 1830s OL4./ HOUSE BOOKS [OL5.]	TENEMENT VALUATION 1855–6 FICHE	1841–1851 CENSUS SEARCHES Cen /s/11
Abbey	121	41			
Abbeygormacan	112	41	[1026], [3833]	11.A.2., 2.B.2., 10.G.14., 14.B.4.	1624-1625, 1774-1794
Abbeyknockmoy	41	40	0540, 051 0542, [0964]	6.A.2., 15.C.2., 17.B.12.	2408-2427
Addergoole	10	37		16.C.4.	825-871
Ahascragh	78	40	[0996], [2727/28]	2.A.6., 11.G.2., 1.E.12., 11.E.12., 11.F.14.	655-673, 702, 1184-1200, 1274-1280
Annaghdown	36	38	0543 /44, [0965]	6.A .3., 15.C.2.	471-508
Ardrahan	66	39	0588, [1018], [1037]	8.G.2., 9.F.10., 7.G.10., 9.B.14., 10.C.14.	703-712, 1438-1443, 1917-1919 ·
Athenry	69	39	0520, 0545 0546, 0547 [0966], [3825], [2729/30]	6.B.4., 5.E.4., 5.C.14., 9.D.12.	49-67, 509-510, 713
Athleague				11.G.4.	1281-1290
Augheart	123	41			
Aughrim	77	40	[0997/98], [2731/32]	1.F.1., 1.B.9.	674-675, 1201-1204
Ballinchalla	No Tab	37	[1044]	13.G.8.,	2292-2301
Ballindoon	4	37	0537, [0960], [3831]	2.E.12.	289-300
Ballinrobe	No Tab	37	[1045]	13.G.10.	2302-2317
Ballymacward	46	39	[0999/100]	2.A.12., 10.B.12., 12.C.14., 1.F.7., 11.F.1.	1205-1216, 2428-2452
Ballynacourty	56	39		5.E.6.	714-729
Ballynakill	19	38	0528 , [0952], [2739/40]	7.D.10.	79-117?, 1626-1718?
Ballynakill		39	0538	11.G.9.	301-347?
Ballynakill	105	41	[0961], [3834]	11.B.12., 14.F.10.	1291-1295?
Beagh	90	40	[1019]	8.A.1.	1444-1494
Belclare	30	38	0548, [0967]	15.C.7.	511-518
Boyounagh	18	38	0529, [0953], [1047a]	6.F.12., 6.D.12.	118-127, 2453
Bullaun	91	40	[1043]	10.D.1.	1920-1922
Cargin	31	38	0549, 0550, [0968]	15.C.7.	519-521
Claregalway	55	39	0551/52/53, [0969]	6.B.8., 5.F.1.	522-533, 728-735
Clonbern	22	38	0530	6.G.12., 17.D.8.	128-169
Clonfert	111	41		2.C.8., 14.B.4.	1795-1821
Clonkeen	45	39		10.B.13., 12.D.4.	2454-2463
Clonrush	107	41		17.G.12.	1719-1726
Clontuskert	81	40		1.B.10., 2.B.8.	676-682
Cong	8	37	[1046]	13.E.4.	2318-2351
Cummer	34	38	0554/55/56, [0970]	15.D.13.	534
Derrymacloughney	122	41			
Donaghpatrick	26	38	0557 /58, [0971]	15.D.13.	535-559
Dunamon	21	38	0532, [0955]	17.F.1.	177
Donanaghta	115	41	[1027/29]	14.B.5.	1822-1834

PARISH	TITHES 1823–38 TAB 11/	FILM	VALUATION FIELD BOOKS 1830s OL4./ HOUSE BOOKS [OL5.]	TENEMENT VALUATION 1855–6 FICHE	1841–1851 CENSUS SEARCHES Cen /s/11
Dunmore	11	37	0533, [0956/57], [2745]	16.D.2., 7.A.7., 17.D.11.,	178-211, 872-967
Drumatemple	17	38	0531, [0954]	7.A.5.	170-176
Drumacoo	61	39	0592	5.F.10., 8.G.9.	736-750
Duniry	103	41	[1030], [3834], [3840]	11.A.4., 14.G.13.	1727-1739
Fahy	114	41		14.B.11.	1835-1843
Fohanagh	71	39	[1001]	1.F.12., 11.F.4., 1.C.8.	1217-1236
Grange	74	40	[1002/03]	10.A.10., 10.D.3.	1237-1243
Inishcaltra	106	41	[3835]	18.A.7.	1740-1747
Inisheer	84	40	0517, [3822]	5.D.4.	1-7
Inishmaan	83	40	0518, [3823]	5.D.5.	8-21
Inishmore	82	40	0519, [3824]	5.D.7.	22-48
Isertkelly	93	40	[3843]	10.D.3.	1923-1924
Kilbarron		41		18.A.14.	
Kilbeacanty	89	40	[1020]	8.B.5.	1495-1526
Kilbegnet	20	38	[0958]	7.E.10., 17.F.2.	212-226
Kilbennan	13	37		16.F.1.	968-993
Kilchreest	95	40	0593, [0983], [3844]	9.F.12., 10.D.4.	1925-1927
Kilcloony	80	40		1.C.8.	683-691, 699
Kilcolgan	63	39	0594	8.G.13.	751-762
Kilconickny	68	39	0521, 0595, [0984], [3826]	9.F.14., 9.E.10., 10.D.6.	763, 1928-1930
Kilconierin	68	39	0522, 0596, [0985], [3827]	9.G.5., 9.E.11., 10.D.12.	68-69, 764
Kilconla	12	37	[0972]	16.F.11.	994-1032
Kilconnell	72	40	[1004], [2774]	1.F.13.	1244-1250
Kilcooly	100	40	[3836]	11.A.7.	1748-1750
Kilcoona	33	38	0559, 0560	15.E.7.	560-567
Kilcroan	16	38	[0959]	7.B.4.	227-241
Kilcummin	23	38	[3846]	5. B.4., 12.G.14.	1964-2065
Kilgerrill	79	40	[1005/06]	1.G.6., 1.E.3.	692-698
Killinny	86	40			
Kilkerrin	39	38	[1047b/47c]	6.E.2.	2464-2527
Kilkilvery	29	38	[0973/74]	15.E.12.	568-570
Killaan	75	40	[1007]	1.G.7., 10.B.7., 10.D.13.	1931, 1251-1254
Killallaghtan	76	40	0587, [1008]	1.G.11., 1.E.7.	1255-1259
Killannin	24	38	[3845]	4.G.14., 13.C.7.	2054-2241
Killeany	32	38	0562, 0563, [0975]	15.F.1.	571-579
Killeely	58	39		9.A.4.	765-773
Killeenadeema	96	40	[1038]	10.D.13.	1932-1936
Killeenavarra	65	39		9.A.12.	774-785
Killeeneen	59	39	[0986]	9.B.3., 9.G.9.	786-788
Killererin	35	38	0534, 0564, 0565, [0976]	16.G.5., 17.C.11. 17.D.12., 15.F.6.,	242-243, 580-598, 1033-1035, 2487

PARISH	TITHES 1823–38 TAB 11/	FILM	VALUATION FIELD BOOKS 1830s OL4./ HOUSE BOOKS [OL5.]	TENEMENT VALUATION 1855–6 FICHE	1841–1851 CENSUS SEARCHES Cen /s/11
Killeroran	48	39	[1017]	11.G.12.	1296-1353
Killian	47	39	[1016]	12.B.2.	1354-1415
Killimorbologue	116	41	[1031/32]	14.B.14.	1844-1849
Killimordaly	73	40	0523/25, [3828], [1010/11]	10.C.5., 9.E.12., 10.A.13.	70, 1260-1265, 2528
Killinny			[1021]	8.C.2.	1527-1534
Killinan	94	40	[0987], [1039]	12.B.2.	1937-1939
Killogilleen	67	39	[0988], [1040]	9.G.11., 10.E.14.	789-791, 1940
Killora	60	39	[0989]	9.G.14.	792-799
Killoran	109	41	[1017], [3837]	1.E.10., 11.A.9., 2.B.11.	700-701, 1753 1850-1863
Killoscobe	42	40		12.D.4.	2529-2558
Killosolan	43	39	[1009]	12.D.13., 11.F.8.	1266-1273, 2559-2581
Killower	27	38	[0977]	15.G.3.	599-604
Killursa	28	38	[0978]	15.G.6.	605-629
Kilmacduagh	88	40	[1022]	8.C.7.	1535-1561
Kilmalinogue (Portumna)	120	41		14.C.12.	1864-1867
Kilmeen	99	40	[3838], [1043]	10.F.1., 11.A.9.	1751-1752, 1941
Kilmoylan	37	38	[0979]		630-631
Kilquain	113	41		14.D.2.	1868-1878
Kilreekill	98	40	[3839]	2.A.10., 11.A.12.	
Kiltartan	87	40	[1023]	8.D.6.	1563-1584
Kilteskill	101	40	[1041], [3840]	10.F.1., 11.B.2.	1585-1590
Kilthomas	97	40	[1042]	8.E.4., 10.B.10, 9.C.1.	1585-1590 1942-1952
Kiltormer	110	41	[1033]	2.C.1.	1879-1887
Kiltullagh	70	39	0526, [1012/13], [3829]	9.E.13., 10.B.5.	71-78
Kinvarradoorus	85	40	[1025]	8.E.7.	1591-1623
Lackagh	38	38	[0980]	6.B.13., 16.B.4.	632-642
Leitrim	102	41	[3841]	11.B.4.	1754-1761
Lickerrig		39	[0990]	10.A.7., 9.F.9.	
Lickerrig	64	39	0527, [3830]	10.F.4.	800
Lickmolassy (Portumna)	119	41	[1034/35]	14.D.6.	1888-1905
Liskeevy	12/9	37		16.G.6.	1036-1082
Loughrea	92	40	[1043], [2778/81]	10.F.5.	1953-1963
Meelick	118	41		14.E.9.	1906-1911
Monivea	44	39	[0981], [1014/15], [1047d]	6.C.9., 5.G.14. 10.C.6., 17.C.13.	2582-2606
Moycullen	25	38	[3847]	5.B.6.	2242-2289
Moylough	40	39	[2782/83]	6.F.9., 12.E.10., 17.D.7., 12.C.6.	1416-1422, 2607-2655
Moyrus	3	37	[0962]	3.A.8., 3.F.6.	348-429
Omey	2	37	0539, [0963], [3832]	3.D.7.	430-470

PARISH	TITHES 1823–38 TAB 11/	FILM	VALUATION FIELD BOOKS 1830s OL4./ HOUSE BOOKS [OL5.]	TENEMENT VALUATION 1855–6 FICHE	1841–1851 CENSUS SEARCHES Cen /s/11
Oranmore	52	39	[2784/87]	4.F.4., 4.G.10., 3.G.8., 4.B.2., 5.F.10.	801-821, 1109-1111
Rahoon	53	39	[3848]	5.C.10., 4.F.8., 4.C.10.	1112-1141, 2290-2291
Ross	7	37	[1047]	13.F.2., 14.A.1.	2352-2407
St Nicholas & Islands	54	39		4.F.7., 3.G.11., 4.B.3., 4.F.1.	1142-1162
Stradbally	57	39		5.G.9., 9.B.12	822-824
Taghboy		39		12.C.10.	1423-1437
Templetogher	15	38	0535	7.B.11.	244-287
Tiranascragh	117	41		14.F.1.	1912-1913
Tuam	14	37	0536, [0982], [2792/6]	16.G.14., 17.D.12., 16.A.11	288, 643-654, 1083-1108
Tynagh	104	41	[1036], [3840], [3842]	11.B.10., 15.A.1., 14.F.4.	1762-1773, 1914-1916

TOWNS & VILLAGES	VALUATION HOUSE BOOK 1830s [OL5.]
Ballinasloe	[2733/36]
Ballygar	[2737/38]
Ballynakill (Woodford)	[2739/40]
Clarin Bridge	[2741]
Clifden	[2742/43]
Craughwell (Killora)	[2744]
Eyrecourt	[2746]
Portumna	[2746, 2788/89]
Killimor	[2746]
Galway City	[2747/67] [1163-1183]
Gort	[2768/70]
Headford	[2771/73]
Killimor	[2775]
Kinvarra	[2776/77]
Roundstone	[2790/91]

PARISH	TITHES 1823–38 TAB 12/	FILM	VALUATION FIELD BOOKS 1830s OL4./ HOUSE BOOKS [OL5.]	TENEMENT VALUATION 1855–6 FICHE	1841–1851 CENSUS SEARCHES Cen /s/12
Aghadoe			[1135/38]	5.D.10., 9.G.12.	
Aghavallen	2	42	[1111/12]	6.F.12.	487-528
Aglish	74	44	[1139/43]	10.A.14.	935-945
Annagh	53	43	2571/2604, [1056/57], [1185]	2.G.12., 11.E.14.	1068
Ardfert	25	42	2572/2573/2605, [1048]	1.B.2., 11.F.10	1-15, 1069-1074
Ballincuslane	56	44	2576/77/ 2606	11.F.14.	1075-1114
Ballinvoher	40	43	[1058/59]	2.G.14.	151-173
Ballyconry	8	42		7.A.8.	
Ballyduff	28	42	[1060/61]	3.A.13.	174
Ballyheige	16	42		1.C.2.	16-21
Ballymacelligott	49	43	2578/2607	12.A.6.	1115-1121
Ballynacourty	39	43	[1062/63]	3.B.2.	175
Ballynahaglish	45	43	2579/2607a	12.B.8.	1122-11252
Ballyseedy	54	44	2580/81	12.B.14.	1126
Brosna	52	43	[1186]	12.C.6.	
Caher	65	44	2559, [1120/21]	8.C.8.	639-658, 660-672
Castleisland	51	43	2587, [2802/03]	12.D.4.	1173-1233
Cloghane	27	42	[1064/65]	3.B.9.	191-196
Clogherbrien	46	43	2588/2609	12.F.4.	1234
Currans	59	44	2589/2610, [1144/46]	12.F.10., 10.B.6.	1235-1241
Dingle	35	43	[1066/67], [2806/07]	3.C.3.	197-210
Drumod	70	44	2560, [1122/23]	8.E.7.	673-731
Duagh	15	42	[1113]	7.A.12., 1.D.8.	22-48, 529-530
Dunquin	41	43	[1068/69]	3.E.4.	211-217
Dunurlin	32	43	[1070/71]	3.E.10.	
Dysert	13	42	2590	7.B.2., 1.D.12.	49-52, 531-534, 1242-1249
Dysert	61	44		12.G.2.	
Fenit	44	43	2591	12.G.8.	1250-1252
Finuge	14	42	[1049]	1.F.2.	53-60
Galey	6	42		7.B.6.	535-545
Garfinny	36	43	[1072/73]	3.E.14.	218
Glanbehy	67	44	2561, [1124/25]	8.G.9.	732-771
Kenmare	84	45	2554, [2808]	5.G.14.	448-460
Kilbonane	74	44	[1147/49]	10.B.8.	946-953
Kilcaragh	19	42	[1050]	1.F.8.	61-68
Kilcaskan	87	45	2555	6.B.7.	
Kilcolman	62	44	2592/93, [1150/51]	12.G.10., 10.C.6.	954-961, 1253-1267
Kilconly	1	42		7.C.4.	546-554
Kilcredane	76	44	[1152/55]	10.C.10.	
Kilcrohane	82	45	[1096/102]	4.D.14.	303-444
Kilcummin	77	45	[1156/59]	10.C.14.	962-1013
Kildrum	43	43	[1074/76]	3.F.3.	219-220
Kilfeighny	20	42		1.F.12.	69-83
Kilflyn	24	42	[1051]	1.G.8.	84-85
Kilgarrylander	57	44	2611, [1187]	13.A.8.	1268-1273
Kilgarvan	85	45	2556	6.B.14.	461-468
Kilgobban	31	43	[1077/78]	3.F.9.	221-233
Killaha	81	45	2569/70, [1160/62]	10.F.14.	1014-1019
Killahan	17	42	[1052]	2.A.2.	123-124

PARISH	TITHES 1823–38 TAB 12/	FILM	VALUATION FIELD BOOKS 1830s OL4./ HOUSE BOOKS [OL5.]	TENEMENT VALUATION 1855–6 FICHE	1841–1851 CENSUS SEARCHES CEN S|12|
Killarney	80	45	[1163/66], [2809/14], [3850]	10.F.14.	1020-1027
Killeentierna	60	44	2594 /2612, [1167/70]	13.B.8., 11.B.12.	1037-1039, 1274-1292
Killehenny	4	42	[1114]	7.C.12.	572-574
Killemlagh	68	44	[1126/27] 2562	9.B.2.	772-812
Killinane	66	44	2563, [1128/29]	9.C.3.	813-834
Killiney	30	42	[1079/80]	3.G.1.	126-134, 234-245
Killorglin	63	44	2545/2546/2564, 2595/2613, [1130/31], [1171/73], [2815/16]	13.C.2., 9.D.6 5.D.11., 11.B.14.	248, 264-272, 1028-1036, 835-848, 1293-1332
Killury	11	42	[1053]	2.A.8.	125
Kilmalkedar	34	43	[1081/84]	4.A.4.	246-247
Kilmoyly	22	42		2.B.12.	86-104
Kilnanare	73	44	[1174/77]	11.C.3.	1040-1046
Kilnaughtin	3	42	[1115]	7.D.10.	555-571
Kilquane	26	42	[1083/84]	4.A.11.	
Kilshenane	21	42	2542/2543, [1054]	2.C.10.	105-119
Kiltallagh	58	44	2596/97	13.D.12.	1334-1335
Kiltomy	18	42		2.D.6.	120-122
Kinard	37	43	[1085/87]	4.B.2.	249-253
Knockane	71	44	2549/2551, [1103/06]	5.E.5., 5.B.1.	273-301
Knockanure	10	42		7.F.2.	575-583
Lisselton	5	42	[1117]	7.F.6.	584-591
Listowel	9	42	[1118/19], [2817/18]	7.F.14.	592-618
Marhin	33	43	[1088/89], [1116?]	4.B.7.	
Minard	38	43	[1090/91]	4.B.10.	254-258
Molahiffe	72	44	[1178/80]	11.C.10.	1047-1059
Murher	7	42		8.A.6.	619-637
Nohaval	55	44	2598/2614	13.E.8.	
Nohavaldaly	78	45	[1181/84]	11.D.6.	1060-1067, 1336-1340
O Brennan	50	43	2599	13.E.8.	1341-1344
O Dorney	23	42	[1055]	2.E.2.	135-143
Prior	69	44	2565, [1132], [3849]	9.D.12.	849-903
Ratass	48	43	2600/2615	13.E.14.	1345-1353
Rattoo	12	42		8.B.6., 2.E.12.	144-150, 638
Stradbally	29	42	[1092/93]	4.C.3.	259-261
Templnoe	83	45	2550/2552/2553, [1007/10]	5.G.2., 5.B.2.	302, 445-447
Tralee	47	43	2601/2616, [1188], [2823]	13.F.10+14 [2824/33]	1354-1361
Tuosist	86	45	2557/2558	6.D.1.	469-486
Valencia	64	44	2566/2567/8, [1133/34]	9.E.13.	
Ventry	42	43	[1094/95]	4.C.9.	262-263

TOWNS	VALUATION HOUSE BOOK 1830s [OL5.]
Ballylongford	[2796a]
Blennerville	[2797/99]
Cahersiveen	[2800/01]
Castlemaine	[2804]
Chapelstown	[2805]
Milltown	[2819/20]
Sneem	[2821/22]
Tarbert	[2823]

PARISH	TITHES 1823–38 TAB 13/	FILM	VALUATION FIELD BOOKS 1830s OL4./ HOUSE BOOKS [OL5.]	TENEMENT VALUATION 1851 FICHE	1841–1851 CENSUS SEARCH Cen /s/13
Ardkill	10	46	0703	4.B.7.	1
Ardree (Tankardstown)	104	49	0738, [3873]	1.F.8.	
Ballaghmoon	115	49	0739, [3874]	1.F.9.	
Ballybought	81	48	0763, [3887]	4.E.14.	77
Ballybrackan	86	48	0800	2.B.7.	
Ballymany	63	47	0784, [3902]	6.C.8.	
Ballymoreustace	77	48	0762, [3888]	4.F.1.	79
Ballynadrumny	1	46	0704, [3851]	4.B.11.	2
Ballynafagh	30	46	0714, [3855]	5.E.10	14-15
Ballysax	64	47	0785, [3903]	2.E.14., 6.D.5.	135
Ballyshannon	92	48	0786/0801, [3904]	2.E.14., 6.C.8., 2.B.13	
Balraheen	16	46	0728, [3866]	3.D.14.	59
Belan	107	49	0740	1.F.10.	
Bodenstown	36	47	0753, [3951]	6.A.2.	
Brannockstown	78	48	0764, [3889]	4.F.11.	80
Brideschurch	35	47	0715, [3856]	5.E.13.	17-18
Cadamstown	4	46	0705, [3852]	4.C.1.	3-5
Carbury	9	46	0706, [3853]	4.C.6.	6-8
Carn	65	47	0787, [3905]	2.E.14., 6.C.9.	136-137
Carnalway	75	48	0765, [3890]	4.F.12.	81-84
Carragh	34	47	0716	5.F.1.	19-27
Carrick	5	46	0707	4.C.8.	
Castledermot	111	49	0741, [3875], [2840/42]	1.F.11., 2.F.2.	67-74
Castledillon	46	47	0823, [3941]	3.C.6.	
Churchtown	96	48	0779, [3897]	1.B.2.	108-110
Clane	33	47	0717, [3857], [2845/46]	5.F.4.	16, 28
Clonaghlis	48	47	0824, [3942]	3.C.7.	
Cloncurry	12, 56	46, 47	0729/0788, [3867], [3906]	3.E.6.	60-61, 138-140
Clonshanbo	15	46	0730, [3868]	3.E.2.	
Coghlanstown	76	48	0766, [3891]	4.G.3.	
Confey	21	46	0813, [3919], [3920]	2.G.7.	
Davidstown	99	48	0772	1.D.12.	111-114
Donadea	18	46	0731, [3869]	3.E.12.	
Donaghcumper	44	47	0814/0825, [3921]	2.F.12., 3.C.8., 3.D.1.	
Donaghmore	22	46	0815, [3922/23]	3.A.2.	
Downings	31	46	0718, [3858]	5.G.1	29-31
Duneany	84	48	0802	2.C.1.	
Dunfierth	7	46	0708, [3854]	4.C.11.	
Dunmanoge or Monmahennock	110	49	0742, [3876]	1.G.7.	
Dunmurraghill	17	46	0732, [3869]	3.E.13.	
Dunmurry	58	47	0789, [3907]		
Feighcullen	68	47	0721/0790, [3861], [3908]	4.A .2., 5.A.4.	37-39
Fontstown	93	48	0773/0803	2.C.3., 1.E.2.	115-118
Forenaghts	52	47	0826, [3943]	5.D.13.	
Gilltown	79	48	0767, [3892]	4.G.4.	85-86
Graney	113	49	0743	1.G.10.	
Grangeclare	58	47	0791, [3909]	4.A.14., 6.C.13.	
Grangerosnolvan	106	49	0744, [3878]	1.G.14.	

PARISH	TITHES 1823–38 TAB 13/	FILM	VALUATION FIELD BOOKS 1830s OL4./ HOUSE BOOKS [OL5.]	TENEMENT VALUATION 1851 FICHE	1841–1851 CENSUS SEARCH Cen /s/13
Greatconnell	72	48	0722, [3862]	5.A.8.	40-49
Haynestown	53	47	0827, [3944]	5.D.13.	
Harristown	89	48	0804	2.C.6.	
Jago	80	48	0768, [3893]	4.G.7.	87
Johnstown	41	47	0754, [3952]	6.A.4.	
Kerdiffstown	39	47	0755, [3953]	6.A.5.	
Kilberry	95	48	[3898]	1.B.13.	
Kilcock	13	26	0733, [3870], [2847/49], [4255]	3.F.1.	
Kilcullen	94	48	0736, [2850/51]	5.D.1.	63-66
Kildangan	87	48	0805	2.C.11.	
Kildare & Bishopscourt	61	47	0723/0792, [3910], [2852], [2853], [2854]	4.B.3., 6.D.11., 5.A .14.	141
Kildrought	26	46	0816, [3925], [3926/27]		147
Kilkea	109	49	0745, [3879]	2.A.1.	
Kill	50	47	0769/0828, [3945], [3894]	5.D.13., 4.G.8.	
Killadoon	27	46	0817, [3928], [3929]	2.G.5.	
Killashee	73	48	0756 /0770, [3895]	6.A .6.	88-90
Killelan	108	49	0746, [3880]	2.A.3.	
Killybegs	32	46	0719, [3859]	5.G.6.	32-35
Kilmacredock	23	46	0818, [3930]	2.G.7.	
Kilmeage	66	47	0724/0793, [3911]	6.C.13.	50-51
Kilmore	8	46	0709	4.C.14.	
Kilpatrick	11	46	0710	4.D.2.	9-10
Kilrainy	2	46	0711	4.D.5.	
Kilrush	91	48	0806	2.C.11.	
Kilteel	51	47	[3946]	5.E.3.	148-149
Kineagh	112	49	0747, [3881]	2.A.9.	
Knavinstown	83	48	0807	2.C.14.	
Lackagh	82	48	0808, [3918]	2.D.1.	
Ladytown	71	48	0725, [3864]	5.B.14.	
Laraghbryan	20	46	0819, [3931/32]	3.A.2.	150
Leixlip	24	46	0820, [2855/56], [3933/4], [3859]	2.G.9.	151-153
Lullymore	54	47	[3912]	4.A.4.	
Lyons	47	47	0830, [3947]	3.C.12	154
Mainham	19	46	0734, [3871]	3.E.3.	61
Monasterevin	85	48	0809, [2853], [2861/62]	2.D.9.	142
Moone	103	49	0748/0774/0794, [3882], [3913]	6.C.14., 1.E.4., 2.A.11	
Morristownbiller	69	47	0726, [3865]	5.C.1.	52-55
Mylerstown	3	46	0712	4.D.7.	11-13
Narraghmore	101	48	0749/0775/0781, [3883], [3899]	1.C.7., 1.E.6.	75-76, 119-124
Naas	40	47	[3954], 0757, [2864]	6.A.6.	91-101
Nurney	6, 90	46, 48	0713, 0810	4.D.10., 2.E.8.	143
Oldconnell	70	48	[3863]	5.C.7.	56-58
Oughterard	49	47	0831, [3948]	5.E.7.	
Painestown	114	49	0750, [3884]	2.B.2.	
Pollardstown	62	47	0796, [3914]	6.D.10.	
Rathangan	55	47	0797/0811, [3915], [2853], [2868]	6.C.14., 4.A.5., 2.E.12.	144

PARISH	TITHES 1823–38 TAB 13/	FILM	VALUATION FIELD BOOKS 1830s OL4./ HOUSE BOOKS [OL5.]	TENEMENT VALUATION 1851 FICHE	1841–1851 CENSUS SEARCH Cen /s/13
Rathernan	67	47	0727	5.C.11.	
Rathmore	43	47	0758, [3955]	6.B.10.	102-105
Relictstown	116	49			
Scullogestown	14	46	0735, [3872]	3.E.14.	
Sherlockstown	38	47	0759, [3956]	6.C.2.	
St John's	98	48	0782, [3900]		77, 125
St Michael's	97	48	0751/0783, [3885], [3901]		126
Stacumny	45	47	0832, [3949/50]		155
Straffan	28	46	0821, [3935/36]	3.A.14	156
Taghadoe	25	46	0822, [3937/38]	3.B.3.	
Tankardstown Ardree	105	49	0752/0776, [3886]	1.E.13., 2.B.2.	
Thomastown	57	47	0798, [3916]	4.B.2.	
Timahoe	29	46	0720 [3860]	5.G.11.	36
Timolin	102	49	0777, [2870]	1.E.13.	127-128
Tipper	42	47	[3957]	6.C.2.	106-107
Tipperkevin	74	48	0771, [3896]	4.G.13.	
Tully	60	47	0737/0799, [3917]	2.E.14., 6.D.2., 2.F.1., 5.D.12.	145
Usk	100	48	0778	1.F.4., 6.E.11.	129-134
Walterstown	88	48	0812	2.E.12.,	
Whitechurch	37	47	0761, [3958]	6.C.5.	

TOWNS	VALUATION HOUSE BOOK 1830s [OL5.]
Athy	[2834/37]
Ballitore	[2837/38]
Ballymore Eustace	[2839, 2851]
Celbridge	[2843/44, 2860]
Johnstown	[2864, 2869]
Kildare	[2852, 2853, 2854]
Kill	[2864]
Kilmeage	[2865/67]
Leixlip	[2855/56]
Maynooth	[2857/59] [3961]
Newbridge	[2865/67]
Prosperous	[2846]
Robertstown	[2865/67]
Sallins	[2864, 2869]

PARISH	TITHES 1823–38 TAB 14/	FILM	VALUATION FIELD BOOKS 1830s OL4./ HOUSE BOOKS [OL5.]	TENEMENT VALUATION FICHE 1849–50	1841–1851 CENSUS SEARCH Cen /s/14
Abbeyleix	14	50	0854, [3978]	2.C.4.	14
Aghaviller	104	54	0959, [3982]	8.C.2.	196-200
Aglish	140	55	0935	6.G.10.	137-139, 138A
Aharney	10	50	0872	3.E.2.	67-69
Arderra	136	55	0936	6.G.12.	
Attanagh	13	50	0855, [3962]	2.C.5.	15-17
Balleen	7	50	0873	3.E.8.	70
Ballycallan	41	51	0836	1.D.9.	
Ballinamara	38	51	0835	1.D.6.	
Ballybur	52	52	0975	9.A.6.	
Ballygurrim	119	54	0919	5.F.12.	
Ballylarkin	32	51	0837	1.E.3.	3-4
Ballylinch	83	53	0884	4.B.8.	
Ballytarsney	135	55	0937	7.A.2.	140
Ballytobin	97	54	0949	7.E.14.	
Blackrath	66	52	0885	4.B.9.	82
Blanchvilleskill	74	53	0886	4.B.10.	83
Borrismore	6	50	0874	3.E.11.	
Burnchurch	56	52	0976	9.A.6.	
Callan	47	51	0833, [2875/77]	1.A.4.	1-2
Castlecomer	15	50	0856, [3963], [3878/9] [4000/01]	2.C.7., 2.D.9.	18-25
Castleinch	51	52	0977	9.A.10.	
Clara	70	53	0877	4.B.11.	
Clashacrow	36	51	0838	1.E.5.	
Clomantagh	28	50	0839	1.E.6.	5-8
Clonamery	112	54	0920	5.G.2.	
Clonmore	131	55	0938	7.A.3.	141
Columbkille	89	53	0888	4.B.14.	84-87
Coolaghmore	93	54	0950	7.F.3.	
Coolcashin	8	50	0875	3.E.12.	
Coolcraheen	22	50	0857, [3964]	3.B.8., 1.E.10.	
Danesfort	57	52	0979	9.A.12.	226
Derrynahinch	106	54	0960, [3983/84]	8.C.11.	201-206
Donaghmore	18/	50	0858	2.C.12.	26-45
Dunbell	73	53	0889	4.C.6.	
Dungarvan	81	53	0890		
Dunkitt	121	55	0921	5.G.8.	119-123
Dunmore	26	50	0859, [3965]	3.B.9., 3.B.14.	46
Dunnamaggan	98	54	0961	7.F.9., 8.D.5.	
Durrow	11	50		3.E.13.	
Dysart	21	50	0860, [3966]	2.G.6., 3.A.11., 3.B.1.	47-49
Dysartmoon	113	54	0922	6.A.6.	
Earlstown	59	52	0979	9.B.3.	
Ennisnag	60	52	0980, [3985]	9.B.5., 8.D.6.	
Erke	1	50	0877	3.E.13.	71-72
Famma	91	53	0891	4.C.14.	
Fertagh	4	50	0841	3.F.11., 1.E.10.	73-76
Fiddown	128	55	0963, [3986]	8.D.6., 7.A.7.	142-149
Freshford	33	51	0842, [2880], [4002]	1.E.11.	9-9a
Garranamanagh	29	50	0843	1.F.7.	

PARISH	TITHES 1823–38 TAB 14/	FILM	VALUATION FIELD BOOKS 1830s OL4./ HOUSE BOOKS [OL5.]	TENEMENT VALUATION FICHE 1849–50	1841–1851 CENSUS SEARCH Cen /s/14
Gaulskill	122	55	0923	6.A.14.	124-126
Glashare	2	50	0879, 2695	3.G.6.	
Gowran	71	53	0892, [2883]	4.C.14.	
Graiguenamanagh	86	53	0893, [2884/5]	4.D.13.	88-97
Grange	50	52	0981	9.B.7.	
Grangekilree	58	52	0982	9.B.9.	
Grangemaccomb	19	50	0861, [3967]	2.D.7., 3.A.3., 3.B.10., 3.C.6., 3.C.8.	50-51
Grangesilvia	76	53	0894, [2882]	4.F.3.	98-99
Inistiogue	92	53	0895, [2886]	4.F.10.	101-103
Jerpointabbey	88	53	0896, [3979]	4.G.9.	
Jerpointchurch	102	54	0964, [3987]	8.D.7	207
Jerpointwest	108	54	0965, [3988]	4.G.11., 8.D.13.	
Kells	95	54	0984, 2696	9.B.10., 7.F.14.	170-178
Kilbeacon	110	54	0966, [3989]	8.E.1.	208
Kilbride	117	54	0925	6.B.4.	
Kilcoan	118	54	0926	6.B.8.	
Kilcolumb	123	55	0927	6.B.12.	127, 136
Kilcooly	34	51	0844	1.F.8.	
Kilderry	67	52	0898	4.G.13.	
Kilfane	85	53	0899	5.A.1.	
Kilferagh	54	52	0985	9.B.11.	
Kilkeasy	105	54	0967, [3990]	8.E.9.	209-212
Kilkenny	43-46	51	2694, [2889-2914], [4003-4007]	9.D.14., 9.F.13. 9.G.11., 10.A.11. 10.B.2.	185-195
Kilkerril	141	55			
Kilkieran	63	52	0900	5.A.5.	
Killahy	35, 109	51, 54	[3991] 0845	1.F.8., 8.E.12.	
Killaloe	48	52	0986, 0834	1.F.9., 9.B.12.	
Killamery	96	54	0953	7.G.7.	
Killarney	79	53	0901	5.A.6.	
Kilmacahill	72	53	0902	5.A.6.	104
Kilmacar	20	50	[3968]	2.G.10., 3.A.6.	52-54
Kilmacow	138	55	0940	7.D.8.	150
Kilmademoge	27	50	0863, [3969]	3.C.2.	
Kilmadum	62	52	0903, [3970]	3.A.2., 3.C.4., 5.A.11.	
Kilmaganny	100	54	0954	7.G.14.	179-183
Kilmakevoge	124	55	0928	3.C.2.	128
Kilmanagh	40	51	0847	1.F.10.	
Kilmenan	17	50	0865, [3971]	2.D.8., 8.A.10	55-56
Kilree	99	54		8.A.10	184
Knocktopher	103	54	0969, [3992] [2872]	8.F.4.	213-220
Lismateige	107	54	0970, [3994]	8.F.13.	221-223
Listerlin	115	54	0929, [3981], [3993]	8.G.2.	129
Mallardstown	94	54	0956	8.A.13.	
Mayne	22	50	0866, [3972]	3.B.10.	
Mothell	24	50	0904	2.G.13., 3.A.13., 3.B.2., 5.A.14.	57-59

PARISH	TITHES 1823–38 TAB 14/	FILM	VALUATION FIELD BOOKS 1830s OL4./ HOUSE BOOKS [OL5.]	TENEMENT VALUATION FICHE 1849–50	1841–1851 CENSUS SEARCH Cen /s/14
Muckalee	25	50	0868, [3973], [3995]	2.G.14., 3.B.6.	60-61, 224
Muckalee	130	55	0972	8.G.3., 7.C.3.	60-61, 224
Odagh	39	51	0848, [3974]	3.B.12., 3.C.6.	10
Outrath	53	52	0987	9.C.2.	227
Owning	127	55	0942	7.C.3.	163
Pleberstown	90	53	0905	5.A.14.	
Pollrone	134	55	0943	7.C.8.	164-165
Portnascully	139	55	0944	7.D.2.	166
Powerstown	82	53	0906	5.B.1.	105-107
Rossinan	111	54	0973, [3996]	8.G.5., 6.E.10.	
Rathbeagh	30	50	0880, [3976]	3.G.9., 2.D.8.	62-65
Rathcoole	64	52	0907	5.B.8.	
Rathkieran	133	55	0930	7.D.7.	167
Rathlogan	5	50	0881	3.G.12.	
Rathpatrick	125	55	0930	6.D.8.	130
Rathaspick	16	50	0870, [3975]	2.G.12.	
Rosbercon	116	54	0931, [2917]	6.E.2.	131-133
Rosconnell	12	50	0871, [3977]	2.C.10.	66
Shanbogh	120	55	0933	6.E.12.	134
Shankill	68	52	0911, [3980]	5.C.9.	108-110
Sheffin	9	50	0849	3.G.13., 1.G.7.	77-78
St Canice's	42	51	0850	1.G.8., 9.C.7.	
St John's	43	51	0908	5.B.10.	
St Martin's	69	53	0909	5.C.6.	
St Mary's	44	51	[4003/05]	9.G.11.	
St Maul's	45	51	[4006]	5.C.8.	111-112
St Patrick's	46	51	0991, [4007]	9.C.9.	228
Stonecarthy	61	52	0988, [3997]	9.C.5.	225
The Rower	114	54	0934		135
Thomastown	84	53	0912, [2919/21]	5.D.2.	113-117
Tibberaghny	129	55	0945	7.D.12.	168
Tiscoffin	65	52	0913	5.D.13.	
Treadingstown	77	53	0914	9.D.1., 5.E.4.	
Tubbrid	132	55	0946	7.D.13.	
Tubbridbritain	31	51	0851	1.G.14.	11
Tullaghanbrogue	49	52	0852	2.A.5.	12
Tullaherin	80	53	0915	5.E.6.	
Tullahought	101	54	0958	8.B.2.	
Tullamaine	45	52	0993	9.D.4.	
Tullaroan	37	51	0853	2.A.6.	13
Ullard	87	53	0916	5.E.10.	118
Ullid	137	55	0947	7.E.1.	
Urlingford	3	50	0883, [2922]	4.A.1.	79-81
Wells	75	53	0917	5.F.1.	
Whitechurch	126	55	0948	7.E.3.	169
Woolengrange	78	53	0918	5.F.1.	

TOWNS	VALUATION HOUSE BOOKS 1830s [OL5]
Ballyhale	[2871/72] [3998/99]
Ballyragget	[2873]
Bennettsbridge	[2874]
Goresbridge	[2881/82]
Higginstown	[2872]
Johnstown	[2807/88]
Mullinvat	[2872] [2916]
St Canice	[2889/93, 2903/05]
St John's	[2894/96, 2906/08]
St Mary's	[2897/900, 2909/11]
St Maul's	[2901, 2912/13]
St Patrick's	[2902, 2914/15]
Stoneyford	[2872] [2918] [4008]

PARISH	TITHES 1823–38 TAB 24/	FILM	VALUATION FIELD BOOKS 1830s OL4./ HOUSE BOOKS [OL5.]	TENEMENT VALUATION FICHE 1850/51	1841–1851 CENSUS SEARCH Cen /s/24
Abbeyleix	41	85	1537, 1550, 1564, [2932/35]	3.F.10., 1.D.12., 3.B.2.	44-47
Aghaboe	23	85	1528, 2702	2.C.6., 1.E.2.	5-12, 29-32
Aghmacart	32	85	1538	1.F.2.	33
Aharney	36	85	1539	1.G.2.	
Ardea	5	84	1566, [2954/59]	5.A.6.	82-84
Attanagh	37	85	1540	1.G.4.	
Ballyadams	43	85	1575, [4010]	6.D.2., 1.A.8.	
Ballyroan	38	85	1551, [2939]	3.C.4.	
Bordwell	29	85	1529, 1541	2.D.4., 1.G.7.	34
Borris	10	84	1558, [2940]	4.D.6.	52-54
Castlebrack	1	84	1585	7.A.8.	
Clonenagh & Clonagheen	9	84	1552, 1559, 1565 [2952/53]	3.F.12., 4.F.1., 3.D.4.	55, 59-81
Cloydagh	53	86	1569	5.F.6.	
Coolbanagher	6	84	1567	5.B.12.	
Coolkerry	31	85	1530, 1542	2.D.6., 1.G.10.	
Curraclone	18	85	1576, [4011]	6.D.4.	
Donaghmore	25	85	1531, [2944]	2.D.8.	
Durrow	33	85	1543, [2945/47]	1.G.14.	35-39
Dysartenos	14	84	1560, 1577, [4012]	4.F.6., 6.D.10.	103
Dysartgallen	42	85	1553	3.D.5.	48
Erke	27	85	1532, 1544	2.E.2., 2.A.12.	13-15
Fossy or Timahoe	40	85	1554, 1578, [4013]	4.F.8., 6.E.2., 3.E.7.	49-51
Glashare	35	85	1545	2.B.2.	
Kilcolmanbane	13	84	1555, 1561	4.F.12., 3.E.14.	
Kilcolmanbrack	39	85	1556	3.F.1.	
Kildellig	28	85	1546	2.B.4.	
Killabban	49	86	1521, 1570, [2938, 4009]	5.F.10.	1, 88-93
Killenny	15	84	1579, [4015]	6.E.4.	
Killermogh	30	85	1547	2.B.6.	40-41
Killeshin	51	86	1571	6.A.8.	94-98
Kilmanman	2	84	1586, [2942/3]	7.B.4.	106-107
Kilteale	12	84	1562, 1580, [4014]	4.F.8., 6.E.6.	
Kyle	21	85	1533	2.E.6.	16-21
Lea	7	84	1568, [1189]	5.C.8.	85-87
Moyanna	16	84	1581, [4016] [2961/63]	6.E.10.	104
Mountrath					
Monksgrange	48	86	1522	1.C.2.	2-3
Offerlane	8	84	1589	7.F.14.	111-135
Rahan			[1189A]		
Rathaspick	47	85	1523, 1572	1.C.4., 6.B.14.	4, 99-101
Rathdowney	24	85	1534, 1548, [2948, 2967/68]	2.E.14., 2.B.10	22-25
Rathsaran	26	85	1535	2.G.14.	26
Rearymore	3	84	1587	7.C.10.	
Rosconnell	34	85	1549, 1557	2.B.12., 3.F.2.	42-43
Rosenallis	4	84	1588, [2954/60]	7.D.8.	108-110
Shrule	50	86	1573	6.C.6.	102
Skirk	22	85	1536	3.A.4.	27-28
Sleaty	52	86	1574	6.C.8.	

PARISH	TITHES 1823–38 TAB 24/	FILM	VALUATION FIELD BOOKS 1830s OL4./ HOUSE BOOKS [OL5.]	TENEMENT VALUATION FICHE 1850/51	1841–1851 CENSUS SEARCH Cen /s/24
St John's	44	85	1524	1.C.10.	
Straboe	11	84	1563	4.G.1.	56-58
Stradbally	27/17	84	1582, [4017], [2969/72]	6.F.4.	105
Tankardstown	46	85	1525	1.C.12.	
Tecolm	45	85	1526	1.D.2.	
Timahoe/Fossy			[4018]		
Timogue	19	85	1583, [4018]	6.G.4.	
Tullomoy	20	85	1584, [4019]	6.G.6., 1.D.4.	

TOWNS	VALUATION HOUSE BOOK 1830s [OL5.]
Abbeyleix	[2932/35]
Arless	[2951]
Ballickmoyler	[2951]
Ballinakill	[2936/37]
Ballybrittas	[2960]
Ballylynan	[2938, 2951]
Ballyroan	[2939]
Castletown	[2941, 2947]
Clonaslee	[2942/43, 2960]
Erril	[2948]
Graigue	[2949/50, 2951]
Maryborough	[2952/53]
Mountmellick	[2954/59, 2960]
Portarlington	[2964/66]

PARISH	TITHES 1823–38 TAB 16/	FILM	VALUATION FIELD BOOKS 1830s OL4./ HOUSE BOOKS [OL5.]	TENEMENT VALUATION 1856 FICHE	1841–1851 CENSUS SEARCH Cen /s/16
Annaduff	13	61	1057, 1062	3.A.2., 6.D.4., 4.A.8., 6.E.10.	494-504, 675-680
Carrigallen	15	61	1047	1.E.14., 6.A.12.	1-39
Cloonclare	5	60	1051, 1065, 2699, [4257]	5.D.4., 4.B.8.	137-193, 752-769
Cloone	17	61	1048, 2698, [4256], [2924]	6.C.4., 6.F.5.	40-60, 681-722
Cloonlogher	4	60	1052	4.D.8.	194-202
Drumlease	3	60	1053 [4258]	4.D.12.	203-252
Drumreilly	9	60	1049, 1054, [4256], [4020], [4259]	2.F.2., 1.F.13	61-92, 253-311
Fenagh	12	61	1050, 1058, 1063	6.D.5., 2.A.14., 7.B.13.	93-94, 505-512, 723-727
Inishmagrath	8	60	2697, [4021], [4260]	4.E.14.	312-379
Killanummery	6	60	1055, [4261],	5.A.8.	380-426
Killarga	7	60	1056, [4022], [4262]	5.B.11.	427-493
Killasnet	2	59	1066, 2700	5.E.1.	770-808
Kiltubbrid	11	61	1060	3.F.1.	595-669
Kiltoghert	10	60	1059, [4023]	3.A.12.	513-594
Mohill	16	61	1061, 1064, [2931]	4.A.6., 6.E.5.	670-674, 728-751
Oughteragh	14	61	[4256]	2.A.14., 6.D.2.	95-136
Rossinver	1	59	1067, 2701	1.A.12., 5.F.14.	808-870

TOWNS	VALUATION HOUSE BOOK 1830s [OL5.]
Ballinamore	[2923]
Drumahaire	[2925]
Drumkeeran	[2926]
Drumsna	[2927]
Keshkerrigan	[2928]
Manorhamilton	[2929/30]

PARISH	TITHES 1823–38 TAB 17/	FILM	VALUATION FIELD BOOKS 1830s OL4./ HOUSE BOOKS [OL5.]	TENEMENT VALUATION FICHE 1850/52	1841–1851 CENSUS SEARCH Cen /s/17
Abbeyfeale	74	65	2749, [1252/54], [2973]	6.B.14.	318-352
Abington	61	64	2703-04, 2769-2771	1.A.14., 8.C.2.	532-537
Adare	89	66	2757-58-59, [1221/22], [1250], [2974/75]	7.E.8., 7.E.12., 11.G.5., 13.A.2.	268-272, 446-448
Aglishcormick	60	64	2705, [1237]	1.B.6., 3.E.2.	1-3
Anhid	93	66		13.B.1.	
Ardagh	11	62	2790, [1255/56]	10.F.12., 6.D.6.	353, 583-586
Ardcanny	27	62	2760	7.E.8., 7.F.4.	449-450
Ardpatrick	121	67	2728	4.D.6.	182-183
Askeaton	14	62	[1190/91], [1190/91] [2976/77]	2.E.10.	60-65
Athlacca	95	66		13.B.3.	273-276
Athneasy	131	67	2729, 2800, [1270]	9.E.14., 4.D.8.	184-185
Ballinacurra	131	67	[3040]		
Ballinard	109	66	2801, [1271/72]	9.F.4.	
Ballingaddy	122	67	2730	4.D.14.	186
Ballingarry	81	65	[1223/25], [1243/44]	11.G.6.	66-67, 93-108, 187-191
Ballingarry	125	67	2731-32, [4024], [2978/81]	4.E.6.	66-67, 93-108,187-191
Ballinlough	111	66	2802, [1271/72]	9.F.8.	663
Ballybrood	57	64	2706	1.B.8.	4
Ballycahane	38	63	2777, 2803, [1273/74]	8.F.8., 8.F.12., 9.F.12	542-544
Ballylanders	126	67	[1245], 4025/26	4.F.2.	192-211
Ballynamona	110	66	2804, [1275]	9.F.14.	
Ballynaclogh	66	64		3.E.4.	
Ballyscadden	119	66	2734		
Bruff	96	66	[2982/83]	13.B.8.	277-283
Bruree	84	65	[1226/28], [2983]		109-110, 284-285
Caheravally	50	63		1.B.12.	
Caherconlish	53	64	[2985]	1.C.4.	5-15
Cahercorney	106	65	2805, [1271/72]	9.G.2.	
Caherelly	55	64	2707	1.D.4.	
Cahernarry	51	63	2708	1.D.10.	
Cappagh	17	62	[1192/95], [1192/95]	2.F.10.	68-69
Carrigparson	49	63	2709	1.D.14.	
Castletown	64	64	[1238]	3.F.4.	
Chapelrussell	26	62	2761-62	7.E.8.	451
Clonagh	19	62	[1196], [1196a/97]	2.F.13.	70
Cloncagh	80	65	[1229]	12.C.8.	111-115
Cloncrew	85,86	65		12.C.14.	116
Clonelty	73	65	2750, [1257/58]	6.C.7.	355-357
Clonkeen	47	63		1.E.4.	
Clonshire	18	62	[1198/200]	2.G.1.	
Colmanswell	87	65		12.D.2.	117
Corcomohide	83	65	[1230/31]	12.D.5.	118-132
Crecora	35	63	2778	8.G.2.	545-546
Croagh	22	62	2721, [1201/02]	2.G.2.	71-74
Croom	91	66	2779, [1222], [1232], [2987/88]	8.G.8.	286-300
Darragh	129	67	2735 [1246]	4.G.2.	212-227

PARISH	TITHES 1823–38 TAB 17/	FILM	VALUATION FIELD BOOKS 1830s OL4./ HOUSE BOOKS [OL5.]	TENEMENT VALUATION FICHE 1850/52	1841–1851 CENSUS SEARCH Cen /s/17
Derrygalvin	46	63	2710	1.E.6.	
Donaghmore	48	63	2711	1.E.10.	
Doon	63	64	2772-73	8.E.2., 3.E.8., 3.F.6.	172-177, 538
Doondonnell	20	62	2722, [1203]	2.G.14.	75
Drehidtarsna	90	66	[1222]	12.E.9., 13.D.9.	
Dromcolliher			[2989/90]		133-143
Dromin	97	66		13.D.9.	301-304
Dromkeen	58	64	2712	1.E.14.	
Dunmoylan	7	62		10.G.7.	587-588
Dysert	92	66		13.D.14.	
Effin	102	66	2736, [4027/28]	13.E.1., 4.G.10.	228-230, 305-307
Emlygrennan	117	66	2737	4.G.14.	231
Fedamore	104	66	2713, [1276/77], [2993]	1.F.4., 9.E.8., 9.G.4.	664-674
Glenogra	105	66	2806, [1278/79]	10.A.4.	675
Galbally	120	67	2738, [4029], [2991]	5.A.6.	232-237
Grange	72	65	2751, [1259]	6.D.12.	358-359
Grean	65	64	2714, [1239]	1.F.6., 3.G.14.	
Hackmys	100	66		13.E.6.	308-310
Hospital	112	66	2807-08, [1280], [4032], [2994]	9.E.9., 10.A.10.	
Inch St Lawrence	56	64	2715	1.F.10.	
Iveruss	24	62	2763-64	7.E.9., 7.F.14.	76, 452-455
Kilbeheny	130	67	2739, [4030]	5.B.14.	238-247
Kilbolane	88	65		12.F.6.	
Kilbradran	9	62	2791, [1196], [1203]	10.G.12., 3.A.2.	
Kilbreedy	101	66	2740	13.E.8.	248-249
Kilbreedy Major	115	66	2809, [1247]	10.B.8., 5.D.6.	
Kilcolman	8	62	2792	11.A.2.	589
Kilcornan	25	62	2765-66	7.E.9., 7.G.8.	456-461
Kilcullane	108	66	2810, [1281]	9.E.9.	676-677
Kildimo	28	62	2767-68	7.E.9.	462-468
Kilfergus	2	62	2793	11.A.5.	590-611
Kilfinnane	124	67	2741, [1248], [4031], [2995]	5.D.12.	250-251
Kilfinny	79	65	[1222], [1233/34]	12.F.7.	144
Kilflyn	128	67	2742, [1249]	5.F.10.	253-258
Kilfrush	113	66	2811, [1282]	10.C.2.	
Kilkeedy	29	62	2780-81, 2789	8.F.8., 8.G.14.	547-552
Killagholehane	78	65	2752, [1260]	6.E.1.	360-366
Killeedy	77	65	2753, [1261]	6.E.7.	354, 367-412
Killeely	30	62	[3011], [3035]	14.B.2., 14.B.10., 13.G.8., 13.G.12.	178
Killeenagarriff	43	63	2716	1.F.14.	31-32
Killeenoghty	37	63	2782	9.B.6., 13.E.10.	553
Killonahan	34	63	2783	8.F.8., 9.B.8., 13.E.11.	311-313
Kilmallock (Sts. Peter & Paul)			[2996/7]		

PARISH	TITHES 1823–38 TAB 17/	FILM	VALUATION FIELD BOOKS 1830s OL4./ HOUSE BOOKS [OL5.]	TENEMENT VALUATION FICHE 1850/52	1841–1851 CENSUS SEARCH Cen /s/17
Kilmeedy	82	65	[1235/36]	12.F.12.	145-171
Kilmoylan	6	62	2794	11.B.12.	612-619
Kilmurry	42	63	2717	1.G.10.	33-36
Kilpeacon	103	66	2784, 2812, [1283/84]	9.B.12., 10.C.4.	678
Kilquane	127	67	2743	5.G.8.	259-261
Kilscannell	23	62	2723, [1196a/97], [1204/05]	3.A.2.	77
Kilteely	69	64	2813, [1271/72]	3.E.9., 4.A.12.	178, 679
Knockainy	107	66	2814 ,[1285] [2994]	9.E.9., 10.C.6.	680-681
Knocklong	118	66	2744	5.G.12.	262-264
Knocknagaul	36	63	2785	9.B.14.	
Limerick city			[2998-3035]		474-531
Lismakeery	15	62	[1206/08]	3.A.6.	
Loghill	3	62	2795	11.C.12.	620-626
Ludden	52	64		2.A.2.	37-38
Mahoonagh	76	65	2754. [1262/63]	6.G.2.	413-416
Monagay	75	65	2755, [1264/67]	7.A.1.	417-443
Monasteranenagh	39	63	2786, 2815, [1286/87]	8.F.9., 9.C.4., 13.E.13.	682-685, 554-560
Morgans	12	62	2724, [1209/11]	3.A.9.	
Mungret	32	63	2787	8.F.9., 9.C.10.	561-577
Nantinan	16	62	2725, 2796, [1212/15]	11.D.6., 3.A.11.	78-80, 627-632
Newcastle	71	64	2756, [1266/69]	11.D.7., 7.C.1.	444-445
Oola	68	64	[1240]	3.E.9., 4.B.2.	179
Particles	123	67	2745-46-47	6.A.6.	265-267
Rathjordan	59	64		2.A.6.	
Rathkeale	21	62	2726, [1216/18, 3041/44]	3.B.5.	81-92
Rathronan	10	62	2797	11.D.8.	633-659
Robertstown	5	62	2798	11.E.8.	
Rochestown	54	64		2.A.10.	
Shanagolden	4	62	2799, [3045]	11.D.6.	660-662
St John's	1	62	[3007]	14.B.2., 14.C.3., 2.A.10.	
St Lawrence's	44	63	2718, [3012]	14.B.3., 14.E.7., 2.A.12.	
St Michael's	33	63	2788, [3006]	14.B.3., 14.F.10., 8.F.9., 9.D.10.	493-499, 530-531, 578-580
St Munchin's	31	63	2789, [3014], [3034], [3035]	14.B.5., 15.C.14., 13.G.8., 14.A.2.	500-508, 581-582
St Nicholas	45	63	2719, [3015], [3032], [3035]	15.D.5., 13.G.8., 14.A.6., 2.B.2.	39
St Patrick's	41	63	2720, [4034], [3033]	14.B.5., 15.D.10.	40-41, 509-529
St Peter's & St Paul's	114	66		7.D.6.	469-473
Stradbally	40	63		2.C.2.	42-59
Tankardstown	99	66		13.E.14.	
Templebredon	70	64	[1240/42]	4.B.14.	180-181
Tomdeely	13	62	2727, [1219/20]	3.D.9.	
Tullabracky	94	66	2816, [1251], [1288/89]	13.F.2.,	314-316

PARISH	TITHES 1823–38 TAB 17/	FILM	VALUATION FIELD BOOKS 1830s OL4./ HOUSE BOOKS [OL5.]	TENEMENT VALUATION FICHE 1850/52	1841–1851 CENSUS SEARCH Cen /s/17
Tuogh	62	64	2774-2776	8.C.2., 8.E.6.	539-541
Tuoghcluggin or	67	64		4.C.4.	
Cluggin					
Uregare	98	66	2817 [1290]	13.F5., 10.E.10.	317, 686-687

TOWNS	VALUATION HOUSE BOOK 1830s [OL5.]
Cappamore	[2986]
Castleconnel	[2985]
Glin	[2992]
Herbertstown	[2993]
Killeely	[3011, 3035]
Limerick No. 1 & 2	[2998]
Limerick No. 3	[2999]
Limerick No. 4	[3000]
Limerick No. 5	[3001]
Limerick No. 6	[3002]
Limerick No. 7	[3003]
Limerick No. 8	[3004]
Limerick No. 9	[3005]
Montpelier	[2985]
Moroe	[3036]
No. 1-14	[3016/29]
Pallas Green	[3037]
Pallaskenry	[3038]
Patrickswell	[3039/40]
St John's 11	[3007]
St John's 12	[3008]
St John's 13	[3009]
St John's 14	[3010]
St Lawrence	[3012]
St Mary's	[3013] [4033]
St Mary's	[3030/31]
St Michael's 10	[3006]
St Munchin's	[3014, 3034, 3035]
St Nicholas	[3015, 3032, 3035]
St Patrick's	[3033]

PARISH	TITHES 1823–38 TAB 18/	FILM	VALUATION FIELD BOOKS 1830s OL4./ HOUSE BOOKS [OL5.]	TENEMENT VALUATION 1854 FICHE	1841–1851 CENSUS SEARCH Cen /s/18
Abbeylara	7	68	1116-17, [1291]	2.D.8.	25-31
Abbeyshrule	23	69	1158-59, [1294]	1.F.12.	331-332
Agharra	24	69	1160-61	1.G.2.	
Ardagh	9	68	1099, 1134-35, 2818	4.A.4., 3.E.4.	1-3
Ballymacormick	14	69	1100-01, 1136-37	4.B.3., 3.E.7.	292
Cashel	19	69	1147-48	1.A.14., 3.G.4.	313-318
Clonbroney	5	68	1102 03, 1118-19, 2819, [1293]	2.B.12., 2.E.4.	32-65
Clongesh	3	68	1124-25	4.D.6.	161-165
Columbkille	4	68	1120-21	2.F.7., 5.C.8.	66-111
Forgney	25	69	1162-63, 1162-63	1.G.4.	333-337
Granard	6	68	1104-05, 2819/20, [1292], [3062/65]	2.B.12., 3.A.1.	112-133
Kilcommock	20	69	1138, 1149-50, 1164	1.D.12., 1.C.4., 1.G.11.	292-299, 319-322
Kilglass	16	69	1106-07, 1139-40, 1165	1.F.4., 4.B.9., 1.E.3., 1.G.12.	300, 339-341
Killashee	13	69	1126-27, 1141-42	4.F.3., 1.E.7., 3.F.1.	301-304
Killoe	1	68	1122-23, 1128-29	3.C.8., 5.C.8., 2.D.6., 4.F.7.	134-160, 166-282
Mohill	2	68	1130-31	4.E.12.	283-286
Mostrim	10	68	1108-09	2.B.13.	4-14
Moydow	15	69	1143-44	1.E.7., 3.F.12.	305-309
Noughaval	26	69	1151-52, 1166-67	1.C.12., 1.G.14.	
Rathcline	18	69	1153-54	1.C.12., 3.G.4.	323-329
Rathreagh	12	68	1110-11	1.F.6.	15-16
Shrule	21	69	1155, 2821	1.C.12.	330
Street	11	68	1112-13	2.D.1.	17
Taghsheenod	17	69	1145-46, 1168-69	1.E.10., 2.A.5.	310-312
Taghshinny	22	69	1156-57, 1170-71	1.D.10., 2.A.6.	338, 342
Templemichael	8	68	1114-15, 1132-33	4.B.10., 5.B.11.	18-24, 287-291

TOWNS	VALUATION HOUSE BOOK 1830s [OL5.]
Ballymahon	[3056, 3057]
Drumlish	[3058/59]
Edgeworthstown	[3058, 3060/61]
Longford	[3058]
Newtownforbes	[3058, 3061]
Keenagh	[3066]
Lanesboro[ugh]	[3067]
Longford	[3068/69]

PARISH/TOWN	TITHES 1823–38 TAB 20/	FILM	VALUATION FIELD BOOKS 1830s OL4./ HOUSE BOOKS [OL5.]	TENEMENT VALUATION 1854 FICHE	1841–1851 CENSUS SEARCH Cen /s/20
Ardee	29	71	1172, 2822, [3071/2]	1.A.14.	1-9
Ballybarrack	14	70	1199, [4049-50]	5.A.13.	189
Ballyboys	3	70	1195, [4045]	6.A.9.	110-111
Ballymakenny	62	72	1193 & 3a, 1214, 2848, [4035-36]	2.E.14., 2.D.12.	280
Ballymascanlan	1	70	1196, 1200, 2843, 2844, [4046, 4051]	6.A.12., 5.A.14.	112- 154, 190-92
Barronstown	10	70	1201	5.B.1.	193
Beaulieu	61	72	1215, 2849, [1300]	2.F.2.	281
Cappoge	38	71	1173, 2823	1.C.10.	10
Carlingford	2	70	1197, 2845, [4047]	6.C.13.	155-188
Carrickbaggot	51	71	1216, 2850	2.F.4.	
Castlebellingham (Gernonstown)			[3073]		
Castletown	11	70	1198, 1202 ,[4052-53, 1295]	6.G.13., 5.B.5.	194
Charlestown	27	71	1174, 2824	1.C.12.	11-12
Clogher	57	72	1217, 2851, [3074]	2.F.6.	
Clonkeehan	21	71	1236, 2866, [4070]	2.C.8.	336
Clonkeen	26	71	1175, 1176, 2825	1.D.2.	13-17
Clonmore	46	71	1218	2.F.13.	282
Collon	48	71	1219, 2842, [3075]	2.A.12.	282-297
Creggan	6	70	1203, [4054]	5.B.8.	195-198
Darver	20	71	1237, 2867, [4071]	4.F.2.	
Drogheda			[3076/90, 3100, 4037-4043]		79-109
Dromin	37	71	1177, 2826	1.D.9.	
Dromiskin	19	71	1238, 2868, [4072]	4.F.4.	337-344
Drumcar	35	71	1178	1.D.13.	18-21
Drumshallon	55	72	1220, 2853, [1296]	2.G.2.	298-301
Dunany	43	71	1221, 2854, 2855	2.B.9.	302-303
Dunbin	13	70	1204, [4055-56]	5.B.13.	199-211
Dundalk	12	70	1205, 2846, [3101/9, 4044, 4057-58]	5.C.4., 5.F.2.	213-241
Dunleer	44	71	1222, 2856, [1297, 3110]	2.B.12.	304
Dysart	45	71	1223, 2857	2.G.8.	305
Faughart	5	70	1206, 2847, [4059]	5.D.5.	242-257
Gernonstown	32	71	1179, 2828	1.E.6.	22-25
Haggardstown	15	70	1207, 2847, [4060-61]	5.D.13.	258-265
Haynestown	16	70	1208, 2847, [4062-63]	5.E.2.	
Inishkeen	9	70	1209, 1239, 2847	5.D.2., 4.F.13.	266-268
Kane	8	70	1210, 2847	5.E.3.	269
Kildemock	40	71	1180, 2829	1.E.11.	26-28
Killanny	23	71	1181, 2830	4.E.6.	29-35
Killincoole	18	71	1240, 2869, [4073]	4.F.13.	
Kilsaran	31	71	1182, 2831	1.F.2.	36-47
Louth	17	70	1183, 1211, 1241, 2832, 2870, [4065-66, 4074]	5.E.5., 2.C.8., 4.G.2., 4.E .11.	270-272 345-354
Manfieldstown	22	71	1242, [4075]	2.C.10.	
Mapastown	28	71	1184, 2833	1.F.7.	48-49
Marlestown	50	71	1224, 2858	2.G.11.	306
Mayne	56	72	1225, 2859	2.G.12.	
Monasterboice	54	72	1226, 2860, [1298]	2.G.14.	307-309

PARISH	TITHES 1823–38 TAB 20/	FILM	VALUATION FIELD BOOKS 1830s OL4./ HOUSE BOOKS [OL5.]	TENEMENT VALUATION 1854 FICHE	1841–1851 CENSUS SEARCH Cen /s/20
Mosstown	41	71	1185, 2834	1.F.9.	50-51
Mullary	49	71	1227, 2861, [1299]	3.A .5.	310-315
Parsonstown	53	71	1228	3.A.10.	
Philipstown	7	70	1212	5.E.9.	52-56, 273
Philipstown	24	71	1186, 2835 [4067]	1.G.1.	
Philipstown	59	72	1229, 2862 [1301]	3.A.10.	
Port	47	71	1230	3.A.11.	
Rathdrumin	52	71	1231, 2863	3.B.1.	316
Richardstown	34	71	1187, 2836	1.G.8.	
Roche	4	70	1213, 2847 [4068]	5.E.10.	274-279
Salterstown	42	71	1232	2.C.6.	
Shanlis	36	71	1188, 2837	1.G.10.	
Smarmore	39	71	1189, 2838	1.G.12.	
Stabannan					58-62
St Mary's (Drogheda)	64	72	[4040, 4069]	3.E.10.	66-70
St Peter's	63	72	1194, 1233, 2842 [4041]	2.D.13., 3.G.2.	71-78
Stickillin	33	71	1191, 2840	2.A.7.	
Tallanstown	25	71	1192, 2841	2.A.8.	63-65
Termonfeckin	60	72	1234, 2864 [3111]	3.B.4.	317-320
Tullyallen	58	72	1235, 2865	3.C.6.	321-335

PARISH	TITHES 1823–38 TAB 21/	FILM	VALUATION FIELD BOOKS 1830s OL4./ HOUSE BOOKS [OL5.]	TENEMENT VALUATION FICHE 1855–57	1841–1851 CENSUS SEARCH Cen /s/21
Achill	19	74	1243, [4077]	11.A.2.	1-142
Addergoole	16	74	1298, [4167]	1.A.14., 7.A.14.	2586-2628
Aghagower	48	75	1244, 1294, 2904	14.C.12., 14.G.8.	143-161, 2421-2446
Aghamore	70	76	1268, [4127]	8.G.8., 12.A.12.	640-817
Aglish	24	74	1249, 2872, [4089-90]	5.D.14.	313-337
Annagh	73	76	1269, [4128]	8.G.12.	818-930
Ardagh	14	74	1299, [4168]	1.A.14.	2629-2641
Attymass	36	75	1277, 2889	2.B.10.	1655-1704
Balla	59	75	2884	6.F.14.	469-475
Ballinchalla	52	75	1287, [4150]	2.G.10.	2255-2263
Ballinrobe	50	75	1288, [4151-52, 3119/23]	3.A.4.	2264-2288
Ballintober	30	74	1245, 1250, 2873, [4078, 4091-92]	14.D.10., 2.E.10., 5.G.1.	162, 338-345
Ballynahaglish	18	74	1300, [4169-71]	1.B.7.	2641-2669
Ballyhean	27	74	1251, 2875, [4093-94]	6.A.1.	346-356
Ballyovey	34	75	1252, 2874, [4096]	2.E.11.	357-380
Ballysakeery	12	73	1301, [4172]	1.C.8.	2670-2689
Bekan	72	76	1270, [4131]	9.B.14.	931-975
Bohola	43	75	1278, 2890	6.G.10., 13.A.4.	1705-1766
Breaghwy	26	74	1253, 2876, [4099-4102]	6.A.13.	381-382
Burriscarra	31	74	1254, 2877, [4103]	2.F.10., 6.B.6.	383-387
Burrishoole	20	74	1246, [4079-80]	11.C.12.	163-240
Castlemore	69	76	1271, [4135]	7.E.4.	976-1009
Cong	55	75	1289, [4153-55, 3135]	3.C.7.	1441-1596, 2289, 2290-2310
Crossboyne	63	76	1262	8.A.12.	476-511
Crossmolina	13	73	1302, [4175-76, 4191]	1.D.6.	2690-2737
Doonfeeny	3	73	1303, [4177]	10.A.12.	2738-2762
Drum	29	74	1255, 2878, [4106]	6.B.8.	388-390
Inishbofin (Island)	46	75	1295, 2902	9.G.4.	2447-2454
Islandeady	23	74	1247, 1256, 2879 [4081, 4109]	14.D.11.	241-252, 391-409
Kilbeagh	66	76	1272, [4138]	7.F.1., 12.C.10.	1010-1117
Kilbelfad	17	74	1304, [4181]	1.F.14.	2763-2779
Kilbride	4	73	1305, [4179]	10.B.14.	2780-2794
Kilcolman	61	76	1263, 1273, [4141]	8.C.7. 7.F.3.	512-577, 1118-1176
Kilcommon	2	73	2885-2887	4.D.4., 11.F.12.	1441-1596 2289, 2311-2361
Kilcommon	51	75	2898, [4156]	3.D.14., 9.E.12.	
Kilconduff	41	75	1279, 2891, [4146]	13.B.2.	1767-1862
Kilcummin	5	73	1306, [4180]	10.C.6.	2795-2824
Kildacommoge	42	75	1257, 1280, [4112, 4147]	6.D.2., 6.G.10	410-418, 1863-1876
Kilfian	7	73	1307	1.G.11., 10.D.1.	2825-2859
Kilgarvan	35	75	1281, 2892	2.C.9.	1877-1966
Kilgeever	47	75	1296, 2903, 2905	15.D.6.	2445-2501
Killala	10	73	1308, [4182, 3138/39]	10.E.1.	2860-2865

PARISH	TITHES 1823–38 TAB 21/	FILM	VALUATION FIELD BOOKS 1830s OL4./ HOUSE BOOKS [OL5.]	TENEMENT VALUATION FICHE 1855–57	1841–1851 CENSUS SEARCH Cen /s/21
Killasser	38	75	1282, 2893	13.D.4.	1967-2028
Killedan	44	75	1283, 2894, [4148]	13.E.14.	2029-2160
Kilmaclasser	22	74	1248, [4082]	14.E.7.	253-270, 311-312
Kilmainebeg	56	75			2362-2369
Kilmainemore	54	75	1291, [4159]	3.F.10.	2370-2392
Kilmeena	21	74	2871, [4083]	11.F.7., 14.F.14.	271-310, 311-312
Kilmolara	53	75	2899	3.G.11.	2393-2394
Kilmore	1	73	2888	4.G.13.	1597-1654
Kilmoremoy	15	74	1309, [4185]	2.A.1.	2866-2902
Kilmovee	68	76	1274, [4143]	12.F.5.	1177-1371
Kilturra	65	76	1275, [4144]	12.G.14.	1372-1379
Kilvine	64	76	1264, [4085]	8.E.7.	578-609
Knock	71	76	1265, 1276, [4086, 4145]	8.F.1., 9.D.13.	610-627, 1380-1440
Lackan	6	73	1310	10.E.11.	2903-2925
Manulla	28	74	1258, 2880 [4115]	6.D.7.	419-425
Mayo	60	76	1266, 1292 [4087, 4162]	4.A.3., 2.G.8., 6.G.7., 8.F.3.	628-631, 2395
Meelick	40	75	1284, 2895	13.G.11.	2161-2198
Moorgagagh	57	75	2900	4.A.6.	
Moygawnagh	11	73	1311, [4187]	10.F.5.	2926-2937
Oughaval	45	75	1297, 2906, [4166]	15.A.8.	2502-2585
Rathreagh	8	73	1312, [4188]	10.F.12.	2938-2941
Robeen	49	75	1293, [4163]	4.A.7.	2396-2409
Rosslee	32	75	1259, 2881, [4118]	2.G.1., 6.E.1.	426-427
Shrule	58	75	2901, [4164, 3144/45]	4.B.5.	2410-2420
Tagheen	62	76	1267, [4088]	8.F.11.	632-639
Templemore	39	75	1285, 2896	7.A.3.	2199-2232
Templemurry	9	73	1313, [4190]	10.G.2.	2942-2954
Toomore	37	75	1286, 2897, [4149]	14.A.11.	2233-2254
Touaghty	33	75	1260, 2882, [4121]	2.G.3.	428-429
Turlough	25	74	1261, 2883, [4124]	6.E.3.	430-468

TOWNS	VALUATION HOUSE BOOKS 1830s [OL5.]
Ballaghadereen	[3112,3113]
Ballyhaunis	[3113, 3124/35]
Ballina	[3114/17]
Ballindine	[3118]
Ballyharris	[3124/25]
Belmullet	[3126/27]
Castlebar	[3128/31]
Clare	[3132/33]
Claremorris	[3134]
Foxford	[3136/37]
Kiltamagh	[3140]
Louisburgh	[3141]
Newport	[3142/43]
Swineford	[3146]
Westport	[3147/49]
Westport Quay	[3150/51]

PARISH	TITHES 1823–38 TAB 22/	FILM	VALUATION FIELD BOOKS 1830s OL4./ HOUSE BOOKS [OL5.]	TENEMENT VALUATION FICHE 1855–57	1841–1851 CENSUS SEARCH Cen /s/22
Agher	138	80	1314, 1323, 2907	9.A.4., 9.A.12.	4
Ardagh	17	77	1386 (Part Missing), 2960, [4206]	5.C.12., 5.C.6.	
Ardbraccan	50	78	1404	7.E.10.	197-202
Ardcath	102	79	1344, 2922	2.G.14.	47-49
Ardmulchan	79	79	1434	7.C.6.	263
Ardsallagh	57	78	1405	7.F.6.	203-207
Assey	116	79	1315	7.D.14.	
Athboy	70	78	1381, [3152]	9.F.12.	134-139
Athlumney	80	79	1435	7.C.9.	264-271
Balfeaghan	141	80	2909, 2915	4.F.6.	
Ballyboggan	110	79	1399	4.G.10.	
Ballygarth	100	79	1345, 2923-24	3.A.7.	
Ballymagarvey	68	78	1331, 2917	7.B.6.	12
Ballymaglassan	135	80	1422	4.B.7.	
Balrathboyne	36	77	1372, 1406, [4197]	6.A.8., 6.A.2.	107-109, 208
Balsoon	117	79	1316, [1302]	7.E.1., 9.A.4.	
Bective		79	1415	7.E.2.	
Brownstown	84	79	1436	7.C.14.	272
Burry	35	77	1373, [4198]	6.A.11.	
Castlejordan	111	79	1400	4.G.14.	187-189
Castlerickard	108	79	1382, 1401	10.A.1., 9.E.12.	
Castletown	11	77	1387	5.C.14., 6.F.4.	144-145
Churchtown	55	78	1407	7.F.7.	209
Clonalvy	106	79	1346, 2925	3.A.8.	18-19
Clonard	109	79	1402	5.A.8., 9.F.1.	190-196
Clongill	15	77	1388	6.F.7.	
Clonmacduff	73	79	1416	8.F.12.	
Collon		78	1460	2.E.12.	294-297
Colp	61	78	1332, 2918	3.C.1.	13-17
Cookstown	129	80	1423	4.B.9.	
Crickstown	128	80	1424, 2956	4.B.10.	
Cruicetown	5	77	1362	5.D.14.	72-75
Culmullin	137	80	1324, 1425, 2908	4.B.11., 3.G.7.	5-8
Cushinstown		79	1437	4.D.11.	273-274
Danestown	88	79	1333, 1438, 2919	7.B.7., 7.D.1.	
Derrypatrick	123	80	1317	3.F.12.	1-3
Diamor	29	77	1356	8.B.10.	
Donaghmore	52	78	1408	4.B.11.	?
Donaghmore	133	80	1426	7.E.9.	210-216
Donaghpatrick	38	78	1374, 1409, [4199]	6.A.14., 7.E.6., 7.F.14.	110-111
Donore		78	1334, 2920	3.C.11.	20-25
Dowdstown	85	79	1439	7.D.2.	275
Dowth	48	78	1461	2.G.8.	298-299
Drakestown	12	77	1389	6.F.8.	
Drumcondra	18	77	1455, [4207]	2.C.13., 5.C.11.	282-287
Drumlargan	139	80	1325, 2910	9.A .13.	
Dulane	33	77	1375, [4200]	6.A 14.	112
Duleek	64	78	1335, 1347, 2926-27	3.D.2., 3.A.11.	26-41, 50-55
Duleek Abbey		79	1348, 2928-29	3.B.3.	
Dunboyne	145	80	1354, 2939, [4194-95, 3154]	4.A.6.	

PARISH	TITHES 1823–38 TAB 22/	FILM	VALUATION FIELD BOOKS 1830s OL4./ HOUSE BOOKS [OL5.]	TENEMENT VALUATION FICHE 1855–57	1841–1851 CENSUS SEARCH Cen /s/22
Dunmoe	53	78	1410	7.G.1.	
Dunsany	95	79	1440	4.D.12.	
Dunshaughlin	126	80	1427, 2948, 2949, [4212, 1307]	4.B.13.	257-260
Emlagh	7	77	1363	5.E.1.	76
Ennisken	9	77	1364, 1390	5.E.1., 5.C.14.	
Fennor	58	78	1336, 2921	7.B.7.	
Follistown	82	79	1441	7.D.3.	276
Gallow	140	80	1326, 2911	9.A.13.	
Galtrim	121	79		9.A.6.	
Gernonstown	41	78	1462	6.G.8.	300-302
Girley	39	78	1376, 2941 [4201]	6.B.4.	113-114
Grangegeeth		78	1463	2.E.14.	303-305
Greenoge	134	80	1428	4.C.7.	
Inishmot	20	77	1456, [4208]	2.D.8.	
Julianstown	66	78	1337, 1349, 2930-31 [4192]	3.E.4., 3.B.3.	
Kells		77	1377, [4213, 3155/57]	6.B.7.	115-117
Kentstown	67	78	1338	7.B.8	
Kilbeg	4	77	1365, [4196]	5.E.5.	77-84
Kilberry	16	77	1391	6.F.10.	146-151
Kilbrew	125	80	1429, 2950	4.C.8.	261
Kilbride	24	77	1357	4.B.4.	?
Kilbride		80	1355	8.B.12.	56-57
Kilcarn	81	79	1442	7.D.4.	277
Kilclone	143	80	1327, 2911	3.G.10.	
Kilcooly	78	79	1417	8.F.14.	256
Kildalkey	71	79	1383	10.A.1.	140
Killaconnigan	72	79	1384	10.A.11.	141-142
Killallon	30	77	1358	8.B.13.	58
Killary	23	77	1457, 2961, [4209]	2.D.9.	288-290
Killeen	94	79	1443	4.D.13.	
Killegland	130	80	1430, [4205]	4.C.10.	
Killeagh	26	77	1359	8.C.6.	59-61
Killyon	107	79	1403	5.B.6., 9.F.7.	
Kilmainham	2	77	1366	5.E.11.	85-93
Kilmessan	120	79	1318	3.F.13.	
Kilmoon	98	79	1444	4.E.1.	
Kilmore	136	80	1328, 2913	3.G.12.	9-10
Kilsharvan	65	78	1339, 1350, 2932-33	3.E.7., 3.B.4.	
Kilshine	14	77	1392	6.G.3.	
Kilskeer	31	77	1378, [4202-03]	6.C.12., 8.E.8.	118-120
Kiltale	122	80	1319	3.G.2.	
Knock	13	77	1393	6.G.5.	152
Knockcommon	63	78	1340	7.B.10.	42-43
Knockmark	124	80	1320	3.G.4.	
Laracor	113	79	1395, 2942, [1303]	9.B.4.	157-160
Liscartan	51	78	1411	7.G.1.	
Lismullin		79	1145	7.D.6.	
Loughan (Castlekeeran)	32	77	1379	6.D.8.	121-129
Loughbrackan	19	77	2962	2.E.2.	291
Loughcrew		77	1360	8.C.12.	62

PARISH	TITHES 1823–38 TAB 22/	FILM	VALUATION FIELD BOOKS 1830s OL4./ HOUSE BOOKS [OL5.]	TENEMENT VALUATION FICHE 1855–57	1841–1851 CENSUS SEARCH Cen /s/22
Macetown	97	79	1446	4.E.4.	
Martry	49	78	1412	6.A.3.	217-219
Mitchelstown	21	77	1458, 2962a, [4210]	2.E.5.	292
Monknewtown		78	1464	2.G.10.	306-312
Monktown		79	1447	7.D.7.	278-279
Moorechurch	101	79	1351, 2934-35	3.B.5.	
Moybolgue	1	77	1367	5.F.2.	94
Moyglare	144	80	1329, 2916	4.A.2., 4.F.7.	
Moylagh	27	77	2940	8.D.2.	63-68
Moymet	75	79	1418	8.G.1.	
Moynalty	3	77	1368	5.F.8.	95-103
Navan	54	78	1413, [4214, 3160]	7.G.3.	220-251
Newtown	6	77	1369	5.G.11.	
Newtownclonbun	77	79	1419	8.G.4.	
Nobber	10	77	1370, 1394	5.G.12., 5.D.5.	153-156
Oldcastle	25	77	1361, [3161]	8.D.9.	69-71
Painestown	62	78	1341	7.B.14.	46
Piercetown	105	79	1342, 1352, 2936	7.C.4., 4.A.3.	
Rataine	56	78	1414	8.A.12.	253-254
Rathbeggan	132	80	1431, 2951, 2957	4.C.11.	
Rathcore	115	79	1330, 1396, 2914, 2943, [1304]	9.B.14., 9.B.2.	11, 161-171
Rathfeigh	92	79	1448	4.E.6.	
Rathkenny	40	78	1465	6.G.11.	313-341
Rathmore	69	78	1385	10.B.5.	143
Rathmolyon	114	79	1397, 2944-47, [1305, 3162]	9.C.11.	172-182
Rathregan	131	80	1432, 2952	4.C.13.	
Ratoath	127	80	1433, 2953-54, 2958-59 [3163]	4.C.14.	262
Rodanstown	142	80		4.F.9.	
Scurlockstown	119	79	1321	9.A.9.	
Siddan	22	77	1459, [4211]	2.E.6.	293
Skreen	91	79	1449	4.E.7.	280
Slane	44	78	1466	7.A.5.	342-347
St Marys	60	78	1343	3.E.9.	44-45
Stackallan	46	78	1467	7.B.1.	348-349
Staffordstown	83	79	1450	7.D.9.	
Staholmog	8	77	1371	5.G.13.	104-106
Stamullin	104	79	1353, 2937-38	3.B..9	
Tara	89	79	1451	7.D.9.	
Teltown	20/37	78	1380, [4204]	6.D.14.	130-133
Templekeeran	86	79	1452	7.D.11.	
Timoole	93	79	1453	4.E.12.	
Trevet	96	79	1454, 2955	4.E.12., 4.D.10.	281
Trim	112	79	1398, 1420, [1306, 3167/70]	8.G.5., 9.D.8.	183-186, 255
Trubley	118	79	1322	9.A.11.	
Tullaghanoge	74	79	1421	9.A.2.	
Tullyallen	45	78	1468	2.G.13.	

TOWNS	VALUATION HOUSE BOOK 1830s [OL5.]
Clonee	[3153]
Dunboyne	[3154]
Kells	
Longwood	[3158]
Mornington	[3159]
Robinstown	[3164]
Summerhill	[3165/66]

PARISH/TOWN	TITHES 1823–38 TAB 23/	FILM	VALUATION FIELD BOOKS 1830s OL4./ HOUSE BOOK [OL5.]	TENEMENT VALUATION c.1858–61 FICHE	1841/1851 CENSUS SEARCH Cen /s/3
Aghabog	12	82	1481/2, 2967/8	4.D.10., 5.E.12., 8.G.12.	241-291
Aghnamullen	18	82	1469/70, 2963/4	2.C.8., 3.E.2., 5.D.6.	1-87
Ballybay	17	82	1471/2, 1502/3, [3171] [3173/74]	4.A.4., 3.A.B.	88-121
Carrickmacross					
Castleblayney			[3175]	2.G.11.	
Clones	9	81	1483/4, 1504/5, 2969-76, [1309/10], [3172]	4.D.14., 7.C.10., 9.A.2.	292-323 647-663
Clontibret	15	82	1473/4, 2965, [1308]	3.B.6., 8.E.12.	122-213
Currin	13	82	1485/6, 2977-8	4.G.9., 5.F.12.	324-345
Donagh	2	81	1518, 3012, [1313]	6.C.8.	797-812
Donaghmoyne	20	83	1492/3, 2990	1.A.14., 3.G.6.	411-520
Drummully	11	82	1487	5.A.6.	346-348
Drumsnat	5	81	1506-7, 3003	7.D.8.	664-666
Ematris	14	82	1488-9, 2981	5.G.8.	349-367
Emyvale (Donagh)			[3177]		
Errigal Trough	1	81	1519, 4437 [3176]	4.B.8., 6.F.5.	813-866
Glaslough (Donagh)					
Inishkeen	21	83	1494, 3002	9.B.13.	521-542
Killanny	23	83	1496/7, 2993/4	1.D.14.	543-554
Killeevan	10	82	1490/1, 2982/5	5.A.13., 9.A.4.	368-410
Kilmore	6	81	1508/9, 3004	7.E.8.	667-677
Magheracloone	22	83	1498/9, 2994/6	2.A.8.	555-569
Magheross	19	83	1500/1, 3001/2, [3173/4]	1.E.11.	570-646
Monaghan	7	81	1510/11, 3005/6, [1311], [3178/80], [3181]	8.B.3.	678-717
Newbliss (Killeevan)					
Smithborough (Clones)			[3182/3]		
Muckno	16	82	1475/6, [3175]	2.E.2.	214-238
Tedavnet	3	81	1512/3, 3010	6.G.10.	718-765
Tehallan	4	81	1514/5, 3011, [1312]	8.A.2., 8.G.7.	239-240, 766-770
Tullycorbet	8	81	1516/7	7.F.14., 8 .G.3.	771-796

PARISH	TITHES 1823–38 TAB 15/	FILM	VALUATION FIELD BOOKS 1830s OL4./ HOUSE BOOKS [OL5.]	TENEMENT VALUATION 1854 FICHE	1841–1851 CENSUS SEARCH Cen /s/15
Aghancon	38	58	1005, 3018, 3036 [1319, 1349]	7.C.6., 6.D.1.	12-15, 79-80
Ardnurcher (Horseleap)	3	56	1031, 3069, [1389]	4.G.9.	
Ballyboy	27	57	3014, [1314/16, 3184]	2.B.7.	1-7
Ballyburly	6	56	3084, [1394/95, 1409/10]	1.E.7., 1.D.10.	334- 336, 352-354
Ballycommon	21	57	1036, 3075, [1396/97]	4.C.14.	
Ballykean	29	57	1040, 3068, [1384, 1403/05]	6.A.2., 4.E.12.	337-340
Ballymacwilliam	7	56	1044, 3085, [1411/12]	1.E.11	355
Ballynakill	24	57	1018, 3032	1.A.12.	127 130
Birr	34	58	0994, 3019, [1320/21]	2.E.10., 3.A.1.	16-36
Borrisnafarney	51	58	1006 [1350]	6.D.12.	81
Castlejordan	5	56	1019, 1045, 1046, [1362, 1413/14]	1.F.1.	131, 356-359
Castletownely	48	58	1007, 3038, [1351]	6.D.14.	
Castropetie (Monasteroris)	23	57			
Clonyhurk	30	57	1041, 3079, [1406]	7.F.8.	341
Clonmacnoise	8	56	1023, 3060, [1369]	3.B.9.	151-179
Clonsast	25	57	3034, [1363/64]	1.B.3.	132-137
Corbally	40	58	0995, 1008, 3039 [1322, 1352]	7.C.12., 6.E.2.	
Croghan	19	57	1037, [1398]	1.D.13.	341
Cullenwaine	50	58	3040, [1353]	6.E.4.	82-84
Drumcullen	32	57	1021, 3058, [1366/67]	1.G.10.	148-149
Dunkerrin	46	58	1010, 3041, [1354]	6.E.12.	
Durrow	15	56	1001, [1338/40]	5.C.1.	54-55
Eglish	31	57	1022, 3059, [1368]	2.A.8.	150
Ettagh	43	58	0996, 3021, [1323, 1355]	7.C.14., 6.F 8.	85-95
Finglas	49	58	1012, 3034, [1356]	6.F.14.	
Gallen	12	56	1024, 3061, [1370/71]	3.A.3.	180-199
Geashill	28	57	1030, 3080, 3081, [1385/87, 1407/08]	7.G.10., 6.A.2., 1.E.4., 4.E.12.	284-305, 343-346
Kilbride	4	56	1032, 1002, 3070, 3031, [1390/91]	4.G.13.	56-62, 306-326
Kilbride (Tullamore)	17	57	[1341/42]	5.C.9.	
Kilclonfert	20	57	1038, 3077, [1399/400]	4.D.5.	347-348
Kilcolman	41	58	1013, 3023, 3044, 3055, [1324/25, 1356a]	2.C.13., 6.G.2.	37-40, 96-102
Kilcomin	45	58	3046, [1357]	6.G.6.	
Kilcumreragh	1	56	1033, 3072, [1392]	5.B.2.	
Killaderry	22	57	1039, 3078, [1401/02]	4.D.13.	349-351
Killagally (Wheery)	11	56	[1381/83]	4.A.6.	274-283, 349-351
Kilmurryely	42	58	1014, [1358]	6.C.12.	104-107
Killoughy	26	57	3015-3016, [1317/18]	4.F.5.	8-11
Kilmanaghan	2	56	1034, 3073, [1393]	5.B.6.	327-333
Kinnitty	36	58	0997, 3024, [1326/27, 3198/99]	2.D.2.	41
Lemanaghan	9	56	1025, 3062-3063, [1372]	3.F.5., 5.B.14.	200-242
Letterluna	33	58	0998, 3025, [1328/29]	2.D.10.	42-46

PARISH	TITHES 1823–38 TAB 15/	FILM	VALUATION FIELD BOOKS 1830s OL4./ HOUSE BOOKS [OL5.]	TENEMENT VALUATION 1854 FICHE	1841–1851 CENSUS SEARCH Cen /s/15
Lusmagh	14	56	3065, [1373/75]	3.D.3.	243-250
Lynally	18	57	1003, [1343/45]	5.F.1.	63-67
Monasteroris (Edenderry)	23	57	3035, [1365]		138-147
Rahan	16	56	1004, [1346/48]	5.F.10.	68-78
Reynagh	13	56	1026, 3066, [1376/78]	3.E.1.	251-267
Roscomroe	37	58	3028, [1330/32]	2.E.2.	47-48
Roscrea	39	58	1015, 3026, [1333/34, 1359]	7.D.4., 7.A.4.	49-50, 108-110
Seirkieran	35	58	1000, 3029, [1335/37]	2.E.4., 7.D.8.,	51-53
Shinrone	44	58	1016, 3049, [1360, 3212/13]	7.A.8.	111-123
Templeharry	47	58	1017, 3050, [1361]	7.B.4.	124-126
Tisaran	10	56	1027, 3067, [1379/80]	3.G.12.	268-273
Wheery/Killagally				4.A.6.	274-283

TOWNS	VALUATION HOUSE BOOK 1830s [OL5.]
Ballycumber	[3185]
Banagher	[3186/87]
Birr (See Parsonstown)	
Crinkell	[3188/89]
Clara	[3190/91]
Edenderry	[3192/94]
Frankford	[3195]
Ferbane	[3196/97]
Moneygall	[3200/01]
Parsonstown	[3202/06]
Philipstown	[3207/08]
Portarlington	[3209/10]
Shannon Bridge	[3211]
Tullamore	[3214/17]

PARISH	TITHES 1823–38 TAB 25/	FILM	VALUATION FIELD BOOKS 1830s OL4./ HOUSE BOOKS [OL5.]	TENEMENT VALUATION 1857–8 FICHE	1841–1851 CENSUS SEARCH Cen /s/25
Ardcarn	4	87	1617	2.G.6., 4.D.12.	378-414
Athleague	44	89	[3218]	5.A.12.	1-13
Aughrim	19	88	1636	4.G.4.	888-892
Ballintober	18	88	1625	8.E.2.	523-534
Ballynakill	35	88	1612	6.D.12.	349
Baslick	16	88	1626	8.E.8.	535-549
Boyle	2	87	1613, [3222/25]	3.B.2.	415-446
Bumlin	26	88	1637	7.C.4.	893-921
Cam	51	89	1590	1.E.7.	14-31
Castlemore	98	87	1630	9.D.12.	638-647
Clooncraff	21	88	1638	4.G.14., 7.C.14.	922-935
Cloonfinlough	28	88	1639	6.E 10., 7.D.8.	936-942
Cloontuskert	40	89	1606-07	5.F.8.	273-293
Cloonygormican	34	88	1613	6.D.13., 8.D.6.	350-365
Creagh	57	90	1634	2.D.4.	862-864
Creeve	13	87	1631, 1640	4.F.12., 7.E.5.	648-653
Drum	56	90	1591	1.A.14.	32-42
Drumatemple	33	88	1614	8.D.10.	366-371
Dunamon	37	88	1615	6.E.1.	
Dysart	53	89	1592	1.F.5.	43-50
Elphin	22	88	1641, [3227]	7.E.6.	943-985
Estersnow	6	87	1619	3.D.10.	447-461
Fuerty	43	89	1593	5.B.11.	52-77
Kilbride	38	88	1608, 1642	7.F.11., 5.G.4.	294-316, 956
Kilbryan	3	87	1620	3.E.4.	462-463
Kilcolagh	11	87	1632	3.G.14., 3.G.4.	654-668
Kilcolman	9a	87	3088	9.E.1.	669-677
Kilcooley	25	88	1643	7.F.12.	987-989
Kilcorkey	14	88	1627	8.F.4.	550-554, 697-698
Kilgefin	39	89	1609	6.A.5.	317-332
Kilglass	31	88	1603, 1644	7.G.4., 6.F.12.	185-217
Kilkeevin	15	88	1628	8.F.13.	571-601
Killinvoy	46-?	89	1594	2.A.1., 5.C.14.	78-84
Killukin	7	87	1621	3.E.9., 4.E.1.	464-468, 990-995
Killukin	27	88	1645	7.G.4.	
Killummod	8	87	1623	3.E.11., 4.E.8.	469-477
Kilmacumsy	12	87	1633	4.A.8.	678-688
Kilmeane	45	89	1595	5.D.9.	85-90
Kilmore	45	88	1604	4.C.10.	218-226
Kilnamanagh	9	87		4.B.1., 9.E.2.	689-696
Kilronan	1	87	1623	3.E.12.	478-501
Kilteevan	42	89	1610	6.B.3.	333-337
Kiltoom	52	89	1596	1.F.12.	91-100
Kiltrustan	23	88	1646	7.G.12.	996-1001
Kiltullagh	17	88	1629	9.B.5.	603-637
Lissonuffy	29	88	1647	8.A.9.	1002-1034
Moore	58	90	1635	2.E.1.	865-887
Ogulla	24	88	1648	8.B.8.	1035-1047
Oran	36	88	1616	6.E.3.	372-377
Rahara	48	89	1597	2.B.10.	101-106
Roscommon	41	89	1611, 3087, [3231/33]	6.C.1.	338-347

PARISH	TITHES 1823–38 TAB 25/	FILM	VALUATION FIELD BOOKS 1830s OL4./ HOUSE BOOKS [OL5.]	TENEMENT VALUATION 1857–8 FICHE	1841–1851 CENSUS SEARCH Cen /s/25
Shankill	20	88	3090	4.B.8., 8.B.13., 10.B.12.	1048-1052
St John's	49	89	1598	2.A.12., 5.E.9.	107-117
St Peter's	55	90	1599	1.C.11.	118-139
Taghboy	50	89	1600	2.A.2., 5.E.9.	140-153
Taghmaconnell	54	89	1601	1.C.2., 2.C.10.	51, 154-171
Termonbarry	32	88	1605	7.A.8.	227-264, 348
Tibohine	10	87	3089	9.E.6., 10.C.14.	699-861
Tisrara	47	89	1602	5.E.9.	172-184
Tumna	5	87	1624	3.G.10., 4.E.13.	502-505, 522

TOWNS	VALUATION HOUSE BOOK 1830s [OL5.]
Athlone (Part)	[3219]
Ballyfarnham	[3220]
Bellanagare	[3221]
Castlereagh	[3226]
Frenchpark	[3230]
Keadew	[3220]
Knockcroghery	[3228]
Lanesborough	[3229]
Loughglynn	[3230]
Roosky	[3231]
Strokestown	[3234]

PARISH/TOWN	TITHES 1823–38 TAB 26/	FILM	VALUATION FIELD BOOKS 1830s OL4./ HOUSE BOOKS [OL5.]	TENEMENT VALUATION 1858 FICHE	1841–1851 CENSUS SEARCH Cen /s/26
Achonry	19	93	1675	6.G.10.	375-491
Aghanagh	38	94	1683	1.F.4.	776-803
Ahamlish	1	91	1649, 1650	3.F.10.	1-24
Ballymote			1667, [3238]		
Ballynakill	31	93	1684	6.A.10.	804-828
Ballysadare	16	93	1676, 1685, [3239]	5.E.4., 5.F.2., 6.G.8.	492-498, 829-839
Ballysumaghan	30	93	1686	6.A.4.	840-850
Calry	4	91	1651, 1652, 3091	4.E.2.	25-34
Castleconor	14	92	3092	2.C.4., 3.A.1.	580-593
Cloonoghil	23	93	1668	6.F.6.	239-245
Dromard	13	92	1679	3.D.11.	594-605
Drumcliff	3	91	1653-54	4.B.5.	35-74
Drumcolumb	32	93	1687	1.G.3.	851-858
Drumrat	27	93	1669	1.D.6.	246-260
Easky	9	92	1680	2.E.10.	606-642
Emlaghfad	21	93	1670	1.D.13., 6.D.1., 6.G.2.	261-297
Kilcolman	40	94	1664	1.A.12.	121-150
Kilfree	39	94	1665	1.B.5.	151-214
Kilglass	8	92	1681	2.F.14.	643-660
Killadoon	35	94	1688	1.G.3.	859-870
Killaraght	41	94	1666	1.C.9.	215-238
Killaspugbrone	5	91	1655-56	4.F.9.	75-78
Killerry	28	93	1689	5.G.6.	871-887
Killoran	17	93		5.E.4., 7.D.8.	499-525
Kilmacallan	34	93	1690	1.G.9., 6.B.6.	888-899
Kilmacowen	7	91	1657-58	4.G.7.	79-82
Kilmacshalgan	10	92	1682	3.A.13.	661-691
Kilmacteige	20	93	1677	7.E.12.	526-555
Kilmactranny	37	94	1691	1.G.11.	900-935
Kilmoremoy	15	92	3093	2.C.6.	692-732
Kilmorgan	22	93	1671	6.C.8.	298-309
Kilross	29	93	1692	5.G.1.	936-941
Kilshalvy	26	93	1672	1.E.1., 6.G.4.	310-331
Kilturra	25	93	1673	6.G.4.	332-339
Kilvarnet	18	93	1678	7.E.6.	556-561
Rossinver	2	91	1659-60	4.A.12.	83-91
Shancough	36	94	1693	2.A.12.	942-949
Skreen	12	92	3094	3.C.10.	733-747
St John's	6	91	1661-63	5.C.14., 5.A.14., 5.A.2., 5.B.4., 4.E.13.	92-120
Sligo Town			[3241/53]		562-579
Tawnagh	33	93	1694	6.C.4.	950-954
Templeboy	11	92	3095	3.B.12.	748-775
Toomour	24	93	1674	1.E.9., 6.E.2.	340-374

TOWNS	VALUATION HOUSE BOOK 1830s [OL5.]	TOWNS	VALUATION HOUSE BOOK 1830s [OL5.]
Aclare	[3235]	Collooney	[3239]
Ardnaree	[3236/37]	Riverstown	[3254]
Bellahy	[3240]	Tobercurry	[3254]

PARISH/TOWN	TITHES 1823–38 TAB	FILM	VALUATION FIELD BOOKS 1830s OL4./ HOUSE BOOKS [OL5.]	TENEMENT VALUATION 1848–51 FICHE	1841–1851 CENSUS SEARCH Cen /s/27
Abington	27N/28	96		17.F.8.	
Aghacrew	27S/4	98	3208, 3218-20	7.F.14.	134-136
Aghnameadle	27N38	96	3273, [1787/93	14.F.10.	251-255, 257-260
Aglishcloghane	27N/4	95	3250, [1727/28]	15.G.8.	184-186
Ardcrony	27N/13	95	3251, [1729/30]	16.A.2.	187-191
Ardfinnan	27S/94	100	3170, [1555/56, 3259]	5.A.4.	91-93
Ardmayle	27S/37	99	3235, [1632/34]	8.D.12.	152-153
Athnid	27N/71	97	3137, [1496]	12.A.14.	
Ballingarry	27N/10	95	3252, [1731/36, 3260]		192-196
Ballingarry	27S/77	100	3293, [1854/61, 3260]	16.A.8., 10.E.2.	339-349
Ballintemple	27S/77	98	3209, 3228, [1607]	7.F.4.	
Ballybacon	27S/97	101	3171-72, [1557]	5.A.8.	
Ballycahill	27N/68	97	3230, [1468/69]	6.E.12.,12.A.14.	
Ballyclerahan	27S/101	101	[1510, 3261]	3.D.12.	55
Ballygibbon	27N/29	96	3274, [1794/95]	14.G.6.	256, 261
Ballygriffin	27S/14	98	[1415/16]	1.A.14.	
Ballymackey	27N/31	96	[1796/99]	14.G.11.	262-263
Ballymurreen	27N/79	97	3138, [1470/71]	12.B.4.	
Ballynaclogh	27N/36	96	[1800/03]	15.A.8.	264-265
Ballysheehan	27S/38	99	3237, [1635/37]	8.E.6.	154
Baptistgrange	27S/68	99	3238, [1638/39]	8.F.2.	
Barnane-ely	27N/51	97	3190, [1581]	13.D.12.	
Barrettsgrange	27S/60	99	3238, [1640/41	8.F.6.	
Borrisokane	27N/8	95	3253, [1737/38, 4219, 3264/66]	16.A.14.	197-204
Bourney	27N/45	97	3192, 3204-05, [1584/87, 1599]	13.E.2.	121-122
Boytonrath	27S/56	99	3239, [1642]	8.F.10.	155
Brickendown	27S/43	99	3240, [1643, 1680]	8.F.12.	156
Bruis	27S/27	98	3097, [1417/18]	1.B.6.	1
Buolick	27S/72	99	3294, 3311, [1862/64]	10.F.10.	350-352
Burgesbeg	27N/22	96	3282-83, 3289, [1834]	17.F.14.	
Borrisnafarney	27N/47	97	3191, [1582/83]	13.D.14.	
Caher	27S/91	100	3147, [1558/59, 3270/73]	5.B.6., 3.D.2.	94-98
Carrick	27S/116	101	3148, [1514/16]	3.D.4.	56-59
Cashel (See St John Baptist)					
Castletownarra	27N/19	96	3284, [1835]	17.G.12.	301-304
Cloghprior	27N/12	95	3254	16.B.12.	205
Clonbeg	27S/33	98	3098, 3123, 3124, [1418]	1.B,10.	2-4
Clonbullogue	27S/32	98	3099, 3125, [1421]	1.C.12.	5
Cloneen	27S/54	99	3241, 3295-96, [1644/45, 1688/90, 1865/67]	8.F.14., 10.G.6.	
Clonmel St Mary's	27S/114	101	[1550/51, 3296/3309]	4.D.2.	75-88
Clonoulty	27S/3	98	3211, 3222, [1609]	7.G.8., 1.D.4.	137, 139-140
Clonpet	27S/28	98	3127, [1433]	1.D.6.	
Clogher	27S/1	98	3210, 3221, [1608]		138
Colman	27S/66	99	3238 ,[1646/48]	8.G.6.	
Cooleagh	27S/45	99	[1649/51]	8.G.8.	
Coolmundry	27S/63	99	3241, [1652]	8.G.12.	
Corbally	27N/43	97	3192, 3206, [1588/91, 1599]	13.F.4.	123-124
Cordangan	27S/29	98	3100, 3124, 3128, 3136 [1422/24]	1.D.10.	6

PARISH/TOWN	TITHES 1823–38 TAB	FILM	VALUATION FIELD BOOKS 1830s OL4./ HOUSE BOOKS [OL5.]	TENEMENT VALUATION 1848–51 FICHE	1841–1851 CENSUS SEARCH Cen /s/27
Corroge	27S/25	98	3136, [1425/26]	1.E.10.	
Crohane	27S/78	100	3297, 3313, [1868/69]	10.G.8.	353
Cullen	27S/17	98	3101, [1427/29, 3295]	1.E.14.	7-11
Cullenwaine	27N/46	97	3193, [1592/93]	13.G.2.	
Dangandargan	27S/49	99	[1430/31, 1653/54, 1663]	1.F.6., 8.G.14.	
Derrygarth	27S/92	100	3171-72, [1560/61]	5.D.6.	
Dogstown	27S/57	99	[1655/58]	9.A.2.	
Dulla	2/N/35	96	[1804/05]	15.A.12.	265a-271
Donaghmore	27S/67	99	3149, 3238, [1659]	9.A.4., 3.F.6.	
Donohill	27S/2	98	3102, 3212-13, 3223-24, [1432, 1434, 1610/11]	8.A.10., 1.F.8.	
Doon	27N/57	97	[1622/23]	6.F.2.	143
Dorrha	27N/2	95	3255, [1743/45]	16.C.2.	206-209
Drangan	27S/48	99	[1660/62, 1664]	9.A.6.	157-159
Drom	27N/62	97	[1472/73]	12.B.6.	
Dromineer	27N/15	96	3256, [1746/48]	16.D.2.	
Emly	27S/22	98	3103, [1435/36, 3310]	1.G.2.	12
Erry	27S/39	99	[1665/67]	9.A.14.	160
Fennor	27S/71	99	3298, 3311, 3322, [1870/72]	11.A.2.	354
Fertiana	27N/74	97	[1474/75]	12.B.12.	
Fethard	27S/62	99	3238, [1668/70, 3311/15]	9.B.2.	161-164
Finnoe	27N/7	95	3257, [1749/52]	16.D.5.	210
Gaile	27S/36	99	3242, [1671, 1672/73]	9.C.6.	165-166
Galbooly	27N/75	97	[1476/77]	12.C.1.	
Garrangibbon	27S/106	101	3150, 3299, 3313, [1517/20, 1873/76]	11.A.10., 3.F.8.	
Glenbane	27S/23	98	3104, 3129, [1437]	2.A.4.	
Glenkeen	27N/54	97	[1624/25]	6.F.5.	144-147
Grangemockler	27S/84	100	3300, 3313, [1877/80, 1924/25]	11.A.14.	
Graystown	27N/74	100	3237, 3301, 3312, 3313, [1881/82]	9.C.8., 11.B.4.	355
Holycross	27S/73	97	3139, [1478]	9.C.10., 12.C.3.	42 [166a]
Holycross	27S/35	98	3242, [1672/73, 1674/75]		
Horeabbey	27S/41	99	[1675a/77]	9.C.12.	
Inch	27N/66	97	[1479/80]	12.C.11.	
Inishlounaght	27S/102	101	3151, [1521/23]	3.F.10.	
Isertkieran	27S/102	100	3302, 3313, [1883/85]	11.B.12.	
Kilbarron	27N/6	95	[1753/56]	16.D.12.	
Kilbragh	27S/59	99	[1678, 1679]	9.C.14.	
Kilcash	27S/107	101	3152, [1524/26]	3.G.8.	60-61
Kilclonagh	27N/67	97	3137, [1496]	12.D.3.	
Kilcomenty	27N/24	96	3285, [1836/37]	18.B.10.	305-306
Kilconnell	27S/51	99	3243, [1681/83, 1680]	9.D.2.	
Kilcooly	27N/77	97	[1481/82]	11.B.14., 12.D.3.	
Kilcooly	27S/73	99	3303, 3312, 3313, 3314, [1886/91]		356-359
Kilcornan	27S/16	98	3106, [1433/40]	2.A.6.	13-15
Kilfeakle	27S/20	98	3107, [1441/42]	2.A.10.	16
Kilfithmone	27N/61	97	[1483/84]	12.D.4.	
Kilgrant	27S/110	101	3153, [1527/29]	3.G.12.	62

PARISH/TOWN	TITHES 1823–38 TAB	FILM	VALUATION FIELD BOOKS 1830s OL4./ HOUSE BOOKS [OL5.]	TENEMENT VALUATION 1848–51 FICHE	1841–1851 CENSUS SEARCH Cen /s/27
Kilkeary	27N/37	96	3275, [1806/07, 1810]	15.B.4.	
Killaloan	27S/115	101	[1530]	4.A.4.	
Killardry	27S/31	98	3105, 3125, 3130, [1443/44]	2.B.2.	17-19
Killavinoge	27N/49	97	3195, 3202, [1594]	13.G.4.	125
Killea	27N/48	97	3196, [1595]	13.G.14.	126
Killeenasteena	27S/55	99	[1684, 1717]	9.D.6.	167
Killenaule	27S/75	100	3304, 3312, 3313, [1892/94, 3317/19]	11.C.14.	360
Killodiernan	27N/11	95	3258, [1757/60]	16.E.8.	223
Killoscully	27N/25	96	3286, [1838/39]	18.C.9.	307-312
Killoskehan	27N/50	97	3197, [1596]	14.A.6.	
Kilmastulla	27N/23	96	3287[1840]	18.D.9.	313
Kilmore	27N/34	96	3276, [1811/15]		272-283[A]
Kilmore (Oughterleague)	27S/7	98	3214, 3226, [1612]	8.B.10., 15.B.6.	141-142
Kilmucklin	27S/12	98	[1445, 1450]	2.B.12.	
Kilmurry	27S/112	101	3154, [1431/33]	4.A.6.	63
Kilnaneave	27N/39	96	3277, [1816/17]	15.G.12.	284-288
Kilnarath	27N/27	96	3288, [1841/43]	18.E.6.	314-319
Kilpatrick	27S/5	98	3215, 3227, [1613/15]	8.B.14.	
Kilruane	27N/30	96	3278, [1761/62, 1818/20]	16.E.12., 15.D.5	289-291
Kilshane	27S/30	98	3108, 3136, [1446/47]	2.B.14.	
Kilsheelan	27S/111	101	3155, [1534/36]	4.A.14.	64-67
Kiltegan	27S/109	101	3156, [1437/39]	4.B.6.	
Kiltinan	27S/69	99	3238, [1685/87, 1688/90]	9.D.8.	168
Kilvellane	27N/26	96	3284, [1844/45]	18.F.6.	320-334
Kilvemnon	27S/83	100	3305, 3312, 3313, 3315-16, [1895/902]	11.D.14.	361-363
Knigh	27N/16	96	3260, [1763/65]	16.E.14.	
Knockgraffon	27S/64	99	3244, [1691/92]	9.D.12.	169-170
Laginstown	27S/117	101			
Latteragh	27N/40	96	3279, [1821/23]	15.D.9.	292
Lattin	27S/26	98	3109, [1417, 1448]	2.C.7.	20-24
Lickfinn	27S/76	100	3306, 3313, 3317, [1903/05]	11.F.4.	
Lisbunny	27N/32	96	3279, [1824/26]	15.D.13.	
Lismalin	27S/80	100	3307, 3318, [1906/11]	11.F.6.	364
Lisronagh	27S/104	101	3157, [1540]	4.B.8.	68
Lorrha	27N/1	95	3261, [1769/71]	16.F.4.	211-216
Loughkeen	27N/5	95	3262, [1766/68]	16.G.4.	217-221
Loughmoe East	27N/64	97	3140-42, [1485/86]	12.D.5.	
Loughmoe West	27N/63	97	[1487/89]	12.D.14.	43
Magorban	27S/44	99	3245, [1693/95]	9.E.8.	
Magowry	27S/47	99	[1696/99]	9.E.12.	
Modeshil	27S/81	100	3308, 3313, 3323, [1912/14]	11.F.10.	
Modreeny	27N/14	96	3263, [1772/74]	17.A.2.	222, 224-234
Molough	27S/99	101	3173-74, [1564]	5.D.11.	99-101
Monsea	27N/17	96	3264, 3289, [1775/77, 1846/47]	17.B.7., 18.G.10.	
Mora	27S/65	99	3246, [1700/02]	9.F.2.	171-172
Mortlestown	27S/86	100	3175, [1562/63]	5.D.14.	

PARISH/TOWN	TITHES 1823–38 TAB	FILM	VALUATION FIELD BOOKS 1830s OL4./ HOUSE BOOKS [OL5.]	TENEMENT VALUATION 1848–51 FICHE	1841–1851 CENSUS SEARCH Cen /s/27
Mowney	27S/79	100	3319, [1915/17]	11.F.14.	365
Moyaliff	27N/59	97	[1626]	7.A.8.	148-150
Moycarky	27N/78	97	[1490/91]	12.E.6.	44-45
Moyne	27N/65	97	[1492]	12.E.11.	46
Neddans	27S/98	101	3176-77, 3186, [1565]	5.E.2.	
Nenagh	27N/18	96	3265, 3279, [1778/79, 1827/29, 3325/33]	17.B.12., 15.E.3.	235-248, 293
Newcastle	2/S/100	101	3187, [1566/68]	5.E.5.	102-106
Newchapel	27S/102	101	3158, [1541/44]	4.B.10.	69-74
Newtownlennan	27S/113	101	3159, 3309, [1545/46, 1918]	11.G.2., 4.C.4.	
Oughterleague	27S/8	98	3110, 3131, 3216, 3228, [1431, 1449, 1616]	8.C.6., 2.C.8.	
Outeragh	27S/70	99	3246, [1703/05]	9.F.6.	173
Peppardstown	27S/53	99	3241, [1706/08]	9.F.8.	
Rahelty	27N/72	97	[1493/94]	12.F.4.	47-49
Railstown	27S/50	99	[1709, 1717]	9.F.12.	
Rathcool	27S/52	99	3241, [1710/11]	9.F.14.	
Rathkennan	27S/1a	98	3217, 3229	8.C.12.	
Rathlynin	27S/13	98	3111, [1450, 1451]	2.C.10.	25
Rathnaveoge	27N/44	97	3198, [1597/98, 1599]	14.A.8.	127
Rathronan	27S/108	101	3160, [1547/49]	4.C.10.	
Redcity	27S/61	99	3238, [1712]	9.G.6.	
Relickmurry and Athassel	27S/21	98	3132, 3096, 3236, [1452/56]	2.C.14., 9.G.8.	26-29
Rochestown	27S/93	100	[3568, 1569/70]	5.F.4.	
Roscrea	27N/42	97	3207, [1600/03, 3334/44]	14.A.14.	128-132
Shanrahan	27S/88	100	3179, [1571/72]	5.F.5.	108-112
Shronell	27S/24	98	3112, 3133, [1417, 1457]	2.E.7.	30
Shyane	27N/70	97	3137, [1495, 1496]	12.F.9.	
Solloghhodbeg	27S/11	98	3113, [1458/59]	2.E.10.	31
Solloghodmore	27S/10	98	3114, 3134, [1460/61]	2.E.14.	32-35
St John Baptist (Cashel)	27S/42	99	3247, 3310, 3312, 3320, [1713/16, 1717, 1919/21]	9.G.10., 11.G.4.	174-182
St Johnstown	27S/46	99	[1718/20]	10.B.8.	
St Patricksrock	27S/40	99	3248-49, [1721/22]	10.B.12.	
Temple	27S/34	98			
Temple-etney	27S/105	101	3162, [1552/54]	4.F.14.	89-90
Templeachally	27N/21	96	3290, [1848/51]	18.C.11.	335-337
Templebeg	27N/56	97	[1627/28]	7.B.8.	
Templebredon	27S/15	98	3117, [1462/64]	2.F.10.	
Templederry	27N/41	96	3280, [1830/32]	15.E.8.	294-297
Templedowney	27N/33	96	[1810, 1833]	15.F.2.	298-300
Templenoe	27S/19	98	3116, [1450, 1466]	2.G.12.	
Templemichael	27S/85	100	3311, 3321, [1922/23, 1924/25]	11.G.6.	366
Templemore	27N/60	97	3145, 3199, [1497/98, 1604, 3346/51]	14.D.2., 12.F.10.	50-51
Templeneiry					36-38
Templeree	27N/52	97	3200, [1605]	14.D.6.	133
Templetenny	27S/87	100	3179, 3188, [1573/75]	5.G.11.	113-118
Templetoughy	27N/53	97	3201, [1499, 1606]	14.D.12., 12.G.13.	

PARISH/TOWN	TITHES 1823–38 TAB/	FILM	VALUATION FIELD BOOKS 1830s OL4./ HOUSE BOOKS [OL5.]	TENEMENT VALUATION 1848–51 FICHE	1841–1851 CENSUS SEARCH Cen /s/27
Terryglass	27N/3	95	3265a, [1780/83]	17.D.10.	248-250
Thurles	27N/69	97	[1500/04, 3352/60]	12.G.13.	52-53
Tipperary	27S/18	98	3118, 3136, [4218, 3361/67]	3.A.4.	39-41
Toem	27N/58	97	[1629]		
Toem	27S/9	98	3119, 3135, [1469]	3.B.14., 7.B.14.	
Tubbrid	27S/89	100	[1576]	6.B.9.	119-120
Tullaghmelan	27S/95	100	3180-81, 3189, [1577]	6.C.7.	74
Tullaghorton	27S/96	100	3182-83, [1578]	6.C.11.	
Tullamain	27S/58	99	3246, [1679, 1723/26]	10.C.14.	
Twomileborris	27N/76	97	[1505/09]	13.C.3.	54
Upperchurch	27N/55	97	[1630/31]	7.D.2.	151
Uskane	27N/9	95	3266, [1784/86]	17.E.7.	
Whitechurch	27S/90	100	3184, [1579/80]	6.D.3.	
Youghalarra	27N/20	96	3291, [1852/53]	19.B.12.	338

TOWNS	VALUATION HOUSE BOOK 1830s [OL5.]
Abbey	[3255/58]
Ballyporeen	[3262]
Bansha	[3263]
Borrisoleigh	[3267/69]
Cappagh White	[3274/75]
Carrick-on-Suir	[3276/82]
Cashel	[3283/90]
Clogheen	[3291]
Cloghjordan	[3292/94]
Cullen	[3295]
Golden	[3316]
Killenaule	[3317/19]
Marlfield	[3320/21]
Mullinahone	[3322/24a]
Silvermines	[3345]
Toberaheena	[3368/69]
Toomevarra	[3370/72]

PARISH/TOWN	TITHES 1823–38 TAB 29/	FILM	VALUATION FIELD BOOKS 1830s OL4./ HOUSE BOOKS [OL5.]	TENEMENT VALUATION 1848–51 FICHE	1841–1851 CENSUS SEARCH Cen /s/29
Affane	19	102	3365-66, [1944/46]	4.A.4.	
Aglish	68	104		2.E.5., 2.E.12.	62-65
Ardmore	69	104	3356, 3357-59	2.E.5., 2.F.14.	66, 72
Ballygunner	58	103	3407, [1985/87]	6.D.6.	130
Ballylaneen	34	103	3367-72, [1947, 4220]	4.B.2.	73-76
Ballymacart	74	104		2.E.5., 3.B.10.	67
Ballynakill	51	103	3408. [1988/91]	6,D,9,	
Clashmore	71	104	3360, 3361	2.E.5., 3.B.14.	68
Clonagam	11	102	3465, 3479, 3495, [2118/19]	8.D.14.	244-250
Clonea	32	103	3373-75, [1948/50]	4.C.2.	
Colligan	27	102	3376, [1951/52]	3.G.8., 4.C.6.	77-78
Corbally	66	104	3409, [1992/95]	6.D.11.	131
Crooke	60	104	3410, [1996/99]	6.D.12.	132-136
Drumcannon	47	103	3436-37, [2000/03, 2073/82]	7.D.14., 6.E.2.	186-220
Dungarvan	30	103	3377, [1953/54], [3383]	3.G.8., 4.C.12.	79-87
Dunhill	44	103	3438-39, [2083/86]	7.F.8.	221-226
Dysert	6	102	3466, 3480, 3489, 6496, [2120/21, 4227]	8.E.13.	
Faithlegg	53	103	[2004/09]	6.E.2.	137-139
Fenoagh	8	102	3467, 3481, 3490, 3497, [2122/23]	8.F.4.	
Fews	25	102	3378, [1955, 4226]	4.G.8.	88
Guilcagh	12	102	3468, 3482, 3498, [2124/26, 4226]	8.F.9.	251
Inishlounaght	1	102	3426a-3428, [2067/68]	7.A.14.	178-179
Islandikane	48	103	3440-41, [2087/91]	7.G.4.	227-232
Kilbarry	54	103	3411, [2010/14]	6.E.6.	
Kilbarrymeadan	36	103	3379-80, [1956]	4.G.12.	89-91
Kilbride	46	103	3442-43, [2092, 2103]	7.G.10.	233-235
Kilburne	42	103	3444-45, [2093/95, 4223]	7.G.14.	236
Kilcaragh	57	103	[2015/18]	6.E.8.	
Kilcockan	17	102	3331, [1926/28]	1.A.14., 1.B.2.	1-2
Kilcop	59	104	3412, [2019/22]	6.E.9.	
Kilculliheen	13	102	3435, [2023/24, [2072]	7.C.14., 9.D.10., 9.D.14.	280
Kilgobnet	23	102	3381-82	5.A.10.	92-98
Kill St Lawrence	55	103	3419, [2025/28]	6.F.4.	
Kill St Nicholas	52	103	3414, [2029/31]	6.F.5.	
Killaloan	4	102	3469, 3483, 3499, [2127/28]	8.F.11.	
Killea	65	104	3413, [2032/36]	6.E.10.	140-154
Killoteran	38	103	3464, [2096/97]	8.A.4.	
Killure	56	103	[2037/40]	6.F.12.	155
Kilmacleague	62	104	3415, [2041/44]	6.F.12.	156-162
Kilmacomb	63	104	[2045/48]	6.G.3.	163
Kilmeadan	37	103	3449-50, 3470, 3484, 3491, 3500, [2098/100, 2129/30]	8.F.13., 8.A.8.	237-238
Kilmolash	28	103	3361, 3383-84, [1957/58]	5.B.14., 3.C.14.	69
Kilmoleran	7	102	3471, 3476, 3485, 3501, [2131/32]	8.G.1.	252
Kilrossanty	24	102	3385-86, [1959/60, 4221]	3.G.9., 5.C.4.	99-100

PARISH/TOWN	TITHES 1823–38 TAB 29/	FILM	VALUATION FIELD BOOKS OL4./ HOUSE BOOKS [OL5.]	TENEMENT VALUATION 1848—1 FICHE	1841–1851 CENSUS SEARCH CEN S|29|1
Kilronan	2	102	3430-33, [2069/71]	7.B.6.	180-185
Kilronan	43	103	3451-52, [2101/02, 2103]	8.B.4.	
Kilrush	31	103	3387-88, [1961/62]	5.D.8.	
Kilsheelan	5	102	3472, 3486, 3502, [2133/34]	8.G.12.	
Kilwatermoy	28/16	102	3332, [1930]	1.B.10.	3-4
Kinsalebeg	72	104	3362-63	2.E.6., 3.D.4.	
Leitrim	13a	102	3333, [1931/32]	1.C.6.	
Lickoran	21	102	3390-91, [1963]	5.E.2.	101-103
Lisgenan or Grange	73	104		3.E.4.	70, 104
Lismore and Mocollop	14	102	3334-35, 3350-54, [1933/38], [3387]	1.A.14., 1.C.8.	5-51
Lisnaskill	41	103	3453, 3464, [2104/07]	8.B.6.	239
Modelligo	20	102	3392-93, [1964/67]	3.G.9., 5.E.6.	105 [105a]
Monamintra	61	104	[2049/51]	6.G.6.	
Monksland	35	103	3394-95, [1968/71]	3.G.9., 5.F.4.	
Mothel	10	102	3473-74, 3487, 3492-93, 3503, [2135/36, 4228]	8.G.14.	253
Newcastle	40	103	3396-97, 3454-55, 3464, [1972/74a, 2108/11]	5.F.10., 8.B.10.	240
Newtownlennan	75	104			
Rathgormuck	9	102	3475, 3488, 3494, 3504, [2137, 4224]	9.A.11.	254-264
Rathmoylan	67	104	3420, [2052/56]	6.G.6.	164-172
Reisk	45	103	3456-57, 3464, [2112/15]	8.B.14.	241
Ringagonagh	70	104	3364	2.E.6., 3.E.14.	71
Rossduff	64	104	3421, [2057/60]	6.G.10.	173-174
Rossmire	26	102	3398-99, [1975/77, 2138/39]	9.B.5., 3.G.9., 5.F.12.	106-110
Seskinan	22	102	3400, [1978/79]	3.G.9., 5.G.8.	111-125
St John's [without]	50	103	3424, [2061/64, 3415/17]	9.D.10., 9.E.14.	278, 175-177, 273, 284
St Mary's Clonmel	3	102	3478, 3505-07, [2140, 4225]	9.B.5.	265-269
Stradbally	33	103	3389, 3401, [1980/82]	3.G.10., 6.A.10.	126-127
Tallow	15	102	3346, [1939/41, 3394]	1.A.14., 2.B.10.	52-56
Templemichael	18	102	3347, 3348, 3355, [1942/43]	1.A.14., 2.C.14.	57-61
Trinity without	39	103	3458-59, [2116/17, 3426/35]	8.C.6., 9.D.11., 10.B.8.	242-243
Waterford City Parishes	49	103	(see below)		270-294
Whitechurch	29	103	3402-03, [1983/84]	3.G.10., 6.B.10.	128-129

TOWNS	VALUATION HOUSE BOOK 1830s [OL5.]
No. 1 Kilculliheen	[3399]
No. 2 St John's Within	[3400] [3414]
No. 3 St John's Without	[3401] [3415/17]
No. 4 St Michael's	[3402] [3418]
No. 5 St Olave's	[3403] [3419]
No. 6 St Patrick's	[3404] [3420]
No. 7 St Peter's	[3405]
No 8 St Stephen's Within	[3406] [3421]
No. 9 St Stephen's Without	[3407] [3422/24]
No. 10 Trinity Within	[3408] [3425]
No. 11 Trinity Without	[3409] [3426/35]
No. 12 Trinity Without	[3410]
No. 13 Trinity Without	[3411]
No. 14 Trinity Without	[3412]
No. 12? Trinity Without	[3413]
Waterford (Town)	[3438]
Abbeyside	[3373]
Cappoquin	[3374/75]
Carrickbeg	[3376/78]
Carrick-on-Suir	[3379/81]
Clonmel	[3382]
Dunmore	[3384, 3389]
Kilmacthomas	[3385/86]
Passage	[3388/89]
Portlaw	[3390/93]
Tramore	[3395/98]

PARISH/TOWN	TITHES 1823–38 TAB 30/	FILM	VALUATION FIELD BOOKS 1830s OL4./ HOUSE BOOKS [OL5.]	TENEMENT VALUATION 1854 FICHE	1841–1851 CENSUS SEARCH Cen /s/30
Ardnurcher (Horseleap)	50	106	1747	5.D.10., 7.A.10.	164-167
Athlone			[3439/41]		1-12
Ballyloughloe	46	106	1695	1.E.3.	18-19
Ballymore	36	106	1761	1.G.14., 2.F.2.	214-218
Ballymorin	38	106	1762	4.G.8.	219
Bunown	30	105	1740	1.B.8.	123-127
Carrick	59	107	1722	5.G.2.	83
Castlelost	63	107	1723	5.G.4.	84-85
Castletowndelvin	27	105	3511-12, [3446/7]	3.A.4.	45-55
Castletownkin-delan	51	107	1748, [2144, 3448]	5.E.2.	168-183
Churchtown	40	106	1763	4.G.10.	220-223
Clonarney	24	105	1710-11	3.B.9.	
Clonfad	62	107	1724	5.G.11.	86-88
Conry	39	106	1764, 3524	4.G.14.	
Delvin					56-68
Drumraney	32	105	1741, [2143]	1.D.4., 2.D.10.	128-136
Durrow	54	107	1749, 3522	7.A.13.	184-185
Dysart	43	106	1744, 1750-51, [4232]	5.A.2., 6.D.12., 5.F.5.	147, 186
Enniscoffey	58	107	1725	6.A.2.	
Faughalstown	7	105	1732	3.D.3., 4.A.2.	96-101
Foyran	1	105	1733, 3515	4.A.3.	102-106
Kilbeggan	52	107	1752-53, [2145, 3449]	7.C.6.	187-188
Kilbixy	13	105	3523, [3455]	4.E.6.	199-201
Kilbride	60	107	1726, 3516	6.A.5.	89-91
Kilcleagh	47	106	1696-97	1.F.5.	20-28
Kilcumny	23	105	1712-13, [2141]	3.B.12.	
Kilcumreragh	49	106	1698-99, 1754, [2146]	1.D.8., 1.A.14.	189-192
Kilkenny West	31	105	1742 [4230]	1.C.1., 2.E.5.	137-141
Killagh	28	105	1714-15	3.C.2.	
Killare	37	106	1765, 3525, [3444]	2.F.8.	224-225
Killua	25	105	1716-17	3.C.4.	
Killucan	44	106	1718-19, 3513, [4229]	3.C.12., 6.B.8., 3.F.11.	74-82
Killulagh	26	105	1720-21, [2142]	3.C.12.	69-73
Kilmacnevan	12	105	[3455]	4.F.2.	202-203
Kilmanaghan					29-30
Kilpatrick	8	105	1734	3.D.7.	
Lackan	15	105	1702	5.B.8.	31-33
Leny	17	105	1703	5.B.11.	34
Lickbla	2	105	1735, 3517	3.D.9., 4.A.10.	107-109
Lynn	56	107	1727	6.A.8.	
Mayne	3	105	1736	4.B.2.	110-112
Moylisker	57	107	1728	6.A.12.	92-93
Mullingar	42	106	1729, 1745, 3520, [3451/54, 4231]	6.E.13., 6.A.14.	148-158
Multyfarnham	16	105	1704, 3509, [3443]	5.C.3.	35
Newtown	53	107	1730, 1755-56	5.F.5., 6.B.1.	94-95, 193-198
Noughaval	29	105	1743	1.D.2., 2.E.6.	142-146
Pass of Kilbride	61	107	1731	6.B.4.	

PARISH/TOWN	TITHES 1823–38 TAB 30/	FILM	VALUATION FIELD BOOKS 1830s OL4./ HOUSE BOOKS [OL5.]	TENEMENT VALUATION 1854 FICHE	1841–1851 CENSUS SEARCH Cen /s/30
Piercetown	33	106	3526	2.F.13., 5.A.10.	226-228
Portloman	22	105	1705	5.C.8.	
Portnashangan	19	105	1706	5.C.12.	36
Rahugh	55	107	1757, [2147]	5.F.14., 7.C.1.	
Rathaspick	11	105	1758, [3455]	4.B.12., 4.F.9.	204-210
Rathconnell	41	106	1746	6.E.1.	159-163
Rathconrath	34	106	1766, 3521	2.G.2., 5.A.11.	229-231
Rathgarve	4	105	1737, 3518	3.D.9., 4.B.10.	113-116
Russagh	10	105		4.C.2.	211-212
St Feighin's	5	105	1738	3.E.8.	117-120
St Mary's (Athlone)	6	105	1739, 3519	2.A.4.	1-17, 121-122
St Mary's	45	106	3508	3.F.6.	
Stonehall	18	105	1707	5.C.14.	37-38
Street	9	105	1759	4.C.5., 4.G.1.	
Taghmon	21	105	1708	5.D.3.	39-43
Templeoran					213
Moygoish	14	105			
Templepatrick	35	106		2.G.3.	
Tyfarnham	20	105	1709, 3510	5.D.7.	44

TOWNS	VALUATION HOUSE BOOK 1830s [OL5.]
Ballinagore	[3442]
Ballinalack	[3443]
Ballymore	[3444]
Ballynacarrigy	[3445]
Castlepollard	[3443]
Clonmellan	[3447]
Collenstown	[3443]
Finnea	[3443]
Killucan	[3443]
Moate	[3450]
Rathowen	[3445]
Rochfordbridge	[3456]
Tyrrellspass	[3457/58]

PARISH/TOWN	TITHES 1823–38 TAB 31/	FILM	VALUATION FIELD BOOKS 1830s OL4./ HOUSE BOOKS [OL5.]	TENEMENT VALUATION 1853 FICHE	1841–1851 CENSUS SEARCH Cen /s/31
Adamstown	50	109	1792-93, 3542, [2169]	6.G.4.	44-47
Ambrosetown	102	111	1828, 3555, [2191]	10.C.11.	174-178
Ardamine	30	109	1767, [2148]	5.C.2.	1-3
Ardcandrisk	71	110	1918, [2282]	8.C.4.	
Ardcavan	85	110	1910, 3646, [2273a]	8.F.2.	449-453
Ardcolm	86	110	1911, 3647, [2274]	8.F.6.	454
Artramon	84	110	1912, 3648, [2275]	8.F.11.	455-458
Ballingly	80	110	1919, [2283]	8.C.6.	475
Ballyanne	46	109	1794, [2170]	6.G.11.	48-56
Ballybrazil	89	110	1897, 3620, [2261]	5.G.12.	402
Ballybrennan	136	111	1841, [2204]	9.A.4.	210-216
Ballycanew	24	109	1867, 3583, [2228/29]	4.A.14.	263-268
Ballycarney	6	108	3604, [2247]	1.E.3.	299-302
Ballyconnick	103	108	1829, 3556, [2192]	10.C.14.	
Ballyhoge	53	109	1795-96, 1920, 3543, [2171, 2284]	2.D.6., 1.B.4.	
Ballyhuskard*	58	110	1768, 3527, [2149]	3.D.8.	4, 21-25
Ballylannan	79	110	1921, [2285]	7.F.8.	476-479
Ballymitty	81	110	1922, [2286]	8.C.7.	480
Ballymore	129	111	1842, [2205]	9.A.6.	217-218
Ballynaslaney	64	110	1769, 1913, 3649 [2150, 2276]	3.C.13., 1.B.9.	
Ballyvaldon	62	110	1771, [2151]	3.C.4.	26
Ballyvaloo	68	110	1770, 3528	3.B.6.	
Bannow	105	111	1830, 3557, [2193]	10.D.2.	179-180
Carn	138	111	1843, [2206]	9.A.10.	219
Carnagh	54	109	1797-98, 3544, [2172]	7.A.4.	57-63
Carnew	3	108	1868, 1184, 3584, 3605 [2230, 2248]	5.A.13., 3.B.6., 4.B.7	303-310
Carrick	78	110	1923, [2287]	8.C.9.	481
Castle-Ellis	60	110	1772, 3529, [2152]	3.B.9.	27
Chapel	44	109	1799, [2173]	2.D.9.	64-66
Clone	11	108	1885, 3606, [2249]	1.E.10.	311-314
Clongeen	72	110	1924, [2288]	7.F.12.	
Clonleigh	42	109	1800, 3545, [2174]	7.A.6.	67-71
Clonmines	97	111	1898, 3621, [2262]	6.A.1.	
Clonmore	45	109	1801-02, 1925, [2175, 4234]	2.D.14., 1.B.6	72-73
Coolstuff	76	110	1926, [2289]	8.D.1.	
Crosspatrick	13	108	3585-75, [2231]	4.B.5.	
Donaghmore	31	109	1773, 1869, 3530, 3587 [2153/54, 2232]	4.B.7., 5.C.10.	5-7
Doonooney	51	109	1803, [2176]	11.A.13.	
Drinagh	120	111	1844, [2207]	9.B.12.	
Duncormick	106	111	1831, 3558, [2194]	10.C.12.	181-182
Edermine	63	110	1774	3.F.10.	28
Ferns	7	108	1870, 1886, 3588, 3607 [2233, 2250]	1.D.3., 5.B.5., 1.B.12.	315-316
Fethard	99	111	1899, 3623, [2263]	6.A.2.	403-418
Hook	100	111	1900, 3624, [2264]	6.B.1.	
Horetown	74	110	1927, [2290]	7.G.5.	482-483
Inch	16	108	1871, 3589, [2234]	7.G.11.	

PARISH/TOWN	TITHES 1823–38 TAB 31/	FILM	VALUATION FIELD BOOKS 1830s OL4./ HOUSE BOOKS [OL5.]	TENEMENT VALUATION 1853 FICHE	1841–1851 CENSUS SEARCH Cen /s/31
Inch	73	110	[1928, 2291]	4.B.7.	269, 484
Ishartmon	133	111	1845, [2208]	9.B.5.	
Kerloge	117	111	1846, [2209]	9.B.7.	
Kilbride	8	108	1887, 3608, [2251]	5.B.5., 1.D.1.	317-319
Kilbrideglynn	77	110	1929, [2292]	8.D.4.	485-486
Kilcavan	19	108	1872, 3590, [2235]	4.E.3., 5.D.5.	
Kilcavan	101	111	1775, 1832, 3531, 3559 [2155, 2195]	8.A.10., 10.E.8.	183-184, 270-271
Kilcomb	4	108	1888, 3609, [2252]	5.B.6.	320-322
Kilcormick	25	109	1776, 1873, 3532, 3591 [2156, 2236]	1.B.12., 3.A.5., 5.E.8.	8-9, 272-273
Kilcowan	107	111	1833, 3560, [2196]	10.E.11.	185-186
Kilcowanmore	52	109	1804-05, [2177]	2.E.7.	
Kildavin	118	111	1847, [2210]	9.B.8.	220-221
Kilgarvan	69	110	1930, [2293]		487-490
Kilgorman	17	108	1874, 3592, [2237]	4.F.10.	
Killag	109	111	1834, 3561, [2197]	10.F.1.	
Killann	36	109	1806-07, 3546, [2178]	2.E.1.	74-88
Killenagh	29	109	3534, 3548	5.D.6.	
Killesk	93	111	1901, [2265]	6.B.5.	419
Killiane	122	111	1848, [2211]	9.C.1.	
Killegney	43	109	1808-09, 3547, [2179]	2.F.10.	89-104
Killila	61	110	1777, 3533	3.G.3.	29
Killincooly	33	109	1778, 3535, [2157]	3.A.11.	10
Killinick	125	111	1849, [2212]	9.C.3.	
Killisk	59	110	1779, 3536, [2158]	3.E.7.	30-32, 419
Kilmacree	123	111	1850, [2213]	9.C.7.	222
Kilmakilloge	21	108	1780, 1875, 3593, [2159, 2238]	4.G.2., 5.E.5.	33-34, 274-277
Kilmallock	65	110	1781, 3537, [2160]	3.D.2.	35-38
Kilmannan	104	111	1835, 3562, [2198]	10.F.4.	
Kilmokea			1902		420
Kilmore	110	111	1836, 3563, [2199]	10.F.11.	187-189
Kilmuckridge	34	109	1782, 3538, [2161]	3.A.14., 5.E.9.	
Kilnahue	18	108	1876, 3594, [2239]	4.D.2.	278-281
Kilnamanagh	32	109	1783, [2162]	5.D.12.	11-14
Kilnenor	15	108	1877, 3595, [2240]	5.A.3.	282
Kilpatrick	83	110	1914, 3605, [2278]	1.B.10., 8.G.1.	459-462
Kilpipe	14	108	1878, 3597, [2241]	4.A.10.	283
Kilrane	131	111	1851, [2214]	9.C.9.	223-224
Kilrush	2	108	1889, 3610, [2253]	1.C.3.	323-335
Kilscanlan	55	109	1810, 3549, [2180]	9.A.9.	105-109
Kilscoran	130	111	1852, [2215]	9.C.12.	225-234
Kiltennell	28	109	1784, [2163]	5.D.14.	15
Kiltrisk	27	109	1785, 1879, 3539, 3598 [2242]	4.C.12., 5.D.14.	284
Kilturk	111	111	1837, 3564, [2200]	10.G.8.	
Lady's Island	136	111	1853, [2216]	9.D.3.	
Liskinfere	23	108	3599-3600, [2243]	4.C.1.	285
Maudlintown	116	111	1854 ,[2217, 3518/21]		235
Meelnagh	35	109	1786, [2164]	3.A.14., 5.E.14.	16-18

PARISH/TOWN	TITHES 1823–38 TAB 31/	FILM	VALUATION FIELD BOOKS 1830s OL4./ HOUSE BOOKS [OL5.]	TENEMENT VALUATION 1853 FICHE	1841–1851 CENSUS SEARCH Cen /s/31
Monamolin	26	109	1787, 1880, 3601, [2165, 2244]	4.F.1., 5.F.1.	19-20, 286-288
Monart	10	108	1890, 3611, [2254]	2.C.5.	336-350
Moyacomb	1	108	1891, 3612, [2255]	1.D.3, 3.B.9.	351-356
Maglass	124	111	1855, [2218]	9.D.5.	236
Mulrankin	108	111	1838, 3565, [2201]	10.G.12.	190-201
Newbawn	49	109	1811-12, 1932, [2181, 2294]	7.A.11., 8.A.5.	110-113, 491-494
Oldross	48	109	1813, 3550, [2182]	7.A.14.	114-126
Owenduff	91	111	1903, 3627, [2267]	6.B.14.	421-424
Rathaspick	119	111	1856, [2219]	9.D.12.	
Rathmacknee	121	111	1857, [2220]	9.E.3.	237
Rathroe	95	111	1904, 3628, [2268]	6.C.10.	425-428
Rossdroit	38	109	1814-15, [2183]	2.G.3.	127-130
Rosslare	128	111	1858, [2221]	9.E.7.	238-246
Rossminoge	20	108	1881, 3602, [2245]	4.C.6.	289-293
Skreen	67	110	1790, 1916, 3540, 3651, [2280, 3509]	11.B.10., 8.G.10.	39-40, 463-466
St Helen's	132	111	1859, [2222]	9.F.5.	247
St Bridget's			[3522/23]	10.C.9.	
St. Doologes			[3524/26]	10.C.7.	
St Iberius				10.B.9.	
St Iberius	135	111	1860, 3572-73, [2223, 3527/30]	9.F.6.	248-249
St James & Dunbrody	94	111	1905, [2269]	6.C.13.	429-440
St John's	40	109	1816-17, 3551, [2184, 3531/36]		
St John's	113	111	1861	9.G.2.	
St Margaret's	137	111	1862, [2166, 2224]	9.F.10., 8.G.6.	
St Margaret's	87	110	1788, 1915, 3652, [2279]	11.B.10.	250, 467-468
St Mary's	47	109	1818, 3574-75, [2185, 3537/39]	10.C.4.	131-145, 251, 357-364
St Mary's (Enniscorthy)	12	108	1892, 3613, [2256]		
St Mary's (N Barry)	5	108	1893, 3614, [2257]		357-364
St Michael's	127	111	1789, 1863-64, 3576, [2225, 3540/43, 3544]	9.F.11.	
St Michael's of Feagh			[3540/44]	10.A.7.	
St Mullin's	41	109	1819-20, [2186]	7.E.6.	
St Nicholas	66	110	[2167]	3.C.3.	41
St Patrick's			[3545/48]		
St Peter's	115	111	1865, 3579, [2226, 3544, 3549/52]	9.G.14.	
St Selskar's			[3553/55]	10.B.2.	
Tacumshin	134	111	1866, [2227]	9.E.13.	
Taghmon	75	110	1839, 1933, 3566, [2202, 4236] [3510/11]	8.A.9., 8.D.12	202-204, 495-502
Tellarought	90	110	1906, 3629, [2270]		441-442
Templescoby	39	109	1823-24, [2188]	3.A.2.	171
Templeshanbo	9	108	1894, [2258]	2.B.10.	365-395

PARISH/TOWN	TITHES 1823–38 TAB 31/	FILM	VALUATION FIELD BOOKS 1830s OL4./ HOUSE BOOKS [OL5.]	TENEMENT VALUATION 1853 FICHE	1841–1851 CENSUS SEARCH Cen /s/31
Templeshannon	57	109	1791, 1895, 3541, 3615-16, [2168, 2259]	1.E.2., 3.E.13.	41-43
Templetown	98	111	1907, 3630, [2271]	6.E.3.	443
Templeludigan	37	109	1821-22, 3552, [2187]	7.E.12.	146-170
Tikillin	82	110	1917, 3653, [2281]	8.G.11.	469-474
Tintern	96	111	1908, 3631, [2272]	6.E.13.	444-446
Tomhaggard	112	111	1840, 3567, [2203]	11.A.6.	205-209
Toome	22	108	1882, 1896, 3603, 3617, [2246, 2260]396-401	5.B.11., 4.F.7.	294-298, 396-401
Wexford Town	114	111			251-262
Whitechurch	88	110	1825, 1909, 3553, 3632, [2189, 2273] [3460]	7.F.7., 6.F.11.	447-448
Whitechurchglynn	56	109	1826-27, 1934, 3554, [2190]	11.A.14.	172-173

* Enniscorthy workhouse included.

TOWNS	VALUATION HOUSE BOOK 1830s [OL5.]
Arthurstown	[3459, 3460, 3464]
Ballaghkeen	[3461]
Ballycanew	[3490]
Ballygarret	[3463]
Ballyhack	[3464]
Blackwater	[3462]
Camolin	[3465/66]
Castlebridge	[3467]
Clohamon	[3468/69]
Clonroche	[3470]
Coolgreany	[3471, 3490]
Courtown	[3472]
Duncannon	[3460, 3464]
Duncannon	[3473]
Enniscorthy	[3474/84]
Ferns	[3485]
Ford	[3487]
Fethard	[3460, 3486]
Gorey	[3463, 3488/89, 3490]
Monamolin	[3491]
New Ross	[3492/506]
Newtownbarry	[3512/16]
Oilgate	[3507]
Riverchapel	[3508]
Saltmills	[3486]
Screen	[3509]
Watch House	[3517]

PARISH/TOWN	TITHES 1823–38 TAB 32/	FILM	VALUATION FIELD BOOKS 1830s OL4./ HOUSE BOOKS [OL5.]	TENEMENT VALUATION 1852–4 FICHE	1841–1851 CENSUS SEARCH Cen /s/32
Aghowle	55	114	1969, 3736-39, [2338]	6.B.6.	72-75
Ardoyne		114	1970, 3740-42, [2339]	6.B.14.	76
Arklow	50	114	1935, 3653a-3654, [2295, 3556/58]	4.A.8.	1-12
Ballinacarrig			1994		
Ballinacor	34	113	3691-93, [4237]	5.A.7.	38
Ballintemple	47	114	1936, 3655-56, [2297]	4.C.5.	
Ballymacsimon (Glenealy)			3715		39
Ballynure	15	112	1984, 3782-84, [2346]	5.A.13.	
Ballykine			3694-98, [4238]	5.A.13.	
Baltinglass	20	112	1986, 3785-87, [2347]	1.E.2., 1.D.10.	113-119
Blessington	2	112	1977, 3765-66, 3564/65, 4246]	2.C.6.	89-91
Boystown	4	112	1978, 3767-68, [4247]	1.B.5., 2.D.2.	92-98
Bray	12	112	3731, [2330/31, 3566/68]	2.F.2.	64
Burgage	3	112	1979, 3769, [4248]	2.D.11.	99
Calary	23	123	1948, 1959, 1965, 3677-79, 3716, [2310, 2314/16, 2332/33]	2.G.4., 5.B.12., 3.C.14.	24-25, 47, 65
Carnew	59	114	1971, 3743-46, [2340, 3569/71]	6.D.3.	77-83
Castlemacadam	44	114	1937, 3657-58, [2296]	4.C.10.	13-14
Crecrin	53	114	1972, 3747-48, [2341]	6.C.2.	
Crehelp	6	112	1980, 3770, [4249]	1.B.9.	
Crosspatrick	57	114	1951, 1973, 3749-51, [2342]	5.F.10., 6.C.2.	84-87
Delgany	13	112	1966, 3732-33, [2334/35]	2.G.8.	66
Derrylossary	24	113	1960, 3680-83, 3717, [2311, 2317/18]	5.C.2.	27-34
Donaghmore	19	112	1986, 3788-91, 3806, [2348]	1.G.5.	120-126
Donard	9	112	1981, 3771-72, [3565, 3572, 4250]	1.B.11.	100
Drumkay	41	113	1938, 1961, 3659-60, [2298]	4.D.13.	15
Dunganstown	43	113	1939, 3661-62, [2299/300]	4.E.2.	16-17
Dunlavin	8	112	1982, 1987, 3773-74, 3792, [2349, 3565, 4251]	1.C.3., 1.F.1.	101-103
Ennereilly	46	114	1940, 3663-64, [2301]	4.F.2.	18-19
Freynestown	16	112	1988, 3793-94, [2350]	1.F.1.	
Glenealy	33	113	1941, 1962, 3665-66, 3718-19, [2302, 2319]	3.D.7., 4.F.4.	
Hacketstown	35	113	1952, 3699-3700, [4239]	1.A.14.	40-41
Hollywood	7	112	1983, 3775-77, [4252]		104-110
Inch	51	114	1942, 3667, [2303]	4.F.5.	
Kilbride	1, 48	112, 114	1943, 3668-69, 3778-80, [2304/05, 4253]	2.D.13. 4.F.6.	111-2
Kilcommon	32, 38	113	1944, 1953, 3670, 3701-03, 3720, [2306, 2320/21, 4240]	3.D.11., 4.F.13., 5.G.2.	42-43,
Kilcoole	27	113	3721-22, [2322]	3.D.13.	50-54
Killahurler	49	114	1945, 3671-72, [2307]	4.G.1.	20
Killiskey	30	113	3723-24, [2323/24]	3.E.8.	55

PARISH/TOWN	TITHES 1823–38 TAB 32/	FILM	VALUATION FIELD BOOKS 1830s OL4./ HOUSE BOOKS [OL5.]	TENEMENT VALUATION 1852–4 FICHE	1841–1851 CENSUS SEARCH Cen /s/32
Kilmacanoge	11	112	1967, 3734, [2336]	3.A.4.	67-68
Kilpoole	42	113	1946, 3673-74, [2308]	4.G.4.	21
Kilpipe	40	113	1954, 3704-07, [4241]	5.B.8., 6.A.3.	
Kilranelagh	21	112	1989, 3795-97, [2351/52]	1.F.3.	127
Kiltegan	22	112	1955, 1990, 3798-99, 3806, [2353/54, 4242]	2.A.6., 1.B.1.	44-45, 128-130
Knockrath	25	113	1949, 1956, 3684-86, 3708, [2312]	5.D.3., 5.B.7.	35-36
Liscolman	52	114	1974, 3752-3756, [2343]	6.C.6.	
Moyacomb	58	114	1975, 3757-3761, [2344]	6.C.7.	88
Moyne			1957, 3709-11, [4243]	6.A.10.	46
Mullinacuff	56	114	1976, 3762-64, [2345]	6.C.11.	
Newcastle Lower & Upper	29	113	1963, 3725/26, [2325/27]	3.F.3., 3.F.7.	56-60
Powerscourt	10	112	1968, 3735, [2337, 4245]	3.A.14.	69-71
Preban	39	113	1958, 3712-13, [4244]	6.B.1.	
Rathbran		112	1991, 3800-02, [2356]	1.F.8.	131-134
Rathdrum	26	113	1950, 3687-90, [2313, 3575/77]	5.D.12.	37
Rathnew	31	113	1964, 3727-30, [2328/29, 3578]	3.G.3.	61-62
Rathsallagh	14	112	1992, 3805-04, [2357]	1.G.2.	
Rathtoole	17	112	1993, 3805, [2357a]	1.G.3.	
Redcross	45	114	1947, 3675-76, [2309, 3579/80]	5.A.1.	22-23
Tober	5	112	3781, [4254]	1.D.8.	
Wicklow Town			[3587/89]		63

TOWNS	VALUATION HOUSE BOOK 1830s [OL5.]
Ballinlea	[3559]
Baltinglass	[3560/63]
Enniskerry	[3568, 3573]
Newtownmountkennedy	[3574]
Stratford	[3581/83]
Tinahely	[3584/86]

GLOSSARY

ACT OF UNION
In 1800, legislation in Dublin and Westminster created the United Kingdom of Great Britain and Ireland, dissolved the Irish parliament in Dublin, and brought Ireland into one parliament at Westminster, effective 1 January 1801. The 1798 Rebellion was the immediate impetus for this legislation. The Act of Union was controversial from the outset, and efforts in Ireland were launched almost immediately to repeal it. The momentum for Home Rule intensified towards the end of the nineteenth century, and led eventually to the **partition** of Ireland in 1922. The term 'Unionist' designates those who support continued political union of Northern Ireland with Great Britain.

Alumni Dublinensis
This provides a list of registered students of Trinity College Dublin from 1593 to 1860, giving place of birth, father's name and profession, teacher or school attended, and degrees taken (G.D. Burtchaell and T.U. Sadleir (eds), two volumes, 1935).

BARONY
A unit used in Ireland between the sixteenth and nineteenth centuries for administrative (census, taxation and legal) purposes. Drawn on pre-existing Gaelic divisions – the *triocha ced* – the baronies consisted of large groupings of **townlands** within a county. They were superseded as an administrative unit by the creation of county councils in 1898. The 1891 census is the last to use the barony as an administrative unit.

BOARD OF GUARDIANS
See POOR LAW UNION

CATHOLIC CHURCH
The largest of the churches in Ireland and Northern Ireland. More than 90 per cent of the population in the Republic identifies itself as Catholic, as does 45 per cent of the population of Northern Ireland. The Catholic Archbishop of Armagh and Primate of All Ireland is based in Armagh City. *See* CATHOLIC EMANCIPATION.

CATHOLIC EMANCIPATION

From the 1690s through the 1720s, a series of anti-Catholic laws – popularly called the Penal Laws – were passed by the Irish parliament that severely restricted or denied most civil and religious rights to Catholics, including the right to practise their religion freely, buy or inherit land from Protestants, hold public office, travel abroad for education, operate schools, practise law, serve on **Grand Juries** or in the military, and to vote. While these laws may have been applied only regionally and intermittently, their overall effect was to copper-fasten the Protestant Ascendancy and to create the highly unusual situation of religious discrimination against a majority population. Political resistance to these restrictions gradually escalated in the late eighteenth century, and various Catholic Relief Acts were passed towards the end of the century. In the 1820s, under the flamboyant and effective leadership of Daniel O'Connell, the Catholic Association successfully forced the British Government to pass the final Catholic Relief Act in April 1829, conceding the right of Catholics to sit in parliament.

CENSUS RETURNS

The earliest census taken, for which partial records are extant, is the census of 1659, edited by Seamus Pender in 1939. It is a poll tax list, not a true census, but is of historical significance for recording proportions of settler and native families, the names of principal landowners and tabulations of the most numerous Irish families for each barony. In 1749 Bishop Edward Synge initiated an impressively detailed census for his Church of Ireland Diocese of **Elphin**. There are partial returns of individuals of different denominations in the 1766 census. The first modern census in Ireland began in 1821 and has been held every ten years subsequently, though after independence Ireland conducted a census in 1926, 1936, 1946 and thereafter at five-year intervals. Northern Ireland took a census in 1926, 1937, 1951 and every five years thereafter.

The decennial census remains the most important, however. The individual returns up to 1901 were largely destroyed, partially in World War I, when they were pulped as part of the war effort, and partially in the Irish Civil War in 1922. However, abstracts were published and those since 1841 provide important information by individual parish on population, religion, housing, occupation, literacy etc. The first full census for which the individual returns survive is that of 1901: its records, with those from 1911, are publicly available for all 32 counties.

Arranged by county, district, electoral division and townland, it provides each occupant's name, age, religion, occupation, ability to read or write, marital status, relationship to householder, county of birth or country if not born in Ireland, and ability to speak English and/or Irish. Details of houses are also provided, including the number of rooms occupied by each family, type of roof and number of windows. Many of the institutions listed in this guide hold copies of the returns on microfilm for both 1901 and 1911, in whole or in part. The returns for 1901 and 1911 are available online at the National Archives of Ireland website: **www.census.nationalarchives.ie.**

CHURCH OF IRELAND

The Church of Ireland, affiliated with the Anglican/Episcopalian tradition, was the established church in Ireland from the Reformation in the sixteenth century to its formal disestablishment in 1869, effective in 1870. Members of other religious denominations, notably Catholics and Dissenters, were forced to pay tithes to maintain the Church of Ireland. It is the largest Protestant denomination in the Republic of Ireland and on the island of Ireland, but second in numbers to the Presbyterian Church in Northern Ireland. The Church's leader, the Archbishop of Armagh and Primate of All Ireland, is based in Armagh.

CIVIL SURVEY (1654)
This mid-seventeenth century survey records the principal property holders in each county.

COUNTY
The county system as a form of territorial division was introduced into Ireland shortly after the Norman Conquest in the late twelfth century. The creation of counties or shires was gradual, however, and did not reach into Ulster until after the **Flight of the Earls** in 1607. The final configuration of 32 counties was not achieved until the early part of the eighteenth century. The Sheriff was the chief administrative officer in the county and was vested with considerable powers, including public safety and administration. In 1898 the primary administrative duties were assigned to county councils, which remain the principal administrative body in the Republic but were abolished in Northern Ireland in 1972 with the introduction of Direct Rule by the British Government. Counties remain a powerful focus of local allegiance, symbolised by the use of the unit as the basis for the organisation of the **GAA** games of hurling and Gaelic football.

DÁIL ÉIREANN
The Irish parliament, first convened in January 1919 to declare Ireland's independence. The Dáil's 166 members, **TDs**, are elected by proportional representation. Each Dáil sits for a term of up to five years.

ELPHIN CENSUS
In 1749 the Church of Ireland bishop Edward Synge (1691–1762) organised a census of the people in his diocese, which at that time covered County Roscommon and a large part of Counties Sligo and Galway. This census encompasses all inhabitants, regardless of religious affiliation.

ENCUMBERED ESTATES RECORDS
In 1849, parliament passed legislation setting up Encumbered Estate Courts to settle claims against the growing number of estates bankrupted by the Famine. The courts freed up complicated land titles and placed thousands of estates on the open market. Their printed sales brochures frequently contain detailed lists of townlands, tenants, and leases. These brochures can be found at various locations in Ireland, including the NATIONAL ARCHIVES OF IRELAND, the NATIONAL LIBRARY OF IRELAND and the PUBLIC RECORD OFFICE OF NORTHERN IRELAND.

FLIGHT OF THE EARLS
On 4 September 1607, Hugh O'Neill, Earl of Tyrone, and Rory O'Donnell, Earl of Tyrconnell, together with a contingent of their followers, sailed from the port of

Rathmullan in County Donegal for Spain, but were diverted to France and eventually to Italy. The 'Great O'Neill' (c. 1550–1616) spent the last years of his life in Rome, where he is buried. The departure of Ireland's greatest chieftains symbolised the end of overt Gaelic resistance and paved the way for the **Ulster Plantation**.

GAELIC ATHLETIC ASSOCIATION (GAA)

The Gaelic Athletic Association was founded in 1884 to promote distinctive Irish sports. It is now probably the world's largest community sporting organisation. There is huge grass roots involvement, especially in rural communities, where clubs represent **parishes**. The GAA principally runs Gaelic football, hurling, handball and camogie (the female version of hurling). Today Gaelic football remains the most popular spectator sport in Ireland, and hurling (the fastest field sport in the world) also attracts huge crowds to GAA headquarters, the impressively rebuilt 80,000 capacity state of the art Croke Park stadium in Dublin. Gaelic football has enough similarity with Australian Rules football for internationals to be played, in which the amateur Irish hold their own against the professional Australians. From its inception, the GAA has been an explicitly nationalist body. Until 1971 members were forbidden to play or watch 'foreign' sports such as soccer ('the Ban'), and until 2001 the security forces in Northern Ireland were barred from membership.

GRAND JURIES

Established in the thirteenth century, Grand Juries were appointed by the High Sheriff in each county and their membership was drawn largely from local landowners. Responsibilities included the maintenance of roads and bridges and the upkeep of courthouses, hospitals and lunatic asylums. The Juries, which kept minute books and presentment books, had their administrative functions transferred to county councils in 1898.

GRIFFITH'S VALUATION (1848–65)

Compiled by Richard Griffith, the purpose of this undertaking was to value house and land holdings to determine the payment of rates, i.e. property taxes. Tax receipts were administered by the Poor Law Guardians, who oversaw the administration of workhouses and certain public projects, such as road maintenance. The meticulously detailed document, more formally known as *The Primary Valuation*, is arranged by **townland** or street within **barony**, or **Poor Law Union** within county. This survey – of the utmost genealogical significance – is held on microfiche and covers the 32 counties. Most institutions listed in this guide hold at least a copy of Griffith's *Valuation* for their region. The Griffith's Valuation is available online from a number of sources the best being, www.askaboutireland.ie

HEARTH MONEY ROLLS

In 1662 the Irish parliament enacted legislation levying a tax of two shillings on every hearth, firing place and stove in Ireland, with exemptions, mostly for the indigent, including widows. Tax evasion was common. The rolls record the names of householders arranged by **parish** or **townland**. Few original rolls survive, but some copies are available. The Public Record Office fire destroyed the originals, but many copies had been transcribed and are still available.

INCUMBERED ESTATES RECORDS
See ENCUMBERED ESTATES RECORDS

INDEXES TO WILLS
Published indexes to wills, compiled before the destruction of the Public Record Office, providing important information on wills that are no longer extant.

INDOOR WORKHOUSE REGISTERS
Registers often included the following information: date of admission; first name and last name; sex and age; marital status; occupation; religion; name of spouse and number of children; electoral division or townland of residence; date the person left the workhouse or died; and date of birth if born in the workhouse.

IRISH FOLKLORE COMMISSION SCHOOLS SCHEME PROJECT
Over a period of 18 months between 1937 and 1938, the Irish Folklore Commission, founded in 1935, organised a project that involved Irish schoolchildren in collecting and documenting a wide range of Irish folk material, including folk tales and folk legends, riddles and proverbs, songs, customs and beliefs, games and pastimes, and traditional work practices and crafts. The stories and information collected have been preserved on microfilm and offer a good deal of useful historical and genealogical information.

KING'S INNS ADMISSION PAPERS
This printed volume lists legal students who were admitted to the King's Inns from 1607 to 1867, giving name of father and maiden name of mother, place of birth and qualifications gained. *See* THE HONORABLE SOCIETY OF KING'S INNS

METHODIST CHURCH
The Methodist Church is the third largest Protestant denomination in Ireland, with a total membership of about 60,000, most of whom reside in Northern Ireland. A chairman is elected annually.

ORDNANCE SURVEY
Though inaugurated in England in the early 1790s for military purposes, the mapping of Ireland commenced in 1825 for civil purposes, in anticipation of *Griffith's Valuation*. More than 2,000 workers carried out the survey, county by county, completing their work in 1841. In all, some 1,900 maps were drawn, the most detailed mapping of an entire country ever carried out up to that time, and an invaluable record of the state of the Irish landscape on the eve of the Great Famine. From 1825 until 1841, all of Ireland was mapped at the intimate scale of six inches to the mile. At this scale field fences and houses are marked. These are particularly useful for family research, as they help locate holdings listed in *Griffith's Valuation*.

ORDNANCE SURVEY LETTERS AND MEMOIRS
As the country was being mapped, John O'Donovan and other members of the **Ordnance Survey** teams sent erudite and entertaining letters back to headquarters describing the countryside, monuments, placenames, big houses etc. These were never

published, but are held in typescript copies. They are arranged by county. For much of Ulster and some of the counties that border it, detailed memoirs were also compiled for each parish, and these have been published in a 40 volume series by the Institute of Irish Studies, Queen's University, Belfast (Angélique Day and Patrick McWilliams, eds). See www.qub.ac.uk/iis/publications.html.

PALMER'S INDEX TO THE TIMES 1790–1905 ON CD-ROM
This index provides a wealth of information about Irish affairs in the nineteenth century. It is especially useful for genealogists wishing to glean information about people, places and social events.

PARISH
This territorial division refers to both civil and ecclesiastical boundaries. Civil parishes largely follow the pattern that was established in medieval times, drawn largely along ecclesiastical lines. Ecclesiastical parishes do not always coincide with civil parish boundaries, however. Following the Reformation in the sixteenth century, the Church of Ireland maintained the pre-Reformation arrangement, but low populations forced it to expand its parishes into large groupings of civil parishes. When the Catholic Church began its institutional re-emergence in the late eighteenth and nineteenth centuries, it had to construct an entirely new network of Catholic parishes. The Irish system of parishes is therefore very complex indeed.

PARISH REGISTERS
See Appendix: Karel Kiely's 'A brief guide to the Irish Family History Foundation and the main sources for tracing Irish ancestors'.

PARTITION
The Government of Ireland Act, passed by the British parliament in 1920, created two separate Home Rule parliaments, one based in Dublin for the 26 counties in the south and north-west, the other based in Belfast for the six north-eastern counties that were to become Northern Ireland in 1921. The latter area is often referred to as Ulster, but in fact includes only six of the nine counties in the province of Ulster, namely Antrim, Armagh, Derry or Londonderry, Down, Fermanagh and Tyrone. The three Ulster counties that came under Dublin's jurisdiction were Cavan, Donegal and Monaghan. The south rejected Home Rule, and in 1922 became the Irish Free State, with dominion status.

PENAL LAWS
Starting in 1695, the Irish parliament passed a series of draconian measures that were intended to limit not only the civil and religious rights of Catholics, but also the rights of all Dissenters, i.e. those who did not belong to the Church of Ireland. Catholics, however, suffered the most severe restrictions. *See* CATHOLIC EMANCIPATION.

PENDER'S CENSUS (1659)
See CENSUS RETURNS

PLANTATION
See ULSTER PLANTATION

POOR LAW UNION
Under the Poor Law Act of 1838 Ireland was divided initially into 130 Poor Law Unions, each administered by an area Board of Guardians, responsible in turn to the Poor Law Commission. The Boards were chiefly responsible for supervising the running of the workhouses and administering poor relief in their unions. Later health services were added to their responsibilities. In 1898 the Local Government Act removed health matters from the Boards and assigned these to Rural District Councils. The Boards of Guardians and the Rural District Councils were abolished in 1930.

PRESBYTERIAN CHURCH
The second largest Protestant denomination in Ireland. Its membership is largely concentrated in the northern counties of the Republic and in Northern Ireland, where it slightly outnumbers the **Church of Ireland**. Its leader is the Moderator, elected annually by the General Assembly of the Church.

PROVINCES
There are four provinces in Ireland: Ulster in the north, Leinster in the east, Munster in the south, and Connacht or Connaught in the west.

REPUBLIC OF IRELAND
Formally established in 1949 as the successor to the Irish Free State of 1922, it consists of 26 counties in the south and north-west. The Irish Constitution of 1937, Articles 2 and 3, laid territorial claim to all 32 counties, but this claim was revoked by referendum as part of the Good Friday Agreement of 10 April 1998.

ROMAN CATHOLIC CHURCH
See CATHOLIC CHURCH

ROYAL IRISH CONSTABULARY (RIC)
Founded originally in 1836 as the Irish Constabulary, the RIC was a national, armed force that took on a distinct military character for much of the nineteenth century. It was disbanded in 1922 and replaced in the Republic by the Garda Síochána and in Northern Ireland by the Royal Ulster Constabulary (**RUC**). The latter was disbanded in 2001 and replaced by the Police Service of Northern Ireland.

ROYAL ULSTER CONSTABULARY (RUC)
Founded in 1922 with the establishment of Northern Ireland, the Royal Ulster Constabulary was controversial from the outset. Overwhelmingly Protestant and Unionist in composition, it was widely distrusted by the Catholic community. The Good Friday Agreement of 10 April 1998 specifically called for its reform. The subsequent Patten Commission recommended sweeping changes, and the Police Service of Northern Ireland replaced it in 2001.

RURAL DISTRICT COUNCILS
See POOR LAW UNION

TAOISEACH
Prime Minister of Ireland.

TD
Teachta Dála, i.e. member of the Irish parliament or Dáil.

TITHE APPLOTMENT BOOKS (1823–37)
The tithe books were compiled for each civil parish to assess payment of tithes to the **Church of Ireland**, the established church in Ireland until 1869. All occupiers of land, regardless of their religious affiliation, were required to pay these tithes. Recorded is the name of the occupier, the acreage and quality of his holding and the amount of tithe payable. The landlord's name is also listed. These records, with variable degrees of detail, are held on microfilm and cover the 32 counties. The tithe books for the 26 counties of the Irish Republic have been made available online by the National Archives of Ireland at: **www.titheapplotmentbooks.nationalarchives.ie**.

TOWNLAND
This is the smallest administrative territorial unit in Ireland, varying in size from a single acre to over 7,000 acres. Originating in the older Gaelic dispensation, townlands were used as the basis of leases in the estate system, and subsequently to assess valuations and tithes in the eighteenth and nineteenth centuries. They survive as important markers of identity and as postal addresses.

ULSTER PLANTATION
Following the **Flight of the Earls**, the British crown set about 'planting' settlers from England and Scotland, on the confiscated lands of the Gaelic lords such as the O'Neills and the O'Donnells. The 'official' Plantation affected six of Ulster's counties – Armagh, Cavan, Donegal, Fermanagh, Londonderry and Tyrone. In Antrim and Down there were privately-sponsored settlements. There were various waves of migration, the largest taking place in the 1690s when as many as 50,000 Scots crossed the North Channel into Ulster, many of them fleeing severe famine conditions in their homeland. Of the four Irish provinces, Ulster attracted the largest group of newcomers in seventeenth-century Ireland, contributing to a distinctive identity for the province.

WORKHOUSES
See POOR LAW UNION
and INDOOR WORKHOUSE REGISTERS

For more detailed information on these and other terms, please consult such works as S.J. Connolly's *The Oxford Companion to Irish History* (second edn, Oxford, 2002); William Nolan's *Tracing the Past* (Dublin, 1982); and Donal Begley's *Handbook on Irish Genealogy: How to Trace your Ancestors and Relatives* (sixth edition, Dublin, 1984).

BIBLIOGRAPHY

A select list of general books and monographs only is included here. Monographs primarily of a local interest or serial-type publications, such as Parnham's *1911 Census Ireland References*, or memorial inscriptions of cemeteries, are not included because of space considerations. For articles and CD-ROMs, as well as monographs dealing with local history, consult bibliographies in works listed above, especially James Ryan's works, as well as the catalogues and websites of major distributors of genealogical publications, such as the Ulster Historical Foundation (www.ancestryireland.com), the New England Historic and Genealogical Society (www.newenglandancestors.org), Kennys Bookshop and Art Galleries (www.kennys.ie), Flyleaf Press (http://www.flyleaf.ie/) and the Genealogical Publishing Company (www.genealogical.com).

ALLEN, F.H.A., KEVIN WHELAN, and MATTHEW STOUT. *Atlas of the Irish Rural Landscape*. Cork: Cork University Press, 1997.

ANDREWS, J.H. *A Paper Landscape: the Ordnance Survey in Nineteenth Century Ireland*. Oxford: Oxford University Press, 1975; reprint Dublin: Four Courts Press, 2001.

BARDEN, JUDITH, ed. *Directory of British and Irish Law Libraries*. 4th edn. Hebden Bridge: Published for the British and Irish Association of Law Librarians by Legal Information Resources Limited, *c.* 1992.

BARDON, JONATHAN. *A History of Ulster*. Belfast: Blackstaff Press, 1992; new edition, 2001.

_____. *The Plantation of Ulster*. Dublin: Gill & Macmillan, 2011.

BAXTER, ANGUS. *In Search of Your British & Irish Roots: A Complete Guide to Tracing Your English, Welsh, Scottish, & Irish Ancestors*. 4th edn. Baltimore, MD: Genealogical Publishing Company, 2000.

BEGLEY, DONAL F. *Handbook on Irish Genealogy*. 6th edn. Dublin: Heraldic Artists, 1984.

_____. *Irish Genealogy: a Record Finder*. Dublin: Heraldic Artists, 1981.

BLESSING, PATRICK J. *The Irish in America: A Guide to the Literature and the Manuscript Collections*. Washington, DC: Catholic University of America Press, 1992.

Boylan, Henry, ed. *A Dictionary of Irish Biography*. 3rd edn. Dublin: Gill & Macmillan, 1998.

BRIGGS, ELIZABETH. *Access to Ancestry: A Genealogical Resource Manual for Canadians* Tracing Their Heritage. Winnipeg: Westgarth, 1995.

Calendar of Fiants of the Tudor Sovereigns 1521–1603, with Index of Personal and Placenames. 4 vols. Dublin: E. Burke, 1994.

Calendar of State Papers Relating to Ireland. 24 vols. London: 1860–1912.

CARROLL, FRIEDA, Comp. *Ireland School Registers, 1861–1872; 1891–1939.* Irish Genealogical Source No. 6. Dún Laoghaire: Dún Laoghaire Genealogical Society, 1998.

Church of Ireland Parish Register Series. Dublin: Representative Church Body Library, 1994–2001.

CONNOLLY, S. J. *The Oxford Companion to Irish History.* 2nd edn. Oxford: Oxford University Press, 2002.

DAY, ANGÉLIQUE, and PATRICK McWILLIAMS, Eds. *The Ordnance Survey Parish Memoirs of Ireland.* 40 vols. Belfast: Institute of Irish Studies, Queen's University, in association with the Royal Irish Academy, 1990–1998.

DE BRÚN, PÁDRAIG, and Máire Herbert. *Catalogue of Irish Manuscripts in Cambridge Libraries.* Cambridge (UK), New York: Cambridge University Press, 1986.

DELANEY, ENDA. *Demography, State and Society. Irish Migration to Britain, 1921–1971.* Liverpool: Liverpool University Press, 2000.

DICKSON, R.J. *Ulster Emigration to Colonial America 1718-1775.* Belfast: Ulster Historical Foundation, 2009.

DONOVAN, BRIAN C., and DAVID EDWARDS. *British Sources for Irish History, 1485–1641: A Guide to Manuscripts in Local, Regional and Specialised Repositories in England, Scotland and Wales.* Dublin: Irish Manuscripts Commission, 1997.

DOOLEY, TERENCE. *Sources for the History of Landed Estates in Ireland.* Dublin: Irish Academic Press, 2000.

DUFFY, GODFREY F., and HELEN MEEHAN. *Tracing Your Donegal Ancestors.* Glenageary, Co. Dublin: Flyleaf, Press, *c.* 2008.

ELLIOTT, MARIANNE. *The Catholics of Ulster: A History.* London: Allen Lane, 2000.

FANNING, CHARLES, ed. *New Perspectives on the Irish Diaspora.* Carbondale, IL: Southern Illinois University Press, 2000.

FLANAGAN, DEIRDRE, and LAURENCE FLANAGAN. *IrishPlace Names.* Dublin: Gill & Macmillan, 2002.

FOSTER, JANET, and JULIA SHEPPARD. *British Archives: A Guide to Archive Resources in the United Kingdom.* 4th edn. London: Palgrave Macmillan, 2002.

FOSTER, R.F. *Modern Ireland, 1600–1972.* London: Penguin, 1988.

FOWLER, SIMON. *Tracing Irish Ancestors.* Richmond, UK: Public Record Office, 2001.

The Genealogical Office, Dublin. A Guide. Dublin: Irish Manuscripts Commission, 1998.

GIBBEN, ARTHUR, and RUTH-ANN HARRIS, eds. *The Great Famine and the Irish Diaspora in America.* Amherst: University of Massachusetts Press, 1999.

GLAZIER, MICHAEL. *The Encyclopedia of the Irish in America.* Notre Dame, IN: University of Notre Dame Press, 1999.

GRENHAM, JOHN. *Tracing Your Irish Ancestors: The Complete Guide.* 4th edn. Dublin: Gill & Macmillan, 2012.

GRIFFIN, WILLIAM D. *The Book of Irish Americans.* New York: Random House, 1990.

HACHEY, THOMAS E., and LAWRENCE J. MCCAFFREY. *The Irish Experience Since 1800: A Concise History.* 3rd edn. Armonk, NY and London: MM.E. Sharpe, 2010.

HAMROCK, JOHN. *A Guide to Tracing Your Roscommon Ancestors.* Dublin, Ireland: Flyleaf Press, *c.* 2007.

HANDRAN, GEORGE B. *Townlands in Poor Law Unions: A Reprint of Poor Law Union Pamphlets of the General Registrar's Office with an Introduction, and Six Appendices Relating to Irish Genealogical Research.* Salem, MA: Higginson Book Company, 1997.

HARTY, PATRICIA, ed. *Greatest Irish Americans of the 20th Century.* Dublin: Oak Tree Press, 2001.

HAYES, R.J. *Manuscript Sources for the Study of Irish Civilisation. 11 vols, plus supplement* (3 vols). Boston: G.K. Hall, 1965–79.

HELFERTY, SEAMUS, and Raymond Refaussé, Eds. *Directory of Irish Archives.* 5th edn. Dublin: Four Courts Press, 2011.

HERITY, MICHAEL. *Ordnance Survey Letters [of John O'Donovan, 1830s], Counties Donegal, Down, Dublin, Kildare, Meath.* Dublin: Royal Irish Academy, *c.* 1999–.

HOUSTON, CECIL J., and WILLIAM J. SMYTH. *Irish Emigration and Canadian Settlement: Patterns, Links, and Letters.* Toronto: University of Toronto Press, 1990.

JACKSON, ALVIN. *Ireland, 1798–1998.* Oxford: Blackwell, 1999.

KEANE, E., E. ELLIS, and P.B. EUSTACE. *Registry of Deeds, Dublin, Abstracts of Wills.* Vols. I–III (1708–1832). Dublin: Stationery Office, 1954–1984.

KEANE, E., P.B. PHAIR, and T.U. SADLIER. *King's Inn's Admission Papers, 1607–1867.* Dublin: Stationery Office, 1982.

KENNY, KEVIN. *The American Irish: A History.* Harlow, UK; New York: Longman, 2000.

KILLEN, JOHN. *A History of the Linen Hall Library, 1788–1988.* Belfast: Linen Hall Library, 1990.

KIRKPATRICK, LAURENCE. *Presbyterians in Ireland: An Illustrated History.* Booklink, 2006.

LALOR, BRIAN. The *Encyclopedia of Ireland.* New Haven, Conn.: Yale University Press, 2003.

MCCAFFREY, LAWRENCE J. *The Irish Catholic Diaspora in America.* Washington, DC: Catholic University of America Press, 1997.

MCCARTHY, TONY and TIM CADOGAN. *Tracing Your Cork Ancestors.* Dublin: Flyleaf Press, 1998.

MAC CONGHAIL, MÁIRE, and PAUL GORRY. *Tracing Irish Ancestors: A Practical Guide to Irish Genealogy.* London: Harper Collins, 1997.

MCGUIRE, J.I., and James Quinn. *Dictionary of Irish Biography: From the Earliest Times to the Year 2002.* Cambridge: Cambridge University Press; Royal Irish Academy 2009.

MCKAY, PATRICK. *A Dictionary of Ulster Placenames.* Belfast: Institute of Irish Studies, Queen's University, 1999.

MACLYSAGHT, EDWARD. *The Surnames of Ireland.* 6th edn. Dublin: Irish Academic Press, 1985. (Originally published in 1957 as *Irish Families,* followed in 1960 by *More Irish Families,* and in 1964 by a *Supplement to Irish Families.*)

MCREDMOND, LOUIS, gen. ed. *Modern Irish Lives: Dictionary of 20th-century Irish Biography.* Dublin: Gill & Macmillan, 1996.

MCTERNAN, JOHN C., Ed. *Sligo: Sources of Local History: A Catalogue of the Local History Collection, with an Introduction and Guide to Sources.* New edn. Sligo: Sligo County Library, 1994.

MCWILLIAMS, PATRICK, Ed. *The Ordnance Survey Memoirs of Ireland. Index of People & Places.* Belfast: Institute of Irish Studies, Queen's University Belfast, in association with the Royal Irish Academy, 2002.

MASTERSON, JOSEPHINE. *Ireland: 1841/1851 Census Abstracts (Northern Ireland).* Baltimore: Genealogical Publishing Company, 1999.

_____. *Ireland: 1841/1851 Census Abstracts (Republic of Ireland).* Baltimore: Genealogical Publishing Company, 1999.

MAXWELL, IAN. *Researching Armagh Ancestors: A Practical Guide for the Family and Local Historian.* Belfast: Ulster Historical Foundation, 2004.

_____. *Tracing Your Ancestors in Northern Ireland.* Edinburgh: Stationery Office, 1997.

MITCHELL, BRIAN. *A Guide to Irish Parish Registers.* Baltimore: Genealogical Publishing Company, 1997.

_____. *A New Genealogical Atlas of Ireland.* Baltimore: Genealogical Publishing Company, 2001.

Moody, T.W., F.X. Martin, and F.J. Byrne, eds. *Early Modern Ireland, 1534–1691.* Vol. III in *A New History of Ireland.* Oxford: Oxford University Press, 1976.

Moody, T.W. and W.E. Vaughan, eds. *Eighteenth-Century Ireland, 1691–1800.* Vol. IV in *A New History of Ireland.* Oxford: Oxford University Press, 1986.

MOODY, T.W., F.X. MARTIN, and F.J. BYRNE, eds. *Maps, Genealogies, Lists.* Vol. IX in *A New History of Ireland.* Oxford: Oxford University Press, 1976.

MORRIN, JAMES, ed. *Calendar of the Patent and Close Rolls of Chancery in Ireland, Henry VIII–Elizabeth.* 2 vols. Dublin, 1861–62.

MOSCINSKI, SHARON. *Tracing Our Irish Roots.* Santa Fe, NM: J. Muir Publications, 1993.

NOLAN, WILLIAM. *Tracing the Past.* Dublin: Geography Publications, 1982.

Ó CÉIRÍN, KIT, and CYRIL Ó CÉIRÍN. *Women of Ireland: A Biographic Dictionary.* Newtownlynch, Kinvara, Co. Galway: Tír Eolas, 1996.

O'CONNOR, JOHN. *From The Workhouses of Ireland: The Fate of Ireland's Poor.* Dublin: Anvil Books, 1995.

O'CONNOR, MICHAEL H. *A Guide to Tracing Your Kerry Ancestors.* Glenageary, Co. Dublin, Ireland: Flyleaf Press, 1990.

O'CONNOR, THOMAS, MARIE DALY, and EDWARD L. GALVIN. *The Irish in New England.* Boston: New England Historic Genealogical Society, 1985.

O'DOWD, PEADAR. *Tracing your Galway Ancestors.* Glenageary, Co. Dublin: Flyleaf Press, 2010.

O'FARRELL, PADRAIC. *Irish Surnames*. Dublin: Gill & Macmillan, 2002.

O'FARRELL, PATRICK. *The Irish in Australia, 1788 to the Present*. Cork: Cork University Press, 2001.

O'NEILL, ROBERT KEATING. *A Visitors' Guide: Ulster Libraries, Archives, Museums & Ancestral Heritage Centres*. Belfast: Ulster Historical Foundation, 1997.

OWEN, DOLORES B. *Guide to Genealogical Resources in the British Isles*. Metuchen, NJ: Scarecrow Press, 1989.

PENDER, SEAMUS, ed. *A Census of Ireland, circa 1659. With Supplemental Material from the Poll Money Ordinances (1660–1661)*. 1939, reprinted 1997 by Clearfield Publishing Company, Baltimore, MD.

PERCEVAL-MAXWELL, M. *The Scottish Migration to Ulster in The Reign Of James I*. Belfast: Ulster Historical Foundation, 1990.

PHILLIMORE, W.P.W., and GERTRUDE THRIFT, eds. *Indexes to Irish Wills*. London: Phillimore & Co., 1909–20, reprinted 1997.

QUINN, SEAN E. *Tracing Your Irish Ancestors*. Bray: Magh Itha Teoranta, *c*. 1989.

RADFORD, DWIGHT A., and KYLE J. BETIT, *A Genealogist's Guide to Discovering Your Irish Ancestors: How to Find and Record Your Unique Heritage*. Cincinnati: Butterway Books, 2001.

REFAUSSÉ, RAYMOND. *Church of Ireland Records*. Dublin: Four Courts Press, 2006.

_____. *The Register of the Parish of St. Thomas, Dublin, 1750 to 1791*. Dublin: Representative Church Body Library, *c*. 1994.

REFAUSSÉ, RAYMOND, and COLM LENNON. *The Registers of Christ Church Cathedral, Dublin*. Dublin: Four Courts Press *c*.1998.

ROULSTON, WILLIAM. *Researching Scots-Irish Ancestors: The Essential Genealogical Guide to Early Modern Ulster, 1600-1800*. Belfast: Ulster Historical Foundation, 2005.

RYAN, JAMES G., and BRIAN SMITH. *Tracing Your Dublin Ancestors*. Dublin: Flyleaf Press, 2009.

RYAN, JAMES G., ed. *Irish Church Records: Their History, Availability and Use in Family and Local History Research*. Glenageary, Co. Dublin: Flyleaf Press, 2001.

_____, ed. *Irish Records: Sources for Family and Local History*. Rev. edn. Salt Lake City, UT: Ancestry, *c*. 1997.

_____, Comp. *Sources for Irish Family History: A Listing of Books and Articles on the History of Irish Families*. Glenageary, Co. Dublin: Flyleaf Press, 2001.

_____. *Tracing Your Sligo Ancestors*. Dublin: Flyleaf Press, 2012.

SMITH, BRIAN. *Tracing Your Mayo Ancestors*. Dublin: Flyleaf Press, 2010.

VAUGHAN, W.E., ed. *Ireland under the Union I: 1801–1870*, Vol. V in *A New History of Ireland*. Oxford: Oxford University Press, 1989.

_____., ed. *Ireland under the Union II: 1870–1921*, Vol. VI in *A New History of Ireland*. Oxford: Oxford University Press, 1996.

VICARS, SIR ARTHUR. *Index to Prerogative Wills of Ireland: 1536–1810*. (Dublin: E. Ponsonby, 1897), reprinted 1997.

WOODS, C. J. *Travellers' Accounts as Source-Material for Irish Historians*. Dublin: Four Courts Press, 2009.

INDEX